RoSPA

Health and Safety Practice

Jeremy W. Stranks MSc, MIEH, MIOSH, MBOHS

Malcolm Dewis LLB, MIOSH

Guest Contributors

Lawrence Bamber BSc, DIS, MBIM, MIOSH
Colin A. Stanley DSc, FRIPHH, FIEH, MIOSH
Peter Waterhouse PhD, BSc, CChem, MRSC, MIOSH
Edwin G. Hooper MPhil, CEng, FIEE, FIOSH
Douglas A. Payne

Consultant Editors

Peter W. P. Anderson MA(Cantab), FIOSH
David Bowman BSc, MSc, MEd, MIEH
John Hart BTech

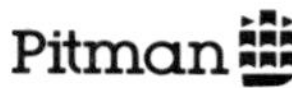

PITMAN PUBLISHING
128 Long Acre, London WC2E 9AN

A Division of Longman Group UK Limited

First published in Great Britain 1986
Reprinted 1989

British Library Cataloguing in Publication Data

Dewis, Malcolm
ROSPA Health and safety practice.
1. Industrial hygiene —— Great Britain
2. Industrial safety —— Great Britain
I. Title II. Stranks, Jeremy
363.1′1′0941 RC963.7.G7
ISBN 0 273 02599 6

Printed in Great Britain at The Bath Press, Avon

Contents

Preface v
Acknowledgements vii
Foreword 1 viii
Foreword 2 x
Foreword 3 xi
Table of Statutory Instruments and Statutory Rules and Orders xii
Table of Statutes xv
Table of Cases xviii
List of Abbreviations xxi

Part I Health and safety law

1 Origins of health and safety law 3
2 Common law liability and workplace injuries 14
3 Health and Safety at Work etc., Act 1974 – administration and duties 26
4 Enforcement 37
5 Health and safety and industrial relations law 46

Part II Health and safety management

6 Safety management and policy 57
7 Investigation, reporting and recording of accidents 67
8 Health and safety monitoring 77
9 Fatal and major accidents and emergencies 89
10 Health and safety training 96
11 The cost of accidents 111

Part III Accident prevention

12 Principles of accident prevention 119
13 Safe systems of work 130

Part IV The working environment

14	The organisation of the working environment	157
15	Temperature, lighting and ventilation	163
16	Welfare amenity provision	178
17	Cleaning and hygiene	186

Part V Occupational health and hygiene

18	Toxicology and health	195
19	Occupational diseases and conditions	202
20	Occupational health practice	242
21	Noise and vibration	252
22	Dust and fumes	265
23	Radiation and radiological protection	277
24	Personal protection	292
25	Occupational hygiene practice	305
26	Control strategies in occupational hygiene	311
27	Ergonomics	317
28	Manual handling	322
29	First aid	339
30	Stress	348

Part VI Safety technology

31	Machinery safety	359
32	Fire	391
33	Lifting machinery and equipment	420
34	Pressure vessels	450
35	Electrical safety	469
36	Construction safety	486
37	Mechanical handling	509
38	Dangerous substances	532
39	Specific processes and activities	563
40	Health and safety in agriculture, forestry, horticulture and associated activities	574
	Bibliography and further reading	590
	Index	605

Preface

In the last decade health and safety at work has taken great strides forward. Above all, it has become 'institutionalised' as part of the normal process of industry and commerce, and is no longer viewed in isolation as previously. The Health and Safety at Work Act, 1974, with its emphasis on individual responsibilities of directors, managers, employees, occupiers, contractors, manufacturers and designers, has had a profound effect on attitudes towards this multi-disciplinary subject. Moreover, people are coming to realise that a safe company can be a profitable one, that accidents and occupational ill-health cost money, and that poor standards of health and safety performance can result in losses to the organisation.

This movement away from a purely legalistic approach to one concerned with loss prevention, asset protection, accountability, consultation and the actual management of the health and safety operation in organisations has meant that many people, who under the old system would never have been involved, have been obliged to take an interest in health and safety at work.

Whilst this book is aimed largely at the health and safety practitioner, it is also intended as a standard reference for managers, employees, trade union safety representatives, contractors, personnel managers, training officers and environmental health officers. It is particularly appropriate to the last mentioned group and is written to accommodate the Health and Safety component of the Diploma in Environmental Health and that Institution's Diploma in Health and Safety at Work. It is also aimed at the Diploma in Health and Safety (with special reference to the food trades) of the Royal Institute of Public Health and Hygiene.

Finally, we must thank our consultant editors, Peter Anderson of the Institution of Occupational Safety and Health, David Bowman of the Institution of Environmental Health Officers and John Hart of the

Royal Society for the Prevention of Accidents, together with staff of the RoSPA Training Centre, for reviewing the chapters and providing helpful comments. We must also thank our guest writers whose names are shown at the head of the appropriate chapters. Special thanks must also be given to Monica Davy for her untiring efforts in typing and re-typing the chapters.

Jeremy Stranks
Malcolm Dewis

Acknowledgements

The authors wish to place on record their thanks to the following organisations and companies for their assistance in the preparation of RoSPA's Health and Safety Practice:

British Standards Institution
Draeger Safety
Health and Safety Unit, Department of Chemical Engineering, University of Aston
Doug Payne Kinetics Limited
National Vulcan Engineering Insurance Group Limited
Royal Society for the Prevention of Accidents
G. W. Sparrow & Sons Plc
Weller Engineering Limited

The law is stated as at 31st March, 1986

Foreword 1

Frederick Creber's *Safety for Industry* was published in 1967 and for many years was used as a standard reference by safety practitioners and by students attending the wide range of safety training courses run by the Society. Despite its popularity as a practical book the increased emphasis on occupational health, safety and welfare brought about by the Health and Safety at Work Act, 1974 led us to believe that there was a need for a new comprehensive and readable text book on health and safety practice which would appeal not only to safety practitioners but to all those involved – managers, occupational health nurses, environmental health officers, health and safety specialists, safety representatives and members of safety committees, safety engineers, insurance company specialists, personnel and training specialists – and many others with an involvement in this very broad field of activity.

The first part of the book outlines the legal aspects of safety and health at work, but the principal emphasis of the rest of the book is on practice, with a view to assisting readers in such areas as the design and development of safe systems of work, improvement of the working environment, the control of dangerous substances and the safe use of plant and machinery. I am pleased to see that the book also deals with occupational health and stress, subjects of increasing importance to everyone concerned with health and safety at work.

RoSPA is pleased to be associated with two well-established professional institutions, the Institution of Occupational Safety and Health and the Institution of Environmental Health Officers, in the preparation of this book.

Whatever the approach to the subject may be; enforcement of legal requirements, the giving of advice, dissemination of information, or discussion and consultation, the practice of occupational health and safety has one basic objective, that of eliminating or reducing the pain, suffering and cost to the individual and the country brought about by ill health and accidents associated with work activities. I am sure this book will do much to assist in the achievement of this objective.

R. M. Warburton
Director General
RoSPA

Foreword 2

For over a century environmental health officers have had a direct involvement in securing improvements in occupational health, safety and welfare in a wide range of industrial and commercial premises. The Institution, therefore, welcomes RoSPA's Health and Safety Practice, which is written to cover the Health and Safety module of the Diploma in Environmental Health and the Institution's Post-Diploma Qualification in Health and Safety at Work.

Both practising environmental health officers and students of environmental health will find this book of considerable value in their enforcement and advisory role and in the study of this multi-disciplinary subject.

The Institution is pleased to be associated with the Royal Society for the Prevention of Accidents and the Institution of Occupational Safety and Health in the publication of this book and wishes to place on record its thanks to David Bowman, Assistant Chief Environmental Health Officer, Leicester City Council, for reviewing the text of this book on its behalf.

Kenneth J. Tyler FIEH
Secretary
The Institution of Environmental Health Officers
1985

Foreword 3

The Institution of Occupational Safety and Health welcome the publication of this book which deals with the basic knowledge needed by people who have a managerial responsibility or a junior advisory responsibility for occupational safety and health.

Over the past few years the realisation has grown that occupational safety and health is not a fringe activity which requires no more than managerial or supervisory experience and an ability to persuade the workforce to work safely. It is now a broad based activity which is influenced by and has an influence on all aspects of the business of an enterprise. If it is to play its full part in the success of an enterprise it requires both understanding and ability in the management who have the responsibility and in advisers who assist them. The three organisations which have been involved in the writing of this book, the Institution of Occupational Safety and Health, The Institution of Environmental Health Officers and the Royal Society for the Prevention of Accidents, illustrate a co-operation between the broad spectrum of occupationally involved safety and health advisers, an association of enforcement officers and a voluntary organisation with links outside the occupational field. This co-operation shows the importance of increased ability in occupational safety and health and, in particular, the relative unimportance of the difference in role between occupational advisers and the regulatory officers.

Members of the Institution of Occupational Safety and Health who have contributed to this book are particularly conscious of the work of Peter Anderson who has acted as editor for their efforts.

P. Waterhouse
President
The Institution of Occupational Safety and Health
1985

Table of Statutory Instruments and Statutory Rules and Orders

This Table includes, in chronological order, all relevant Statutory Instruments and Statutory Rules and Orders. Where these are discussed in the text, the appropriate page number is given.

Factories Locomotives in Sidings Regulations 1906 530
Factories (Horsehair Processes) Regulations, 1907 4, 47, 187
Factories (Electrical Energy) Regulations, 1908 4, 144, 471, 502
Factories (Tin or Terne Plates Manufacturing) Order, 1917
Tanning (Two-Bath Process) Welfare Order, 1918
Dyeing (Use of Bichromate of Potassium or Sodium) Welfare Order, 1918
Factories (Glass Bottle Manufacturing Welfare) Order, 1918
Factories (Saw Mills and Wooden Articles Welfare) Regulations, 1918
Fruit Preserving (Welfare) Order, 1919
Laundry Workers (Welfare) Order, 1920
Gut-Scraping and Tripe Dressing (Welfare) Order, 1920
Factories (Gutting, Salting and Packing Herring Welfare) Order, 1920
Factories (Glass Bevelling Welfare) Order, 1921
Celluloid (Manufacture, Etc.,) Regulations, 1921 47
Factories (Hollow-ware and Galvanising Welfare) Order, 1921
Chemical Works Regulations, 1922 47
Electric Accumulator Regulations, 1925 6
Herring Curing (Scotland) Welfare Order, 1926
Woollen and Worsted Textiles (Lifting of Heavy Weights) Regulations, 1926 322
Bakehouses Welfare Order, 1927
Herring Curing Welfare Order, 1927
Sacks (Cleaning and Repairing) Welfare Order, 1927
Biscuit Factories Welfare Order, 1927
Manufacture of Cinematograph Film Regulations, 1928 48
Horizontal Milling Machines Regulations, 1928 (and 1934) 383
Oil Cake Welfare Order, 1929
Cement Works Welfare Order, 1930

Tanning Welfare Order, 1930
Sugar Factories Welfare Order, 1931
Chains, Ropes and Lifting Tackle (Register) Order, 1938 435
Sanitary Accommodation Regulations, 1938 179
Cinematograph Film Stripping Regulations, 1939
Electricity (Factories Act) Special Regulations, 1944 123, 143, 144, 471, 502
Patent Fuel Manufacture (Health and Welfare) Special Regulations, 1946 6
Magnesium (Grinding of Castings and Other Articles) Special Regulations, 1946 48
Clay Works (Welfare) Special Regulations, 1948
Jute (Safety, Health and Welfare) Regulations, 1948 322
Dry Cleaning Special Regulations, 1949 570
Pottery (Health and Welfare) Special Regulations, 1950 48, 322
Factories (Testing of Aircraft Engines and Accessories) Special Regulations, 1952 48
Iron and Steel Foundries Regulations, 1953 179
Petroleum Spirit (Conveyance by Road) Regulations, 1957 48, 527
Agriculture (Ladders) Regulations, 1957 585
Agriculture (Power Take-off) Regulations, 1957 576
Agriculture (Avoidance of Accidents to Children) Regulations, 1958 580
Agriculture (Circular Saws) Regulations, 1959 580
Agriculture (Safeguarding of Workplaces) Regulations, 1959 574, 575
Agriculture (Stationary Machinery) Regulations, 1959 580, 586
Agriculture (Lifting of Heavy Weights) Regulations, 1959 580, 582
Agriculture (Threshers and Balers) Regulations, 1960 322, 580, 587
Factories (Cleanliness of Walls and Ceilings) Order, 1960 507
Shipbuilding and Ship-repairing Regulations, 1960 438
Construction (General Provisions) Regulations, 1961 143, 486–508
Construction (Lifting Operations) Regulations, 1961 420, 426, 430, 435, 445, 486–508
Agriculture (Field Machinery) Regulations, 1962 577, 580, 586
Hoists Exemption Order, 1962 430
Non-Ferrous Metals (Melting and Founding) Regulations, 1962 17
Washing Facilities Regulations, 1964 179
Sanitary Conveniences Regulations, 1964 179
Examination of Steam Boilers Regulations, 1964 454
Prescribed Dangerous Machines Order, 1964 17
Examination of Steam Boilers Reports (No.1) Order, 1964 454
Power Presses Regulations, 1965 17, 123, 364, 381
Construction (Working Places) Regulations, 1966 20, 122, 143, 486–508
Construction (Health and Welfare) Regulations, 1966 179, 182, 187, 486–508

Carcinogenic Substances Regulations, 1967 557
Offices, Shops and Railway Premises (Hoists and Lifts) Regulations 1968 (as amended in 1974) 420, 430
Asbestos Regulations 1969 187, 557
Abrasive Wheels Regulations 1970 8, 133, 364
Food Hygiene (General) Regulations 1970
Foundries (Protective Footwear and Gaiters) Regulations 1971 303
Highly Flammable Liquids and Liquefied Petroleum Gases Regulations 1972 48, 70, 504, 535
Organic Peroxides (Conveyance by Road) Regulations 1973 48
Agriculture (Tractor Cabs) Regulations 1974 577, 578
Industrial Tribunals (Improvement and Prohibition Notices Appeals) Regulations 1974 41
Sanitary Accommodation (Amendment) Regulations 1974 179
Woodworking Machines Regulations 1974 133, 364, 385, 489
Protection of Eyes Regulations 1974 18, 293, 295, 381, 383
Employers' Health and Safety Policy Statements (Exception) Regulations 1975 27, 29, 57
Protection of Eyes (Amendment) Regulations 1976
Safety Representatives and Safety Committees Regulations 1977 6, 26, 27, 30, 51–3, 60, 61
Health and Safety (Enforcing Authority) Regulations 1977 38, 39
Motor Vehicles (Construction and Use) Regulations 1978 557
Control of Lead at Work Regulations 1980 6, 48, 50, 179, 226, 312
Safety Signs Regulations 1980 160
Dangerous Substances (Conveyance by Road in Road Tankers and Tank Containers) Regulations 1981 532, 547, 551, 552
Diving Operations at Work Regulations 1981 219
Health and Safety (Dangerous Pathogens) Regulations 1981 6
Health and Safety (First Aid) Regulations 1981 6, 61, 123, 339
Notification of Installations Handling Hazardous Substances Regulations 1982
Notification of New Substances Regulations 1982 38, 200, 553, 554
Asbestos (Licensing) Regulations 1983 6
Control of Industrial Major Accidents Hazards Regulations 1984 557
Criminal Penalties, etc. (Increase) Order 1984 11, 44
Classification, Packaging and Labelling of Dangerous Substances Regulations 1984 6, 532–3, 553–6
Poisonous Substances in Agriculture Regulations 1984 48, 581, 582, 589
Social Security (Industrial Injuries) (Prescribed Diseases) Regulations 1985 202, 205, 207, 209, 216, 217, 218, 220
Reporting of Injuries, Diseases and Dangerous Occurrences Regulations 1985 70, 71, 72, 89, 91, 501
Ionising Radiations Regulations 1985 284–6, 557

Table of Statutes

This Table includes, in chronological order, all relevant Statutes. Where these are discussed in the text, the appropriate page number is given.

Health and Morals of Apprentices Act 1802 3
Factory Act 1833 3
Mines and Collieries Act 1842 4
Workshop Regulation Act 1867 3
Metalliferous Mines Regulation Act 1872 4
Explosives Act 1875 44, 47
Factory and Workshop Act 1878 4
Employers' Liability Act 1880 14
Shop Hours Regulation Act 1886 5
Factory and Workshop Act 1901 4
Alkali etc Works Regulation Act 1906 44, 505
Coal Mines Act 1911 4
Anthrax Prevention Act 1919 44
Employment of Women, Young Persons and Children Act 1920 5, 44
Celluloid and Cinematograph Film Act 1922 45
Explosives Act 1923 45
Petroleum Consolidation Act 1928 45, 527
Children and Young Persons Act 1933 579
Hours of Employment (Conventions) Act 1936 5, 45
Petroleum (Transfer of Licences) Act 1936 45
Public Health Act 1936 505
Children and Young Persons (Scotland) Act 1937 579
Factories Act 1937 4, 8, 16, 24
Hydrogen Cyanide (Fumigation) Act 1937 45
Public Health (Drainage of Trade Premises) Act 1937 505
Young Persons (Employment) Act 1938 5
Law Reform (Contributory Negligence) Act 1945 23
Ministry of Fuel and Power Act 1945 45
Coal Industry (Nationalisation) Act 1946 45
Radioactive Substances Act 1948 45

Factories Act 1948 4
Law Reform (Personal Injuries) Act 1948 14, 21, 22
Shops Act 1950 5, 178
Rag Flock and Other Filling Materials Act 1951 187
Rivers (Prevention of Pollution) Acts 1951–61 505
Fireworks Act 1951 45
Agriculture (Poisonous Substances) Act 1952 45
Emergency Laws (Miscellaneous Provisions) Act 1953 45
Mines and Quarries Act 1954 4, 37
Agriculture (Safety, Health and Welfare Provisions) Act 1956 4, 45, 580, 582
Clean Air Act 1956 (and 1968)
Occupiers' Liability Act 1957 32, 500
Factories Act 1959 4
Radioactive Substances Act 1960 290
Factories Act 1961 Chapters 1–4, 8, 12–17, 24, 28, 31, 33–4
Public Health Act 1961 45, 505
Offices, Shops and Railway Premises Act 1963 Chapters 1–4, 12–17, 28, 33, 36
Nuclear Installations Act 1965 45
Civil Evidence Act 1968 7
Trade Descriptions Act 1968 35
Employers' Liability (Compulsory Insurance) Act 1969 11, 22, 23
Employers' Liability (Defective Equipment) Act 1969
Public Health (Recurring Nuisances) Act 1969 505
Equal Pay Act 1970
Fire Precautions Act 1971 417
Industrial Relations Act 1971 48, 50
Mines Management Act 1971 45
Employment Medical Advisory Service Act 1972 45
Control of Pollution Act 1974 505
Health and Safety at Work etc Act 1974 Chapter 3 and throughout
Trade Union and Labour Relations Act 1974
Water Resources Act 1974 505
Limitation Act 1975
Sex Discrimination Act 1975
Social Security Act 1975 202
Social Security (Consequential Provisions) Act 1975 10
Fatal Accidents Act 1976 10
Food and Drugs (Control of Premises) Act 1976
Race Relations Act 1976
Road Traffic Regulation Act 1976
Trade Union and Labour Relations (Amendment) Act 1976
Criminal Law Act 1977

Unfair Contract Terms Act 1977 22
Employment Protection (Consolidation) Act 1978 25, 29, 46, 50, 51, 62
Refuse Disposal (Amenity) Act 1978 505
Employment Act 1980 50, 51
Limitation Act 1980 13
Magistrates' Courts Act 1980 43
Local Government, Planning and Land Act 1980 506
Administration of Justice Act 1982 10
Derelict Land Act 1982 505
Employment Act 1982 50
Social Security and Housing Benefits Act 1982 114
Supply of Goods and Services Act 1982
Criminal Justice Act 1982 11, 44
Food Act 1984
Road Traffic Regulation Act 1984 161

Table of Cases

This Table includes, in alphabetical order, all relevant Cases. Where these are discussed in the text, the appropriate page number is given.

Abercrombie *v.* Alexander Thomson & Son	[1975] IRLR 326	48
Armour *v.* Skeen	1977 SLT 71	30
Ashworth *v.* Needham & Sons Ltd	1977 COIT No. 681/78, Case No. 20161/77	49
Barkway *v.* South Wales Transport Co. Ltd	[1950] 1 AER 392	19
Bendall *v.* Paine & Betteridge Ltd	[1973] IRLR 44	48
Bonnington Castings *v.* Wardlaw	[1965] 1 AER 615	390
Boyle *v.* Kodak Ltd	[1969] 2 AER 439	12
Bradford *v.* Robinson Rentals Ltd	[1967] 1 AER 267	16
Brazier *v.* Skipton Rock Company Ltd	[1962] 1 AER 955	144
British Railways Board *v.* Liptrot	[1967] 2 AER 1072	530
Brydon *v.* Stewart	(1855) 2 Macq 30	16
Burgess *v.* Thorn Consumer Electronics Ltd	HSIB 93 (1983)	
Bux *v.* Slough Metals Ltd	[1974] 1 AER 262	17, 123
Century Insurance Co. Ltd *v.* Northern Ireland Road Transport Board	[1942] AC 509	20
Clifford *v.* Challen & Sons	[1951] 1 KB 495 and [1951] 1 AER 72	302
Close *v.* Steel Company of Wales Ltd	[1962] 2 AER 953	
Davies *v.* Thomas Owen & Co. Ltd	[1919] 2 KB 39	8
Ebbs *v.* James Whitson & Co. Ltd	[1952] 2 QB 877	222
Edwards *v.* National Coal Board	[1949] 1 AER 743	8
Ferguson *v.* John Dawson & Partners (Contractors) Ltd	[1976] IRLR 346	20
Gardiner *v.* Motherwell Machinery & Scrap Co. Ltd	[1961] 3 AER 831	12
Ginty *v.* Belmont Building Supplies Ltd	[1959] 1 AER 414	494
Greaves & Co. (Contractors) Ltd *v.* Baynham Meikle & Partners	[1975] 1 WLR 1095	158, 526
Groves *v.* Lord Wimborne	[1898] 2 QB 402	12

Henry *v.* Vauxhall Motors Ltd
COIT No. 664/85, Case No. 25290/77 46
Heslop *v.* Metalock (Great Britain) Ltd,
Observer, 29 November 1981 207
Hosking *v.* de Havilland Aircraft Ltd [1949] 1 AER 540
Hudson *v.* Ridge Manufacturing Co. Ltd [1957] 2 AER 229 49
ICI Ltd *v.* Shatwell [1964] 2 AER 999 23
Irwin *v.* White, Tomkins & Courage Ltd [1964] 1 AER 545 34
Kilgollan *v.* Cooke & Co. Ltd [1956] 2 AER 294 22
Latimer *v.* AEC Ltd [1953] 2 AER 449 16
Lister *v.* Romford Ice & Cold Storage Co Ltd
[1957] 1 AER 125 24, 29, 62
Liptrot *v.* British Railways Board [1967] 2 AER 1067 162
Lochgelly Iron & Coal Co. *v.* M'Mullan [1934] AC 1 15
Lovell *v.* Blundells & Crompton & Co. Ltd [1944] 2 AER 53 18
Machray *v.* Stewarts & Lloyds Ltd [1964] 3 AER 716 18
McCarthy *v.* Daily Mirror Newspapers Ltd [1949] 1 AER 801 182
McGibbon *v.* Gillespie Building Co. Ltd [1973] IRLR 105 48
Marsh *v.* Judge International Housewares Ltd
[1976] COIT No. 511/57, Case No. 23119/76 295
Marshall *v.* Gotham & Co. [1954] 1 AER 9379
Martin *v.* Yorkshire Imperial Metals Ltd
COIT No. 709/147, Case No. 32793/77 30
O'Shea *v.* Kimberley-Clark Ltd The Guardian, 8 October, 1982 206
Priestley *v.* Fowler (1837) 13 M & W 1 14
R *v.* Swan Hunter Shipbuilders Ltd The Times, July 1981 501
Rankine *v.* Garton Sons & Co. Ltd [1979] 2 AER 1185
Ready Mixed Concrete (South-East) Ltd *v.*
Minister of Pensions and National Insurance
[1968] 1 AER 433 19
Roberts *v.* Dorothea Slate Quarries Co. Ltd [1948] 2 AER 201
Rose *v.* Plenty [1976] 1 AER 97 20, 489
Rylands *v.* Fletcher (1868) LR 3 HL 330
Schwalb *v.* Fass(H) & Son (1946) 175 LT 345 8
Secretary of State *v.* ASLEF [1972] 2 AER 949 29
Smith *v.* Baker & Sons [1891] AC 325 23
Spartan Steel & Alloys Ltd *v.* Martin
(Contractors) & Co. Ltd [1972] 3 AER 557 120
Stokes *v.* GKN Sankey Ltd [1968] 1 WLR 1776 301
Summers (John) & Sons Ltd *v.* Frost [1955] 1 AER 870 7, 8
Taylor *v.* Alidair Ltd [1978] IRLR 82 50
Tesco Stores Ltd *v.* Nattrass [1971] 2 AER 127 35
Thompson, Gray, Nicholson *v.*
Smiths Ship Repairers (North Shields) [1984] IRLR 93–116 207

Uddin *v.* Associated Portland Cement Manufacturers Ltd [1965] 2 AER 213 24, 363
Vineer *v.* Doidge & Sons Ltd [1972] 2 AER 794
Vosper Thornicroft (UK) Ltd. *v.* HSE, Crown Court, Portsmouth 1978 (Unreported)
Walker *v.* Bletchley-Flettons Ltd [1937] 1 AER 170 70, 365, 516
Waugh *v.* British Railways Board [1979] 2 AER 1169 74
Wilsons & Clyde Coal *v.* English [1938] AC 57 15, 17
Westwood *v.* The Post Office [1973] 3 AER 184 21
Wheat *v.* E. Lacon & Co Ltd [1965] 2 AER 700 32, 33
Woods *v.* Durable Suites Ltd [1953] 2 AER 391 18
Woolmington *v.* D.P.P. [1935] AC 462 42

List of Abbreviations

Organisations/Publications

ACAS	Advisory, Conciliation and Arbitration Service
BS	British Standard
Cmnd	Command Paper
COIT	Central Office of the Industrial Tribunals
DHSS	Department of Health and Social Security
HSC	Health and Safety Commission
HSE	Health and Safety Executive
HMSO	Her Majesty's Stationery Office
TUC	Trades Union Congress

Statutes/Statutory Instruments

EPCA	Employment Protection (Consolidation) Act 1978
FA	Factories Act 1961
HSWA	Health and Safety at Work etc Act 1974
OLA	Occupiers' Liability Act 1957
OSRPA	Offices, Shops and Railway Premises Act 1963
PHA	Public Health Act 1936
TULRA	Trade Union and Labour Relations Act 1974
UCTA	Unfair Contract Terms Act 1977
Reg	Regulation
SI	Statutory Instrument
SR&O	Statutory Rule and Order
Sch	Schedule
Sec	Section

Case citations

AC	Appeal Cases

AER	All England Reports
HSIB	Health & Safety Information Bulletin
IRLR	Industrial Relations Law Reports
Macq	Macqueen (Scot) (ended 1865)
KB	Kings Bench
QB	Queens Bench
SLT	Scottish Law Times
TLR	Times Law Reports
WLR	Weekly Law Reports

Legal terminology

J	Mr Justice, a junior judge, usually sitting in a court of first instance
LJ	Lord Justice, a senior judge, usually sitting in a court of appeal
plaintiff	the person presenting a claim in a civil action
defendant	the person against whom the claim is brought in a civil action
appellant	the person bringing an appeal in a civil action
respondent	the person against whom the appeal is brought in a civil action
tort	a species of civil action for injury or damage where the remedy or redress is an award of unliquidated damages
volenti non fit injuria	literally 'to one who is willing no harm is done'; a defence in a civil action.

PART I

Health and safety law

1

Origins of health and safety law

Origins

The law relating to health and safety at work has its origins in statute and common law going back to the early nineteenth century and the industrial revolution.

Statute

The legislative history of occupational health and safety has been patchy. Indeed, until the Health and Safety at Work, etc., Act (HSWA) was passed in 1974, thereby creating a new consultative approach to occupational health and safety problems (*see* Chapter 3), the history of protective industrial legislation consisted of a series of statutes which were aimed mainly at manufacturing industry. Passed on an ad hoc basis, they attempted to control safety and health hazards.

The first statute (the Health and Morals of Apprentices Act) was passed in 1802 to combat the appalling conditions in the textile industry in which children worked. Its purpose was to limit the working hours of apprentices in the cotton industry and to establish minimum standards of heating, lighting, ventilation, etc. Enforcement was by visitors appointed to factories by local magistrates.

As steam power superseded water power, the textile industry moved from rural districts to towns, with the result that large factories proliferated in the growing urban areas. Children were forced to work excessively long hours in unhealthy and dirty conditions. This resulted in the first Factory Act in 1833, which established four factory inspectors who had effective means of entry and enforcement. Factories and mills had to open their gates to state inspectors. In 1864 statutory protection was extended beyond the textile industry to the matchmaking and pottery industries. In 1867 the Workshop Regulation Act introduced some measure of safety and, to a lesser extent, health protection into smaller working establishments (i.e. workshops). With the passing of the Factory and Workshop Act 1878, a consolidating measure, the distinction between factories and workshops became obsolete, both being embraced under the heading 'factory', thus facilitating administration of the law. From then onwards statutory protection was enforced in factories.

A further consolidating Act, the Factory and Workshop Act, passed in 1901, introduced a pattern of legislation which has continued uninterrupted to the present day, namely a built-in statutory power enabling the Minister or Secretary of State to pass ad hoc Regulations to meet dangers arising from certain industries and processes. Many of the Regulations made under the Factory and Workshop Act 1901 are still in force, e.g. the Factories (Horsehair Processes) Regulations 1907 and the Factories (Electrical Energy) Regulations 1908.

A further Factories Act was passed in 1937 (the predecessor of the current Factories Act), with additional ones in 1948 and in 1959. The latter two provisions made minor amendments to the principal Act of 1937 as well as (in the case of the 1959 Act) strengthening the (then) Fire Regulations. The Factories Act 1937 was important because it abolished the distinction between the various types of factory premises, viz. workshops, textile factories, etc. It was the first Act to provide detailed legislation on health, safety and welfare.

Present protective factory legislation, largely consolidating earlier law, but with some modifications, is contained in the Factories Act 1961. It should, however, be understood that, in conjunction with other extant protective legislation (see below) and Regulations, this is being repealed and replaced by Regulations passed under HSWA – though the process is a gradual one.

Although the series of Factories Acts constitutes the most important statutory assault on poor and indifferent occupational health and safety conditions and standards, legislation has penetrated progressively to workplaces other than factories.

Coal mining was an early candidate for protective legislation. In 1842 the Mines and Collieries Act was passed, regulating the conditions and hours of work of women and children in the mines. In the following year the first Inspectorate of Mines was established. Working conditions and hours of employment in quarries came to be regulated by the Metalliferous Mines Regulation Act 1872. Further consolidation of the law followed in 1911 with the passing of the Coal Mines Act. The present law is to be found in the Mines and Quarries Act 1954 and the various regulations passed under it.

In 1956 agriculture received a first protective Act, the Agriculture (Safety, Health and Welfare Provisions) Act, under the umbrella of which many health and safety as well as welfare Regulations have since appeared (*see* Chapter 40).

Protective legislation for office and shop workers came about later. The Shops Hours Regulation Act 1886 controlled the hours of employment of young persons (i.e. persons over 16 and under 18), but it was not until 1963, when the Offices, Shops and Railway Premises Act (OSRPA) was passed, that the health, safety and welfare of employees in offices, shops and some railway premises came to be regulated through enforcement. The law relating to hours of employment, holidays, etc., for employees in shops is contained in the Shops Act 1950, and, for the employment of women and young children in industries generally, in the Employment of Women, Young Persons and Children Act 1920, the Hours of Employment (Conventions) Act 1936 and the Young Persons (Employment) Act 1938. Enforcement of most of the above Acts is by local authorities, though health and safety provisions (for instance, in OSRPA) may be enforced by HSE (*see* Chapter 4).

Emphasis of protective legislation prior to HSWA

Prior to HSWA, as the titles of the various Acts explained, protection was concentrated on *place* of work rather than on fact of work or the existence of employment (as exemplified by the contract of employment). Thus, principal places of work, such as factories, offices, shops, mines, etc., were (and still are) subject to statutory protection, with statutory duties being enforced by the various state inspectorates (now the unified HSE, *see* Chapter 3). However, since the key to statutory protection was not the contract of employment, inevitably certain important places of work were not covered. Examples were hospitals, schools, universities, theatres and fairgrounds. This was unfortunate, as it implied that certain parts of the nation's workforce were entitled to more protection than others. This defect in statute law was remedied by HSWA.

Common law

Common law is the decisions of the courts which have been bound by the doctrine of precedent into a corpus of authoritative principles and rules. It is judge-made law and accounts for the greater part of the law of contract and tort, both of which – but particularly the latter (*see* Chapter 2) – have played a significant role in the development of civil liability relating to occupational health and safety. Common law is synonymous with case law and its rules and principles and doctrines are to be found in the law reports. Case law is a self-endorsing process, being perpetuated either by previous binding cases or by the interpretation of legislation. The main contribution of common law to the law relating to occupational health and safety is the body of rules developed in connection with the right of employees and their dependants to sue employers for damages for personal injury, disease or death at work, i.e. the civil liability of employers is to be found mainly in the rules of tort (*see* Chapter 2).

Nature of occupational health and safety law

Occupational health and safety law consists of statute law and common law (or case law). Predominant, however, is the level of statute law, consisting of Acts of Parliament (HSWA is an example of an enabling Act, and the Factories Act 1961 is predominantly a non-enabling Act), and even more proliferating is the volume of statutory instruments (SIs) and statutory rules and orders (SR&Os) made under parent protective Acts. These latter may conveniently be described as 'subordinate' legislation. Subordinate legislation relating to workplace health and safety consists of statutory instruments proposed by the Health and Safety Commission (HSC), after consultation with industry and local authorities and other relevant bodies, to the Secretary of State, and subsequently laid before Parliament. Before 1948, however, subordinate legislation relating to occupational health and safety consisted entirely of statutory rules and orders, and many of these are still in existence, e.g. the Electric Accumulator Regulations 1925 (SR&O 1925, No. 28) and the Patent Fuel Manufacture (Health and Welfare) Special Regulations 1946 (SR&O 1946, No. 258).

Since 1974, when HSWA was introduced, all Regulations concerning workplace health and safety have been passed in furtherance of HSWA, a process which is well under way, e.g. the Safety Representatives and Safety Committees Regulations 1977, the Control of Lead at Work Regulations 1980, the Health and Safety (Dangerous Pathogens) Regulations 1981, the Health and Safety (First Aid) Regulations 1981 and the Classification, Packaging and Labelling of Dangerous Substances Regulations 1984. Moreover, draft Regulations relating to the protection of hearing from noise at work are likely to become law shortly. These impose penalties on employers and manufacturers of machinery where noise levels at work exceed a statutory limit or limits. Additionally, there have recently been passed the Asbestos (Licensing) Regulations 1983, limiting the use and handling of asbestos and the licensing of contractors who engage in the removal of asbestos insulation, etc. Unlike previous subordinate legislation, however, Regulations passed under HSWA place considerable reliance on approved codes of practice (*see* Chapter 3).

Division into criminal and civil liability

Criminal liability

Criminal liability refers to the responsibilities under statute and the penalties which can be imposed by criminal courts, i.e. fines, imprisonment and remedial orders. The criminal courts in question are the magistrates' courts, which handle the bulk of health and safety offences (the less serious offences), and the Crown Courts, which deal with the more serious health and safety offences (*see* Chapter 4).

There are appeal procedures to the High Court, and beyond to the Court of Appeal and, assuming that leave is given, to the House of Lords. Appeals against decisions of magistrates' courts and Crown Courts on points of criminal law involving occupational health and safety are few. Employers and factory occupiers when found guilty tend to pay the fine and there the matter ends. After all, although not insignificant, a fine is generally much smaller than the civil remedy of an award of damages. Moreover, convictions for health and safety offences can be used as evidence of negligence in subsequent civil cases, in accordance with the Civil Evidence Act 1968, sec 11.

Criminal liability is either

(a) statutory; or
(b) common law, e.g. murder, manslaughter.

As far as occupational health and safety law are concerned, criminal liability is exclusively of statutory origin (but see the remarks about the General Duties of HSWA on page 28).

Statutory criminal liability – interpretation of penal duties

Penal duties in relation to occupational health and safety are strictly construed. This means that the courts only interpret words appearing in the statute or statutory instrument, and not words which do not appear. Examples of this occur often (and can sometimes have strange, if not irritating, commercial consequences). Here the chief way of 'rectifying' the law is by recourse to subsequent legislation, correcting the previous 'maverick' decision. The reversal by subsequent legislation of the House of Lords' decision in *John Summers & Sons Ltd* v. *Frost* [1955] 1 AER 870 provides a good illustration. Here the respondent was employed by the appellant as a maintenance fitter in a steelworks. His thumb was caught in a revolving grindstone, when grinding a piece of metal on a grinding machine. The machine had horizontal shafts at each end driven by an electric motor. The grindstones revolved downwards when the operator faced the machine and were enclosed to an extent commensurate with performing normal grinding operations (i.e. a small portion of each wheel remained exposed opposite its tool rest). It was held by the House of Lords that the grindstone was a 'dangerous part of machinery' for the purposes of the Factories Act 1937, sec 14(1) (the predecessor of the current Act). The legal view was that the machine was not 'securely fenced', as required, even though the consequence of 'securely fencing' would have been to make the machine commercially useless. (This matter was later 'rectified' by the Abrasive Wheels Regulations 1970, though not until more than 15 years later. Broadly these Regulations now require that abrasive wheels shall be guarded to the greatest extent that is practicable having regard to the work to be performed.)

Types of statutory criminal liability

Statutory duties can be (a) absolute, (b) practicable and (c) reasonably practicable.

Absolute requirements: Where the risk of injury, etc., is inevitable if safety precautions are not taken, the statutory duty may well be absolute (i.e. liability is not referable to negligence, or failing to take practicable or reasonably practicable safety measures).

An example, perhaps the most important one in terms of factory safety, of an absolute statutory duty is the Factories Act 1961, sec 12(1). This requires that 'every flywheel directly connected to any prime mover and every moving part of any prime mover ... shall be securely fenced, whether the flywheel or prime mover is situated in an engine house or not'.

If, in consequence, a machine becomes commercially impracticable or mechanically unusable when it has been securely fenced, this is irrelevant (*John Summers & Sons Ltd* v. *Frost* [1955] AC 746); alternatively, if the machine cannot be securely fenced, this is no defence (*Davies* v. *Thomas Owen & Co. Ltd* [1919] 2 KB 39).

Practicable requirements: A statutory obligation which has to be carried out so far as is practicable, must be carried out if, in the light of current knowledge and invention, it is feasible. And this even though it may be difficult, inconvenient and costly (*Schwalb* v. *Fass (H) & Son* (1946) 175 LT 345).

Reasonably practicable requirements: A statutory duty which has to be carried out so far as is reasonably practicable, must allow for the balancing of costs and benefits. Thus, in the leading case of *Edwards* v. *National Coal Board* [1949] 1 AER 743, Asquith L. J. said,

> 'Reasonably practicable' is a narrower term than 'physically possible', and seems to me to imply that a computation must be made by the owner in

which the quantum or risk is placed on one scale and the sacrifice involved in the measures necessary for averting the risk (whether in money, time or trouble) is placed on the other, and that, if it be shown that there is a gross disproportion between them—the defendants discharge the onus on them. Moreover, this computation falls to be made by the owner at a point of time anterior to the accident.

Comparing 'practicable' and 'reasonably practicable' duties, Lord Reid in the leading case of *Marshall* v. *Gotham & Co.* [1954] 1 AER 937 observed, 'If a precaution is practicable it must be taken unless in the whole circumstances that would be unreasonable. And as men's lives may be at stake it should not lightly be held that to take a practicable precaution is unreasonable....'

To summarise a complex point, if a duty is required to be carried out 'so far as is reasonably practicable', the owner or occupier of the work premises, or any other person upon whom the duty is placed, can afford to run the risk of not instituting safety measures, procedures, etc., if the overall benefit, in terms of reducing accidents or improving health and safety conditions, is minimal compared with the cost and inconvenience of introducing the measures, etc.

Common law criminal liability

Although it is inaccurate to refer to common law criminal liability in connection with health and safety offences, it is worth remembering that the General Duties contained in HSWA, secs 2–9, are, in essence, duties existing at common law.

Enforcement agencies

Criminal law is enforcement law. Its statutory provisions are enforced by state enforcement agencies, e.g. the police, trading standards departments and, in the case of occupational health and safety, HSE inspectors and environmental health officers. Breach of penal duties takes the form, on conviction, of a fine or imprisonment. Alternatives are also possible, e.g. remedial orders. By contrast with civil liability in tort, criminal liability cannot be insured against by either employers, directors or employees. It is, however, lawful to insure against court costs and the legal expenses of counsel in connection with a prosecution for health and safety offences. Many reputable insurers offer such cover.

Statutory civil liability

Civil liability refers to the 'penalty' which can be imposed by a civil court, i.e. the County Court; the High Court; the Court of Appeal (Civil Division); or the House of Lords. In general terms, the first two courts are courts of first instance (i.e. they try cases for the first time), whereas the latter two courts are courts of appeal. Such liability consists of awards of damages for injury, disease and/or death at work

(a) in circumstances disclosing breach of common law and/or statutory duty (i.e. normally negligence) on the part of an employer/factory occupier (*see* Chapter 2 for an analysis of 'negligence', common to actions for both breach of common law and statutory duty); and
(b) arising out of and in the course of employment (*see further* Chapter 2).

Normally the employer is insured against this liability (*see* Chapter 2) and payment to the injured employee is made by the employer's insurer.

General and special damages

The damages which can be recovered following injury-causing accident/disease/death fall into two categories:

(a) General damages – which relate to losses incurred after the hearing of the action, viz. actual and probable (not merely 'possible') loss of future earnings following the accident.
(b) Special damages – relating to quantifiable losses incurred before the hearing of the case, and consisting mainly of
    (i) medical expenses incurred before the hearing of the case, and
    (ii) loss of earnings incurred before the hearing of the case.

In the case of fatal injury, compensation for death negligently caused is payable under the Fatal Accidents Act 1976, sec 1; moreover, a fixed lump sum (currently £3,500) is payable, under the Administration of Justice Act 1982, sec 3, in respect of bereavement.

Deduction of social security payments

As far as assessment of future probable earnings under the heading of 'general damages' is concerned, such future earnings are assessed net, i.e. as if tax had been deducted. Moreover, where, as is likely, an injured worker is in receipt of social security benefits, the Social Security (Consequential Provisions) Act 1975 (2 Sch 8) provides that half of the value of certain social security benefits, including particularly sickness benefit and disablement benefit, must be deducted from the subsequently awarded damages.

Parties to the action

Unlike criminal action, civil action is usually initiated by a private individual or by a company suing another private individual, company or local authority. This is known as a private interparty or adversarial action (or litigation). Where workplace injuries are concerned, such action is normally commenced by an injured worker, or, in the case of a fatality, by his dependants. If the worker is a member of a trade union, the union branch may initiate proceedings. Although brought against his employer or the factory occupier, the action is, very often, a claim on the employer's insurance company. If the employer is found legally liable (i.e. personally, or, more likely, vicariously negligent, *see* Chapter 2), the insurer will pay out to the injured worker.

Compulsory employers' liability insurance for negligence

Liability insurance cover is compulsory for most employers. Exceptions occur in the case of workplaces where the family and/or relatives of the employer are the only persons employed in the workplace, also the nationalised industries, local authorities, nuclear power installations and the police authorities, as well as certain other bodies financed out of public funds. Cover is provided in respect of injury, death or disease which is the result of legal liability on the part of the employer. Such legal liability may arise from (a) breach of common law duty or (b) breach of statutory duty or (c) breach of both types of duty. Insurance cover must be up to £2 million in respect of any one occurrence and most employers (with the exceptions mentioned above) must display a certificate of insurance in respect of such cover in a prominent place in the factory, shop or office, etc., so that employees may see it. This is required by the Employers' Liability (Compulsory Insurance) Act 1969 and Regulations passed under it. Failure to obtain and, if necessary, renew liability cover is a serious criminal offence, and is punishable by a maximum fine of £1,000 (Criminal Justice Act 1982); moreover, failure to display a certificate of insurance attracts a maximum fine of £500 (Criminal Justice Act 1982, sec 35, and Criminal Penalties, etc., (Increase) Order 1984).

'Guarantee' of compensation: The existence of large funds of insurance monies, guaranteed by compulsory liability insurance legislation, has led to awards of damages being made in circumstances where the risk of injury (and certainly the risk of death) has not necessarily been reasonably foreseeable – the test necessary to establish liability for negligence (*see* Chapter 2). In consequence, the base of liability has gradually moved away from fault in the direction of strict liability.

Civil liability arising from statutory duties in protective legislation

Breach of statutory duties relating to occupational health and safety results principally in criminal liability. With the exception of the General Duties of HSWA, which can only give rise to civil liability at common law (*see above*), statutory duties can also create civil liability, i.e. breach can lead to prosecution (and conviction) in a criminal court *and* to an award of damages in a civil action. This point, relating to breach of safety provisions, was first established in *Groves* v. *Lord Wimborne* [1898] 2 QB 402, where a boy lost his arm when working at machinery in an ironworks and was later successful in his action for damages against the employer. Suing for breach of the fencing requirements of the Factories Act 1961 is a standard practice today, and most injured employees sue their employers for breach of both statutory duty and common law duty, in what has become known as a double-barrelled action (*see* Chapter 2).

Breach and causation

Where there is a breach of statutory safety and/or health duty, before the injured workman can succeed in his action for damages, it is generally accepted that he must establish the three ingredients of negligence (i.e. statutory negligence), viz. duty of care; breach of duty; and injury, disease or death caused substantially by the breach. The first two ingredients normally present no problems because, where a statutory instrument lays down a health and/or safety duty on an employer, this establishes the existence of a duty of care for the purposes of civil liability. But the third ingredient, causation, can, and all too often has, generated many problems for injured employees.

The law is that an injured employee, or a deceased employee's dependant, must show that statutory breach was the substantial cause of his injury, disease or death, i.e. he must show that the injury, disease or death was predominantly caused by breach rather than his own failure to act correctly and properly in the interests of his own health and safety. A leading case setting down the law on causation in relation to statutory health and safety duties is *Gardiner* v. *Motherwell Machinery & Scrap Co. Ltd* [1961] 3 AER 831 where Lord Reid said,

> When a man who has not previously suffered from a disease contracts that disease after being subject to conditions likely to cause it, and when he shows that it starts in a way typical of disease caused by such conditions, he establishes a prima facie presumption that his disease was caused by those conditions.

The distinctive nature of criminal and civil law in the field of occupational health and safety was succinctly elucidated by Lord Diplock in the leading case of *Boyle* v. *Kodak Ltd* [1969] 2 AER 439 when he said, 'When considering the civil liability engrafted by judicial decision upon the criminal liability imposed by statute, it is no good looking to the statute and seeing from it where the criminal liability would lie, for we are concerned only with civil liability. We must look to the cases.'

Time for bringing actions

All civil actions for personal injury, disease and death must be brought within 3 years of the injury (Limitation Act 1980, sec 11). Normally, where accidents causing injuries or fatality are concerned, this 3-year limitation period causes no problems. But where certain (usually fatal) occupational diseases are concerned, manifesting themselves tardily over a 20- or 30-year period, the rule causes serious hardship. This is particularly true in the case of diseases such as occupational cancer, asbestosis and pneumoconiosis.

2

Common law liability and workplace injuries

Common law

Common law is law consisting of decisions of courts bound together by precedent into a body of authoritative rules. It is judge-made and accounts for the greater part of contract and tort.

History of common law and workplace injuries

The relationship of common law to workplace injuries and employers' liability goes back to the middle of the nineteenth century. Originally, the number of successful actions against employers was few owing to some hostility on the part of judges and tardiness on the part of Parliament in introducing 'progressive' legislation to eliminate anachronistic judicial doctrines. Examples are

(a) the doctrine of common employment, whereby if one employee negligently injured another employee during the course of employment, the employer was held not liable for the injury (per Lord Abinger CB in *Priestley* v. *Fowler* (1837) 3 M&W 1). This obstacle was partially removed by the Employers' Liability Act 1880 which made employers liable in limited circumstances, and completely by the Law Reform (Personal Injuries) Act 1948 which finally abolished the doctrine of common employment in all employment situations;

(b) volenti non fit injuria (i.e. to one who is willing no harm is done). The effect of this doctrine was that, by virtue of being employed, an employee agreed voluntarily to run the risks ordinarily associated with employment. This was (and still is) a defence available to an employer when sued (*see later*).

Main areas of common law liability

The two main areas of common law civil liability are contract and tort. This chapter examines the duties which the law of tort has placed on employers. Contract law has generally not been concerned with liability for injuries/disease/death at work.

Employers' liability in tort

The rule of common law is that everyone owes a duty to everyone else to take reasonable care so as not to cause them foreseeable injury. Hence an employer will be liable if he fails to take reasonable care to protect his workforce from foreseeable injury, disease and/or death. The basis of liability is negligence. The remedy or redress is unliquidated damages for injury, disease or death suffered at work (*see* Chapter 1).

Negligence

In order to show that an employer was negligent, an employee must establish that the employer

(a) owed him a duty of care;
(b) acted in breach of that duty; and
(c) caused injury, disease or death to the employee (*Lochgelly Iron & Coal Co.* v. *M'Mullan* [1934] AC 1).

Employers' duties at common law

The duties of employers at common law were identified by the House of Lords in the leading case of *Wilsons & Clyde Coal Co.* v. *English* [1938] AC 57 as follows. All employers must provide

(a) a safe place of work, including safe access and egress;
(b) a safe system of work;
(c) safe plant and appliances; and
(d) safe and competent fellow workers.

'I do not mean that employers warrant the adequacy of plant, or the competence of fellow-employees, or the propriety of the system of work. The obligation is fulfilled by the exercise of due care and skill' (per Lord Wright in *Wilsons & Clyde Coal Co.* v. *English*).

Safe place of work

This duty was established in *Brydon* v. *Stewart* (1855) 2 Macq 30. Here some miners had left the pit before the end of the shift. As they were on their way up the pit shaft, a stone fell from the side of the shaft, killing one of them. The cage in which they were travelling to the top was open. It was held that the mine owner was liable, since access to and from the pit was not safe.

A place of work can be outdoors. In *Bradford* v. *Robinson Rentals Ltd* [1967] 1 AER 267 an employee suffered frostbite after being required to drive 500 miles in a van without a heater and a leaking radiator in freezing conditions. He successfully sued his employer for damages, as frostbite was a reasonably foreseeable consequence of being required to drive a defective van. But it is only the foreseeable risk of injury for which provision has to be made (*Latimer* v. *AEC Ltd* [1953] 2 AER 449, a case which concerned section 25 of the Factories Act 1937 (now section 28(1) of the Factories Act 1961)). This section requires that, so far as is reasonably practicable, floors, steps, stairs and passages, etc., should be kept free from obstructions and substances likely to cause persons to slip. During the course of an exceptionally heavy thunderstorm one weekend the factory had become flooded. The rainwater had become mixed with an oil liquid used for cooling machines and, as a result, a slippery film of oil was left on the factory floor. The factory floor was later treated with sawdust but, owing to the large area involved, the factory occupiers were unable to treat the whole floor. An employee slipped on an untreated part of the floor and was injured. It was held that the factory occupier was not in breach of the Factories Act 1937, sec 25(1). He had carried out all reasonably practicable measures to make the floor free from substances likely to cause persons to slip. (The result would be the same under the present requirement of the Factories Act 1961, sec 28(1), relating to floors.) At common law the factory occupier is not required to make provision for the unprecedented and freak hazard.

Safe system of work

This is the most extensive of the duties placed on an employer. The duty ranges from co-ordination of the various interrelated workplace departments to the general conditions of work, such as heating, lighting, ventilation, freedom from foreseeable risk of disease, safe working of lifts etc. In addition, it covers an effective system of supervision and training in the hazards of the job as well as instruction in the use of personal protective clothing and the safe use of appliances. This is in addition to any general or specific statutory duties placed on the employer, for instance by HSWA, sec 2, and Regulations passed under the Factories Act 1961 and the Offices, Shops and Railway Premises Act 1963 (e.g. the Power Presses Regulations 1965 and the Prescribed Dangerous Machines Order 1964, requiring sufficient training or adequate supervision before a young person can work at such machines in factories or offices and shops).

Co-ordination of work departments

In *Wilsons & Clyde Coal Co.* v. *English* [1938] AC 57 an employee in a mine was injured whilst passing along one of the underground haulage roads at the end of the day shift at the same time as haulage plant was set in motion. His employer, the mine owner, was held liable at common law for having failed to provide a safe system of work. The haulage plant should have been stopped at the same time as shifts came to an end.

Effective supervision

This duty is well illustrated by the case of *Bux* v. *Slough Metals Ltd* [1974] 1 AER 262. Here the appellant, who was employed as a die-caster by the respondent, was engaged on piece-work in the die-casting foundry. His work consisted of melting ingots of aluminium alloy in a furnace, lifting out the molten metal with a ladle and pouring it into a die. Goggles had (eventually) been provided and the employee was instructed to wear them. He found, however, that they misted up, told his superintendent that they were unsuitable and stopped wearing them. He was not later exhorted to wear them by any member of management. He was blinded when molten metal splashed into his face. He sued his employer for damages for breach of (a) Regulation 13(1)(*c*) of the Non-Ferrous Metals (Melting and Founding) Regulations 1962, in not having been provided with suitable goggles, and (b) the duty to 'police' a safe system of work through effective supervision at common law. It was held by the Court of Appeal that the employer had carried out his statutory duty but that nevertheless he was liable for breach of the duty of effective supervision at common law. '... it would be idle for the employers to urge that they have fulfilled their duty of reasonable care for the safety of their workmen by simply providing them with goggles and then stand by while the men did dangerous work with their eyes wholly unprotected' (per Edmund Davies LJ).

Safe plant and appliances

The duty of an employer is to 'provide' and 'maintain' safe plant and appliances for the job. The duty to 'provide' is satisfied where the employer makes available plant and appliances and safety equipment, which are readily to hand in an accessible place, and informs accordingly. In the absence of a specific statutory requirement to the contrary (e.g. Regulation 11 of the Protection of Eyes Regulations 1974, requiring that suitable eye protection actually be put into the possession of the employee), it is not necessary for the employer to put the equipment into the physical possession of the worker, even less to 'wet nurse' experienced 'hands'. In *Woods* v. *Durable Suites Ltd* [1953] 2 AER 391 an employee, who was employed in the veneer department of a factory where he was engaged in the spreading of synthetic glue, suffered dermatitis. In order to warn of the risk of dermatitis, management had erected a notice outlining precautions to be taken to avoid dermatitis and instructing the workforce in the use of barrier cream, soap and washing facilities, all of which had been supplied. The appellant was an experienced workman and had been specifically instructed in the use of protective measures. He nevertheless chose to ignore them. In an action against his employer for damages at common law, it was held that the employer was not liable. He had done all that was reasonably expected of him.

Failure to provide plant for a job will involve the employer in liability. In *Lovell* v. *Blundells & Crompton & Co. Ltd* [1944] 2 AER 53 the plaintiff was employed by the defendant to overhaul the boiler tubes of a ship. Being unable to reach all the tubes himself, the employee found some planks and set up his own staging. The planking proved unsatisfactory and the employee was injured. It was held that the employer was liable. Similarly, if a correct quantity of plant for the job is not provided, the employer may well be liable. In *Machray* v. *Stewarts & Lloyds* [1964] 3 AER 716 the plaintiff was employed as a rigger. Whilst he was working 21 metres above ground a loop section of pipe, weighing over 500 kilograms, had to be fixed. In order to accomplish this it was necessary to move the loop section 4 metres. One of the established methods of doing this was by using chain block and tackle. The employee endeavoured to obtain two sets of chain block and tackle, but only one was available at the time. Because he had been told by the chargehand that the job was urgent, the employee used single chain block, in consequence of which the loop section swung out of hand, seriously injuring the plaintiff. He sued his employer for negligence at common law. During the course of giving judgment in favour of the injured workman McNair J. said,

> When I find a workman ... adopting a course of conduct not for the sake of saving himself trouble, but in order to get on with his employer's business, and when I find that he has been prevented from doing the work in the way in which he would have preferred to do by the employer's breach in not providing him with proper tackle, I am very slow to put any blame on him.

Provision of safe plant and appliances includes the monitoring of safety performance accompanied by a regular defects reporting system. No matter how good the system of safety inspection of plant is in the factory, the employer could be liable if he has failed to institute a back-up defects reporting procedure. In *Barkway* v. *South Wales Transport Co. Ltd* [1950] 1 AER 392 the appellant's husband was killed whilst travelling on a bus belonging to the respondent, as a result of a tyre burst. The vehicles were inspected and tested by the company regularly and thoroughly. Nevertheless, the company was held to be liable, because it did not require its drivers to report incidents which could have led to the discovery of hidden defects that might cause a tyre burst.

Duties owed only to employees

The common law duties of employers are owed only to employees. They are not owed to independent contractors and their employees who may be working on the premises. HSWA, sec 3(1), places a duty on an employer not to expose the workforce of an independent contractor to risks to health and safety. But breach of this duty only gives rise to criminal liability, HSWA, sec 47, preventing civil claims being brought in respect of breaches of the General Duties of HSWA. Enforcement of this duty is as much in the interests of the employer's workforce as that of the subcontractor's workforce.

The relationship of employer to employee is a complex one, and the following questions have to be answered in order to determine whether a workman is an employee:

(a) Does the person or company for whom the work is done control the way in which the work is done, e.g. specifying the work to be done, wages/salaries, etc., provision of social security stamps, holidays and hours of work, and the manner of work?
(b) Is a workman, although normally employed by an outside organisation, integrated even temporarily into the organisation of the enterprise in question?
(c) Does the workman trade in his own right as a self-employed person, providing his own insurance, assistants, tools and equipment? (And see generally the remarks made in *Ready Mixed Concrete (South East) Ltd* v. *Minister of Pensions and National Insurance* [1968] 1 AER 433.)

However, the fact that a person styles himself as self-employed does not mean that he cannot be an employee. In *Ferguson* v. *John Dawson*

& Partners (Contractors) Ltd [1976] IRLR 346 it was held that a contract to hire labour-only subcontractors was a contract of employment. The labour-only subcontractor was, therefore, entitled to the protection of Regulation 28(1) of the Construction (Working Places) Regulations 1966, which required that the subcontractor who engaged him should provide a suitable guard rail. As a result of this not having been done, the subcontractor was held liable for injury suffered by the labour-only subcontractor (in spite of the fact that the latter regarded himself as self-employed).

Disobeying safety orders

Where an employee disobeys a safety instruction, he can be prosecuted for breach of HSWA, sec 7 (*see* Chapter 3), as well as dismissed from his job (*see* Chapter 5). It is unlikely, however, that he will lose entitlement to damages, even though they may be reduced as a result of contributory negligence on his part. Moreover, if, whilst disobeying a safety instruction, an employee injures either a co-employee or an innocent member of the public or an employee of an outside workforce, his employer will still be liable. In *Century Insurance Co. Ltd* v. *Northern Ireland Road Transport Board* [1942] AC 509 an employee of the respondent was employed to deliver petrol in tankers to garages. Whilst delivering petrol at a garage forecourt and whilst petrol was being transferred from the tanker to an underground tank at the garage, the employee decided to have a smoke. Having lit a match, he then threw it away, whilst still alight, and it landed by the underground tank. There was an explosion and considerable damage to persons and property. The Court of Appeal held that the respondent employer was liable, since the employee was doing what he was employed to do, namely deliver petrol, even though he was doing his job in a grossly negligent way (i.e. whilst smoking a cigarette).

More recently in *Rose* v. *Plenty* [1976] 1 AER 97 the respondent was employed as a milk roundsman by the Co-op. The latter had gone to great lengths to prevent employees continuing the practice of taking on young children and paying them for delivering bottles of milk and collecting empty bottles. Notices at depots urged 'Children must not in any circumstances be employed by you in the performance of your duties'. Contrary to this directive the respondent 'employed' a young boy. The latter was injured when he rode on the milk float with one leg dangling over the side so that he could jump off quickly to deliver bottles of milk. Evidence showed that the respondent drove negligently, with the result that the boy's leg was trapped and crushed between the wheel and the kerb. The trial judge ruled that the employee was 75 per cent to blame and the boy 25 per cent. On an appeal to the Court of Appeal to determine whether the employer was liable, it was held that he was. The fact was that the employee was doing what he was employed to do but was doing it negligently.

A case where an employee, whilst disobeying a safety instruction, suffered fatal injury and where damages were awarded to his widow was *Westwood* v. *The Post Office* [1973] 3 AER 184. The appellant's husband had been employed by the respondent. One day he went onto the flat roof of the telephone exchange building for his mid-morning break. The door to the roof was locked and so he entered the lift motor room, getting onto the roof through a window. The door to the lift motor room was normally locked but on this occasion it was slightly ajar. On the door was a prominent notice: 'Only the authorised attendant is permitted to enter.' The employee was not an authorised attendant. There was a floor in the lift motor room with a trap door which was not of sound construction, as required by section 16 of the Offices, Shops and Railway Premises Act 1963 (OSRPA). On his return the employee jumped from the roof onto the trap door, which gave way, and fell on a concrete floor and was killed. Though the Court of Appeal ruled that the employee was a trespasser and, therefore, not entitled to damages, the House of Lords took a different view. Giving judgment, Lord Kilbrandon said,

> the sole act of negligence giving rise to this accident was the respondents' breach of statutory duty. Any fault on the part of the deceased was a fault of disobedience, not a fault of negligence, because he had no reason to foresee that disregard of the order to keep out of the lift motor room would expose him to danger. It would indeed not have done so, had it not been that, unknown to him, the respondents were in breach of their duty to take care for the safety of those employed in the premises.

Vicarious liability

Once the doctrine of common employment was finally abolished by the Law Reform (Personal Injuries) Act 1948, vicarious liability became a reality. The importance of vicarious liability cannot be underlined too strongly, since it is generally on this ground that employers are held liable at common law. The substance of the doctrine is that if an employee, whilst acting in the course of his employment, negligently injures another employee or an employee of an outside contractor working on the premises, or even a member of the public, the employer will be liable for the injury. And since most accidents at work happen in this way, rather than as a result of the personal negligence of the employer, vicarious liability is the ground on which most claims for injury-causing accidents are successful.

Vicarious liability arises on the part of an employer simply because of his status as an employer. It must be insured against under the provisions of the Employers' Liability (Compulsory Insurance) Act 1969 and employers cannot contract out of this liability, since it is prohibited by the Law Reform (Personal Injuries) Act 1948 and the Unfair Contract Terms Act 1977. The key to liability is that the accident causing injury/disease/death arises (a) out of and (b) in the course of employment. This does not normally include travelling to and from work, though it would be, as is the case with state benefit, if the mode of transport to and from work was within the employer's control, or provided by or in arrangement with him.

Notwithstanding vicarious liability, the employee can be sued instead of or in addition to the employer where he has been negligent (*see later Lister* v. *Romford Ice & Cold Storage Co. Ltd* [1957]). For obvious reasons this would be restricted to senior employees.

Breach of common law and statutory duties – the double-barrelled action

Because an injured employee is entitled to sue his employer for damages for injury resulting from a breach of (a) common law duty and (b) statutory duty, this has led to the emergence of the 'double-barrelled' action against employers; in such cases employees sue separately (though simultaneously) for breach of both duties on the part of the employer. This development can be traced back to the decision in *Kilgollan* v. *Cooke & Co. Ltd* [1956] 2 AER 294.

Employers' defences

There are two defences available to an employer sued for breach of common law, viz. (a) assumption of risk of injury (volenti non fit injuria) and (b) contributory negligence. The first is a complete defence and means that no damages will be payable; the second is a partial defence and means that the injured worker's damages will be reduced to the extent to which he is adjudged to blame for his injuries.

Volenti non fit injuria

This means 'to one who is willing no harm is done', and applies to the situation where an employee, being fully aware of the risks he is running in not complying with safety instructions, duties, etc., after being exhorted and supervised, and having received training and instruction in the dangers involved in not following safety procedures and statutory duties, suffers injury, disease and/or death as a result. Here it is open to an employer to argue that the employee agreed to run the risk of the injury, etc., involved. If this defence is successfully pleaded, the employer will be required to pay no damages.

This defence has not generally succeeded in actions by injured workmen, since there is a presumption that employment and the dangers sometimes inherent in it are not voluntarily accepted by workers; rather employment is an economic necessity. This has been the position since the decision of *Smith* v. *Baker & Sons* [1891] AC 325 where the appellant, who was employed to drill rocks, was injured by stones falling from a crane operated by a co-employee. Although the appellant knew of the risk he was running from the falling stones, it was held by the House of Lords that he had not agreed to run the risk of being injured.

An exception to the general position occurred in *ICI Ltd* v. *Shatwell* [1964] 2 AER 999. Here two brothers, the respondents, were employees of the appellant, being employed as skilled shotfirers in rock blasting, for which they were highly paid. A statutory duty was placed on the two employees personally (not on the employer) to take specific safety precautions when shotfiring was about to begin. The two employees had been thoroughly briefed in the dangers of the work and the risks involved, e.g. premature explosion. They knew of the statutory prohibition in question. Nevertheless, they decided to test although a cable was too short to reach the shelter, rather than wait a few minutes before a workmate could go and get another cable. One brother handed the other brother two wires and the latter applied them to the galvanometer terminals. An explosion occurred injuring both employees. On an appeal to the House of Lords (which reversed the decision of the Court of Appeal) it was held that the employer was not liable. The reasons given were as follows:

(a) the employer was not in breach of statutory duty; the breach of statutory duty was committed by the employees;
(b) the two employees were highly skilled operatives, part of a well-paid workforce elite and knew the dangers involved in taking short cuts where safety was concerned.

Contributory negligence

The Law Reform (Contributory Negligence) Act 1945, sec 1(1), provides that where injury is caused by the fault of two or more persons, liability or fault (and, in consequence, damages) must be apportioned in accordance with the extent to which both or more were to blame. If, therefore, following an employee's injury, it is established that both employer and employee were at fault (e.g. in breach of statutory requirements), when sued for damages, the employer can plead that the employee, through his negligence in failing to look after his own health and safety, should be held partly to blame and have his damages reduced to that extent. A classic case illustrating the operation of this rule (which is applied quite extensively in practice by judges) is *Uddin* v. *Associated Portland Cement Manufacturers Ltd* [1965] 2 AER 213. Here an employee, who was a machine minder, in an effort to retrieve a pigeon, leaned across a revolving shaft in a part of the factory in which he was not authorised to be, and was injured, losing an arm. His employment was confined to the cement-packing plant but his injury occurred in the dust-extracting plant. He sued his employer for breach of section 14(1) of the Factories Act 1937 (the predecessor of the current Factories Act 1961). It was held that the employer was liable under that section, but that the employee's damages would be reduced by 80 per cent to account for his own contributory negligence.

Employers' compulsory liability insurance

Under the provisions of the Employers' Liability (Compulsory Insurance) Act 1969, and Regulations passed under it, employers (with notable exceptions, such as local authorities, the police, etc.) are required to take out insurance against (*inter alia*) common law liability to their employees resulting in injury, disease and/or death. Failure to do so is a criminal offence (*see* Chapter 1).

Redress of employer's insurer

In the law of insurance there is a doctrine, known as subrogation, which entitles an insurer who has indemnified an insured (employer) in respect of his legal liability, to recover his losses as far as he can, and, in particular, to take over any action which his insured might have had against a third party. This principle has been applied to industrial injuries claims. In *Lister* v. *Romford Ice & Cold Storage Co. Ltd* [1957] 1 AER 125 the appellant was employed by the respondent as a lorry driver. His father was also employed by the same company. One day, whilst reversing the lorry, the appellant negligently injured his father, and his father was paid damages under the principle of vicarious liability (*see earlier*). The insurer who had paid the damages sought to recover that amount (£1,600) from the negligent employee, on the ground that it is an implied term of an employment contract that an employee carry out his employment with due care and skill (*see* Chapter 5). On an appeal to the House of Lords it was held that the employee had broken the duty of care and skill implied in his contract, and that as a consequence the insurer could recover the sum paid by way of damages.

Employees' duties at common law

Employees owe duties at common law towards employers, e.g. the duty to perform their work with reasonable care and skill. These are implied terms of the contract of employment and have, to a large extent, been superseded in importance by the law relating to unfair dismissal, as laid down in the Employment Protection (Consolidation) Act 1978 (EPCA). It is, therefore, better to consider them under that heading (*see* Chapter 5).

3

Health and Safety at Work etc., Act 1974 – administration and duties

Prelude – Report of the Robens Committee

The *Report of the Committee on Safety and Health at Work* (Cmnd 5034), published in July 1972 (the Robens Report), proposed the following changes in law and administration relating to occupational health and safety:

(a) The introduction of an enabling Act placing broad General Duties upon employers, employees, manufacturers of industrial products, the self-employed and occupiers of buildings where people work.
(b) Within the broad framework of the General Duties, regulations, often accompanied by approved codes of practice, following consultation with industry.
(c) The amalgamation of the previous inspectorates into one unified inspectorate, i.e. the Health and Safety Executive (HSE), presided over by a director general.
(d) The establishment of a new policy-making body, the Health and Safety Commission (HSC), consisting of employers' and workers' representatives as well as representation from local authorities and educational establishments, which would submit proposals, forming the basis of new regulations, to the Secretary of State for Employment, who would lay them before Parliament.
(e) The conferment of wider, more effective accident prevention powers upon HSE inspectors, viz.
    (i) improvement notices and
    (ii) prohibition orders (*see* Chapter 4).
(f) Less statutory regulation and more voluntary participation on the part of management and workers. An example of such an approach is the Safety Representatives and Safety Committees Regulations 1977, empowering union-appointed safety representatives from the workforce to carry out inspections of the workplace with a

view to identifying and/or monitoring workplace hazards and making recommendations to management.

Health and Safety at Work etc., Act 1974 (HSWA)

This Act implemented the majority of the proposals of the Robens Report. More exactly, it

(a) established the Health and Safety Commission (HSC);
(b) established the Health and Safety Executive (HSE);
(c) conferred accident prevention powers on HSE inspectors (*see* Chapter 4);
(d) placed broad general duties on employers, employees and manufacturers of industrial products as well as on the self-employed and occupiers of buildings where people work (*see below*);
(e) provided for participation of management and workers in the identification and monitoring of workplace hazards by requiring the appointment of union safety representatives from the workforce to carry out periodic inspections of the workplace, and by requiring that changes and improvements in occupational health and safety be discussed at meetings of safety committees consisting of management and union representation. These requirements were laid down in the Safety Representatives and Safety Committees Regulations 1977.

Health and safety regulations

One of the principal functions of the Health and Safety Commission is to propose regulations on health and safety at work to the Secretary of State for Employment. Health and safety regulations can do one of the following:

(a) repeal or modify any of the existing 'relevant statutory provisions' (for the meaning of this expression, *see* Chapter 4);
(b) exclude or modify any of the 'existing statutory provisions'. An example of the power of modification is the Employers' Health and Safety Policy Statements (Exception) Regulations 1975, which exempts employers employing fewer than five employees from complying with HSWA, sec 2(3), and having to issue a written company safety policy, and revise it as often as necessary;
(c) make a specified authority responsible for the enforcement of any of the 'relevant statutory provisions'. An example of the exercise of this power is the enforcement of some of the 'relevant statutory provisions' by HSE and others by local authorities (*see* Chapter 4) (HSWA, sec 15(3)).

Areas likely to be the subject of future statutory regulation are outlined in HSWA, Schedule 3.

Issue and approval of codes of practice

The Health and Safety Commission is empowered to approve and issue codes of practice for the purpose of providing guidance on health and safety duties laid down in statute or regulations. A code of practice can be drawn up by HSC or some other body. In every case, however, any relevant government department, or other body, must be consulted beforehand and the approval of the Secretary of State must be obtained (HSWA, sec 16). Any code of practice approved in this way is an 'approved code of practice' (HSWA, sec 16(7)). (For the effect of codes of practice in civil and criminal proceedings, *see* Chapter 4.)

Health and Safety at Work etc., Act – the General Duties

HSWA places broad General Duties upon five separate classes of persons, viz.

(a) employers;
(b) employees;
(c) manufacturers and suppliers of industrial products;
(d) the self-employed; and
(e) occupiers of buildings in which persons work, other than one's own employees.

Duties of employers

It is the duty of every employer, so far as is reasonably practicable, to ensure the health, safety and welfare at work of all his employees (HSWA, sec 2(1)). More particularly, this includes

(a) the provision and maintenance of plant and systems of work that are safe and without health risks (HSWA, sec 2(2)(*a*));
(b) arrangements for ensuring safety and absence of health risks in connection with the use, handling, storage and transport of articles and substances (HSWA, sec 2(2)(*b*));
(c) the provision of such information, instruction, training and supervision as is necessary to ensure the health and safety at work of employees (HSWA, sec 2(2)(*c*));
(d) the maintenance of any place of work under the employer's control in a condition that is safe and without health risks, including means of access and egress (HSWA, sec 2(2)(*d*));

(e) the provision and maintenance of a working environment for employees that is safe and free from health risks, with adequate facilities and arrangements for employees' welfare (HSWA, sec 2(2)(*e*)).

Health and safety policy

Employers must prepare and, as often as is necessary, revise a written Statement of Health and Safety Policy (HSWA, sec 2(3)). There is an exception to this requirement in the case of employers employing at any time fewer than five employees (Employers' Health and Safety Policy Statements (Exception) Regulations 1975). (For further information relating to Health and Safety Policies, *see* Chapter 6.)

Legal importance of Health and Safety Policy statements

Requirements detailed in the Statement of Health and Safety Policy (and preferably published in works rules, handbooks or codes of practice relating to specific tasks) probably do not constitute terms of a contract of employment. Nevertheless the rule book may be construed (and, indeed, has been so construed) as constituting reasonable orders which an employer is entitled to give to an employee. Failure on the part of an employee to obey such rules would amount to a breach of contract of employment. The matter was summarised as follows by Roskill L. J. (referring to the employers' rule book) in *Secretary of State* v. *ASLEF* [1972] 2 AER 949:

> It was not suggested that strictly speaking this formed part of the contract of employment as such. But every employer is entitled within the terms and scope of the relevant contract of employment to give instructions to his employees and every employee is correspondingly bound to accept instruction properly and lawfully so given. The rule book seems to me to constitute instructions given by the employer to the employee in accordance with that general legal right.

The importance of the law relating to the contractual rights and duties of employers and employees has been largely superseded by the law relating to unfair dismissal, as contained in the Employment Protection (Consolidation) Act 1978 (EPCA). The present position would, therefore, seem to be that failure to carry out an order based on a rule or procedure in a Statement of Health and Safety Policy (assuming that the employee was well aware of it) could lead to the dismissal of the employee. Or, if an employer was in breach, to the constructive dismissal of an employee (*see* Chapter 5). This view is supported by the fact that it was always an implied term of an employment contract at common law that an employee would carry out his duties honestly and with due care and skill (*Lister* v. *Romford Ice & Cold Storage Co. Ltd*

[1957] 1 AER 125). A case confirming this approach is *Martin* v. *Yorkshire Imperial Metals Ltd*, COIT No. 709/147, Case No. 32793/77, where an employee was held to have been fairly dismissed for having removed a guard from a machine so that he might get his work done more quickly.

Failure to bring the contents of a Statement of Health and Safety Policy to the attention of employees, albeit even on a departmental basis, can have serious consequences, as illustrated in the case of *Armour* v. *Skeen* 1977 SLT 71. Here two painters employed under a direct labour contract by Strathclyde Regional Council fell from scaffolding erected for the work. One was killed. Both the Regional Council and its Director of Roads were prosecuted for having failed to comply with HSWA, sec 2(1) and (3) and sec 37(1) – the last section concerning offences committed by a body corporate and individual functional directors. Although the council had issued a statement of safety policy, as required by section 2(3), which had been circulated to the various departments, instructing directors and heads of departments to ensure safe conditions of work, as well as an 'Advisory Bulletin' instructing each department to issue a safety statement specifically related to the work being carried out, including training and instruction in safe practices, the director of roads had not brought this to the attention of his employees and persons carrying out contracts for the council. He was fined £125 and his appeal against conviction under section 37(1) was turned down. Moreover, the council was found guilty of breach of HSWA, sec 2(1), and fined £500. (For more about section 37, see later in this chapter.)

Duty of consultation and establishment of safety committees

Employers are required, in the interests of making and maintaining arrangements to enable them and their employees to co-operate in promoting and developing measures to ensure the health and safety at work of employees and in monitoring the effectiveness of such measures,

(a) to consult with workplace representatives (known as 'safety representatives', whose powers and functions are set out in the Safety Representatives and Safety Committees Regulations 1977 – *see* Chapter 5); and
(b) to set up a safety committee, if requested to do so by two or more safety representatives, to monitor measures taken to ensure the health and safety of employees (HSWA, sec 2(6)).

Duties of employees

Employees, whilst at work, must

(a) take reasonable care for their own health and safety, and that of other persons (including members of the public) who may foreseeably be affected by their acts or omissions at work; and

(b) co-operate with their employer so far as is necessary for him to comply with any duty or requirement under any of the 'relevant statutory provisions' (for the meaning of this expression, *see* Chapter 4) (HSWA, sec 7(*a*) and (*b*));
(c) not intentionally or recklessly interfere with or misuse anything provided for the purpose of health and safety at work in furtherance of a statutory requirement (HSWA, sec 8).

In addition, employees owe employers a contractual duty to carry out their work with care and skill. Failure to do this can lead to dismissal as being in breach of a term of their contract of employment (*see* Chapter 5).

As for the definition of 'employee' and the legal problems involved in determining the existence of an employer/employee relationship, *see* Chapter 2.

Consequences of breach of duties in HSWA by employers and employees

Breach by employer

An employer who is in breach of his duties under HSWA, sec 2, can be

(a) prosecuted by an HSE inspector, and, if found guilty, made to pay a fine, or possibly sent to prison (*see* Chapter 4);
(b) sued for negligence at common law if the breach causes injury to an employee. An action for breach of statutory duty does not lie for breach of the General Duties of HSWA (HSWA, sec 47) (*see* Chapter 2);
(c) sued for constructive dismissal before an industrial tribunal by an employee if the breach constitutes a fundamental term of the contract of employment (*see* Chapter 5).

Breach by employee

An employee who is in breach of his duties under HSWA can

(a) be prosecuted by an HSE inspector and made to pay a fine, if convicted;
(b) if his breach causes injury to himself or to other employees or to a member of the public, involve his employer in vicarious liability (*see* Chapter 2), though, where the injury is to himself, his damages will be reduced on the ground of his contributory negligence;
(c) be dismissed from his employment for being in breach of the term of his contract of employment that he will carry out his work with proper care and skill. If the employer has gone through the necessary procedures set out in the ACAS Code, 'Disciplinary Practice

and Procedures in Industry', an industrial tribunal may well declare such dismissal fair (*see* Chapter 5).

Duties of employers to persons other than their employees

Every employer must conduct his undertaking in such a way as to ensure, so far as is reasonably practicable, that persons not in his employment are not exposed to risks to health or safety (HSWA, sec 3(1)).

Duties of occupiers of premises to persons other than their employees

Health and safety duties are placed on persons in control of premises for the benefit of persons working in such premises, but who are not their employees, or who use plant and substances made available to them for their use there (HSWA, sec 4(1)). An example of the operation of this section would be factory or other work premises owned and leased out by a local authority. Here it is the duty of the person or persons or body in control to take steps to ensure, so far as is reasonably practicable, that (*a*) the premises, (*b*) the means of access and egress, and (*c*) the plant and substances provided for use there, are safe and without health risks (HSWA, sec 4(2)). The protection under this section extends to visitors who are

(a) workers, e.g. employees of a contract window-cleaning firm engaged to clean windows on a local authority owned or privately owned building, and
(b) non-working visitors, who use plant and equipment on premises provided for their use, e.g. visitors to a launderette or schoolchildren visiting a public swimming pool.

Meaning of control

The duty laid down in HSWA, sec 4, is associated with occupation of a building rather than ownership, though it would extend to owner-occupiers. HSWA places responsibility for health and safety upon a person or persons having control 'to any extent' (HSWA, sec 4(2)), and this duty extends to both working and non-working visitors.

In law, control is a synonym for occupation, which includes management of a building. Today occupation or control of a building or buildings is often shared between owner and manager or owner and occupier. Indeed, the idea of single exclusive control based on physical occupation is practically redundant. This much emerged from the decision of the House of Lords in *Wheat* v. *E. Lacon & Co. Ltd* [1965] 2 AER 700, where, following a fatal injury to a visitor at a public house, both owner, the brewery, and the occupier, the licensee, would have been liable (under the Occupiers' Liability Act 1957), had it not been for a technicality of law, the court taking the view that, since the owners could control the use to which the licensee put the premises, they were 'to some extent' in control.

The position under HSWA, sec 4, will, therefore, be as in *Wheat* v. *Lacon* regarding occupation of buildings, unless that position has been modified by contract or lease. Where a contract or lease expressly or by implication places responsibility for

(a) maintenance and/or repair of premises, or
(b) health and safety obligations in connection with plant and substances in premises,

upon a particular person or body, that person or body is deemed to be in control (HSWA, sec 4(3)).

Duties of self-employed persons

HSWA places responsibilities upon self-employed persons. This is the first time that such general statutory duties (as distinct from common law duties, which are applicable to everyone, *see* Chapter 2) have been placed on the self-employed. This is a measure largely designed to remedy certain 'practices' in the construction industry where many self-employed persons are engaged, if only on a temporary basis (but *see also* the case of *Ferguson* v. *John Dawson & Partners* (*Contractors*) *Ltd* in Chapter 2).

Every self-employed person must conduct his undertaking in such a way as to ensure that persons not in his employment are not exposed to health and safety risks (HSWA, sec 3(2)).

Duties of designers, manufacturers and suppliers of industrial products

For the first time in the history of occupational health and safety legislation, general duties have been placed on designers, manufacturers and suppliers of articles and substances for use at work. HSWA, sec 6, requires that, so far as is reasonably practicable, designers, manufacturers (including submanufacturers), importers and suppliers of articles and substances for use at work

(a) ensure that they are designed and constructed so as to be safe and without health risks (HSWA, sec 6(1)(*a*), (2) and (4));
(b) carry out or arrange for the carrying out of testing, research and examination which may be necessary to comply with the duty in section 6(1)(*a*) (*above*) (HSWA, sec 6(1)(*b*) and (5));
(c) take steps which are necessary to secure that adequate information is available about the use for which the product has been designed and tested, and about any conditions necessary to ensure that,

when put to that use, the product will be safe and without health risks (HSWA, sec 6(1)(*c*) and (4)(*c*)).

Special responsibilities of designers and manufacturers

The duty to research and test industrial products rests with designers and manufacturers (*see* sec 6(1), (2), (4) and (5)). The requirements applicable to importers, distributors and suppliers of industrial products are rather less onerous. It is their duty to obtain information, on an on-going basis, from designers and manufacturers of industrial products, so as to be able to advise their client-users how to use safely products which they buy or hire. Provision of data sheets by designers, manufacturers, etc., is not necessarily enough for these purposes. Importers and suppliers are not required to repeat any research and testing already carried out (HSWA, sec 6(6)).

Duties of installers of industrial equipment

Installers and erectors of equipment and machinery for use at work must, so far as is reasonably practicable, ensure that no health and safety hazards arise from the method of installation or erection (HSWA, sec 6(3)). In addition to this requirement, the fencing provisions of the Factories Act 1961 apply to machinery, although not in normal operation, as soon as installation is complete (*Irwin* v. *White, Tomkins & Courage Ltd* [1964] 1 AER 545). Thus, machinery used for demonstration purposes is caught by the Factories Act 1961.

Duties of companies, corporations and their officials

HSWA makes provision for offences committed by companies, corporations and local authorities, as well as by officials. Most directors and other corporate officials are employees, no matter how senior, and so can be dismissed for health and safety offences like any other employee (*see* Chapter 5), in addition to any prosecution which might be brought against them by HSE inspectors. Moreover, the more senior the official, the more severe the penalty imposed by the magistrates is likely to be.

Offences committed by companies and local authorities

Where there has been a breach of one of the 'relevant statutory provisions' (e.g. HSWA, OSRPA and the Factories Act 1961) on the part of a body corporate (i.e. limited company or local authority) and the offence can be proved

(a) to have been committed with the consent or connivance of, or
(b) to be attributable to any neglect on the part of,

any director, manager, secretary or other similar officer of the body corporate, he, as well as the body corporate, can be found guilty and punished accordingly (HSWA, sec 37(1)). Breach of this section has the following consequences:

(a) where an offence is committed through neglect by a board of directors or the council of a local authority, the company itself or the local authority can be prosecuted as well as the directors or council members individually who may have been to blame;
(b) where an individual functional director or executive of a local authority is guilty of an offence, he can be prosecuted as well as the company or local authority;
(c) a company or local authority can be prosecuted even though the act or omission resulting in the offence was committed by a junior official or executive or even a visitor to the company or local authority premises. (This last is made clear in HSWA, sec 36(1) (*see below*).) Thus an offence committed by a training officer or safety officer of a local authority or company can involve the council of the local authority or the board of directors of the company in liability under section 37(1).

Offences committed by other 'corporate' persons

Offences committed by junior corporate officials, e.g. training officers, safety officers, etc., are provided for in section 36(1). Thus,

> Where the commission by any person of an offence under any of the relevant statutory provisions is due to the act or default of some other person, that other person shall be guilty of the offence, and a person may be charged with and convicted of the offence ... whether or not proceedings are taken against the first-mentioned person.

Section 36(1) can be used not only against junior members of management but also against visitors to workplaces. Case law seems to show that 'other person' refers to persons lower down the corporate tree than those mentioned in section 37(1), e.g. safety officers, training officers. This is the effect of the decision (involving the Trade Descriptions Act 1968) in *Tesco Stores Ltd* v. *Nattrass* [1971] 2 AER 127.

Breach of section 36(1) is not a defence for a company or local authority prosecuted under section 37(1). This is made clear in section 36(1) itself. (This was a defence under the Trade Descriptions Act 1968 where the company could show fault on the part of an employee who was not himself of sufficiently senior corporate status to 'commit' the company.) It is thought, however, that breach of section 36(1) would entitle an HSE inspector to use discretion in deciding whether to proceed against the body corporate under section 37(1).

4

Enforcement

Introduction

Before the Health and Safety at Work etc., Act (HSWA) was passed in 1974, the main 'weapon' used in the fight against breach of statutory duty relating to occupational health and safety was prosecution by an inspector. The Robens Report (Cmnd 5034), however, recommended that inspectors be given wider powers than prosecution. These recommendations were implemented in HSWA, secs 21–6. Of these 'new' powers the most important is the power to serve improvement and prohibition notices. A prohibition notice can be served by an inspector, irrespective of whether any statutory offence has been committed, if he believes that there is risk of serious personal injury from a workplace activity or process. Moreover, inspectors can use these executive powers to enforce not only the provisions of HSWA but also pre-HSWA protective legislation, e.g. the Offices, Shops and Railway Premises Act 1963 (OSRPA) and the Mines and Quarries Act 1954 (i.e. 'relevant statutory provisions').

Despite these 'new' executive powers conferred on inspectors, it should not be assumed that prosecution is a thing of the past. On the contrary, prosecution is still an important 'weapon', though of ancillary importance to the improvement or prohibition notice. Employers and employees, whether junior, middle or senior management, including the managing director and individual functional directors, who commit breaches of 'relevant statutory provisions' could be prosecuted instead of being served with an improvement or prohibition notice. This applies also to corporate bodies.

'Relevant statutory provisions'

Enforcement powers and procedures apply to all the 'relevant statutory provisions'. This expression refers to the following statutory requirements:

(a) all the provisions of HSWA, Part 1 (i.e. secs 1–54);
(b) health and safety regulations passed pursuant to HSWA (e.g. the Notification of New Substances Regulations 1982); and
(c) 'existing statutory provisions' (i.e. all enactments specified in HSWA, Schedule 1, including any regulations made under them in so far as they continue in force) (HSWA, sec 53(1)).

(A full list of the 'relevant statutory provisions' is given in the Appendix to this chapter.)

The enforcing authorities

Generally, the enforcing authority is the HSE, except in the following cases:

(a) Where Regulations stipulate that the local authority is the enforcing authority. The Regulations which so stipulate are the Health and Safety (Enforcing Authority) Regulations 1977, as amended by SI 1980 No. 1744 (referred to as the 'Enforcing Authority Regulations').
(b) Where one of the 'relevant statutory provisions' stipulates that some other body is responsible for enforcement (HSWA, sec 18(1), (7)(*a*)).

There are draft proposals to transfer more enforcing powers to local authorities and environmental health officers.

Where HSE is the enforcing authority

HSE is the enforcing authority for

(a) premises occupied by, or under the control of, a local authority or the Crown, e.g. colleges of further education;
(b) the following activities carried on in any premises (whether or not they are the main activity):
    (i) construction work,
    (ii) installation, maintenance or repair of gas, water or electricity systems,
    (iii) areas of responsibility specifically excluded from local authorities (Enforcing Authority Regulations, Regs 4(1) and (2)).

These last (iii) refer to

(a) premises controlled or occupied by a railway undertaking;
(b) sale or storage of water and sewage, or gas;
(c) wholesale distribution of flammable, toxic or certain other dangerous substances, including petrol;
(d) the following premises where consumer services are carried on:
  (i) dry cleaning,
  (ii) radio and television repairs, and
  (iii) the maintenance or repair of motor vehicles (Enforcing Authority Regulations, Reg 3, 1 Sch);
(e) premises occupied or under the control of a fire authority or police authority or the UK Atomic Energy Authority; or
(f) circumstances where responsibility for licensing and enforcement are vested under an 'existing statutory provision' in a county council or a harbour authority (Enforcing Authority Regulations, Regs 4(1), (3)).

Where the local authority is the enforcing authority

The local authority is the enforcing authority in the following situations, where the *main* activity is

(a) sale or storage of goods for retail or wholesale distribution (other than those mentioned in (d)(iii) above);
(b) office activities,
(c) catering services,
(d) provision of residential accommodation,
(e) shop premises providing consumer services (except dry cleaning, radio and television repairs, etc. (mentioned in (d) above)), or
(f) dry cleaning in launderettes. (Enforcing Authority Regulations 1977, Reg 3, 1 Sch.)

Thus local authorities have enforcement powers in respect of offices, shops, public houses, and restaurants and hotels.

Transfer of responsibility

Enforcement of any of the 'relevant statutory provisions' may be transferred by agreement from HSE to local authorities, and vice versa. Moreover, the Health and Safety Commission has power to order such transfer without agreement (Enforcing Authority Regulations, Reg 5).

Enforcement powers of HSE inspectors and local authority officers

The two main enforcement powers of inspectors are

(a) service of improvement and prohibition notices, and
(b) prosecution.

Improvement notices and prohibition orders

Improvement notices

An inspector may serve an improvement notice if he is of the opinion that a person

(a) is contravening one or more 'relevant statutory provisions';
(b) has contravened one or more of those provisions in circumstances that make it likely that the contravention will continue or be repeated (HSWA, sec 21).

The period stipulated in the notice within which the requirement must be carried out must not be less than 21 days – the time allowed for lodging an appeal with an industrial tribunal (HSWA, sec 21).

Prohibition notices

If an inspector is of the opinion that an industrial activity involves or will involve a risk of serious personal injury, he may serve a prohibition notice (HSWA, sec 22(2)). Prohibition notices differ from improvement notices as follows:

(a) in the case of a prohibition notice it is not necessary that an inspector believe that a provision of HSWA or any other statutory provision is being or has been contravened;
(b) prohibition notices are served in anticipation of danger.

Improvement and prohibition notices compared

Unlike an improvement notice, where time is allowed in which to put the offending matter right, a prohibition notice can take immediate effect. 'A direction ... shall take immediate effect if the inspector is of the opinion ... that the risk of serious personal injury is ... or will be imminent' (in any other case it will have effect at the end of a period stipulated in the notice) (HSWA, sec 22(4). Thus a prohibition notice, which is a direction to stop the work activity in question, rather than put the offending matter right, can take effect immediately it is issued; alternatively (and not infrequently) it may allow time to implement certain modifications (it is then known as a 'deferred prohibition notice'). Both immediate and deferred prohibition notices will usually refer to a schedule of work which the inspector will require to be carried out.

Effect of non-compliance with a notice

If, after the time specified in the notice has expired, or, in the event of an appeal, after the expiry of any additional time allowed for compliance by the tribunal, an applicant does not comply with the notice, he can be prosecuted. If convicted by the Crown Court of contravening a prohibition notice, he may be imprisoned (HSWA, sec 33(1)(*g*), (4)(*d*)).

Appeals against improvement and prohibition notices

A person against whom an improvement or prohibition notice is served may appeal to an industrial tribunal within 21 days from the date of service of the notice. The tribunal may extend this time where it is satisfied, on application made in writing (either before or after the expiry of 21 days), that it was not reasonably practicable for the appeal to be brought within the 21-day period. On appeal the tribunal may either affirm or cancel the notice, and if it affirms it, may do so with modifications, in the form of additions, omissions or amendments (HSWA, secs 24(2), 82(1)(*c*); Industrial Tribunals (Improvement and Prohibition Notices Appeals) Regulations 1974, Reg 3 and Sch 2).

Effect of an appeal

Where an appeal is lodged against an improvement notice, that automatically suspends operation of that notice. But a prohibition notice will continue to apply, unless there is a direction to the contrary from the tribunal. More specifically,

(a) in the case of an improvement notice, the bringing of an appeal has the effect of suspending operation of the notice;
(b) in the case of a prohibition notice, the lodging of an appeal only suspends operation of the notice
   (i) if the tribunal directs, on the application of the applicant; and
   (ii) the suspension is then effective from the date when the tribunal so directs (HSWA, sec 24(3)).

Prosecution for breach of the 'relevant statutory provisions'

Prosecutions often follow non-compliance with an improvement or prohibition notice. Alternatively, inspectors may simply prosecute without serving notices. Prosecutions normally take place before the magistrates but HSWA makes provision for prosecution on indictment (HSWA, sec 33(3)(*b*)). The test of prosecution on indictment is gravity of the particular offence.

Burden of proof in criminal cases

Throughout criminal law the general burden of proving guilt is on the prosecution to show that the accused committed the offence (*Woolmington* v. *DPP* [1935] AC 462). While not detracting from this general principle, HSWA makes the burden of the prosecution considerably easier than it otherwise would have been. Thus HSWA, sec 40, provides that it is incumbent upon the accused to show either (a) it was not practicable, or (b) it was not reasonably practicable to do more than was, in fact, done; *or* (c) there was no better practicable means than were, in fact, used to satisfy the statutory requirement.

If the accused cannot discharge this duty, the case will be regarded as proved against him. In this connection the effect of an approved code of practice may be crucial.

Effect of an approved code of practice

A provision in an approved code of practice is not in itself a statutory duty and so cannot of itself be enforced by HSE inspectors. Nor of itself can it give rise to civil liability (HSWA, sec 17(1)). Nevertheless, failure on the part of a person to whom its provisions apply to comply with it can have serious practical consequences, since it brings into operation a presumption that he was in breach of the statutory requirement(s). This applies only in the case of criminal liability (HSWA, sec 17(2)).

Principal offences and penalties

Health and safety offences are of three kinds, viz.

(a) summary offences (i.e. triable by magistrates);
(b) offences triable summarily and on indictment; and
(c) offences triable only on indictment.

By far the greater number of health and safety offences fall into categories (a) and (b).

Summary offences and offences triable either way

The principal health and safety offences which are triable (a) summarily or (b) either summarily or on indictment are the following:

(a) Failure to carry out one or more of the General Duties of HSWA, secs 2–7.
(b) Contravening either of the following sections:
    (i) HSWA, sec 8 – intentionally or recklessly interfering with anything provided for safety;

(ii) HSWA, sec 9 – levying payment for anything which an employer must by law provide in the interests of health and safety (i.e. personal protective clothing).

(c) Contravening any health and safety regulations.

(d) Contravening a requirement imposed under HSWA, sec 14, or under regulations passed pursuant to it (power of HSC to order an investigation).

(e) Contravening a requirement imposed by an inspector.

(f) Preventing or attempting to prevent a person from appearing before an inspector (e.g. a safety representative), or from answering his questions.

(g) Intentionally obstructing an inspector.

(h) Intentionally or recklessly making false statements, where the statement is made

(i) to comply with a requirement to furnish information; or

(ii) to obtain the issue of a document.

(i) Intentionally making a false entry in a register, book, notice, etc., which is required to be kept.

(j) Falsely pretending to be an inspector (HSWA, sec 33(1)).

Summary trial or trial on indictment

Many of these offences are triable either way, i.e. summarily before the magistrates, or on indictment before the Crown Court. The offences mentioned in (d) to (g) as well as (j) are, however, only triable summarily. And in the case of (e) it is only an offence consisting of contravening a requirement imposed by an inspector under section 20 which is triable summarily; contravention of a requirement imposed under section 25, i.e. power to seize and destroy dangerous articles and substances, is triable either way.

Offences triable either way are usually tried summarily before the magistrates. But they could be tried on indictment – for instance, when the magistrates feel that the case is too serious for them to try and accordingly requires the imposition of a penalty greater than they can impose, under their powers under HSWA, sec 33(3)(*a*), as amended by the Magistrates' Courts Act 1980, sec 32(2), i.e. a fine of £2,000. This could well be the situation where the commission of the offence involved serious risk to life, or the offender was a persistent one, or the offence(s) revealed flagrant disregard of health and safety precautions. If the case goes to the Crown Court, that court can impose an unlimited fine (HSWA, sec 33(3)(*b*)(ii)). Moreover, the prosecution may request trial on indictment, or the defendant may refuse to consent to summary trial.

The great majority of the above offences, triable either summarily or on indictment carry a maximum fine of £2,000 on summary conviction.

Offences triable on indictment only

The following are more serious offences and are triable on indictment only:

(a) contravening any of the 'relevant statutory provisions' by doing something unlicensed which requires a licence from HSE;
(b) contravening a term or condition or restriction attached to such licence;
(c) acquiring or attempting to acquire, possessing or using an explosive article or substance in contravention of the 'relevant statutory provisions';
(d) contravening a requirement or prohibition imposed by a prohibition notice under section 33(1)(*g*);
(e) wrongful use or disclosure of information, contrary to section 33(1)(j) (HSWA, sec 33(4)).

Penalties for indictable offences

Offences under section 33(4) are punishable on conviction in the Crown Court by

(a) a maximum of 2 years' imprisonment, or
(b) an unlimited fine, or
(c) up to 2 years' imprisonment and an unlimited fine (HSWA, sec 33(3)(*b*)(i)).

As regards other indictable offences (i.e. those triable either way (*see above*)), the Crown Court can impose an unlimited fine (HSWA, sec 33(3)(*b*)(ii)).

Continuing offences

Where, following conviction, a person continues to contravene an improvement or prohibition notice, he is liable to a maximum fine of £200 for every day that the offence is continued or the contravention continues (Criminal Justice Act 1982, sec 35; Criminal Penalties, etc., (Increase) Order 1984).

Appendix: the 'relevant statutory provisions'

Explosives Act 1875	The whole Act except secs 30 to 32, 80 and 116 to 121
Alkali, etc., Works Regulation Act 1906	The whole Act
Anthrax Prevention Act 1919	The whole Act
Employment of Women, Young Persons and Children Act 1920	The whole Act

Celluloid and Cinematograph Film Act 1922	The whole Act
Explosives Act 1923	The whole Act
Petroleum (Consolidation) Act 1928	The whole Act
Hours of Employment (Conventions) Act 1936	The whole Act except sec 5
Petroleum (Transfer of Licences) Act 1936	The whole Act
Hydrogen Cyanide (Fumigation) Act 1937	The whole Act
Ministry of Fuel and Power Act 1945	Section 1(1) so far as it relates to maintaining and improving the safety, health and welfare of persons employed in or about mines and quarries in Great Britain
Coal Industry Nationalisation Act 1946	Sections 42(1) and (2)
Radioactive Substances Act 1948	Section 5(1)(*a*)
Fireworks Act 1951	Sections 4 and 7
Agriculture (Poisonous Substances) Act 1952	The whole Act
Emergency Laws (Miscellaneous Provisions) Act 1953	Section 3
Agriculture (Safety, Health and Welfare Provisions) Act 1956	The whole Act
Factories Act 1961	The whole Act except sec 135
Public Health Act 1961	Sec 73
Offices, Shops and Railway Premises Act 1963	The whole Act
Nuclear Installations Act 1965	Sections 1, 3 to 6, 22 and 24, Schedule 2
Mines Management Act 1971	The whole Act
Employment Medical Advisory Service Act 1972	The whole Act except secs 1 and 6 and Schedule 1

5

Health and safety and industrial relations law

Need for disciplinary procedure

Established, mutually agreed, in-house disciplinary procedure and practice are essential. This should contain a clearly identifiable appeals procedure. Employees should be permitted to give an explanation of their conduct and management should carry out a thorough investigation of matters leading to the alleged offence (*Henry* v. *Vauxhall Motors Ltd*, COIT No. 664/85, Case No. 25290/77). Moreover, in addition to an in-house procedure, embodying the ACAS Code, a clearly communicable formal system should be instituted. Thus the contract of employment and supporting job description must identify requirements and responsibilities of all employees and management. This can be done by cross-referencing to job description in the contract. Moreover, the company health and safety policy statement should specify the statutory duties under HSWA and other legislation placed on employees and management.

Relevance of company Health and Safety Policy Statement to the contract of employment

Statutory duties under HSWA and other legislation, as well as Regulations made under HSWA and other legislation, should be itemised in the company Health and Safety Policy Statement – itself a requirement of HSWA, sec 2(3). Such duties would then qualify as contractual terms, breach of which could lead to dismissal, though not necessarily instant dismissal, since not all breaches would amount to gross misconduct leading to instant dismissal. The Employment Protection (Consolidation) Act 1978 (EPCA), sec. 1(4), requires that the written particulars of terms of employment, which all full-time employees are entitled to receive by the thirteenth week of employment, include reference to disciplinary rules, procedures etc., or a document specifying such rules, procedures etc. However, sec 1(5) expressly provides that these requirements do not apply to rules, disciplinary decisions and procedures in connection with health and safety at work.

Works rules

Not all works rules will be based on or referable to statutory duties and/or regulations. This may well be the position in respect of self-evident risks taken at work, e.g. skylarking, smoking, drinking, etc., which are not in themselves specific health and safety offences. Most companies wishing to specify in their works rules the 'penalties' for such conduct, would do well to bear in mind, however, that, unless such conduct

(a) constitutes a serious risk of injury to the employee or fellow employees, or
(b) breaches specific health and safety duties and/or regulations, or
(c) is persistent or repeated in contravention of earlier warnings,

it is not likely to be regarded as an implied term of an employment contract but rather as a reasonable order or instruction which an employer is entitled to give to an employee. The practical consequence is, however, probably the same as if it constituted a term of an employment contract. Therefore, an employee who disobeyed such an instruction would be in breach of his general duty to co-operate with his employer and so, after institution of the necessary procedures laid down in the ACAS Code, liable to be dismissed (*see Secretary of State* v. *ASLEF* [1972] 2 AER 949 mentioned in Chapter 3).

General offences

Smoking

There are certain regulations which prohibit smoking either completely or in certain circumstances. Breach of such regulations could lead to instant dismissal, assuming that the employee knew that he was committing an offence and was aware of the risk involved. The specific regulations prohibiting smoking at work are:

(a) Explosives Act 1875, sec 10
(b) Factories (Horsehair Processes) Regulations 1907, Reg 13
(c) Celluloid (Manufacture, etc.) Regulations 1921, Reg 6
(d) Chemical Works Regulations 1922, Reg 4

(e) Manufacture of Cinematograph Film Regulations 1928, Reg 10
(f) Magnesium (Grinding of Castings and Other Articles) Special Regulations 1946, Reg 13
(g) Pottery (Health and Welfare) Special Regulations 1950, Reg 14
(h) Factories (Testing of Aircraft Engines and Accessories) Special Regulations 1952, Reg 20
(i) Petroleum Spirit (Conveyance by Road) Regulations 1957
(j) Highly Flammable Liquids and Liquefied Petroleum Gases Regulations 1972, Reg 14
(k) Organic Peroxides (Conveyance by Road) Regulations 1973
(l) Poisonous Substances in Agriculture Regulations 1984, and the List of Statutory Instruments amended accordingly
(m) Control of Lead at Work Regulations 1980, Reg 10

In other cases smoking in itself, even though a risk may be involved (unless, of course, the risk of danger is high, as, say, in the case of a fire risk), would not normally be enough to justify instant dismissal. In *Bendall* v. *Paine & Betteridge* [1973] IRLR 44 an employee who had smoked for 15 years was told periodically not to do so, as there was a fire risk. One day he was summarily dismissed for smoking. His dismissal was held to be unfair (under the provisions of the Industrial Relations Act 1971, the Act then in force governing unfair dismissal). The dismissal was unfair because previously, although the employee had been warned about smoking, he was not made aware that he was risking instant dismissal. The applicant should have been given a final warning in writing advising him of the likelihood of dismissal, before he was actually dismissed.

Drinking

Like smoking, drinking in itself is probably not sufficient to justify instant dismissal (*McGibbon* v. *Gillespie Building Co. Ltd* [1973] IRLR 105), but if drunkenness constitutes a safety hazard, then the necessary disciplinary procedures should be instituted immediately. If this attracts instant dismissal, the employee should be made aware of this on entering employment, the penalties being spelt out to him in the works rules and the contract of employment. This was made clear in *Abercrombie* v. *Alexander Thomson & Son* [1973] IRLR 326, where the applicant was found drunk whilst operating a crane. Management decided to dismiss him, but this was not done until 2 weeks later. In the interim period the applicant was permitted to carry on working. It was held that the delay in dismissing him made the dismissal unfair.

Other 'dismissible' offences

Other conduct which could give rise to dismissal, instant or otherwise, is

(a) sleeping while employed,
(b) vandalism of company property,
(c) theft of company property,
(d) failure to attend in-plant or residential training courses,
(e) failure to observe hygiene standards in the food industry, e.g. smoking or failing to wash regularly.

General duty on employer to maintain discipline

Because of his status, an employer is vicariously liable for negligent injury caused by an employee to a co-employee or to a member of an outside workforce or the general public (*see* Chapter 2). Nor can he contract out of this liability. For this reason employers must, through line management, ensure that employees are protected from the negligent conduct of other employees. This gives the employer the right (indeed, imposes upon him the duty) to dismiss, either after due warnings, or instantly in the case of gross misconduct, an employee who constitutes a danger to co-employees. 'If a fellow workman ... by his habitual conduct is likely to prove a source of danger to his fellow employees, a duty lies fairly and squarely on the employer to remove the source of danger' (per Streatfield J. in *Hudson* v. *Ridge Manufacturing Co. Ltd.* [1957] 2 AER 229).

Gross misconduct causing health and safety risks

Gross misconduct, involving health and safety risks, is 'punishable' with instant dismissal. The offending employee is not entitled to a warning, oral or in writing, nor does the employer have to abide by the ACAS procedures. What constitutes gross misconduct will normally be specified, for the benefit of employees, in the works rules, the company health and safety policy statement as well as in individual contracts of employment. Normally, however, only the following matters would be construed as serious enough to constitute gross misconduct:

(a) Serious and/or flagrant disregard of or disobedience to health and safety duties, regulations and rules, involving risk of injury to life or property damage. Thus in *Ashworth* v. *Needham & Sons Ltd* 1977 COIT No. 681/78, Case No. 20161/77, an employee who erected a collapsible fence around a cellar, instead of steel or concrete plates, was held to have been fairly dismissed.
(b) Persistent or repeated health and safety offences, or hygiene offences.
(c) Failure to observe safety procedures on the part of a person engaged on an intrinsically dangerous operation. The categories of such occupations are not exhaustive but the following would come

within this category: an airline pilot (*Taylor* v. *Alidair Ltd* [1978] IRLR 82 per Lord Denning MR), a nuclear scientist, the driver of a petrol or chemical container – in all these cases, with one split-second mistake a disaster could ensue.

Law relating to unfair dismissal

The law relating to unfair dismissal was introduced by the Industrial Relations Act 1971 and is currently contained in the Employment Protection (Consolidation) Act 1978 (EPCA), secs 54–81, as amended by the Employment Acts 1980 and 1982. Under this Act an employee can present a claim to an industrial tribunal, and if the complaint is upheld the employer will be ordered to compensate the ex-employee for loss of earnings, or alternatively reinstate or re-engage him.

The following conditions govern applications for unfair dismissal. The applicant is only entitled to present a complaint

(a) if he worked for the employer as an employee and not as an independent contractor;
(b) he has either been dismissed by the employer (actual dismissal) or has resigned in circumstances amounting to constructive dismissal;
(c) he has in general worked for the employer for at least 2 years (as from 1 June 1985); however, if an employee is dismissed on medical grounds in compliance with any law or regulation or code of practice providing for health and safety at work (e.g. Control of Lead at Work Regulations 1980), the qualifying period for presenting a claim is only 1 month (EPCA, sec 64(2); Employment Act 1982, 2 Sch 5).

Actual and constructive dismissal

Dismissal is of two kinds: actual and constructive.

Actual dismissal

Here the employer terminates the contract of employment.

Constructive dismissal

Here the employee voluntarily resigns because of the employer's conduct in breaking a fundamental term of the contract of employment.

Reason for dismissal

In order to determine whether a dismissal was fair or unfair, the employer must identify the reason (or the main reason) for the dismissal and at the same time establish that the reason was one of those cited in EPCA, sec 57(2), or some other 'substantial' reason justifying the dismissal (EPCA, sec 57(1)). For these purposes, reasons that might well be relevant to health and safety at work are those

(a) related to the capability or qualifications of the employee, or
(b) related to the conduct of the employee (EPCA, sec 57(2)).

Once an employer has established the reason for dismissal, it must then be shown that he acted reasonably in treating the reason as sufficient cause for dismissing the employee. This is a matter for the tribunal to decide. Here the tribunal must have regard to the size and administrative resources of the employer's undertaking when determining the reasonableness of the dismissal (EPCA, sec 57(3), and the Employment Act 1980, sec 6). Arguably, a small concern would be treated more sympathetically than a larger one with greater management resources to draw on.

Relevance of ACAS Code

In order to determine whether an employer has acted reasonably in dismissing an employee, regard should be had to the question whether the employer complied with the provisions of the ACAS Code relating to disciplinary procedure and practice, except in cases of gross misconduct, where instant dismissal is justified (*see above*). Failure to follow procedures outlined in the ACAS Code means, in all probability, that the employer would be construed as having acted unreasonably.

Duty of employer to consult with safety representatives

It is the duty of every unionised employer to consult with union-appointed safety representatives so as to make and maintain arrangements which will enable the employer and his workforce to co-operate in both promoting and developing health and safety at work measures and procedures, and monitoring their effectiveness (HSWA, sec 2(6)). Moreover, every such employer must, if requested to do so by two or more safety representatives, establish a safety committee whose purpose is to monitor health and safety at work (HSWA, sec 2(7), and the Safety Representatives and Safety Committees Regulations 1977, Reg 9(1) (hereafter referred to as the Safety Representatives Regulations)).

Definition of a safety representative

A safety representative is an employee appointed by his trade union to represent the workforce in consultations with the employer on all matters affecting health and safety at work, and to carry out periodic inspections of the workplace for hazards. A safety representative appointed by an employer to fulfil the same functions is not a safety representative for present purposes and would not enjoy the powers and immunities given by the Safety Representatives Regulations. In short, he would not be recognised by law.

Role of safety representatives

Safety representatives exist in order to

(a) represent their fellow employees at the workplace;
(b) carry out workplace investigations and inspections;
(c) handle information (e.g. information which an inspector might have disclosed in furtherance of his duty under HSWA, sec 28(8) (*see below*)).

None of the functions of a safety representative confers legal duties upon him (Safety Representatives Regulations, Reg 4(1)).

Disclosure of information to safety representatives by employer

Employers are required to disclose to safety representatives information necessary in order to enable them to carry out their functions (Safety Representatives Regulations, Reg 7(2)). The full list of information is to be found in paragraph 6 of the Approved Code of Practice on Safety Representatives and Safety Committees, and an employer who failed to comply with this code would be deemed to be in breach of the law (*see* Chapter 4). The sort of information referred to is technical information and consultants' reports, information concerning the employer's future plans and any proposed changes in so far as they might affect health, safety and welfare at work.

Disclosure of information to safety representatives by an inspector

HSE inspectors are required by HSWA, sec 28(8), to supply safety representatives with technical information obtained during their visits (e.g. measurements, testing the results of sampling and monitoring), notices of prosecution, copies of correspondence and copies of any improvement notice or prohibition order served upon the employer. An inspector has no discretion in this matter; it is mandatory. During discussions with safety representatives an inspector must inform them what action he proposes to take as a result of his visit to the workplace.

Safety committees

In prescribed cases every employer must establish a safety committee, if requested to do so by two or more safety representatives (Safety Representatives Regulations, Reg 9(1)). The purpose of the safety committee is to monitor health and safety at work measures and procedures (HSWA, sec 2(7)).

When setting up a safety committee the employer must

(a) consult with both
   (i) the safety representatives who made the request, and
   (ii) the representatives of a recognised trade union or unions whose members work in any workplace where it is proposed that the committee will function;
(b) post a notice, stating the composition of the committee and the workplace or workplaces to be covered by it, in a place where it can be easily read by employees; and
(c) establish the committee within 3 months after the request for it was made (Safety Representatives Regulations, Reg 9(2)).

PART II

Health and safety management

6

Safety management and policy

Lawrence Bamber, BSc, DIS, MIOSH, MBIM

The statement of health and safety policy

The Health and Safety at Work etc., Act 1974, requires employers to prepare and, as often as may be appropriate, revise their written statement of general policy with respect to the health and safety at work of their employees, together with the organisation and arrangements in force at the time for carrying out the policy, and to bring the statement, and any revisions, to the notice of all employees. However, employers employing fewer than five employees are excepted from this requirement (Employers' Health and Safety Policy Statements (Exception) Regulations 1975) (*see* Chapter 3). To this end the Health and Safety Executive (HSE) has produced useful guidance on the format and utilisation of health and safety policy statements in industry and commerce. A policy should comprise three parts:

Part 1: General Statement of Intent (Specifying Objectives)
This part should outline the company's overall philosophy in relation to the management of health and safety.

Part 2: Organisation (People and their Duties)
This part should clearly show who is responsible to whom and for what – i.e. the chain of command. (A management structure diagram is of use in this regard.) Also, this part should demonstrate how accountabilities are fixed, how policy implementation is to be monitored, how safety committees and safety representatives are to function, and how individual job descriptions should reflect health and safety responsibilities and associated accountabilities.

Part 3: Arrangements (Systems and Procedures)
This part should detail the practical arrangements in force to

assist in overall policy implementation. These include safety training, safety audits/inspections, accident reporting/investigation, safe systems of work, permit to work systems, noise/environmental control, utilisation of protective equipment, fire safety, liaison with contractors, machine guarding, emergency procedures and medical/welfare considerations. In practice, this part of the policy may be very lengthy and is often best presented in the form of a manual with appropriate cross-references made to it in Parts 1 and 2.

Each policy should be signed by the managing director/chief executive, and should be dated to facilitate revision. The policy should be brought to the attention of *all* employees, i.e. both existing and new, through training sessions, inserts in pay packets, display on notice boards, individual issue and by incorporation in employee handbooks. Any policy revision should also be brought to the attention of all employees.

The HSE publication *Effective Policies for Safety and Health* suggests that a policy statement should incorporate the following elements:

(a) A written safety policy which states the basic objectives and is supplemented by more detailed rules and procedures to cater for specific hazards.
(b) Definition of both the duties and the extent of responsibility of specified line management levels for safety and health, with identification made at the highest level of an individual with overall responsibility.
(c) Clear definition of the function of the safety officer and his relationship to line management made clear.
(d) The system for monitoring safety performance and publishing information about such performance.
(e) An identification and analysis of hazards, together with the precautions necessary on the part of staff, visitors, contractors, etc.
(f) An information system which will be sufficient to produce an identification of needs and can be used as an indicator of the effectiveness of the policy. (The amount of information required by such a system will depend on these needs, bearing in mind that the cost of obtaining the information should be realistically related to the expected benefit.)
(g) A training policy for all management and staff levels.
(h) A commitment to consultation on health and safety and to a positive form of worker involvement.

The HSE further suggests that it is not sufficient to publish a policy, however comprehensive it may be, unless the policy is translated into effective action at all levels within the organisation. Success, in terms of an acknowledged and continuing commitment at all management levels, is more likely where the policy is underwritten by the Board. They need also to make adequate financial provision for bringing the policy into effect. The requirement to monitor performance at a high level in the organisation is of particular importance.

A successfully operated policy ought to result in

(a) high standards of compliance with environmental requirements;
(b) high standards of compliance with the physical requirements, i.e. in regard to plant, machinery and process operations;
(c) carefully designed and observed safe systems of work;
(d) high standards of cleanliness and housekeeping;
(e) maintenance of safe means of access and egress;
(f) control of toxic, corrosive and flammable substances, where such control is relevant;
(g) effective consultation for safety and positive participation by work people; and
(h) training programmes which are well developed and run on a continuing basis for all levels.

The primary aim of the policy must be the motivation and involvement of the workforce. This is best achieved through a demonstrated commitment and concern on the part of management. In this context, first line supervision is of primary importance and more recognition should be given to its role. This means that particular attention should be paid to training in hazard identification and to the support of first line supervision in actions needed and taken. The needs of the worker relate to protective equipment and devices, to training relative to his job and the hazards involved, and to job descriptions. The importance of his contribution can be stressed in terms of the reporting of defects, in inspection and audit of the workplace and in the correct use of rules and procedures relating to safe systems of work.

Health and safety organisation: policy implementation

In order to ensure effective policy implementation, the organisation of health and safety management within a company should:

(a) clearly and unambiguously show, in written and pictogram format, the unbroken and logical delegation of duties through line management operating where risks arise and accidents happen;
(b) identify key personnel, by title rather than name, to be held accountable to senior management for ensuring that detailed

arrangements (systems and procedures) for safe working are developed, utilised and maintained;
(c) define the roles of both line and functional management by the use of specific job descriptions;
(d) provide adequate support through relevant functional management, i.e. safety advisers, medical advisers, designers, chemists, engineers, etc.;
(e) nominate competent persons to measure and monitor overall safety performance;
(f) provide the means/authority to deal with failures to meet the requirements of the policy;
(g) fix management's accountability for health and safety in a similar manner to other management functions;
(h) ensure that the organisation unambiguously indicates to each individual exactly what he must do to fulfil his role; and
(i) ensure that the organisation makes it known, in terms of both time and money, what resources are available for health and safety. The individual must be certain of the extent to which he is actually supported by the policy and the organisation needed to fulfil it.

If the above elements are incorporated into the organisation framework of a company, then the efficiency by which the policy is implemented will be greatly enhanced.

Joint consultation in health and safety

This section examines the complex role of management, workers and health and safety specialists in the development and subsequent implementation of health and safety policies through joint consultation.

In its report, the Robens Committee stated that real progress in the promotion of safety and health at work was impossible without the full co-operation and commitment of all employees. The committee felt that if workpeople were to accept their full share of responsibility, they must first be able to participate in the making and monitoring of arrangements for safety and health at work. These recommendations were later incorporated in the Health and Safety at Work, etc., Act 1974, more specifically section 2(4), (6) and (7), and the Safety Representatives and Safety Committees Regulations 1977 (*see* Chapter 5).

The principal aim, therefore, of joint consultation on, or participation in, health and safety matters is to involve those people at the 'sharp end' who are actually having the accidents and who are, therefore, well placed to identify risks and to assist in the prevention of further accidents. Hence line management, supervisors and workers should be actively encouraged to work together with health and safety specialists by participating in safety audits and safety committees. In this way, they will be given a say in developing a more realistic approach to accident prevention. More specifically, the HSC (1977) booklet *Safety Representatives and Safety Committees* gives excellent guidance on the interaction between the participants in the joint consultation process.

The role of the health and safety specialist in joint consultation is generally that of a catalyst. Primarily, his role is advisory, leaving executive decisions to be made by line management/safety committees, based on advice given to them. In fulfilling this role the health and safety specialist should work closely with management and workers and their representatives, with the object of ensuring a safe and healthy workplace in line with the organisation's health and safety policy.

Provision of information to employees

All employers have to provide such information, instruction, training and supervision as is necessary to ensure, so far as is reasonably practicable, the health and safety at work of their employees (HSWA, sec 2(2)(*c*)). In addition to this general duty there are specific Regulations – e.g. the Safety Representatives and Safety Committees Regulations 1977, Reg 7, and the Health and Safety (First Aid) Regulations 1981, Reg 4 – which require employers to provide relevant information to employees.

Safe systems of work

One of the best methods of communicating health and safety information is through the use of written safe systems of work (*see* Chapter 13). The establishment of safe systems of work is part of the common law duty of care owed by employers to their employees (*see* Chapter 2). In addition, it is a fundamental requirement of HSWA, sec 2(1)(*a*) (*see* Chapter 3). Essentially, all safe systems of work should be:

(a) fully documented in terms of the hazard, the precautions and the detailed safe working conditions;
(b) used increasingly in all aspects of job training, especially induction training; and
(c) referred to in Part 3 (*above*), i.e. the 'Arrangements' section, of the health and safety policy.

More specifically, in connection with the provision of information for employees, written safe systems of work should include details concerning:

(a) the correct use of plant, tools and equipment;
(b) the working environment – heating, lighting, ventilation, etc.;
(c) in-plant safety rules (for the legal effect of company or in-house safety rules, *see* Chapter 5);
(d) the formal issue, proper use and regular maintenance of all necessary protective equipment and clothing;
(e) relevant chemical/product safety literature – what to do in the case of spillage or fire, first aid treatment, etc.; and
(f) correct and safe working methods, incorporating relevant safety precautions.

Generally, when developing written safe systems of work, all hazards should be clearly identified, together with the precautions that should be taken to control them. The technique of Job Safety Analysis is useful in this regard (*see* Chapter 13).

Contracts of employment/employee handbooks

Although a contract of employment need not be in writing, all employees are entitled to receive, after 13 weeks of employment, details in writing of the main terms of their contract (EPCA, sec 1(4)(*a*)). Surprisingly, section 1(5) states that this statutory requirement does not include details relating to health and safety at work. It is, however, a common law requirement that employers take reasonable care for the health and safety of their employees and, therefore, such a term is implied in all contracts of employment (*Lister* v. *Romford Ice & Cold Storage Co. Ltd* [1957] 1 AER 125). To this end employee handbooks are a useful vehicle for disseminating information to the workforce relating to working conditions, health and safety requirements and Regulations as well as codes of practice. Moreover, induction training sessions will assist in this regard, as relevant information can be promptly brought to the attention of all new employees.

Measurement of safety performance

The measurement of safety performance is a complex evaluation and should take into account both positive (accident prevention) and negative (accident statistics) features. Positive features include aspects such as safety audits and inspections, risk identification, evaluation and control, loss control profiling, and fault-free analysis (*see* Chapter 8). Negative features to be incorporated include data collected via the use of accident records (*see* Chapter 7), i.e. accident statistics. Accident statistics may be used to monitor the overall effectiveness of the implementation of a health and safety policy, but a clearer picture will be obtained if other indicators, such as the results of a safety audit, are used in conjunction with statistical data.

Within the UK a number of standard indices are used. These are:

(a) $\text{Frequency Rate} = \dfrac{\text{Total number of accidents}}{\text{Total number of man-hours worked}} \times 100{,}000$

(b) $\text{Incidence Rate} = \dfrac{\text{Total number of accidents}}{\text{Number of persons employed}} \times 1{,}000$

(c) $\text{Severity Rate} = \dfrac{\text{Total number of days lost}}{\text{Total number of man-hours worked}} \times 1{,}000$

(d) $\text{Mean Duration Rate} = \dfrac{\text{Total number of days lost}}{\text{Total number of accidents}}$

(e) $\text{Duration Rate} = \dfrac{\text{Number of man-hours worked}}{\text{Total number of accidents}}$

For the statistics to be of use, the limitations of these indices should be realised. For example, the indices should not be used for comparing one factory or department with another, because of variables such as differing work patterns, differing degrees of risk and different levels of training. Ideally, the indices should only be used to compare the performance of the same factory/department over similar periods of time, i.e. to compare this year with last year. (For a fuller discussion of safety performance see Shipp and Sutton's (1972) Research Paper for the Robens Committee.)

Sources of information

Health and Safety Executive (HSE)

The HSE produces an annual *Publications Catalogue*, available from HMSO, which lists all relevant health and safety literature by subject, with key word cross-referencing, by title of legislation, by title of guidance literature/reports, by title of approved factory forms and by film title. This organisation also produces a 'publications in series' list which identifies all series of publications produced by the HSC and the HSE, such as guidance notes, guidance booklets, codes of practice, occasional papers, research papers and toxicity reviews. Further information sources, including the comprehensive range of material produced by RoSPA, are shown at Appendix 'Information Sources'.

Safety budgets

The economic argument for health and safety is strongly based on the fact that accidents cost money, in terms of both insured and uninsured costs, as well as economic sanctions such as improvement notices, prohibition notices, prosecutions and fines in the courts. (A fuller discussion on the costs of accidents is presented in Chapter 11.) Moreover, the use of accident costs to facilitate budgeting for safety and accident prevention would enable a degree of financial accountability to be built into the overall budgetary control system, as envisaged by the Robens Committee.

Indeed, the Robens Report suggested that better knowledge of accident costs could contribute towards more informed decision making. The report advocates the displaying of accident costs on the balance sheet, so encouraging management to apply the same effort and technique to accident reduction as is customarily applied to other facets of the business. Accident prevention then becomes a part of the standard economic activity of the company.

The present system of accident prevention operating throughout most of industry does not attempt to make line management financially accountable for accidents and uninsured losses, and very little use is made of economic arguments in stimulating management interest in accident prevention. Any arguments put forward rely mainly on legal and humanitarian considerations which, in some instances, fail to convince management that there is a need for accident prevention, at least beyond compliance with statutory duties.

The use of budgetary control would introduce economic accountability into the field of accident prevention. Such a measure would involve the reorganisation of the existing accounting procedures in most companies in order to overcome the lack of accountability for accidents.

When an accident occurs within a factory department, the cost of the accident usually is absorbed into the running costs of the factory as a whole, and will not be itemised on the departmental balance sheet. Nor will many of the indirect costs be paid for from the departmental manager's budget. Furthermore, the direct cost, i.e. insurance premiums such as employer's liability, will generally be paid from a central fund, usually administered by Head Office.

However, when a safety adviser or factory inspector recommends safety measures such as guarding for machinery, the cost is usually charged against the departmental manager's budget, though it is very unlikely that it would be itemised as an accident prevention cost. Thus under accounting systems employed in many companies, accident costs are not charged to the departmental manager's budget, whereas accident prevention is charged. Hence the departmental manager has no economic motivation to undertake any accident prevention, rather the reverse.

A positive economic motivating factor for encouraging accident prevention may be introduced by transposing these items in the budgetary system. For each accident, injury or incidence of damage that occurs in a department, a charge should be made against that department. Any accident prevention expenditure that is required within the department should be financed from a central fund subject to approval by the risk manager or safety adviser. The result, as far as the departmental manager is concerned, would be that it is costly to have accidents but not to prevent them. Thus line management becomes accountable for accidents occurring within their areas of control.

At the end of the financial year, a realistic allowance for accidents will be set within the new budget as a target for the manager to achieve. This allowance will form an integral part of the management plan as with budgetary control in other areas. However, the number, and hence the cost, of accidents budgeted for should be less than that of the previous year so that reduction of accidents becomes part of the management plan. This reorganised system would help to bring about the necessary economic accountability and would make full use of the knowledge and data obtained in establishing what accidents are costing the company in financial terms.

Once the costs of accidents have been established (*see* Chapter 11), the reorganised budgetary system can be implemented. The charges to be made against the departmental manager's budget can then be calculated and allocated on a monthly basis. The departmental manager would receive a monthly report giving information on the costs of accidents and accident prevention expenditure. This would enable him to plan any action necessary to maintain or improve the level of safety within his department. It would also facilitate decision making in connection with the allocation of scarce accident prevention resources. Any deficiencies in the current safety programme would be highlighted in cost terms rather than by a frequency rate, a measure of safety questioned by both management and academics!

On their own, the legal and humanitarian arguments for accident prevention may not be sufficient to achieve a reduction in accidents and other losses, e.g. damage to plant. The addition of economic accountability, through safety budgeting, should greatly assist in the overall aim of minimising losses resulting from accidents.

Safety propaganda

Safety propaganda – publications, posters, slide/tape programmes, films, etc. – is utilised in both formal and informal training situations with the intention of modifying behaviour through attitude change. In order to decide which aspect of safety propaganda is best suited to the needs of the organisation, it is useful to note the following. A person tends to remember:

10% of what he *reads*;
20% of what he *hears*;
30% of what he *sees*;
50% of what he *sees and hears*;
70% of what he *says in conversation*;
90% of what he *says as he does a thing*.

It follows, therefore, that the relative usefulness of safety propaganda will depend to a large extent on the method of communication utilised. For example, a person will tend to remember 50 per cent of a film, slide/tape programme or video as against 90 per cent if he describes a task as he does it under supervision.

Generally, safety propaganda may be communicated through a variety of media:

(a) Publications; programmed learning (*reads*) – 10%
(b) Taped commentaries; lectures (*hears*) – 20%
(c) Slides; posters; overhead transparencies (*sees*) – 30%
(d) Films; slide/tape programmes; videos (*sees* and *hears*) – 50%
(e) Discussion groups (*says in conversation*) – 70%
(f) On the job training; simulation exercises; role playing (*says* as he *does a thing*) – 90%

Pirani and Reynolds (1976) examined the use of five different methods of communication, using different facets of safety propaganda designed to persuade employees to utilise protective equipment. Their results, in rank order from best (highest percentage improvement in utilisation) to worst (little or no improvement), were as follows:

(a) Role playing
(b) Films
(c) Posters
(d) Discussion
(e) Discipline

These results tend to confirm that, for safety propaganda to be effective, active participation is required in order to create the necessary changes in behaviour.

7

Investigation, reporting and recording of accidents

There has been much research over the last century into the actual causes of accidents. These causes are amplified in Chapter 12. In the majority of cases, two factors are directly relevant:

(a) the objective danger, e.g. the inadequately fenced machine, unguarded floor opening, defective ladder; and
(b) the subjective perception of risk of the potential accident victim.

The cause–result accident sequence

All accidents involve one or more events which lead to the accident and possible injury. There are both direct and indirect causes of accidents but, in many cases, the indirect causes are overlooked in the subsequent investigation. Similarly, there are both direct and indirect results of accidents. The indirect results, as with the indirect causes, can be extremely significant, particularly in terms of cost (*see* Chapter 11). The cause–result accident sequence can be summarised as in Fig. 7.1. In order to understand the various components of this sequence, it is necessary to analyse each individually.

INDIRECT CAUSES ⟶ DIRECT CAUSES ⟶ ACCIDENTS ⟶ DIRECT RESULTS ⟶ INDIRECT RESULTS

Fig. 7.1 Cause–result accident sequence

Indirect causes

These are generally associated with two particular aspects, viz. people and the environment, which can be termed 'personal factors' and 'source causes'.

Personal factors

A personal factor is defined as 'any characteristic or condition of a person that causes or influences that person to act unsafely'. Personal factors include

(a) knowledge and skill deficiencies, e.g.
  (i) lack of hazard awareness,
  (ii) lack of job knowledge,
  (iii) lack of job skill, and
  (iv) lack of adequate instruction;
(b) conflicting motivations, e.g.
  (i) saving time and effort,
  (ii) avoiding discomfort,
  (iii) attracting attention,
  (iv) asserting independence,
  (v) seeking group approval, and
  (vi) expressing resentment;
(c) physical and mental incapacities.

Source causes

Source causes are any circumstances that may cause or contribute to the development of an unsafe condition. Major sources include

(a) management, e.g. failure by management and supervision to inform, instruct, maintain and lead in safety procedures;
(b) production employees, e.g. failure to follow a specific safety procedure;
(c) maintenance employees, e.g. inadequate or careless maintenance of plant;
(d) design and engineering, e.g. the provision of insufficient or ineffective safety devices on machinery;
(e) purchasing practices, e.g. failure to write safety requirements into specifications;
(f) normal wear through use resulting in hazardous failure;
(g) abnormal wear and tear;
(h) lack of preventive maintenance; and
(i) the presence or activities of third parties including outside contractors, e.g. unsafe working practices by contractors working on the premises.

Direct causes

Accidents are attributed to

(a) unsafe acts and/or omissions, and
(b) unsafe conditions.

Unsafe acts and/or omissions

An unsafe act is any act that deviates from a generally recognised safe way of doing a job and increases the likelihood of an accident. The following are types of unsafe act:

(a) operating without authority, e.g. unauthorised use of potentially dangerous machinery;
(b) operating at unsafe speed, e.g. internal factory transport;
(c) nullifying safety devices, e.g. operators defeating safety devices on machines;
(d) use of defective equipment;
(e) using equipment unsafely, e.g. home-made 'lash-ups';
(f) taking an unsafe position, e.g. working on a fragile roof without crawl boards;
(g) attempting repair or servicing of moving or energised equipment;
(h) riding hazardous equipment, e.g. conveyor belts; and
(i) horseplay.

Omissions or failures on the part of management and workers can result in accidents. Typical omissions are:

(a) failure to make secure, e.g. the load on a hand truck;
(b) failure to warn or signal, e.g. fork lift truck drivers working in congested areas; and
(c) failure to use personal protective equipment. (Various statutes and regulations require employees and other persons to wear personal protective equipment when engaged in certain work or processes.)

Unsafe conditions

Unsafe conditions are fundamentally associated with the quality of the working environment and may be defined as 'any environmental conditions that may cause or contribute to an accident or occupational illness/disease'. The basic types include

(a) inadequate guards and safety devices;
(b) inadequate warning systems;
(c) fire and explosion hazards;
(d) unexpected movement hazards, e.g. conveyors;
(e) poor housekeeping and cleaning activities;
(f) protruding objects, e.g. nails in scaffold boards;
(g) congestion;
(h) hazardous atmospheric conditions, e.g. during welding operations;
(i) hazardous placement or storage (various statutory requirements regulate the placement and/or storage of dangerous substances,

e.g. the Highly Flammable Liquids and Liquefied Petroleum Gases Regulations 1972);

(j) unsafe equipment and defective equipment (by definition 'a part of machinery is dangerous if it is a possible cause of injury to anybody acting in a way in which a human being may be reasonably expected to act in circumstances which may be reasonably expected to occur' (per du Parcq J in *Walker* v. *Bletchley Flettons Ltd* [1937] 1 AER 170);

(k) inadequate or unsuitable illumination;

(l) noise; and

(m) hazardous personal attire, e.g. wearing loose jewellery or clothing.

The accident

A notifiable/reportable accident, for the purposes of the Reporting of Injuries, Diseases and Dangerous Occurrences Regulations 1985, is an accident arising out of or in connection with work, as a result of which any person

(a) dies; or

(b) suffers any of the following injuries/conditions
   (i) fracture of the skull, spine or pelvis
   (ii) fracture of any bone in the arm or wrist, but not a bone in the hand; or in the leg or ankle, but not a bone in the foot;

(c) amputation of
   (i) a hand or foot, or
   (ii) a finger, thumb or toe, or any part of the same if the joint or bone is completely severed;

(d) loss of sight of an eye, or penetrating injury to an eye, or a chemical or hot metal burn to an eye;

(e) either injury (including burns) requiring immediate medical treatment, or loss of consciousness, resulting in either case from an electric shock from any electrical circuit or equipment, whether or not due to direct contact;

(f) loss of consciousness resulting from lack of oxygen;

(g) decompression sickness (though not diving at work);

(h) either
   (i) acute illness requiring medical treatment, or
   (ii) loss of consciousness,
   resulting in either case from the absorption of any substance by inhalation, ingestion or through the skin;

(i) acute illness requiring medical treatment where there is reason to believe that this resulted from exposure to a pathogen or infected material

(j) any other injury which results in the person injured being admitted immediately into hospital for more than 24 hours.

(Reporting of Injuries, Diseases and Dangerous Occurrences Regulations 1985, Reg 3(2).)

Direct results

One or more of the following are the direct (or immediate) results of an accident:

(a) 'no results' or near misses,
(b) minor injury,
(c) major injury,
(d) property damage.

Indirect results

Indirect results refer to the consequences flowing from the direct results of accidents. They include

(a) for the injured person:
    (i) loss of earnings and of earning capacity,
    (ii) disrupted family life,
    (iii) disrupted personal life, and
    (iv) other consequences, e.g. continued pain and suffering;
(b) for the company:
    (i) injury costs;
    (ii) production loss costs;
    (iii) property damage costs;
    (iv) reduction in employee morale;
    (v) poor reputation as a result of adverse media publicity;
    (vi) poor customer relations following adverse media publicity;
    (vii) lost time – supervisors, workers and others;
    (viii) product damage costs;
    (ix) first aid and medical costs;
    (x) increased employer's liability premiums;
    (xi) legal costs, e.g. fines imposed by courts, legal representation fees;
    (xii) cost of changes in practice arising from prosecution or as a result of enforcement action, e.g. prohibition or improvement notice; and
    (xiii) training costs, e.g. retraining of injured employee, training of replacement labour.

(*See further* Chapter 11.)

Accident investigation

There are very good reasons for the effective and thorough investigation of accidents, viz.

(a) on a purely humanitarian basis, no one likes to see people killed or injured;
(b) the accident may have resulted from a breach of statute by the organisation, the accident victim, the manufacturers and/or suppliers of articles and substances used at work, or other persons, e.g. contractors, with the possibility of civil proceedings being instituted by the injured party against his employer;
(c) the accident may be reportable to the enforcing authority under the Reporting of Injuries, Diseases and Dangerous Occurrences Regulations 1985);
(d) the accident may result in lost production;
(e) from a management viewpoint, a serious accident, particularly a fatal one, can have a long-term detrimental effect on the morale of the workforce;
(f) there may be damage to plant and equipment, resulting in the need for repair or replacement, with possible delays in replacement; and
(g) in most cases, there will be a need for immediate remedial action in order to prevent recurrence of the accident.

Humanitarian reasons apart, all accidents represent losses to the organisation, both directly and indirectly (*see* Chapter 11). There are, therefore, legal and financial reasons for investigating accidents to identify causes and produce strategies to prevent recurrences. Above all, the purpose of accident investigation is *not* to apportion blame or fault, though this may inevitably emerge from investigation.

Which accidents should be investigated?

It may be impracticable to investigate every accident, but the following factors are helpful in determining which accidents should be investigated as a priority:

(a) the type of accident, e.g. fall from a height, chemical handling, machinery;
(b) the form and severity of injury, or the potential for severe injury and/or damage;
(c) whether the accident indicates the continuation of a particular trend in accident experience;
(d) the extent of involvement of articles and substances used at work, e.g. machinery, plant, dangerous substances, and the ensuing damage or loss;

(e) the possibility of a breach of the law;
(f) whether the accident is by law reportable to the enforcing authorities; and
(g) whether the accident should be reported to the insurance company as it could result in a claim being made.

Moreover, since an occupational disease or condition, sometimes referred to as a 'slow accident', can have the same effects on an individual as an accident, the above factors should be considered when investigating the possible causes of occupational diseases such as non-infective dermatitis or noise-induced hearing loss.

Practical accident investigation

In any accident situation, particularly a fatal accident, one resulting in major injury, or a scheduled dangerous occurrence, speed of action is essential. This is particularly true when it comes to interviewing the injured person and any witnesses. The following procedure is recommended.

(a) Establish the facts as quickly and completely as possible about:
  (i) the general environment;
  (ii) the particular plant, machinery, practice or system of work involved; and
  (iii) the sequence of events leading to the accident.
(b) Use an instant camera to take photographs of the accident scene.
(c) Draw sketches and take measurements with a view to producing a scale drawing of the accident scene.
(d) List the names of all witnesses, i.e. those who saw, heard, felt or smelt anything; interview them thoroughly in the presence of a third party, if necessary, and take full statements. Do *not* prompt or lead the witnesses.
(e) Evaluate the facts, and individual witnesses' versions of same, as to accuracy, reliability and relevance.
(f) Endeavour to arrive at conclusions as to the *cause* of the accident on the basis of the relevant facts. (Cause here means 'cause in fact' and should not be confused with 'causation' in law. For the latter, *see* Chapter 2 under heading 'Negligence'.)
(g) Examine closely any contradictory evidence. Never dismiss a fact that does not fit in with the rest. *Find out more.*
(h) Learn fully about the system of work involved. Every accident occurs within the context of a work system. Consider the personnel involved in terms of their ages, training, experience and level of supervision, and the nature of the work, e.g. routine, sporadic or incidental.

(i) In certain cases, it may be necessary for plant and equipment to be examined by a specialist, e.g. consultant engineer.
(j) Produce a report for the responsible manager emphasising the causes and remedies to prevent a recurrence, including any changes necessary.
(k) In complex and serious cases, consider the establishment of an investigating committee comprising managers, supervisors, technical specialists and trade union representatives.

The investigators

The investigation of accidents is not the sole prerogative of the employer or his representative. Clearly, the employer, or his health and safety specialist, must endeavour to ascertain the cause of the accident with a view to preventing recurrence and improving the work situation. (The decision of the House of Lords in *Waugh* v. *British Railways Board* [1979] 2 AER 1169 has established that a safety officer's detailed report after an injury-causing accident and/or fatality at work is only privileged from 'discovery' by the plaintiff or his representatives if its dominant purpose is the preparation of the employer's defence in subsequent litigation.) A number of other organisations, however, have a direct interest in the investigation of accidents, in particular the following.

Trade union safety representatives

Such persons have a right to undertake an inspection of that part of the workplace concerned in any reportable or notifiable accident as far as is necessary for determining the cause of the accident. They have a duty to notify the employer of their intention to undertake such an inspection. (*See* Chapter 5 for the specific powers of safety representatives.)

Insurance company surveyor

Whether or not a claim has been made by the injured person, most insurance companies insist on inspection rights, particularly where the accident may identify trends and/or there is potential for a claim being submitted later. (This is extremely advisable also from a legal viewpoint, as the facts themselves may disclose evidence of negligence (res ipsa loquitur).)

Legal representative

In the event of a civil action for negligence, the legal representative of the injured person, as well as the company's legal representative, would expect reasonable access to ascertain the cause of the accident. They may both need to interview witnesses.

Enforcing authority

H M Factories Inspectors and local authority environmental health officers have powers of entry for the purpose of investigating accidents to ascertain whether there has been a breach of statute (*see* Chapter 4).

The outcome of accident investigation

Whether accident investigation is carried out by individuals or by a committee, it is necessary, once the cause has been identified, to submit recommendations to management with a view to preventing a recurrence. The organisation of 'feedback' is crucial in large organisations, especially those which occupy more than one site or premises. An effective investigation should result in one or more of the following recommendations being made:

(a) the issuing of specific instructions by management, perhaps attached to the Statement of Health and Safety Policy, regarding systems of work, the need for more effective guarding of machinery, etc.;
(b) the establishment of a working party or group to undertake further investigation, perhaps in conjunction with a safety committee and/or safety representatives;
(c) the preparation and issue of specific codes of practice or guidance notes dealing with the procedures necessary to minimise a particular risk;
(d) the identification of specific training needs for groups of individuals – e.g. managers, foremen, supervisors, machinery operators, drivers – and the implementation of a training programme designed to meet these needs;
(e) the formal analysis of the job or system in question, perhaps using Job Safety Analysis techniques, to identify specific skill and safety components of the job;
(f) identification of the need for further information relating to articles and substances used at work, e.g. equipment, chemical substances;
(g) identification of the need for better environmental control, e.g. noise reduction at source or improved lighting;
(h) general employee involvement in health and safety issues, e.g. the establishment of a health and safety committee (this may be a legal requirement – *see* Chapter 5); and
(i) identification of the specific responsibilities of groups with regard to safe working practices.

Above all, a system of monitoring should be implemented to ensure that the lessons which have been learned from the accident are put into practice or incorporated in future systems of work, that supervisors have been trained to monitor such systems, and that procedures and operating systems have been produced for all grades of staff (*see further* Chapter 8).

8

Health and safety monitoring

Health and safety monitoring refers to all of those activities which are concerned with ensuring good standards of health and safety management. In order to assess and evaluate standards of health and safety performance, and to bring about improvements which will reduce the potential for accidents, it is essential to operate one or more forms of health and safety monitoring. There may be a case for analysing or evaluating certain tasks from a health and safety viewpoint, or a need to motivate staff, for instance, to use personal protective equipment or to adhere to a specifically designed safe system of work. All these activities come within the scope of 'health and safety monitoring' and, as such, are closely related to the 'arrangements' for ensuring a safe and healthy workplace which must be outlined in the Statement of Health and Safety Policy (*see* Chapter 3).

The various forms of health and safety monitoring are outlined below. The adoption of a specific technique will depend on the hazards present, the number of people exposed to the hazard, the levels of training received, the standards of supervision and control and the climate within the organisation for bringing about improvement.

Safety audits

A safety audit subjects each area of an organisation's activities to a systematic critical examination with the object of minimising injury and loss. Every component of the total system is included, e.g. management policy, attitudes, training, features of processes, personal protection needs, emergency procedures, etc. As in the field of accountancy, an audit aims to disclose strengths and weaknesses in the main areas of vulnerability or risk. Following the safety audit a formal report and action plan is prepared and closely monitored. A specimen safety audit check-list appears at the end of this chapter.

Health and safety surveys

A survey is a detailed examination of a number of critical areas of operation or an in-depth study of the whole health and safety operation of premises. For instance, a survey might examine in depth health and safety management and administration, environmental factors, occupational health and hygiene provisions, the diverse field of safety and accident prevention as it affects the premises, and the current system for health and safety training of staff, from the Board of Directors to shop-floor workers. Contractors and other groups who may enter the premises on a casual or infrequent basis might also be covered. Much will depend on the inherent risks, the number of employees, the location of the premises in relation to urban population, the potential for pollution incidents and the range of products manufactured.

Reporting procedure

Following a survey, a report is published. In most cases, this report is purely critical and produced on an observation and recommendation basis. Recommendations would be phased according to the degree of risk, current legal requirements and the cost of eliminating or reducing the risks. A survey report is mainly concerned with risks and the system for bringing about a gradual upgrading of standards, e.g. in welfare amenity provisions. Recommendations could include the eventual replacement of old and dilapidated buildings which may be totally unsuitable for the work processes being undertaken within. The purpose of the health and safety report is to present management with a phased programme of health and safety improvement covering, say, a 5-year period. Recommendations would be phased as follows.

Phase 1: These recommendations apply to situations where there is a serious risk and/or direct breach of the law, and to situations where relatively minor improvements can be made without capital expenditure, e.g. redecoration, repairs to floors. Phase 1 items would also include recommendations relating to health and safety management and administration, such as updating the Statement of Health and Safety Policy, the publication of specific objectives for the health and safety committee or the establishment of a company code of practice dealing with, perhaps, the supply and use of personal protective equipment. It would be normal to expect implementation of phase 1 recommendations within 6 months of the presentation of the report.

Phase 2: These recommendations would normally be implemented in 1–2 years. They would include items which do not require large-scale expenditure but which are essential for the improvement of working conditions and safety standards, e.g. improvements to lighting in working areas, the installation of specific exhaust ventilation to processes or improvements in access to parts of the premises.

Phase 3: Recommendations in this category are those for which long-term planning is needed, together with approval for capital expenditure, such as for the provision of new amenities, replacement of outdated plant and equipment, provision of improved chemical storage facilities and fire protection measures. In many cases, such improvements can be incorporated in the long-term development plans for factories.

The health and safety survey thus covers the whole field of the working environment, from plant and machinery to systems of safe working and the establishment of training programmes. For the impact of the report to continue, regular monitoring of progress in its implementation is needed by the individual undertaking the survey and by company management, supported by progress reports to senior management.

Safety inspections

Many people are involved in safety inspections, such as company health and safety specialists who may visit on a regular basis, plant safety officers, local management, trade union safety representatives, inspectors of the enforcing authorities and insurance company surveyors. Each of these individuals has different motives for undertaking an inspection. The enforcement agencies carry out inspections to identify breaches of the law regarding the causes of a notified accident. In-company health and safety specialists inspect to identify hazards, to ensure that specific procedures designed to promote safe working are being operated, and to protect their employers from liability. The safety representative carries out inspections to protect members of his trade union from hazards.

Generally, however, a safety inspection is a scheduled inspection of premises or part of same by personnel within that organisation, possibly accompanied by an external specialist. The inspection may examine maintenance standards, employee involvement, working practices and housekeeping levels, and check that work is undertaken in accordance with company codes of practice or procedures. This form of monitoring tends to be a general examination of the situation at a specific point in time rather than the in-depth and broad approach taken with health and safety surveys. Whatever system exists for safety inspection, it is vital that the objectives are clearly defined and made known to the workforce.

Safety tours

This refers to the unscheduled examination of a work area, carried out by a manager, possibly accompanied by health and safety committee members, to ensure that, for instance, standards of housekeeping are at an acceptable level, fire protection measures are being observed and maintained, or personal protective equipment is being used correctly. Safety tours tend to be of limited value unless related to decisions made by local management and/or health and safety committee members. To be effective, it is essential that deficiencies noted during the tour are remedied immediately.

Contact schemes

The objective of a contact scheme is to provide added incentive and facilities to middle and junior management to persuade them to impart information and/or instructions on health and safety matters to the

Table 1: Safety contact scheme

	Operator						
	A	B	C	D	E	F	G
1. Fire protection procedures							
2. Safe systems of work for: (a) (b) (c) (d)							
3. Personal protective equipment							
4. Hand tools							
5. Machinery and plant: (a) (b) (c)							
6. Manual handling							

workers under their control. Many supervisors, for instance, are conscious of the fact that they are not instructors or trainers. Even short talks with workers are not within their scope, quite apart from the fact that such talks tend to disrupt production. If, however, a supervisor tours a section and talks to each person separately he can usually communicate various ideas through this one-to-one relationship. The contact scheme enables him to do this and keep a record of the extent of instruction received by each worker.

A simple system involves the use of a piece of squared paper. Topics for discussion are entered in the left-hand column and names of operators in the row at the top of the page. Subjects to be covered may include the use of personal protection equipment, housekeeping, manual handling techniques or the use of hand tools. The supervisor then prepares his programme for informal discussions and, over a period, ensures that each worker is contacted, a tick being placed in the appropriate square after each contact session.

Safety sampling

This technique is designed to measure, by random sampling, the accident potential in a specific workshop or process by identifying safety defects or omissions. The area to be sampled is divided into sections and an observer appointed to each section. A prescribed route through the area is planned and observers follow their itinerary in the time allowed, about 15 minutes. During the sampling period they note safety defects on a safety sampling sheet, with a limited number of points to be observed, e.g. housekeeping, eye protection being worn, correct handling procedures. Other aspects for observation may include obstructed fire exits, environmental factors such as lighting and ventilation, faulty hand tools and damaged guards to machinery. The staff undertaking the inspections should be trained in the technique and have a broad knowledge of procedures and processes carried out. The results of the sampling activity are collated and presented in graphical form by a specific manager, e.g. safety officer. The system monitors the effectiveness of the overall safety programme.

Hazard and operability studies

These studies incorporate the application of formal critical examination to the process and engineering intentions regarding new facilities, e.g. new production processes. Their aim is to assess the hazard potential arising from incorrect operation of items of equipment and the consequential effects on the facility as a whole. Remedial action is then usually possible at a very early stage of the project with maximum

Table 2: Safety sampling exercise

		Area A	B	C	D
1. Housekeeping/cleaning	(Max 10)				
2. Personal protection	(Max 10)				
3. Machinery	(Max 10)				
4. Chemical storage	(Max 5)				
5. Chemical handling	(Max 5)				
6. Manual handling	(Max 5)				
7. Fire protection	(Max 10)				
8. Structural hazards	(Max 10)				
9. Internal transport e.g. FLTs	(Max 5)				
10. Access equipment	(Max 5)				
11. First Aid boxes	(Max 5)				
12. Hand tools	(Max 10)				
13. Internal Storage (racking systems)	(Max 5)				
14. Structural safety	(Max 10)				
15. Temperature	(Max 5)				
16. Lighting	(Max 5)				
17. Ventilation	(Max 5)				
18. Noise	(Max 5)				
19. Dust and fumes	(Max 5)				
20. Welfare amenities	(Max 10)				
Totals	(Max 140)				

effectiveness and minimum costs. These studies examine the potential for error amongst operators, with regard to new plant and machinery in particular, on the basis that the perpetuation of errors in design can result in accidents, plant stoppage and loss of production. While unsuspected hazards may be revealed by hazard and operability studies, the use of a formal check-list in engineering design departments helps to ensure that account is taken of accumulated experience, knowledge of the technology and best practice in the initial design.

Damage control

The theory of damage control or damage costing is that non-injury accidents are as important as injury accidents. The elimination of non-injury accidents will, in many cases, remove other forms of accident. For example, a pallet stack falls and may just miss a man standing close by. No injury results and an accident is not recorded, but there may be damage to wooden pallets, the building fabric, plant and equipment. However, the next time a pallet stack falls over someone could be seriously injured or killed. The fact is recorded. The elimination of the cause of the first pallet stack falling – e.g. bad stacking or the use of defective pallets or stacking on an uneven floor – might have prevented the injury when the second pallet stack fell.

Damage control aims to ensure a safe working environment and calls for keen observation and co-operation by staff who see or experience a condition which may lead to an accident. It relies heavily on an effective inspection and reporting system for all damage and defects and a programme of preventive maintenance. Moreover, evidence of damage to property and plant is often an indication of poor safety performance.

Job Safety Analysis

Just as productivity can benefit from work study or job analysis, health and safety benefits from Job Safety Analysis. Furthermore, the two are intimately connected. The work study engineer should not ignore safety and the safety specialist should not ignore productivity considerations.

Job Safety Analysis, whether undertaken as part of work study or not, can do much to eliminate the hazards of a job. The analysis isolates each single operation, examines the individual hazards, and indicates remedies to reduce the hazards. It involves the examination of plant and work processes, systems of work, including permit to work systems, the qualifications and training required for the job, and the degree of instruction, supervision and control necessary (*see* Chapter 13).

Permits to work

Permits to work are essential where work with a foreseeably high hazard content must be undertaken with a commensurate need for numerous precautions, e.g. entry into confined spaces (*see* Chapter 13).

Safety incentive schemes

Opinions vary considerably as to the desirability or value of incentives to encourage workers to consider their own safety. However, the principal philosophy behind safety incentive schemes is exactly the same as that behind other incentive schemes for production, sales or marketing, i.e. to motivate people to perform better. The ways of securing motivation are based on

(a) identifying targets, for which a reward can be given if the target is reached; and
(b) making the reward meaningful and desirable to the people concerned.

Essentially these schemes are concerned with two aspects of human behaviour and performance, viz. motivation and attitude. People should be motivated to perform or behave in a particular way and, in many cases, attitude changes should be brought about so that they will behave more safely, thereby bringing about a reduction in accidents. The most successful safety incentive schemes are those which are linked to a programme of safety inspections or safety audits of the workplace. To be effective, inspections should be undertaken on an irregular basis, otherwise there is the danger that workers will become 'conditioned' to the system and not behave as they normally would. The most common system is that of awarding points for areas of health and safety performance, e.g. systems of work, procedures, housekeeping. Inspections should be carried out by a mixed team – e.g. safety specialist, personnel officer, trade union safety representative and the line manager concerned – in order to maintain a degree of fairness. The establishment of the correct targets is important in such schemes. Everyone must fully understand the scheme, and there must be total support from senior and line management if the scheme is to work. Such schemes as the RoSPA Safe Driving Awards for commercial vehicle drivers do much to develop a personal and collective pride in the job and, generally, these schemes are more successful when the final result or reward is achieved by collective effort.

Many existing safety incentive schemes, however, have serious deficiencies. If the rewards are directly related to the number of accidents in a department, this can reduce the incidence of accident reporting in order to attain the target. They can alter the threshold at which accidents are reported and, in many cases, injured persons may be discouraged from obtaining first aid treatment if all treatments are reported as part of the scheme. It does not affect serious accidents which must be reported anyway. One of the principal criticisms of safety incentive schemes is that they tend to be short-lived. There have been accusations of gimmickry, 'nine-day wonders' and lack of organisation and control. They can also shift responsibility from management to worker for the general control of health and safety and, over a relatively short period of time, serious situations can develop over accidents that have not been reported. People may even disclaim knowledge of an accident ever taking place, due to the desire to earn the rewards offered in the scheme.

Generally, however, safety incentive schemes have much to offer in terms of improved operator behaviour and performance, and this should result in a reduction in accidents. These schemes are probably most effective where people are restricted to one area of activity, e.g. driving commercial vehicles or fork lift trucks, and the operation of machinery or well-controlled processes where it is relatively simple to measure and demonstrate safety performance. They do, however, need regular stimulation and rejuvenation, and must have management and trade union support. Additionally, they should be supported adequately by safety propaganda.

Conclusion

The above monitoring systems are commonly used. Their success depends upon the expertise available, the inherent risks and the system for remedying deficiencies. No matter which monitoring system is operated, there is clearly a need to operate some form of system with a view to preventing accidents and occupational disease, rather than undertaking the 'fire-fighting exercise' characteristic of so many situations following an accident.

Appendix: specimen safety audit check-list

1. Documents

(a) Are copies of relevant legislation available to all employees? Do they know where to find them?
(b) Apart from the Health and Safety at Work etc., Act, 1974, what health and safety legislation applies to the premises?
(c) Have you examined the General Register which is required under the Factories Act 1961?
(d) Have all codes of practice and other documents relating to the workplace been studied?
(e) Does the existing Statement of Health and Safety Policy meet current conditions in the factory? Are the organisation and arrangements to implement the policy still adequate?

(f) Are all test certificates and other documents available, e.g. for lifts, pressure vessels?
(g) Are all necessary licences available, e.g. licence to store petroleum spirit?
(h) Has the certificate as to means of escape in the event of fire been examined? Are fire notices and instructions displayed?
(i) Do written systems of work exist for all potentially hazardous operations?
(j) Are the factory safety rules current and adequate?
(k) Are all emergency and disaster control plans available? Have people been trained in the implementation of such plans?
(l) Are health and safety training records maintained?

2. Organisation and arrangements

(a) Are responsibilities for health and safety clearly defined at all levels of the organisation? Have personnel been trained to meet these responsibilities?
(b) Is the title of the senior executive with overall responsibility for health and safety clearly stated?
(c) Are the duties of health and safety specialists accurately described and are such specialists adequately trained?
(d) Are the role and objectives of the health and safety committee fully detailed? Are the procedures for appointing or electing safety committee members and trade union safety representatives clearly defined? Are the available facilities, including training, known to the committee members and representatives?
(e) Are employees fully aware of their duties outlined in the Statement of Health and Safety Policy?
(f) Are there satisfactory arrangements for dealing with contractors' employees, including training, and site visitors?
(g) Are the medical and first aid arrangements adequate for the current hazards?
(h) Are maintenance arrangements for buildings, plant, machinery and equipment satisfactory? Do they ensure that no avoidable hazards are created?
(i) Are there arrangements for regular health and safety monitoring activities?
(j) Do the arrangements ensure that safety implications are considered in any plans for changing premises, processes, products, materials, suppliers or the general organisation of the workplace?
(k) Do all job descriptions adequately describe health and safety responsibilities?
(l) Do employees fully understand process hazards and how to cope with fault situations, i.e. shut down procedures, etc.?

(m) Have significant fire and explosion process risks been identified and dealt with adequately?
(n) Are fire drills detailed, practised and understood by all employees? Are all items of equipment regularly tested and maintained?
(o) Are all fire exits and escape routes marked, kept free from obstruction, and operational?
(p) Are certain employees trained to operate the correct type of fire appliance in the event of fire?
(q) What specific fire hazards exist and are they catered for in the arrangements? Are fire-fighting arrangements adequate for the potential hazards? Are the appliances correctly labelled, sited and maintained?

3. Hazards

(a) Are all dangerous substances correctly identified, handled and stored? Do suppliers provide adequate information on their properties and use?
(b) Is personal protective equipment readily available and are staff trained in its use?
(c) Is there adequate control of all toxic, flammable, explosive and corrosive materials? Are all employees adequately trained in their use, handling and properties?
(d) Are environmental hazards such as noise, dust, fumes, radiation, etc., adequately understood and controlled?
(e) Are levels of temperature, lighting and ventilation adequate and controlled?
(f) Is all machinery guarded to the standard implied in BS 5304 and, in addition, to meet any special requirements of the premises? Are the guards and safety devices regularly inspected and correctly used?
(g) What is the condition of both fixed and portable electrical equipment? What precautions have been taken to avoid risk of electric shock, burns, fire, ignition of flammable substances?
(h) Are warnings and guards for structural hazards adequate, e.g. floor openings, slippery or defective floors, stairways, truck movement areas, overhead cranes?
(i) Is general housekeeping of a high standard, e.g. materials storage, waste disposal, removal of spillages? Have cleaning schedules for all parts of the premises been established and implemented?
(j) Is all materials handling carried out safely? Are employees trained in correct lifting techniques? Are all truck and crane drivers adequately trained, supervised and qualified for the

machines and areas which they use? Are stacking procedures safe? Is all transporting and lifting equipment properly inspected and maintained?

4. General safety

(a) Are safe systems of work documented, taught and used wherever appropriate?
(b) Are all gangways kept clear?
(c) Are all ladders of the correct type, properly maintained and inspected? Are they footed and lashed in use?
(d) Are first aid box contents regularly checked? Are resuscitation and eye wash equipment in good order?
(e) Are welfare facilities adequate, including washing facilities and toilets?
(f) Is health and safety given sufficient promotion within the organisation? Are safety posters, films and demonstrations of personal protection frequently used?
(g) Are there sufficient links with external organisations – e.g. RoSPA, Health and Safety Executive, environmental health officers, university departments, the Institution of Occupational Safety and Health – on health and safety matters?

5. Accident investigation and reporting

(a) Are accident and near miss reporting procedures satisfactory and understood by all who use them? Are the procedures laid down in current legislation fully understood?
(b) Do investigation procedures produce results which can be used to prevent accidents in the future?
(c) Are the causes of accidents and dangerous occurrences recorded and analysed with a view to preventing recurrences?
(d) Are the reporting procedures closely monitored?
(e) Is it possible to determine the direct and indirect costs of accidents to the organisation?
(f) How does the company accident record compare with those of other organisations in the same industry?

6. Final questions

Is there reasonable certainty that the organisation is as safe and healthy as it can reasonably be made? If not, is it known what must be done to achieve that state?

9

Fatal and major accidents and emergencies

Fatal and major injury accidents

The statutory procedure under the Reporting of Injuries, Diseases and Dangerous Occurrences Regulations 1985 is outlined in Chapter 7. Given the possibility of the occurrence of a fatal or major injury accident, it is important that organisations have a clearly established procedure, including the allocation of responsibility for specific tasks, following the accident. Generally, this procedure can be subdivided into two aspects, the notification sequence and the post-accident procedure.

Notification sequence

On receipt of a report of a fatal accident or one causing major injury, a senior manager should immediately contact by telephone the ambulance service, the factory doctor where appropriate and, in the case of a fatal accident, the police. In the case of a fatal accident, the manager, in consultation with the police, should arrange to visit the next of kin to advise that person of the accident.

Following this, the senior manager or safety specialist should inform, by telephone, the following:

(a) the divisional manager, where appropriate;
(b) Health and Safety Executive (HM Factories Inspector or Agricultural Health and Safety Inspector) or local authority environmental health officer, as appropriate;
(c) the head of the central health and safety department, where appropriate;
(d) the personnel manager for the organisation; and
(e) the insurance company.

Post-accident procedure

The area of an accident, including machinery, plant and equipment, should be immediately sealed off by the use of ropes or barriers. Unauthorised access to the scene of the accident must be prevented and the accident area not disturbed, other than to render the situation safe, until permission is given by the officer of the enforcing authority. The actual position of the corpse should be marked out on the floor or other surface prior to removal. (For the position regarding admissibility of evidence for litigation purposes following a fatality, *see* Chapter 5.)

At this stage it is essential that

(a) photographs of the scene of the accident are taken using either an instant camera or standard camera, before any disturbance takes place;
(b) witnesses to the accident are identified;
(c) the trade union shop steward and/or safety representative, where appropriate, are informed (*see* Chapter 5 for the powers of safety representatives);
(d) consideration is given to the establishment of a formal investigating committee; and
(e) a person trained in the taking of statements is briefed.

Statements from witnesses and other persons should be taken as soon as possible by the nominated person or manager whilst the accident is still fresh in the minds of witnesses. Witnesses should be interviewed separately and not allowed to discuss the accident together prior to the taking of statements. A shorthand typist should be made available if possible, and his statement read out to each witness at the completion of the process. All witness statements should be signed and dated.

In the event of involvement with the media (press, radio, television), a bare statement of the facts should be given as follows:

(a) an accident has taken place which is the subject of investigation;
(b) the person involved has been taken to hospital; and
(c) a further statement *may* be made later.

A note should be made of all contacts with the media and a senior manager or a public relations officer (PRO) should be delegated to handle any future contact. Extreme care must be taken to avoid any admission of liability and the making of unnecessary assumptions by the media, e.g. no mention of a 'fatality' should be made at this stage.

Summary

The above procedure is only one way of tackling a fatal or major accident situation. Speed is of the utmost significance, particularly in taking photographs, preparation of sketches and interviewing witnesses. Facts surrounding the accident must be established quickly and accurately, bearing in mind that the accident will be the subject of specific investigation by enforcement agencies, the insurance company, representatives of the deceased or injured person, trade union safety representatives and staff of the Department of Health and Social Security.

Major emergencies

A major emergency is one that may affect several departments within a factory or commercial premises and/or endanger the surrounding communities. It may be precipitated by malfunction of operational plant, or by the intervention of an outside agency such as a crashed vehicle carrying dangerous substances, severe electrical storm, flooding, rail disaster, act of arson or sabotage, or through terrorist activities. Alternatively, the emergency could arise through a scheduled dangerous occurrence (see Schedule 1 of Part 1 of the Reporting of Injuries, Diseases and Dangerous Occurrences Regulations 1985).

Types of emergency

The emergency conditions most likely to arise in the average industrial or commercial premises are

(a) a large or rapidly escalating fire,
(b) an explosion,
(c) a large-scale release of toxic materials,
(d) a large-scale flood, or
(e) a combination of these conditions.

Affected areas

Account should always be taken of areas likely to be affected when considering the kind of emergency that could occur – for instance, the interdependence of plant and buildings; the impact of prevailing wind direction and strength, and the effect these may have on spread of fire and toxic materials. The civil authorities will need information about areas outside the premises which could be affected by, for instance, toxic fume or dust deposits.

Principal stages

A properly conceived emergency scheme or plan will take account of four phases or stages of an emergency.

Phase 1 – preliminary action

This refers to

(a) the preparation of a plan, tailored to meet the special requirements of the site, products and surroundings; including
   (i) a list of all key telephone numbers;
   (ii) the system for the provision of emergency lighting, e.g. hand lamps and torches;
   (iii) designation of exit routes;
   (iv) a plan of the site layout identifying hydrant points and the location of shut-off valves to energy supplies, e.g. gas; and
   (v) notes on specific hazards on site for use by the emergency services;
(b) the familiarisation of every employee with the details of the plan, including the position of essential equipment;
(c) the training of personnel involved, in particular, key personnel;
(d) the initiation of a programme of inspection of potentially hazardous areas, testing of warning systems and evacuation procedures; and
(e) stipulating specific periods at which the plan is to be re-examined and updated.

Phase 2 – action when emergency is imminent

There may be a warning of the emergency, in which case this period should be used to assemble key personnel, to review the standing arrangements in order to consider whether changes are necessary, to give advance warning to external authorities, and to test all systems connected with the emergency scheme.

Phase 3 – action during emergency

If phase 1 has been properly carried out, and phase 2, where applicable, phase 3 proceeds according to plan. However, it is likely that unexpected variations in a predicted emergency will take place. The decision-making personnel, selected beforehand for this purpose, must be able to make precise and rapid judgments and see that proper action follows the decision made.

Phase 4 – ending the emergency

There must be a procedure for declaring plant, systems and specific areas safe, together with an early reoccupation of buildings where possible.

Implementation of procedure

Implementation of an emergency procedure involves the following:

Liaison with external authorities and other companies

The closest contact must be maintained with the fire, police and health authorities, together with the Health and Safety Executive and local authority. A mutual aid scheme involving neighbouring premises is best undertaken at this stage. A major emergency may also involve a failure in the supply of gas, electricity, water and/or telephone communications. Discussions with the appropriate authority will help to determine priorities in re-establishing supply.

Emergency controller

A senior manager, with a thorough knowledge of all processes and their associated hazards, should be nominated Emergency Controller, and a deputy appointed to cover absence, however brief this may be. Out of normal working hours, the senior member of management on site should take initial control until relieved by the Emergency Controller.

Emergency control centre

A sound communication system is essential if a major emergency is to be handled effectively. A control centre should be established and equipped with means of receiving information from the forward control and assembly points, transmitting calls for assistance to external authorities, calling in essential personnel and transmitting information and instructions to personnel within the premises. Alternative means of communication must be available in the event of the main system being rendered inoperative, e.g. field telephones. A fall-back control centre may be necessary in certain situations such as a rapidly escalating fire.

Initiating the procedure

The special procedure for handling major emergencies must only be initiated when such an emergency is known to exist. A limited number of designated senior managers should be assigned the responsibility for deciding if a major emergency exists or is imminent. Only these persons should have authority to implement the procedure.

Notification to local authorities

Notification can be achieved by a predetermined short message, transmitted via an emergency line or by the British Telecom lines. The warning message should mention routes to the premises which may become impassable. Alternative routes can then be used.

Call out of key personnel

A list of key personnel required in the event of a major emergency should be drawn up, together with their internal and home telephone numbers and addresses. The list should be available in control centres and constantly updated.

Immediate action on site

Any emergency would be dealt with by action by supervisors and operators designed to close down and make safe those parts which are affected or likely to be affected. Preservation of human life and the protection of property are of prime importance, and injured persons should be conveyed to hospital with the least possible delay. This may require temporary facilities at points in a safe area accessible to ambulances.

Evacuation

Complete evacuation of non-essential personnel immediately the alarm is sounded is usually advisable, though it may not be necessary or advisable in large factories. In either situation, however, an evacuation alarm system should be installed and made known to all employees, for the purposes of evacuating the premises. Evacuation should be immediately followed by a roll call at a prescribed assembly point to ensure its success.

Access to records

Because relatives of injured and/or deceased employees will have to be informed by the police, each control centre should keep a list of names and addresses of all employees.

External communication

It must be possible to transmit urgent calls from the factory telephone exchange without delay. If this is out of order, alternative means of communication should be available.

Public relations

As a major incident will attract the attention of the media, it is essential to make arrangements for official releases of information to the press and other news services. This is best achieved through a specifically designated Public Relations Officer. Other employees should be instructed not to release information, but to refer any inquiries to the PRO, who should keep a record of any media inquiries dealt with during the emergency.

Catering and temporary shelter

Emergency teams will need refreshment and temporary shelter if the incident is of long duration. Where facilities on the premises cannot be used, it may be possible for the local authority or neighbouring companies to provide facilities.

Contingency arrangements

A contingency plan should be drawn up covering arrangements for repairs to buildings, drying out and temporary water-proofing, replacement of raw materials, alternative storage and transport arrangements.

Training

It is difficult to predict the way people will react in a major emergency situation, but knowledge of the correct procedure will increase the probability of the situation being resolved safely. Training exercises should include the participation of outside services, such as the fire brigade, ambulance service and police. Where mutual aid schemes with neighbouring organisations exist, all possible participants should take part in any form of training exercise.

Familiarisation of all staff concerned with the procedure, together with training exercises at regular intervals, will help reduce the risk of fatal and serious injuries following an emergency. For this reason, the emergency procedure should form an integral part of the company Statement of Health and Safety Policy (*see* Chapter 3).

10

Health and safety training

Training is defined by the Department of Employment as 'the systematic development of attitude, knowledge and skill patterns required by an individual to perform adequately a given task or job'. Given the enormous range, number and level of jobs in industry and commerce, it is easy to see how complex 'training' can be and how it invariably overlaps with 'education'. Prior to the introduction of the Health and Safety at Work etc., Act in 1974, safety training of employees was only a statutory requirement under certain specific Regulations, such as those covering power presses, woodworking machines and abrasive wheels. Now, under HSWA, it is a general requirement applying to all levels of management and the shop floor. Clearly, safety officers and trade union safety representatives require specialised health and safety training.

Systematic training

The term 'systematic' immediately distinguishes such training from the traditional apprenticeship consisting of 'sitting by Nellie', i.e. learning through listening and observation. Systematic training makes full use of skills available in training staff. It attracts recruits, achieves the target of an experienced operator's skill in one half to one third of the traditional time, and creates confidence in the minds of trainees. It guarantees better safety performance and morale, and results in greater earnings and productivity, ease of mind, a sense of security and contentment at work. Furthermore, it excludes misfits and diminishes unrest, whilst facilitating the understanding and acceptance of change.

Systematic training implies the following:

(a) the presence of a trained and competent instructor working with suitable trainees;

(b) defined training objectives;
(c) a content of knowledge broken down into sequential units which can be readily assimilated;
(d) a content of skills analysed by elements;
(e) a clear and orderly training programme;
(f) an appropriate place in which to learn;
(g) suitable equipment and visual aids;
(h) sufficient time to attain a desired standard of knowledge and competence, with frequent testing to ensure trainees understand and know what has to be learned.

A well-designed training programme can be truly educational. First, it is possible to place the specific job knowledge or skill in a wider context, relating it to affiliated topics, to what is already known by the trainee, and to possible future trends and developments. Second, any programme of technical instruction must be supplemented by other courses which enable an operator to relate to his entire sociopolitical environment, and answer his questions about the structure and meaning of society, the destiny of Man, the meaning of law and the lessons of history.

Education, on the other hand, is a lot more than the giving and receiving of information. As Maritain said, it is a 'human awakening'. The acid test of both education and training is the degree and quality of skill which they finally engender – conceptual skills, numerical skills, verbal skills, social skills, administrative and managerial skills.

The training process

Any process of systematic training must take place in a number of clearly defined stages. These stages are outlined below.

Identification of training needs

A training need exists when the optimum solution to an organisation's problem is through some form of training. For instance, a training need may exist where there is damage to stored goods and buildings through fork lift truck activity, or where a particular procedure, such as a permit to work system, is about to be introduced. For training to be effective, it must be integrated with the selection, placement and promotion policies of the organisation. Selection, however, must ensure that the trainees are capable of learning what is to be taught. Promotion must ensure that the promoted person is fully aware of his responsibilities in terms of health and safety at work.

Training needs should be identified with regard to the retraining, or the reinforcement of training, of existing personnel, and the induction training of new recruits. The identification should show:

(a) what kind of training is needed, e.g. safety procedure, duties and responsibilities, general safety training for supervisors;
(b) when such training will be needed, i.e. immediate, medium-term and long-term training requirements;
(c) for how many people training is needed; and
(d) the standard of performance to be attained by the trainees.

Development of the training plan and programme

Training programmes must be co-ordinated with the personnel needs of the organisation. The first step in the development of the training programme is the definition of training objectives. Objectives or aims may be designed by job specification in the case of new training, or by detailed Task Analysis in the case of existing jobs. Safety training objectives may be assessed through the process of Job Safety Analysis (*see* Chapter 13).

Two important factors which need to be considered carefully in the development of a training programme are:

(a) what has to be taught – theoretical and practical areas; and
(b) how it can best be taught.

What has to be taught will be determined by a number of factors, e.g. legal, production, health and safety and industrial relations requirements. A comprehensive job specification for the trainees is relevant in clarifying such matters.

How is the new knowledge and/or skill to be imparted? Is it to be by a process of 'sitting by Nellie' or through a planned training programme? There are great disadvantages to the former, such as

(a) the trainee acquiring bad habits, particularly in relation to safe working and procedures;
(b) Nellie not being able to explain what she is doing or not knowing the best or safest way of doing the job;
(c) the problems of the skilled operator being dissimilar to those of the trainee;
(d) the sizes of the learning stages being too large for the trainee; and
(e) personality clashes developing between trainer and trainee who may be unsuited.

'Sitting by Nellie', however, does have some advantages:

(a) such a system can fit into a planned training programme, particularly if Nellie is a trained trainer and aware of the programme requirements; and

(b) it involves a one-to-one relationship, which is a good training relationship, particularly where detailed safety requirements or procedures must be explained in stages.

Implementation of the training programme

It is important that, at this stage, a distinction is made between 'learning' and 'training'.

Learning goes on all the time. People are continually learning from each other and through their own experiences. It is the process by which manpower becomes and remains effective. If learning does not occur, an organisation will stagnate and soon cease to exist.

Training is simply a way to help people to learn. It may impart skills and/or alter a person's basic characteristics. To be effective, training must be planned and organised, i.e. systematic training.

In the implementation of the training programme, there are three factors which must be considered:

Organising the training

This covers the provision of training staff and equipment, and the training, certification and appointment of trained trainers. The facilities for running the training must be organised in terms of training rooms provided with blackboards, projectors and other equipment. The general environment of the training room with regard to temperature, lighting, ventilation, arrangement of tables and chairs, location of toilets and washing facilities, together with the arrangements for meals and refreshment periods, must also be considered.

Undertaking the training

With many training activities, such as the training of fork lift truck drivers, only trained trainers should be used. There must be a correct mix of both active and passive learning systems, and a system for monitoring the effectiveness of the trainers. (See 'Training Methods and Techniques' later in this chapter.)

Recording the results

It is necessary to record improvements in operator performance and productivity, safety awareness and other factors included among the training objectives. Feedback systems must be incorporated with a view to measuring the effectiveness of the training by observation, questionnaire or the examination results of trainees.

Evaluation of the results

There are two questions that need to be answered at this stage.

(a) Have the training objectives been met?
(b) If they have been met, could they have been met more effectively?

Operator training in industry requires an appraisal of those skills needed to perform the task satisfactorily and safely. It is normal, therefore, to incorporate the results of such appraisals in the basic training objectives. A further objective is to bring about long-term changes in attitude on the part of trainees linked with performance in the job. Any decision, therefore, as to whether training objectives have been met cannot be taken immediately the trainee returns to work or after a short period of time. It may be several months, or even years, before a valid evaluation can be made, and only after continuous assessment of the trainee. A significant factor in training effectiveness is the extent of the transfer of training achieved by the trainee. 'Transfer of training' means the ability to carry over the knowledge acquired in one task to another task.

The answer to the second question can only be achieved through feedback from staff monitoring the performance of trainees, and the trainees themselves. Feedback can usefully be employed in setting objectives for further training, in the revision of training content and in the analysis of training needs of other groups.

Training methods and techniques

Methods and techniques of training are directly related to the way people learn things. A wide range of techniques and methods is available, depending very much on the learning system adopted, e.g. active or passive.

Passive learning systems

Guided reading

The trainee is given standard literature or company produced material, e.g. a procedure for ensuring safe working, to read and comment upon in a structured situation. For self-motivated trainees it can be an effective means of knowledge transfer, but there is always the danger of self-deception. Guided reading forms an integral part of most training courses.

Lecture

The Department of Employment's (1978) *Glossary of Training Terms* defines the lecture as 'a straight talk or exposition, possibly using visual or other aids, but without group participation other than through questions at the conclusion'. Participation is thus of an auditory nature.

A lecture can:

(a) indicate rules, regulations, policies and course resources;
(b) introduce and provide a general survey of a subject, its scope and value;
(c) provide a brief on procedures to be adopted in subsequent learning activities;
(d) set the scene for a demonstration, discussion or presentation;
(e) illustrate the application of rules, principles or concepts; and
(f) recapitulate, add emphasis or summarise.

A lecture is only as good as the lecturer's ability to present his material and maintain the interest of trainees. If well done and appropriately illustrated, it can be an effective means of communication, especially when groups are large. A good lecturer can convey very swiftly the essentials of a topic, lead the group to an understanding of key concepts, fascinate, amuse, provoke, challenge and involve the trainees. The following points, however, should be considered:

(a) Communication is largely one-way; the lecturer prepares and presents the material in his own way, and the trainees sit, listen and possibly take notes.
(b) Lectures are inappropriate for teaching specific skills.
(c) A lecture has limited sense appeal, which is chiefly aural; to hold a trainee's attention, the content of the lecture must be interesting and challenging.
(d) Lecturing encourages passivity; it is difficult to retain a trainee's attention continuously and he is highly susceptible to distraction.
(e) It is difficult to gauge reaction; if an instructor is to do more than merely present information, he must be aware all the time of the trainees' reactions, misconceptions and inattention, and must rectify the situation immediately.
(f) Effective lecturing is a highly skilled task; because interest and attention has to be generated by the lecturer, the latter's vocabulary, enthusiasm, planning, speech technique, humour and use of visual aids are critical.

Demonstration

Here the instructor, by actual performance, shows the trainees what to do and how to do it and, with associated explanations, indicates why, when and where it is done. The demonstration rarely stands alone, but is invariably combined with some other form of training. A demonstration can illustrate

(a) manipulative operations and procedures, e.g. the operation of a lathe;
(b) construction and principles of operation and use;
(c) the functioning and operation of equipment;
(d) standards, e.g. workmanship, operating efficiency; and
(e) operational safety procedures.

The well-constructed demonstration has several advantages in that it

(a) has dramatic appeal, which can arouse interest and sustain attention;
(b) provides perspective by showing the interrelationships between steps in a procedure;
(c) reduces waste and damage by illustrating the correct handling of equipment and materials; and
(d) saves time by reducing explanation and preventing misunderstanding.

The only limit to class size is the ability of everyone to see the demonstration. A demonstration must work and work well. It should set a standard of performance for trainees and must be correct.

Guided practice

Guided practice is defined as 'a method in which the trainee has to perform the operation or procedure being taught under controlled conditions'. There are four basic categories:

(a) independent practice – trainees set their own pace and work individually;
(b) controlled practice – trainees work together at a pace set by the instructor;
(c) team performance – a group of trainees perform together as a team; and
(d) coach and pupil – a method requiring paired trainees, who perform alternately as student and instructor.

Guided practice is usually used in connection with demonstration. It is used as follow-up instruction in teaching manipulative operations and procedures, the functioning and operation of equipment, team skills and safety procedures. Its disadvantages are the constraints imposed by time. There are many advantages, however, in that:

(a) the trainee is given an opportunity to apply his knowledge in a realistic situation, which is possibly the best way of developing confidence and a positive attitude;
(b) active participation is possible which increases both the quantity of learning and its retention;

(c) the correct procedure can be emphasised, thereby contributing to accident prevention;
(d) wastage and damage are reduced by limiting the possibility of trainee error; and
(e) a method of validation is provided, in that the instructor can note whether the desired objective has been achieved, and difficulties and weaknesses in the instruction.

Active learning systems

Group discussion

Discussion methods take three forms. No sharp boundaries exist between them, but they differ in their objectives.

Directed discussion: The object is to assist trainees to acquire a better understanding of, and the ability to apply, facts, principles, concepts, policies and procedures. The instructor attempts to guide the discussion so that these elements are clearly interlinked and applied.

Developmental discussion: The object is to pool the knowledge and past experience of the trainees with a view to developing and improving existing principles, concepts, policies and procedures. Questions for developmental discussion are less likely to have clear-cut answers than those in directed discussion. The instructor's task is to elicit contributions from members of the group, based on their own experience and related to the topic in hand. He should aim for balanced participation.

Problem-solving discussion: This form attempts to discover an answer to a question or a solution to a problem. There is no known best or correct solution. The instructor's functions are to introduce the problem and to encourage free and full participation in a discussion whose goals include identifying the real problem, assembling and analysing data, formulating and testing hypotheses, determining and evaluating possible courses of action, arriving at conclusions and making recommendations to support these conclusions.

Discussion techniques can be used for

(a) developing imaginative solutions to problems;
(b) stimulating interest and constructive thought, and ensuring participation in situations which would otherwise permit passivity;
(c) emphasising principal teaching points;
(d) supplementing reading, lectures, exercises, etc.;

(e) determining the trainees' degree of comprehension of concepts and principles, and their readiness for progression;
(f) preparing trainees for the application of theoretical work to particular situations;
(g) summarising, classifying or reviewing;
(h) preparing trainees for future instruction; and
(i) determining trainees' progress and the effectiveness of previous instruction.

Advantages of discussion methods:
(a) Discussions present a stimulating opportunity to express one's own opinions and to hear those of others. In a well-planned and skilfully directed discussion, interest level is remarkably high.
(b) Trainees participate in the development of the instruction and are more likely to accept the validity and importance of the content. Thus, they become more deeply committed to the decisions or solutions.
(c) The trainer is able to make use of the trainees' experience, knowledge and abilities to the benefit of everyone else in the group.
(d) Discussion demands a very high degree of trainee participation and leads to better learning and retention. Learning takes place in direct proportion to the amount of individual participation.

Disadvantages of discussion methods:
(a) The instructor must remain unobtrusive yet lead the discussion. He must be well informed; he should be able to reduce arguments over trivia, prevent domination by a few trainees and, finally, relate comments to previous discussions, summarise and encourage full participation.
(b) The quality of discussion depends directly upon the thoroughness of the preparation. However, little or no control can be exercised over the preparatory work of trainees.
(c) Discussions are only applicable to certain forms of subject matter, e.g. safety specification, when the basic groundwork or theory has been completed.
(d) Discussion is time consuming, which is frequently the deciding factor in eliminating this approach. The trainer must, therefore, control the discussion to avoid time wastage.
(e) Discussions are only effective with relatively small groups.
(f) The group must be selected carefully if maximum benefit is to be gained.

Syndicate exercises

A large group can be broken into subgroups (syndicates) for discussion or problem-solving exercises – e.g. the design of a safe system of work – with the instructor available for consultation and guidance. This allows for experience sharing, group decision making and discipline in solving a particular problem. In syndicate exercises, objectives must be clearly established and the reporting back of the syndicate's findings is important.

Group dynamics (T-groups)

Situations develop or are induced in which the behaviour of trainees is examined by other trainees. Group behaviour is also examined by the trainee. This is a very effective way of teaching the trainee about his behaviour and its effect on others. Knowledge of the trainee's behaviour and that of the group as a whole increases, together with the skills needed in order to work together and communicate.

This method of training can go badly wrong if the trainer is not trained in the technique. Trainees may, for instance, be hurt by revelations about their behaviour and may opt out, causing the group to break up. The trainer must be aware of this risk and any loss of confidence amongst trainees resolved before the close of the exercise.

Programmed instruction/learning

Programmed instruction, or programmed learning, is defined as a form of instruction/teaching in which the following factors are present:

(a) a clear statement of exactly what the trainee is expected to be able to do at the end of the programme;
(b) the material to be learnt, which is itemised and tested, is presented serially in identifiable steps and/or frames;
(c) trainees follow an actual sequence of frames which is determined for them according to their individual needs; and
(d) feedback on the accuracy of responses is usually given to the trainee before the next frame is presented.

Good instructional programmes have many uses, including:

(a) the provision of remedial instruction and the maintenance of levels of proficiency in infrequently practised skills;
(b) the filling in of gaps in instruction caused by late arrival, absence, etc.;
(c) the 'acceleration' of able trainees, permitting their early completion of a course;
(d) the provision of sufficient common background among trainees to ensure a firm basis for formal classroom work;
(e) the consolidation of learning by review and practice of knowledge skills;

(f) the provision of advanced work or broader contact on the same level within a particular field of study; and
(g) the provision of a control in the study of learning situations.

Advantages of programmed instruction: The advantages mainly stem from the meticulous preparation, testing and validation involved in the production of an instructional programme. The advantages are

(a) a usually reduced failure rate, which can be attributed to the testing and validation of programmes before use, appropriate 'self-pacing' by trainees, a 'forced response' from trainees and immediate confirmation which guarantees attention, indicates and corrects wrong responses, prevents misinterpretation and eliminates repetition of errors;
(b) the self-pacing, forced attention and immediate feedback characteristics of programmes improve learning and retention, and result in improved standards of proficiency among trainees successfully completing a training course;
(c) the elimination of unnecessary material made possible in the programme's development increases the emphasis on learning critical material; self-pacing and forced attention also decrease training time;
(d) instruction can be almost completely standardised;
(e) except for those programmes which depend upon teaching machines, the use of programmes demands no special facilities for accommodation or equipment;
(f) although it is not recommended that programmes be used as a substitute for trainers, they are validated under conditions where they alone do the teaching and are, therefore, effective instructional vehicles, even in the absence of trainers;
(g) they can be designed to meet a wide range of individual needs, and to achieve group or individual progress; and
(h) programmes, through their self-pacing characteristics and adaptability to any class size, can instruct groups or individuals efficiently and economically; they also free instructors from routine and repetitive teaching tasks, permitting them to devote their time to more difficult, demanding aspects of training.

There are two types of programmed learning or instruction:

(a) Basic linear: this entails the learning of small parts in a set sequence.
(b) Branching: in this sytem, the trainee is presented with a text and a multiple-choice question. The answer given directs the trainee back to an appropriate part of the text, depending upon whether that answer is correct or not. If correct, the trainee moves on to the next

question. If incorrect, the trainee goes back and starts again, reconsidering the question asked.

Disadvantages of programmed instruction: The disadvantages stem from the same roots as its advantages:

(a) programmes suitable for specific needs must be produced locally or by special contract; most programmes that are available 'off the shelf' will not match particular company objectives;
(b) few trained programmers are available;
(c) programmes are costly in terms of programmer training, programme writing, testing and validation, or in the use of outside consultants;
(d) programming is unsuitable for subject matter which is prone to frequent and radical change;
(e) many programmes, especially linear ones, can be boring, making heavy demands on instructors, who must be able to motivate their trainees to complete programmes; and
(f) the use of programmes poses administrative problems, due to varying completion times by trainees, such as timetabling and assignment of trainees to jobs.

Role playing/simulation

These techniques increase trainee involvement in the learning process by introducing a realistic element into instruction. They present the trainees with a situation which might be resolved by acting out the roles of those concerned in their situation. The following types are particularly relevant.

In-tray exercises: Each trainee acts the part of, say, an executive faced with an in-tray containing a number of letters, files, memoranda, etc., to be actioned within a certain time limit. This group can also be made part of a larger simulation, e.g. to include telephone calls and interruptions by visitors, and added to or linked with other groups, each with a different in-tray and functions within the simulated organisation.

Case studies: Problem situations are presented to a group of trainees, the group having to ascertain the best solution, usually in the form of a written report with an oral explanation.

Management games: These differ from other forms of role-playing exercise in that they are played to rules laid down before the game starts. Trainees are given management titles and make management decisions, using a model of the real situation. However, their competitive nature and the implied criticism of the 'losers' can introduce adverse responses amongst participants.

Simulation techniques vary, but are generally applied to give trainees practice in the application of job skills and knowledge in safe, controlled conditions. They can isolate part of a task and give special training in that part. Furthermore, they introduce interest and also active participation. They do, however, require a great deal of preparation and time allocation to be effective.

Individual coaching

This is an on-the-job training technique designed to inspire and develop individual skills. The one-to-one relationship between trainer and trainee can be extremely effective provided the trainer is aware of his objectives and adheres to the written training programme. Coaching imparts knowledge, develops skills and forms attitudes during informal, but planned encounters between trainer and trainee. This technique offers sound learning situations within a management development programme.

Projects

The form taken by projects varies immensely, but objectives must be set for the trainee to achieve, together with guide-lines to encourage initiative. A project stimulates creativity, interest and decision making, and information on the trainee's knowledge and personality is fed back to the trainer in consequence of the way the trainee undertakes the project work.

Assignments

An assignment differs from a project in that the task is undertaken following precise guide-lines after a session of information absorption. An assignment encourages learning transfer to the job situation. Realistic assignments should be chosen to avoid frustration, and loss of confidence by the trainee must be avoided.

The role of external organisations in training

Many organisations provide training. They can be classified as follows.

Universities and polytechnics

These organisations run courses on full-time, modular and part-time bases. Certain 'sandwich' courses will include a period spent in industry, with or without a project undertaken during that period. All universities allow suitable graduates to follow particular lines of research and to proceed to higher level degrees, e.g. PhD, MSc.

Colleges of further education and technical colleges

These colleges train students, again in a wide range of courses. Most of the older technical colleges were established to provide training in jobs relative to the industry in that area, e.g. mining or steelmaking. Courses are run on a full-time, part-time, sandwich or modular basis and linked with government organised schemes, such as the Youth Training Scheme. Certain colleges run courses in accordance with a clearly defined syllabus developed by the Institution of Occupational Safety and Health with compulsory independent examination of candidates by the National Examination Board in Occupational Safety and Health. Courses are run at two levels – 'Ordinary' level and 'Higher' level. Success in these examinations accords with the institution's academic requirements for Corporate Membership respectively at 'Associate' and 'Member' levels.

Training centres

Training centres take many forms. They can be national training centres, such as that run by RoSPA, which runs a wide range of health and safety courses taking in students from all over the world. Conversely, they may be run by organisations specifically for training their own staff and/or staff from other organisations in the same industry. There are a number of management training centres, e.g. Coverdale and Henley Staff College, whose principal fields are management training.

In the area of health and safety training many options are available, depending upon training needs and personal career objectives. All these organisations, whether funded by central or local government, industry or by private subscription/fees have a role to play in training. In many cases, courses can be 'tailor-made' to suit a particular set of training objectives.

Conclusion

The identification of training needs, particularly in relation to health and safety, is an important task in any organisation. It has the basic objectives of:

(a) determining the content of the required training;
(b) indicating the best method of undertaking the training;
(c) highlighting the problem of motivating the organisation to implement the recommended training methods or to use the training provided; and

(d) revealing the ultimate problem of motivating the organisation to apply the training once it has been given.

Health and safety training should emphasise certain basic themes summarised below.

(a) The importance of distinguishing between
    (i) accident and injury, and
    (ii) prevention and protection.
(b) The link between safety performance and operational efficiency, and that between accident prevention management and company management as a whole, must be recognised.
(c) Training must be regarded as the creation of learning situations, not simply by systematic instruction, but by better design of organisational structures and the adoption of appropriate management styles. Organisations are viewed as learning systems. This applies in all situations, including health and safety.
(d) The concept of training must be extended to developing people's full potential so that organisations can satisfy human needs by effective utilisation of manpower. It has been said that accidents 'downgrade the system'. In order to ensure effective utilisation of manpower, there is clearly a need for regular health and safety training of all staff, from the Board room downwards.

11

The cost of accidents

The term *accident* refers to personal injury and 'loss' (*see* Chapter 12). Given that a minimum level of profitability is essential for a business, loss prevention is a key factor.

All accidents, whether they result in personal injury, property and plant damage and/or interruption of business, represent losses to an organisation. The aim of this chapter is to consider the range of losses which can be incurred and how such losses can be quantified, and to explain how loss identification can assist in the establishment of priorities where the improvement of health and safety standards is concerned. Although senior management will complain of the 'burden of health and safety at work', it is the escalating costs of accidents which need closer scrutiny by management.

Statistics

In 1981, it was estimated that the cost of accidents at work in 1982 could be between £700 million and £1,400 million (Morgan and Davies, 1981). This estimate included the costs to the nation of lost production, damaged plant and machinery, medical treatment and management administration costs. Moreover, there is the moral cost when 'account is taken also of the pain, grief and suffering borne by the accident victims, their families and friends'. The figures quoted refer to 1981 costs only.

Taking into account claims submitted during 1981 and 1982, insurers estimated that a lost time or major injury accident costed an average of £765; a minor accident, requiring first aid treatment only, £10; while an accident resulting in plant and property damage only, costed £51. The average major injury accident, at the time of writing (1985), costs in excess of £1,000, particularly if there is property and plant damage.

Costs of compensation for industrial injury and disease are also increasing steadily. Many insurers, as a general rule, now suggest that it would be cheaper for the employer, through his insurer, to pay up, as it is becoming increasingly difficult for employers to win cases in court (*see* Chapter 2).

Health and safety – a multiple approach

The reasons for preventing accidents are threefold – legislative, humanitarian and economic.

(a) The legislative approach is based on the enforcement of statutory provisions contained in Acts, Regulations, orders and approved codes of practice. The enforcing authorities are the Health and Safety Executive and local authorities.
(b) The humanitarian or social approach is based on the premise that no one likes to think that his error or omission has been the principal cause of an accident. No two people respond identically in their assessment or quantification of hazards. An approach based on subjective criteria of a situation is, therefore, of very little value.
(c) The economic or financial approach presupposes that accidents and occupational diseases represent financial losses to the employing organisation. The approach aims to persuade managers that money can be saved and profits increased if accidents are reduced.

It should be appreciated that, in the prevention of accidents, all three approaches must be considered together.

The direct costs of accidents

Direct costs, sometimes referred to as 'insured costs', are largely concerned with a company's liabilities as employer and occupier. Direct costs are covered by premiums paid to an insurance company to provide cover against claims made by injured parties. The premiums paid are determined by the claims history of the organisation and the risks involved in the business. (For the legal liabilities of employers and occupiers, *see* Chapter 2.) Other direct costs of accidents are claims by insured persons and users of products manufactured by the organisation, which are settled either in or out of court, together with fines imposed by courts for breaches of health and safety law. (For the law relating to claims and penalties connected with health and safety at work, *see* Chapter 2.) Also included in this category might be substantial legal defence costs.

Direct costs are relatively simple to calculate annually and they may be included in the operating costs of the organisation. The cost of claims and fines, and court costs, are more difficult to predict and quantify.

The indirect costs of accidents

Indirect costs of accidents are many and varied and are often difficult to predict. Some indirect costs may be included, and thus hidden, in other costs, e.g. labour costs, production costs and administration costs. It is common for indirect costs to be ignored owing to the difficulty of separating them from other costs. Some indirect costs, however, are simple to quantify. These are outlined below.

Treatment costs

These can be divided as follows:

(a) First aid – the cost of first aid materials, including any re-treatment or re-dressing of injuries.
(b) Transport – the cost of transport for the injured person to home, doctor or hospital.
(c) Hospital – any charges made by a hospital for emergency or casualty treatment.
(d) Other costs – within these costs can be included attendance charges made by a local doctor, provision of specific medical materials or treatment not provided under the National Health Service, or the services of a specialist after referral by a doctor.

Lost time costs

Lost time costs include the cost of a person being away from the job for which he is normally paid. They are incurred by the injured person, management, first aid staff and others. These costs are assessed on the basis of time (number of hours) away from the job multiplied by the hourly rate for the job.

Production costs

These can be subdivided as follows:

(a) Lost production – production losses as a result of an accident.
(b) Extra staff payments – payment of overtime rates following hold-up in the normal production cycle after an accident.
(c) Damage costs – through damage to property, plant, vehicles, raw materials and finished products as a result of an accident; these costs should be calculated on the basis of:
    (i) replacement and/or repair of materials and plant, and

(ii) labour costs involved in replacement/repair.

(d) Training and supervision costs – where replacement labour is introduced to maintain production, costs should be calculated on the basis of:
   (i) actual man-hours for replacement labour, and
   (ii) specific training costs for replacement labour, i.e. time of trainers and trainees together with other training costs.

Investigation costs

A number of people may be involved in the investigation of an accident – management, safety officer, shop-floor personnel, safety representative, together with the injured person. Investigation costs should be based on the total man-hours involved, with the hourly rates for individuals taken into account.

Miscellaneous costs

Miscellaneous costs may include ex-gratia payments made by the organisation, perhaps to a widow, the replacement costs of personal items belonging to the injured person and others, incidental costs incurred by witnesses, etc.

Costs to the state

These are difficult to quantify but are potentially enormous. They include the costs of medical treatment provided by the National Health Service, including hospitalisation, attendance of medical staff and provision of ambulance services, together with payment of injury/occupational illness benefit under the Social Security Act.

Costs to the injured person(s)

This chapter has previously considered the cost of accidents to the employer and, to a lesser extent, the state. The personal costs (apart from pain and suffering) also need consideration. They can include:

(a) possible loss of earnings, dependent on terms and conditions of employment, for the period of absence from work;
(b) possible total loss of earning capacity due to physical and/or mental injury and resultant inability to do the original job;
(c) possible reduced earning capacity for the reasons given in (b) above;
(d) possible legal costs in pursuing claims for injury where these are not payable by a trade union; and
(e) possible legal costs, both criminal and civil, where the injured person has been found guilty of reckless or negligent behaviour.

An example of a typical accident costing form is shown in Fig. 11.1.

Details of accident			Unit
Date	Time	Place of accident	

Injured person

Name in full ....
Address ....
Occupation .... Age ....
Length of service .... Sex ....
Accident details ....
Injury details ....

Accident costs				
Direct costs			£	p
1. % of occupier's liability premium		These figures to be inserted by the insurance company		
2. % of increased premiums payable				
3. Claims				
4. Fines and damages awarded in court				
5. Court and legal representation costs				
Indirect costs				
6. Treatment	(a) First aid			
	(b) Transport			
	(c) Hospital			
	(d) Others			
7. Lost time	(a) Injured person			
	(b) Management			
	(c) Supervisor(s)			
	(d) First aiders			
	(e) Others			
8. Production	(a) Lost production			
	(b) Overtime payments			
	(c) Damage to plant, vehicles, etc.			
	(d) Training/supervision of replacement labour			
9. Investigation	(a) Management			
	(b) Safety officer			
	(c) Others, e.g. safety reps			
	(d) Liaison with enforcement authority			
10. Other costs	(a) Ex-gratia payment to injured person			
	(b) Replacement of personal items of (i) injured person (ii) other persons			
	(c) Other miscellaneous costs			
		TOTAL COSTS		

Fig. 11.1 Accident costing form

The unquantifiable costs

There are some indirect costs which it is difficult to measure. These costs could conceivably amount to a further 25 per cent increase in actual calculated indirect costs. They may include:

(a) reduced output and performance owing to loss of workforce morale; this is particularly evident following a fatal accident and can affect some people for many months afterwards;
(b) reduced sales as a result of adverse media publicity culminating in customer alienation;
(c) trade union action or reaction; and
(d) increased attention from enforcement agencies.

In total loss control terminology, 'accidents downgrade the system'. They cause losses which increase costs and reduce profits. This must be one of the most cogent motives for improving safety performance.

PART III

Accident prevention

12

Principles of accident prevention

What is an accident?

A number of definitions have been put forward over the last 30 years and they are quoted below.

(a) 'An unforeseeable event, often resulting in injury.'
(b) 'An unplanned and uncontrolled event which has led to or could have caused injury to persons, damage to plant or other loss' (RoSPA).
(c) 'An unexpected, unplanned event in a sequence of events that occurs through a combination of causes. It results in physical harm (injury or disease) to an individual, damage to property, business interruption or any combination of these' (Department of Occupational and Environmental Health, University of Aston in Birmingham).
(d) 'An accident is an undesired event that results in physical harm to a person or damage to property. It is usually the result of a contact with a source of energy (i.e. kinetic, electrical, chemical, thermal, ionising radiation, non-ionising radiation, etc.) above the threshold limit of the body or structure' (Frank Bird, Executive Director, American Institute of Loss Control).
(e) 'A management error; the result of errors or omissions on the part of management.'

A number of significant factors emerge from these definitions. Generally accidents are

(a) unforeseeable, as far as the accident victim is concerned;
(b) unplanned;
(c) unintended; and
(d) unexpected.

In most cases there is a sequence of events leading to the accident and there may be a number of contributory causes. An accident may result in injury, damage to property and plant, stoppage of or interference with the work process and resultant interruption of business, or any combination of these results.

An accident at work causing personal injury and/or death is actionable in civil law if the act or omission discloses negligence on the part of the employer. Moreover, if an employee suffers an injury resulting in absence from work for more than 3 days, such injury arising out of and in the course of his employment, he may claim social security benefit, irrespective of whether or not anyone is negligent. In addition, there is legal liability where an accident causes property damage and business losses if the damage and/or loss is a foreseeable consequence of the accident. Generally, property damage is regarded as foreseeable and so actionable in negligence, whereas purely economic or business loss, or loss of profits following such damage or interruption, is regarded as too remote and so not actionable (per Lord Denning MR in *Spartan Steel & Alloys Ltd* v. *Martin (Contractors) & Co. Ltd* [1972] 3 AER 557).

An analysis of accidents and their causes requires consideration of the events leading up to a specific accident, 'the pre-accident situation'. It is also vital to know what to do after the accident, first to minimise the effects of injuries, and second, to prevent a recurrence.

The pre-accident situation

There are two specific aspects to accidents, viz. danger, and how people perceive or recognise the danger. The element of danger may be associated with processes, machinery, access to buildings, inadequate supervision and control, or use of unsafe materials. How people perceive danger is a feature of their past experiences, training and general attitude to safety. Summarised simply, therefore, accidents are concerned with:

(a) the objective danger at a particular point in time associated with a specific machine, process, system of work or substance used at work; and
(b) the subjective perception of risk on the part of the individual, which varies according to the features mentioned above, and also according to behavioural factors such as their level of arousal prior to the hazard arising, motivation, memory, personality and attitude.

Accident prevention strategies should thus be directed at, first, bringing about a reduction in the objective danger in the workplace, and second, increasing the perception of risk on the part of individual workers. This is brought about, in the first case, by the use of 'safe place' strategies, and in the second case, by 'safe person' strategies, which are outlined below.

'Safe place' strategies

Safe place strategies feature in much of the occupational health and safety legislation that has been enacted over the last century, in particular the Health and Safety at Work, etc., Act 1974. Their principal aim is to bring about a reduction in the objective danger at the workplace through means such as machinery guarding, improvements in the working environment to reduce the risk of occupational disease, or the design of safe systems of work. They may be classified as follows.

Safe premises

This relates to the general structural requirements of industrial and commercial premises, such as stability of buildings, soundness of floors and the load-bearing capacity of beams. Environmental working conditions, such as levels of lighting and ventilation, feature in this classification, together with the system for assessment of environmental stressors and standards used in the evaluation of stress. (Legal requirements concerning floors, lighting, ventilation and temperature control are to be found in the Factories Act 1961, Offices, Shops and Railway Premises Act 1963 and Regulations made thereunder.)

Safe plant

A wide range of plant and machinery, their power sources, location and use are relevant here. The safety aspects of individual processes, procedures for vetting new machinery and plant, and systems for maintenance and cleaning must be considered.

Safe processes

All factors contributing to the operation of a specific process must be considered, e.g. plant and machinery, raw materials, procedures for loading and unloading, the ergonomic aspects of machine operation, dangerous substances used in the process, and the operation of internal factory transport such as fork lift trucks.

Safe materials

Relevant here are the safety aspects of chemical substances, radioactive substances, raw materials of all types and specific hazards associated with the handling of materials. Adequate information on their correct use, storage and disposal must be provided. (There is a general requirement under HSWA, sec 6, to provide materials which are safe for use at work. More specifically, however, dangerous substances, supplied in the ordinary course of industrial use, or conveyed in bulk by road, must be packaged and labelled in accordance with current packaging and labelling requirements.)

Safe systems of work

The design and implementation of safe systems of work is a key feature of any safe place strategy. It incorporates planning, involvement of workers, training, and designing out hazards which may have existed with previous systems of work (*see* Chapter 13).

Safe access to work

This refers to safe access both to the factory or workplace from the road outside and to the working position, which may be several hundred metres up in the air, as with construction workers, or several miles below the Earth's surface in the case of miners. Consideration must be given, therefore, to matters such as factory approach roads, yards, work at high level, the use of portable and fixed access equipment – e.g. ladders and lifts – and the shoring of underground workings. (The legal requirements relating to access to workplaces are outlined in specific Regulations, e.g. the Construction (Working Places) Regulations 1966. Moreover, under the Factories Act 1961, sec 29(1), there must be safe access to any place where a person has at any time to work, not merely to his normal working position.)

Adequate supervision

In all organisations, there must be adequate safety supervision directed by senior management through supervisory management to the shop floor. The responsibilities of directors, senior managers, departmental managers, supervisors, specialists – such as health and safety practitioners – and shop-floor workers must be clearly identified in writing in the Statement of Health and Safety Policy. Moreover, since many workers now have a written form of job description, this should incorporate their various duties and responsibilities related to health and safety. Failure to observe these contractual duties can lead to disciplinary action including, in cases of flagrant abuse, summary dismissal. Supervisory management has a key role in ensuring the maintenance of a safe place of work. They are the 'linkmen' between management and shop floor and, therefore, have the most immediate contact with the workforce. The duties of supervisors should be clearly identified and they should receive sufficient training and management support to discharge these duties effectively. (Failure to have properly trained supervisors can have serious legal consequences. First, there will be a criminal liability on the part of the employer for breach of HSWA, sec 2(2)(*c*) and, second, there may be a civil liability if injury is suffered by an employee as a result of lack of or inadequacy of supervi. *Slough Metals Ltd* [1974] 1 AER 262).)

Competent and trained personnel

The duty to train all staff levels in safe systems of work is laid dowı. HSWA, sec 2(2)(*c*). Every employee will need some form of health anı safety training. This should be satisfied through induction training, on-the-job training, and training in specialised aspects, such as the operation of permit to work systems or driver training. Moreover, persons who are designated 'competent persons' or 'authorised persons', in order to comply with specific statutory requirements – e.g. the Power Presses Regulations 1965, Electricity (Factories Act) Special Regulations 1944 as well as the Factories Act 1961 itself – will also require specific training, as will the various categories of first aiders under the Health and Safety (First Aid) Regulations 1981. A well-trained labour force is a safe labour force and in organisations which undertake safety training accident costs (*see* Chapter 11) tend to be lower. (Legislation which requires both training and supervision by competent persons, although clearly well intentioned, often fails to define, by reference to experience and qualifications, 'competent persons'. This is both an unfortunate and a serious omission because it encourages training by unqualified personnel, some of whom masquerade as health and safety 'consultants'.)

'Safe person' strategies

These strategies are concerned with protecting the individual in specific situations where a Safe Place strategy may not be wholly appropriate or possible to implement. They depend upon the individual conforming to certain prescribed standards, e.g. wearing personal protective equipment. Safe person strategies may be classified as follows:

Care of the vulnerable

In any work situation inevitably there will be some people who are more vulnerable than others to certain specific risks, e.g. where workers may be exposed to toxic substances, to small levels of radiation or to dangerous metals such as lead. Typical examples of 'vulnerable' groups are young persons who, through their lack of experience, may be unaware of hazards; pregnant women, where there may be specific danger to the foetus; and disabled persons, who may be limited in specific tasks which they are able to undertake. In a number of cases there may be a need for the medical surveillance of such persons. In particular, there are certain occupations which require periodic compulsory medical examination. These include persons employed with lead, in certain processes in chemical works, in chromium-plating processes and as divers.

Personal hygiene

The potential for occupational skin conditions caused by contact with certain substances – e.g. solvents, glues, adhesives and the wide range of skin sensitisers – needs consideration. There is also the risk of ingestion of chemical substances as a result of contamination of food and drink and their containers. Personal hygiene is very much a matter of individual upbringing. For instance, washing the hands after using the toilet is a basic hygiene drill instilled in most people by their parents and teachers, but it is amazing how many people fail to carry out this basic drill.

In order to promote good standards of personal hygiene, it is vital that the organisation provides adequate wash-basins, showers, hot and cold water, nail brushes, soap and towels. Soap is best provided in the liquid form from a wall-mounted dispenser, and may incorporate a bactericide, particularly where workers are at risk of suffering minor hand and arm abrasions. Drying facilities in the form of disposable paper towels or wall-mounted cabinets dispensing non-returnable roller towels are recommended as opposed to simple roller towels and washable hand towels.

Personal protective equipment

Personal protective equipment is considered in Chapter 24. Personal protective clothing should be selected carefully for reasons of hygiene and workers should be made aware of the limitations of such equipment.

Careful conduct for the safety of the individual and others

Dangerous behaviour and 'horseplay' at work have always existed to some extent. Examples of dangerous behaviour are the wilful removal of machine guards; fighting; smoking in designated 'no smoking' areas; the dangerous driving of vehicles; abuse of equipment, gases and flammable substances; failure to wear personal protective clothing and equipment, such as eye protection or safety helmets, where the need arises; and the playing of practical jokes which expose workers to risk of injury. HSWA places a duty on every 'employee' while at work to take reasonable care for the health and safety of himself and of other persons who may be affected by his acts or omissions at work.

Caution towards danger

All workers and management should appreciate the risks in the workplace, and these risks should be clearly identified in the Statement of Health and Safety Policy, together with the precautions to be taken by workers to protect themselves from such risks.

Post-accident strategies

Accidents are usually unforeseeable (*see above*). This may be attributable to insufficient research into hazards; the 'it can't happen to me' philosophy, which is particularly prominent among skilled workers; failure on the part of management or manufacturers of articles and substances to provide information; or simple mechanical failures in plant and machinery. Thus, whilst there must be an emphasis on accident prevention through the use of pre-accident strategies, provision must be made, by means of post-accident strategies, to deal with the aftermath of accidents and to learn from mistakes. Post-accident strategies can be classified in the following way.

Disaster/contingency planning

It is important, particularly in any large industrial or commercial enterprise, that a disaster or contingency plan be developed. Depending upon the inherent risks, the plan should be tailored to take account of the procedure in the event of a large fire, an explosion, a sudden release of toxic liquids, gases or fumes, building collapse or a major vehicular traffic accident on the premises (*see* Chapter 9).

Ameliorative strategies

These strategies are concerned mainly with minimising the effects of injuries as quickly and effectively as possible following an accident. They will include the provision and maintenance of first aid services, procedures for the rapid hospitalisation of injured persons and, possibly, a scheme for rehabilitation following major injury (*see* Chapter 29).

Feedback strategies

There is much to be learned following an accident. Investigation must be directed at identifying the causes of the accident and not just the effects. By the study of past accidents, feedback strategies attempt to prevent their recurrence. The correct use and interpretation of statistical information is vital here.

The causes of accidents

No chapter dealing with strategies in accident prevention would be complete without an examination of the causes of accidents. In major injury or multiple accidents, there may be up to twenty factors which contribute to the accident. In disasters such as the Flixborough incident the contributory causes are even greater in number. Whatever the accident situation, almost inevitably there will be some form of human involvement, however. People are unpredictable, they make mistakes, their attitude to safety varies and they forget things. Whilst the 'human factor' features strongly in the majority of accidents, it is only part of the process, and many other factors are relevant. A resumé of the principal causes of accidents is given below.

Design and/or layout of the working area

Bad design and layout of working areas, in many cases producing congestion and overcrowding, is one of the principal contributory causes of accidents. Ideally, work processes should follow a sequential flow with the raw materials coming in at one end of the building and the finished products going out at the other end. However, most manufacturing tends to be something of a compromise. Unless a factory is purpose-built to accommodate a particular process, the process will have been fitted into an existing building with either too much or too little space. Safety considerations must, therefore, be taken into account at the design stage of projects, particularly where existing buildings are to be modified for a new process.

Structural features

The floor is the most important structural feature in any work situation, and every year many workers are injured through slips and falls on defective floors, badly drained floors or slippery floor finishes. Floor finishes should be specified according to the needs of the process and the people who have to operate the process. To facilitate cleaning, floors should be non-slip, resistant to oils, solvents, fats and other spillages, and be maintained in a good state of repair. Other structurally important features are staircases, elevated working platforms and teagle openings, all of which need adequate safeguards to prevent workers falling from one level to another.

Environmental features

Poor standards of temperature, lighting, ventilation and noise control characterise many accidents. They may be associated with people failing to see where they are going, failing to hear warning signals due to high ambient sound pressure levels or becoming lethargic as a result of high temperature and humidity levels. The problems of stress in the working environment are dealt with in Chapter 30.

Mechanical or materials failure

Machinery and plant breakdown frequently occur due to a failure to undertake regular preventive maintenance. Many accidents are associated with these breakdowns, particularly where operators carry out their own temporary maintenance to keep the line running. Maintenance schedules indicating the item of plant or machinery, the system of maintenance, the frequency of maintenance and the responsibility for ensuring that the maintenance is undertaken should be produced and implemented. Raw materials should be inspected on a regular basis to ensure soundness and suitability for use on machinery and plant.

Inadequate machinery guarding

With many machines there is a risk of contact with the moving parts, which can result in various forms of injury (*see* Chapter 31).

Bad housekeeping

Bad housekeeping is found to be the cause of many accidents. This may take the form of failure to clear spillages; articles left on the floor or in gangways, where they can be stepped on or tripped over; inadequate systems for storage of refuse; or a simple failure to adopt the principle of 'clean as you go'. Cleaning and housekeeping tasks are unpopular with workers, because they are considered 'menial', and with management, who often consider them to be 'unproductive'. Therefore, in many cases there is an unacceptably poor level of housekeeping. To combat this problem, cleaning schedules should be introduced and enforced (*see* Chapter 17). Staff whose specific occupation is cleaning should be employed on a permanent basis. They should use, and be trained in the use of, modern mechanically operated cleaning equipment. (It should be noted that women employed solely in cleaning a factory are not protected under the Factories Act 1961, sec 176. They are, of course, within the scope of HSWA, sec 3(1).)

Inadequate supervision and control

The duty of all levels of management to supervise and control safety at work is well established in law (*see* Chapters 2 and 4). Many accidents are a result of a failure of management to do this.

Inadequate training

Management have a duty to train staff in the general and specific areas of health and safety at work. As with supervision and control, the level of training received by workers varies greatly. A clearly defined health and safety training policy should be included in every Statement of Health and Safety Policy, and the training needs of individual groups of workers identified. Poorly trained workers, or workers who have received no health and safety training, are a danger to themselves and others, particularly in high-risk situations. There is a need to establish the principle that a safe worker is an efficient one.

Deficiencies in personal protective systems

Every year many accidents are associated with deficiencies in personal protection. There may be a failure by management to provide the protection; alternatively, workers may refuse to wear or use the protection because it is uncomfortable, hinders their working routine or, in the case of eye protection, reduces their vision owing to misting. There is a need, therefore, to assess individual requirements by consulting the workers. This approach is established in case law, much of which has concerned the suitability of eye protection. In certain cases, the wrong type of personal protection may be provided, e.g. respiratory and hearing protection, with the result that the worker does not receive adequate protection. Moreover, most types of personal protection need regular testing for efficiency and the detection of faults. This presupposes efficient supervision and control with, if necessary, the implementation of disciplinary procedures for persistent offenders.

Inadequate or ineffective rules and instructions

The occupier has a duty to explain the hazards to workers and the precautions necessary to ensure safe working (*see* Chapter 3). Most organisations undertake this activity and use internal codes of practice, working instructions, operating manuals or other forms of documentation. In many cases, rules and instructions are ambiguous, badly worded or simply not available to the people to whom they are directed. Alternatively, where consultation with the workforce has not taken place, workers may consider the instructions so unworkable or unreasonable that they are disregarded. Whatever the cause of this situation, there is clearly a need for training and briefing of operators in any new set of rules or procedures which may be introduced. Moreover, the procedures to be adopted when there are breaches of rules or instructions by workers must be fully understood. This requires vigilance on the part of supervisors and regular reinforcement training of operators. (The legal position regarding health and safety discipline is set out more fully in Chapter 5.)

Physical disability

Whilst not a significant factor in the causes of accidents, there are many people who, because of physical limitations or disabilities, may be prevented from undertaking certain tasks or operations. There is a clear-cut need to assess regularly the physical limitations of disabled persons to ensure that there has not been a deterioration in their ability to perform certain tasks safely. (Such factors have been documented in case law established at industrial tribunals. Many cases concerned with unfair dismissal complaints have underlined the fact that if, through physical or mental disability or both, an employee is a source of danger to himself and/or other employees, the employer has a duty to dismiss him or, at least, transfer him to other, less dangerous work.)

Poor ergonomic design

There is much evidence to support the view that the poor ergonomic design of items such as controls and displays on plant and machinery, and of working positions such as those in crane drivers' and lorry drivers' cabs, has in the past been a contributory factor in accidents. Poor ergonomic design results in stress on the operator in terms of general fatigue, eye strain, discomfort, muscular strain and cramps. This may, in turn, lead to loss of interest, reduced arousal level, reduced perceptual powers and altered patterns of thought. All these effects can contribute to the 'human error' aspects of accidents.

13 Safe systems of work

Definition

A *safe system of work* is defined as 'the integration of personnel, articles and substances in a suitable environment and workplace to produce and maintain an acceptable standard of safety. Due consideration must also be given to foreseeable emergencies and the provisions of adequate rescue facilities'. The Health and Safety at Work, etc., Act 1974 requires the provision and maintenance of plant and systems of work that are, so far as is reasonably practicable, safe and without risks to health (*see* Chapter 3).

Components of a safe system of work

People

People are the human assets of the enterprise. A safe system of work should incorporate safe behaviour, sound knowledge, skills, both mental and physical, willingness to conform to the system, motivation, resistance to pressure to behave unsafely and job experience.

Machinery, plant and equipment

Sound design and safety specification of plant, machinery and equipment, including consideration of ergonomic factors, together with efficient and planned maintenance, are important features of a safe system of work (*see* Chapter 31).

Materials

Materials must be safe during processing and as finished products, meet quality assurance standards, and be safe for disposal as waste products and by-products of manufacture.

Environment

The fourth aspect includes control of temperature, lighting and ventilation, dust, fumes, vapours, radiation, chemical and biological hazards, and provision of safe access and egress, sound levels of welfare amenity provision and safe levels of noise and vibration.

Place of work

This may be a factory workshop, construction site or office. The place of work should be safe in terms of its construction, means of fire protection, including means of escape in the event of fire, and layout.

Requirements for a safe system of work

The principal requirement is planning the safest way to combine people and plant so that the work can be undertaken in a specific area. This includes

(a) a layout which allows for safe access to and egress from the working area and plant within, and adequate space between machines and operating plant;
(b) a correct sequence of operations with materials and products conveyed mechanically, wherever appropriate, to and from work positions;
(c) analysis of tasks, including Job Safety Analysis (*see below*), and the provision of clear job instructions;
(d) identification of safe procedures, both routine and emergency, including requirements that
  (i) the authority for starting and stopping machines is clearly allocated and obvious;
  (ii) clear instructions are given to those allowed to lubricate or carry out maintenance work, including the circumstances under which this work may be done;
  (iii) adequate arrangements are made for removal of materials, components, scrap, trimmings, swarf and dirt from plant and the immediate floor area;
  (iv) preventive maintenance schedules incorporate safety checks; and
  (v) there is a firm commitment to cleaning and housekeeping procedures;
(e) provision of a safe and healthy working environment, in particular:
  (i) illumination levels which prevent glare and sharp contrasts between light and shadow;
  (ii) heating and ventilation systems which avoid extremes of temperature and humidity and which allow circulation of fresh air to all parts of working areas;

(iii) ambient noise levels kept to within the limits imposed by current hygiene standards, otherwise hearing protection may be necessary; and

(iv) localised exhaust ventilation at work stations where dusts, fumes, gases or vapours are emitted from the work process.

Information sources

The importance of information sources in the design of safe systems of work cannot be overstated. Sources include the following.

Existing written information

This may take the form of Statements of Health and Safety Policy (*see* Chapter 3); specific company policies, e.g. on the use and storage of dangerous substances; current agreements with trade unions; company rules, regulations and codes of practice, methods, times, instructions; British Standards; HSE Guidance Notes and approved codes.

Interviews and discussions

These are a useful way of obtaining subjective information, perceptions, ideas and feelings, and for identifying informal roles and relationships, group norms, attitudes, levels of knowledge and skill; the Health and Safety Committee is a valuable information source.

Direct observation

This is the actual observation of work being carried out, which identifies interrelationships, hazards, dangerous practices and occurrences, and risk situations.

Work study techniques

Included here are the results of activity sampling, surveys, method study, work measurement and process flows.

Personal experience

People have their own experiences of particular jobs and the hazards their jobs present. Individual experience of the operation of plant and machinery, systems of work and practices used is a valuable source of information.

Job descriptions

A job description should incorporate a health and safety element. It should take account of the physical and mental requirements and limitations of certain jobs and past modifications to the job description. Representations from operators and safety representatives on safety aspects of their jobs should be taken into account. (There is no strict legal duty to include requirements relating to health and safety performance in the summary of the main terms of the employee's contract, which the employer is bound to furnish after a period of 13 weeks of employment. Employees, however, should be under no illusion that compliance with health and safety requirements is an implied condition of every employment contract, breach of which may result in dismissal.)

Acts, orders and regulations

Legal requirements may impose controls on certain jobs and activities, e.g. mounting abrasive wheels (Abrasive Wheels Regulations 1970) and in the use of woodworking machinery (Woodworking Machines Regulations 1974).

Manufacturers' instructions and information

Information about articles and substances used at work which is provided under HSWA, sec 6, and operating instructions for machinery and plant should be sufficiently comprehensive to enable a judgment to be made on their safe use.

Accident statistics

Statistical information on past accidents may identify unsatisfactory trends in operating procedures. These must be eliminated at the design stage of a safe system of work.

Task Analysis

Information produced from the analysis of tasks, such as mental and physical requirements, manual operations, skills required, influences on behaviour, learning methods and specific hazards, must be taken into account. Job Safety Analysis is a development of Task Analysis.

Job Safety Analysis

Job Safety Analysis is a technique which identifies all accident prevention measures appropriate to a particular job or area of work activity, and the behavioural factors which most significantly influence whether or not these measures are taken. The approach is both diagnostic and descriptive.

This analysis reflects the contribution which should be made by all personnel – managers, supervisors, workers' representatives, health and safety specialists, engineers, contractors – in the creation of an overall 'safety climate' within which the individual receives the maximum support for his own accident prevention role. Hence it is possible to create an integrated approach to accident prevention through analysis which ensures that all functions are involved in a co-operative effort. Having recognised the remedial measures necessary, all functions can then become committed to their adoption. This would include design modification, methods improvement and machinery guarding. The training specialist would extract the relevant parts from the Job Safety Analysis for incorporation in his training analysis. In this way subsequent training programmes would make provision for all functions to be able to fulfil their accident prevention roles. If the training analysis has already been prepared, it can often be used as a basis for Job Safety Analysis.

Job Safety Analysis can be:

(a) job-based, e.g. machinery operators, fork lift truck drivers; or
(b) activity based, e.g. manual handling activities, window cleaning, work at heights.

In all circumstances, however, it is normal to undertake Job Safety Analysis in two stages: Initial Job Safety Analysis and Total Job Safety Analysis.

Initial Job Safety Analysis

The following information is required for effective analysis:

(a) job title;
(b) department or section;
(c) job operations, i.e. a stage-by-stage breakdown of the physical and mental tasks required in the job;
(d) machinery and equipment used;
(e) materials used, i.e. raw materials and finished products;
(f) protection needed, e.g. machinery guarding, personal protective equipment;
(g) the hazards that may be encountered;
(h) degree of risk involved;
(i) work organisation, including the responsibilities of supervisor and operator, current safety requirements and procedures; and
(j) specific tasks – Task Analysis would split the job into various stages, e.g. setting up, feeding, controlling, unloading, machine maintenance and housekeeping aspects.

An example of this initial stage of the process is shown in Fig. 13.1.

Total Job Safety Analysis

From the basic information provided in the Initial Job Safety Analysis, Total Job Safety Analysis proceeds to an examination of the following:

INITIAL JOB SAFETY ANALYSIS	
Job Title	Filing machine operator
Department	Bottling Department
Purpose	Filling mineral water bottles using automatic filler and capper

Machinery and Equipment

Rotary filler incorporating capping press, empty bottle conveyor, marshalling table and filled bottle conveyor; hand tools – spanners and steel lever.

Materials

Empty bottles; mineral water

Protection

Clothing – One piece overall, apron and safety wellingtons, full face protection, hair enclosed in combined drill cap with snood attachment, heavy duty gloves and ear defenders.

Machinery – 2 m high polycarbonate enclosure to filler with interlocked gates at access points; interlocked guard to capping press; fixed guards to conveyor end adjacent to filler.

Intrinsic Hazards

1. Hand contact with moving filler and capping press, and when changing cap supply.
2. Cuts to hands from removal of broken glass from filler.
3. Entanglement in in-running nip to conveyor.
4. Flying glass splinters due to occasional bottle explosions.
5. Broken glass on floor – risk of foot injuries.
6. Noise – risk of occupational deafness.
7. Injuries from slips and falls on wet floor.

Degree of Risk

Assume that four machines of this type are in regular use in the same department. The operator with least experience has been doing this job for 8 months, others having up to 20 years' experience. The principal risks are in the removal of broken glass from the filler and falls due to wet floors.

Work Organisation

Assume further that a bonus system is operated on weekly output and work is mainly repetitive. After setting up, a large order could run for 2 or 3 days. On the other hand, a series of small orders are occasionally processed, which requires re-setting the machine after every 4-minute cycle, when much more time would be spent setting than running the machine. Moreover, operator and assistant are interchangeable, but the operator makes the adjustment to the flow control device to ensure even and smooth running. Little maintenance work is required as the machine is very reliable. Typical maintenance includes replacing the driving belt and adjusting the brake – straightforward operations occupying a short period of time.

Specific Tasks

1. Setting up machine
2. Regulating flow control device.
3. Controlling input of bottles to machine.
4. Removing broken bottles and caps, together with broken glass present.
5. Housekeeping activities, including removal of broken bottles from conveyor and liquid spillages.

Fig. 13.1 Initial job safety analysis

(a) operations;
(b) hazards;
(c) skills required:
  (i) knowledge, and
  (ii) behaviour;
(d) external influences on behaviour:
  (i) nature of influences, e.g. noise;
  (ii) source of influence, e.g. machinery;
  (iii) activities, e.g. loading procedure; and
(e) learning method.

A standard form, which covers the above principal elements of the analysis, is used for this exercise. Four examples of Job Safety Analysis are shown in Table 3.

Finally, one of the principal duties of the employer under HSWA is identifying the hazards and the precautions needed by staff, this information to be itemised in the Statement of Health and Safety Policy (*see* Chapter 3). Job Safety Analysis can be undertaken by groups of workers or as a joint exercise by the health and safety committee, the final analysis being incorporated in codes of practice or documentation which is referred to in the statement.

Permit to work systems

A permit to work system is a formal safety control system designed to prevent accidental injury to personnel, damage to plant, premises and product, particularly when work with a foreseeably high hazard content is undertaken and the precautions required are numerous and complex. The permit to work is essentially a document which sets out the work to be done and the precautions to be taken. It predetermines a safe drill and is a clear record that all foreseeable hazards have been considered and that all precautions are defined and taken in the correct sequence. It does not, in itself, make the job safe, but is dependent for its effectiveness on specified persons carrying it out conscientiously and with a high degree of supervision, control and training of staff.

Permit to work systems have largely grown out of the requirements laid down in the Factories Act 1961. Certain sections of that Act require particular precautions to be taken, e.g. in respect of work involving dangerous substances and fumes (section 30), where there may be lack of oxygen, the presence of flammable or explosive dusts, vapours, gases and other substances, or where staff may need to enter confined spaces.

HSWA, secs 2(1) and 2(2) places a duty on the employer to ensure the health and safety at work of all his employees and, in particular, to provide safe systems of work together with adequate supervision.

Requirements of the system

The system must be formal, but simple to operate, so as to ensure the commitment of those who operate and who are affected by it. Permits to work will involve the engineering function and production and service departments. In some cases, engineering staff may not be involved. In the operation of a permit to work system, the following principles must be observed:

(a) The permit must provide concise and accurate information about who is to do the work, the time span over which the permit is valid, specific work to be undertaken and precautions.
(b) The work instruction in the permit must be considered the principal instruction and, until it is cancelled, this instruction overrides all other instructions.
(c) No one must, in any circumstances, work at a place or on apparatus not indicated as safe by the permit.
(d) No one must undertake any work whatsoever which is not described in the permit to work. In the event of a change in the work programme, the permit must be amended, or cancelled and a new permit issued.
(e) Only the originator, or another person taking over responsibility, may amend or cancel the permit. Anyone taking over a permit, either as a matter of routine or in an emergency, must familiarise himself with and assume full responsibility for the work until he has formally handed the permit back to the originator, or the work is completed.
(f) Anyone accepting a permit is, from that moment, responsible for the safe conduct of the work within the limits of the permit. Above all, he must not allow himself to be persuaded to disregard its conditions.
(g) There must be effective liaison with controllers of other plant or work areas whose activities could be affected by the permitted work.
(h) When work has to be undertaken on part of a site, or on specific plant or equipment, the boundary or limits of the work area must be clearly marked or defined.
(i) Contractors undertaking specific tasks must be included in the permit to work system, including any briefing prior to commencement. Observance of safety rules and procedures, including the use of permits to work, should be a condition of contract. Training may be necessary for contractors' staff together with the provision of advice and assistance in certain cases.

Table 3: Total Job Safety Analysis related to Task Analysis

Task	*Hazards*	*Skills*	*Influences on behaviour*	*Learning method*
1. Sharpening a knife using a steel.	Cutting hand or fingers.	Co-ordination of movement of knife and steel.	Sharpness of knife. Condition of floor. Condition of knife. Space limitations. Other people present.	Demonstration of technique. Repetitive practice until speed increases.
2. Use of bench grinder to sharpen a chisel.	Sparks and metal particles in eyes and face. Hand contact with wheel. Entanglement of sleeve or tie in wheel. Flying fragments from possible wheel burst.	Co-ordination of cutting edge of chisel with rotating wheel. Correct use of tool rest.	Speed and condition of wheel. Condition of bench and floor. Space limitations. Illumination. Condition of chisel. Other people present.	Demonstration of method of operation and use. Repetitive practice at machine using guard. Inspection of tools and wheel – action on defects.
3. Dispensing strong chemical compounds from bulk.	Burns to eyes, face, hands and rest of body. Inhalation of fumes.	Correct use of tap, drum cradle, drip tray and container, and protective clothing.	Strength of chemicals and fumes. Corrosive effects. Illumination and ventilation. Arrangement of system. Space limitations. Condition of floor.	Demonstration of correct dispensing method. Practice using apron, gloves and full face protection. Recognition of hazards from spillage, splashing and fumes.

Table 3: Total Job Safety Analysis related to Task Analysis (*contd.*)

Task	*Hazards*	*Skills*	*Influences on behaviour*	*Learning method*
4. Working on fragile roof.	Falling through roof. Sliding down and falling off edge of roof. Algae on roof causing slips and falls. Cuts from roof sheets while handling. Eye and hand injuries while cutting and shaping roof sheets. Inhalation of dust while cutting. Electrical and mechanical hazards from use of drill, saw and cutting disc.	Correct positioning of access ladder, staging and crawl boards. Correct working position on crawl board. Knowledge of strong and weak points of roof. Correct handling and elevation of roof sheets. Correct placing, lapping, drilling and bolting of roof sheets. Correct use of safety harness. Knowledge of wind effects while handling roof sheets.	Weather conditions, e.g. wind speed. Height of roof. Existing condition of roof. Illumination. Spacing and location of structural roof members. Footwear worn. Provision and use of safety harness.	Demonstration of correct placing and use of ladder and crawl boards, erection and use of access system. Practice in placing, lapping, drilling and bolting roof sheets. Recognition of dangerous conditions on existing roofs.

The system in operation

The decision to issue a permit to work depends upon foreseeable hazards. A permit to work system should be operated for the following activities:

(a) entry into confined spaces, closed vessels and vessels containing agitators or other moving parts;
(b) work involving the breaking of pipe lines or the opening of plant containing steam, ammonia, chlorine, other hazardous chemicals and hot substances, or vapours, gases or liquids under pressure;
(c) work on certain electrical systems;
(d) welding and cutting operations in areas other than workshops;
(e) work in isolated locations, locations with difficult access or at high level;
(f) work in the vicinity of, or requiring the use of, highly flammable, explosive or toxic substances;
(g) work which may cause atmospheric pollution of the workplace;
(h) certain work involving commissioning, particularly pressure testing;
(i) certain fumigation activities using dangerous substances in gaseous form, e.g. methyl bromide;
(j) certain work involving ionising radiations; and
(k) work involving contractors in any of the above activities on or about the premises.

Furthermore, it is necessary to assess the degree of risk to which personnel, contractors' staff, possibly members of the public, property and product are exposed in respect of:

(a) the type of work undertaken;
(b) the working method used;
(c) the location of the work; and
(d) any articles and substances used which may affect, or be affected by, the work.

Operation of permit to work systems

The operation of a system should take place in a number of clearly defined stages as outlined below.

Assessment

This is the most important stage and should be undertaken by an authorised person, appointed in writing by senior management, who is experienced in the work and, where specialist plant is concerned, is familiar with the relevant process, chemistry and engineering. The person appointed must be allowed sufficient time to examine each part of the operation and personally check each stage of the action necessary in the task. Assessment should consider the work to be done, the methods by which the work can be done, and the hazards inherent in the plant in relation to the task. The ultimate objective of the assessment is to determine the steps which should be taken to make the job safe and the precautions which should be adopted during the actual working.

Withdrawal from service

Before plant is prepared for actual work or entry, it should be withdrawn from service and clearly designated by notices and/or fencing as a permit to work area, so that there is no chance of personnel not covered by the permit opening valves or activating machinery whilst others are inside or working on the plant. After withdrawal has been completed, the person in charge of the process must sign to that effect on the permit. This entry on the permit should also state that all operators concerned have been advised of the situation. Warning notices, as appropriate, should be displayed.

Isolation

After withdrawing the plant from service, it should be physically isolated by barriers displaying warning notices, and mechanically or electrically isolated. In certain cases, it is appropriate to indicate the stages in the isolation procedure in an attachment to the permit though, in general, the permit to work form should be specifically designed to take the authorised person through a series of logical precautions included on the form itself and designed to ensure that he does not fail to consider each and every such precaution. A declaration that the plant has been isolated should then be entered on the permit. It may be necessary also to undertake atmospheric testing, particularly if personnel are to enter a confined space within the meaning of the Factories Act 1961, sec 30.

Cancellation of permit to work

When scheduled operations have been completed, the permit to work certificate should be cancelled and returned to the originator, who should ensure that all the work has been completed satisfactorily. This person should sign the declaration that all personnel and equipment have been removed from the plant.

Return to service

The plant should now be returned to service. The person responsible for the plant should first check that the permit has been properly cancelled, and then make the final entry on the certificate accepting responsibility for the plant.

Training

Training in the operation of the system is necessary for management, supervisory staff, engineering staff and operators, including contractors' staff, who may operate a permit to work system.

Administrative procedures for permits to work

The permit to work must be raised, by the senior person responsible for carrying out the work, before the work, or the phase of the work requiring the permit, is commenced. The authority for issuing permits to work should be limited to specified appointed persons. When senior management is considering the appointment of 'authorised persons' for the purposes of signing permits to work, the following factors should be taken into account in relation to the person:

(a) age and experience;
(b) training and academic qualifications;
(c) knowledge of the actual plant or process, etc., involved; and
(d) status and ability to control the permit to work operation.

Only a limited supply of permits to work should be available at any one time.

Work involving permits should be carefully planned to cause the least possible interference with, or interruption of, working processes. One benefit of planning is that time is made available to gain specialist advice or refer to written information sources to ensure adequate knowledge of the situation, the hazards involved and preventive methods needed. In any emergency situation, where a permit may be required quickly, the degree of risk may be much greater; hence the need to remain calm and consider the above factors before preparing a permit. The actual preparation of a permit must, in many cases, be classed as a 'team job'. It may require the knowledge and experience of the engineer, chemist, safety specialist, production manager and other specialists from both inside and outside the organisation. In some cases, it may be necessary to issue a permit in the middle of the night or on a Sunday afternoon, when there may be limited staff available. It is at such times that people may take short cuts in the procedure or fail to consider all the implications at the assessment stage of the operation. Where numerous permits are required, a system of early application may be needed, e.g. a request for a permit is made to the authorised person 24 hours before it is required, thereby giving him time to consider and arrange any necessary precautions, such as atmospheric testing.

All potential permit to work situations should be considered for individual locations for identified types of work, e.g. welding in confined spaces. Check-lists should be prepared, particularly for isolation procedures, to ensure a uniform approach.

Documentation of the permit to work system

The permit to work should be printed in triplicate, self-carbonned and serial numbered, perhaps with different coloured pages for the original, first copy and second copy. These should be distributed by the originator as follows.

(a) The original should go to the person undertaking the work, and possibly posted at the place of work.
(b) The first copy should be given to the person responsible for the department or area in which the work is to be carried out.
(c) The second copy should be retained by the originator.

On completion of the work and final clearance of the permit, all copies should be returned to the originator for destruction, except for the second copy which should be kept for record purposes for a period of not less than 2 years.

Typical examples of permits to work are shown in Figs 13.2–13.6.

Competent persons and authorised persons

One way of ensuring the operation of a safe system of work is by the designation and employment of specifically trained operators who appreciate the risks involved. This may be for undertaking certain inspections, issuing permits to work, or carrying out work where there is a high level of foreseeable risk at frequent intervals.

Competent persons

The expression 'competent person' occurs frequently in construction safety legislation. For example, under the Construction (General Provisions) Regulations 1961 and the Construction (Working Places) Regulations 1966 certain inspections, examinations, operations and supervisory duties must be undertaken by such persons. 'Competent person', however, is not generally defined in law, except in the Electricity (Factories Act) Special Regulations 1944. Therefore the onus is on the employer to decide whether persons are competent to carry out these duties. An employer might do this by reference to the person's training, qualifications and experience. Broadly, a competent person should have practical and theoretical knowledge as well as sufficient experience of the particular machinery, plant or procedure involved to enable him to identify defects or weaknesses during plant and machinery examinations, and to assess their importance in relation to the strength and function of that plant and machinery. He must be able to discover defects and determine the consequences of such defects. This last observation does not constitute a legal definition, but does provide a good working rule (*Brazier* v. *Skipton Rock Company Ltd* [1962] 1 AER 955).

Competent persons are involved in many activities, including:

(a) supervision of demolition work;
(b) supervision of handling and use of explosives;
(c) inspection of scaffold materials prior to erection;
(d) supervision of erection of, substantial alterations or additions to, and dismantling of scaffolds;
(e) inspection of scaffolds every 7 days, and after adverse weather conditions which could affect the strength and stability of a scaffold, or cause displacement of any part;
(f) inspection of excavations on a daily basis;
(g) supervision of the erection of cranes;
(h) testing of cranes after erection, re-erection and any removal or adjustment involving change of anchorage or ballasting; and
(i) examination of appliances for anchorage or ballasting prior to crane erection.

For further examples of the duties of competent persons in the construction industry, reference should be made to the Construction Regulations.

Another area where competent persons have a role to play is electrical supply. Under the Factories (Electrical Energy) Regulations 1908 (Reg 28)

> No person, except an authorised person or a competent person acting under his immediate supervision, shall undertake any work where technical knowledge or experience is required in order adequately to avoid danger; and no person shall work alone in any case in which the Secretary of State directs that he shall not. No person except an authorised person, or a competent person over 21 years of age acting under his immediate supervision, shall undertake any repair, alteration, extension, cleaning or such work where technical knowledge or experience is required in order to avoid danger, and no one shall do such work unaccompanied.

Where a contractor is employed, and the danger to be avoided is under his control, the contractor shall appoint the authorised person, but if the danger to be avoided is under the control of the occupier, the occupier shall appoint the authorised person.

Authorised persons – electrical processes

An *authorised person* is defined in the Electricity (Factories Act) Special Regulations 1944 as the occupier or contractor for the time being under control of the occupier, or a person employed, appointed or selected by the occupier, or by a contractor ... to carry out certain duties incidental to the generation, transformation, distribution or use of electrical energy, such occupier, contractor or person being a person who is competent for the purposes of the Regulations. ...

The generally accepted definition of an authorised person is a competent person authorised orally, but preferably in writing, to carry out specific operations and/or work. The expression 'authorised person' means very little, however, unless it is accompanied by the degree of authorisation. Before authorisation, a person should undergo an oral examination and practical test carried out by a senior supervisor, who should declare his opinion as to suitability in writing to the senior manager or head of department concerned.

Senior authorised person and authorised person

Most large organisations operate a formal system of control, particularly for work in high-voltage switchrooms, and it is normal to distinguish between a senior authorised person and an authorised person as follows:

(a) A senior authorised person is an authorised person appointed in writing by a senior manager to issue and cancel permits to work, sanctions for test, certificates for limitation of access, certificates of isolation, earthing and test, and work instructions.
(b) An authorised person is a competent person over 18 years of age, appointed in writing by the senior authorised person, and endorsed by the senior manager, to carry out specific operations and/or work on high-voltage systems and apparatus and issue certificates for limitation of access.

In appointing the authorised person, the senior authorised person would have regard to that person's basic training, experience, specific training, technical ability, competence and suitability for high-voltage work (*see* Chapter 35).

PERMIT TO WORK CERTIFICATE SERIAL NO: 1414

LOCATION: **ORIGINATOR:** **DATE:**

PART A
Valid from .... (time) to .... (time) on .... (date)
Issued by .... to ....
This permit is issued for the following work ....
in .... department/area/section.

PART B – PRECAUTIONS	YES/NO	N/A	SIGNATURE
1 The above plant has been removed from service and persons under my supervision have been informed.			
2 The above plant has been isolated from all sources of: (a) ingress of dangerous fumes, flammable and toxic substances (b) electrical and mechanical power; (c) heat, steam and/or hot water.			
3 The above plant has been freed of dangerous substances.			
4 Atmospheric tests have been carried out and the atmosphere is safe.			
5 The area is roped off or otherwise segregated from adjacent areas.			
6 The appropriate danger/caution notices have been displayed.			
7 The following additional safety precautions have been taken: (a) the use of safety belt and life line; (b) the use of goggles and/or gloves; (c) the use of flameproof lamps; (d) the use of fresh air/self-contained breathing apparatus; (e) prohibition on naked lights/sources of ignition; (f) .... (g) .... (h)			

Part C – DECLARATION
I hereby declare that the operations detailed in Parts A and B have been completed and that the above particulars are correct.
Signed .... Date .... Time ....

PART D – RECEIPT/ACCEPTANCE OF CERTIFICATE
I have read and understand this certificate and will undertake to work in accordance with the conditions in it.
Signed .... Date .... Time ....

PART E – COMPLETION OF WORK
The work has been completed and all persons under my supervision, materials and equipment have been withdrawn.
Signed .... Date .... Time ....

PART F – REQUEST FOR EXTENSION
The work has NOT been completed and permission to continue is requested.
Signed .... Date .... Time ....

PART G – EXTENSION
I have re-examined the plant detailed above and confirm that the certificate may be extended to expire at .... (time).
Further precautions ....
Signed .... Date .... Time ....

PART H – CANCELLATION OF PERMIT
I hereby declare this Permit to Work cancelled and that all precautionary measures specified have been withdrawn.
Signed .... Date .... Time ....

PART I – RETURN TO SERVICE
I accept the above plant back into service.
Signed .... Date .... Time ....

PART J – REMARKS, SPECIAL CONDITIONS AND EXTRA INFORMATION

....
....
....
....
....
....
....
....

Fig. 13.2 Permit to work – plant

* Delete as appropriate throughout form

PERMIT TO WORK ON/TEST* ESSENTIALLY LIVE ELECTRICAL APPARATUS.

PERMIT No Z 7201

1. DETAILS OF APPARATUS AND WORK/TEST* TO BE CARRIED OUT

.... Contract No ....

.... Location ....

....

2. REASON WHY WORK/TEST* CANNOT BE CARRIED OUT WITH APPARATUS ISOLATED

....

3. PERSON(S) INVOLVED IN WORK/TEST*

* (only Authorised or Competent Persons may work on/test live apparatus at or above 55 volts AC/DC)

COMPETENT/AUTHORISED PERSON	OBSERVER
Name and Initials	Name and Initials ....
Name and Initials	Name and Initials ....

4. PRECAUTIONS AND AUTHORISATION

4.1 SAFETY EQUIPMENT. The following safety equipment will be provided and used through the work/test*

...... PAIRS INSULATING RUBBER GLOVES	– MAX SAFE VOLTAGE ....
...... PAIRS INSULATING RUBBER BOOTS	– MAX SAFE VOLTAGE ....
...... INSULATING RUBBER MATS	– MAX SAFE VOLTAGE ....
...... INSULATING PUSH BARS	– MAX SAFE VOLTAGE ....

OTHER TOOLS AND EQUIPMENT (State type and when to be used) ....

....

4.2 ADJACENT LIVE EQUIPMENT. The following precautions are to be taken to ensure that the persons named in Para 3 cannot come into contact with adjacent live equipment ....

....

....

4.3 DANGER AND CAUTION NOTICES have been posted at ....

....

4.4 ATMOSPHERIC CONDITIONS. The following precautions are to be taken to avoid danger from wet or humid conditions ....

....

....

IMPORTANT – No electrical work is to be carried out in potentially flammable atmospheres unless a hot work permit is in force.

4.5 VALIDATION PERIOD: This permit is effective

From .... hrs Date ....

To .... hrs Date ....

4.6 AUTHORISATION

I declare that all precautions specified in Para 4 are in force and that the work/test* described in Para 1 may now begin.

Signed .... Authorised Person Time .... hrs

Date ....

---

5. ACCEPTANCE BY COMPETENT PERSON(S) AND OBSERVER(S)

5.1 I acknowledge receipt of the Top (Yellow) Copy of this permit, and understand/will use the safety precautions listed in Para 4. I will work only under the surveillance of the Observer, and will return this permit to the Authorised Person when work is complete.

Signed .... Competent Person(s) Time .... hrs

Date ....

5.2 I acknowledge receipt of the first (Pink) Copy of this permit and will monitor the safe progress of the Competent Person. I have been instructed what to do in case of emergency, and will return the permit to the Authorised Person when the work/test is complete.

Signed .... Observer(s) Time .... hrs

Date ....

---

6. CLEARANCE

I hereby declare that the work/test* described in Para 1 is complete. The apparatus is safe and tools/gear have been withdrawn.

Signed .... Competent Person

Date .... Time ....

---

7. CANCELLATION

I hereby declare this permit cancelled. I have received the Yellow and Pink copies of the permit back respectively from the Competent Person and the Observer. These copies have been destroyed.

Signed .... Authorised Person

Date .... Time ....

NOTES

(I) Top Copy (Yellow) and First Copy (Pink) to be issued by Authorised Person respectively to Competent Person and Observer and retained by them during the work/test. Both copies to be returned to Authorised Person for destruction on completion of work/test.

(II) Where the Authorised Person is also the Competent Person he should issue the Top (Yellow) Copy to himself as a check on correct procedure.

Fig. 13.3 Permit to work – electrical apparatus

DANGEROUS CONFINED SPACE WORK PERMIT

Permit Serial No 0028
Date of Issue ....

1. DETAILS AND LOCATION OF WORK TO BE CARRIED OUT
Brief description of confined space ______ Permit Request No. ______

2. THIS PERMIT IS VALID FROM ______ hrs. Date ______ to ______ hrs. Date ______

3. DESCRIPTION OF POSSIBLE HAZARDS WITHIN CONFINED SPACE (Quote actual gases, liquids, dusts, vapours, chemicals, oxygen deficiency/enrichment involved, and quote where possible LEL, UEL & TLV):

4. PRECAUTIONS	YES	NO	COMMENT
Valve(s) isolated			
Spade(s) fitted			
Inert gas purged			
No smoking/naked lights			
Total disconnection			
Closed/open steamed			
Mech. through vent.			
Drained free of liquid			
Explosion proof electrics			
Lighting			
Isolate machinery			
'Don't Touch' labels			
Breathing app. to be worn (specify type)			
Observer/rescue staff outside space			
Ops. to work in pairs			
Lifeline to be worn			
Standby resus. equipment			

	Constant auto alarm monitor			
	Ops. trained in hazards & precautions			
	Other necessary precautions			

5. ATMOSPHERIC TEST RESULTS
Person carrying out tests (print name)________ TITLE________ DATE________ TIME________
Toxic gas results________ ppm. (breathing app. to be worn at 50% of TLV or above.)
Flammable gas test result________ % explosive limit. (Entry not permitted if reading exceeds 0% LEL).
Oxygen sufficiency/deficiency test result________ (Entry not permitted below 20% or above 20.8%).
Dust/fibre count result________ (Breathing app. to be worn at 50% TLV or above).

6. FURTHER SPECIAL CONDITIONS AND PRECAUTIONS:

7. AUTHORISATION: I have personally checked the above conditions & consider it safe to carry out this work.
Authorised Person (print name)________ TITLE________
Signature________ DATE________ TIME________

8. ACKNOWLEDGMENT: I understand the hazards of this work and the precautions to be taken. These have also been fully explained to the operatives carrying out this work, and I consider them competent to do it safely. I will return my copy of this permit to the Authorised Person when the work has been safely completed.
Performing Supervisor (print name)________ TITLE________
Signature________ DATE________ TIME________

9. TIME EXTENSION: Subject to the following further precautions
(mark N/A if none is required) the expiry time of this permit is extended from________hrs. Date________
to________hrs. Date________ Signed________(Authorised Person) Date________

10. CANCELLATION
10.1 I have completed the work detailed in this permit, and have restored the location to a safe and orderly condition. I have returned my copy (yellow) and the display copy (pink) of this permit to the Authorised Person
Signed________ (Performing Supervisor) Date________
10.2 I accept that the work has been safely completed. The top (yellow) and 1st (pink) copy of this permit have been destroyed.
Signed________ (Authorised Person) Date________ Time________

NOTES
PERMIT IS AUTOMATICALLY SUSPENDED UPON SOUNDING OF EMERGENCY ALARMS, INSTRUCTIONS VIA PUBLIC ADDRESS SYSTEM, ETC. CHECK WITH AUTHORISED PERSON BEFORE RECOMMENCING WORK.

Fig. 13.4 Permit to work – dangerous confined space

IONISING RADIATIONS WORK PERMIT

Permit Serial No 0002 ....
Date of Issue ....

1. DETAILS AND LOCATION OF WORK TO BE CARRIED OUT

Permit Request No. ____________

2. THIS PERMIT IS VALID FROM ________ hrs. Date ____________ to ________ hrs. Date ____________

3. DETAILS OF RADIATION SOURCE:
(a) X-ray apparatus (make/type) ____________ Max tube voltage ________ kV
(b) Sealed source type ____________ Strength ____________ Curies
Identification data ____________

4. PRECAUTIONS	YES	NO	COMMENT
Rad. area fenced			
Caution notices posted			
Warning lights, etc., positioned			
Rad. area boundaries monitored			Min. reading = Max. reading =
Scatter shielding			
Rad. meters checked/calibrated			
Audio warning signal			
Remote handling equipment checked			
Sealed source container checked			
Sealed source storage arrangements			
Notification of HMFI			Date
Other special precautions			

Name & initials of overseeing Competent Person

5.	DETAILS OF CLASSIFIED WORKERS CARRYING OUT WORK: Name & initials ____________ Name & initials ____________ Name & initials ____________ Name & initials ____________ Name & initials ____________ Name & initials ____________
6.	AUTHORISATION: I have personally checked the above conditions and consider it safe to carry out this work. Authorised Person (print name) ____________ TITLE ____________ Signature ____________ DATE ________ TIME ________
7.	ACKNOWLEDGMENT: I understand the hazards of this work and the precautions to be taken. These have also been explained to the above Classified Workers, who will wear film badges/personal dosemeters throughout the work. I will return my copy of this permit to the Authorised Person when the work has been safely completed. Performing Supervisor (Competent Person) ____________ (print name) TITLE ____________ Signature ____________ DATE ________ TIME ________
8.	TIME EXTENSION: Subject to the following further precautions (mark N/A if none is required) the expiry time of this permit is extended from ________ hrs. Date ________ to ________ hrs. Date ______ Signed ____________ (Authorised Person) Date ________
9.	CANCELLATION
9.1	I have completed the work detailed in this permit, and have restored the location to a safe and orderly condition. I have returned my copy (yellow) and the display copy (pink) of this permit to the Authorised Person Signed ____________ (Performing Supervisor) Date ________
9.2	I accept that the work has been safely completed. The top (yellow) and 1st (pink) copy of this permit have been destroyed. Signed ____________ (Authorised Person) Date ________ Time ________

NOTES

PERMIT IS AUTOMATICALLY SUSPENDED UPON SOUNDING OF EMERGENCY ALARMS, INSTRUCTIONS VIA PUBLIC ADDRESS SYSTEM, ETC. CHECK WITH AUTHORISED PERSON BEFORE RECOMMENCING WORK.

Fig. 13.5 Permit to work – ionising radiations

PERMIT TO WORK CERTIFICATE

PLANT DETAILS (Location, identifying number, etc.)	
WORK TO BE DONE	
WITHDRAWAL FROM SERVICE	The above plant has been removed from service and persons under my supervision have been informed Signed Date Time
ISOLATION	The above plant has been isolated from all sources of ingress of dangerous fumes, etc. Signed The above has been isolated from all sources of electrical and mechanical power Signed The above plant has been isolated from all sources of heat Signed Date Time
CLEANING AND PURGING	The above plant has been freed of dangerous materials Material(s): Method(s): Signed Date Time
TESTING	Contaminants tested Results Signed Date Time
I CERTIFY THAT I HAVE PERSONALLY EXAMINED THE PLANT DETAILED ABOVE AND SATISFIED MYSELF THAT THE ABOVE PARTICULARS ARE CORRECT *(1) THE PLANT IS SAFE FOR ENTRY WITHOUT BREATHING APPARATUS (2) BREATHING APPARATUS MUST BE WORN Other precautions necessary: Time of expiry of certificate: *Delete (1) or (2)	Signed Date Time
ACCEPTANCE OF CERTIFICATE	I have read and understood this certificate and will undertake to work in accordance with the conditions in it Signed Date Time
COMPLETION OF WORK	The work has been completed and all persons under my supervision, materials and equipment withdrawn Signed Date Time
REQUEST FOR EXTENSION	The work has not been completed and permission to continue is requested Signed Date Time
EXTENSION	I have re-examined the plant detailed above and confirm that the certificate may be extended to expire at: Further precautions: Signed Date Time
THIS PERMIT TO WORK IS NOW CANCELLED. A NEW PERMIT WILL BE REQUIRED IF WORK IS TO CONTINUE	Signed Date Time
RETURN TO SERVICE	I accept the above plant back into service Signed Date Time

Fig. 13.6 Permit to work – confined space

PART IV

The working environment

14

The organisation of the working environment

The term 'environment' is of French origin (*les environs* – the neighbourhood; that which surrounds us: the surroundings). The working environment embraces structural aspects of workplaces and the problems of stress brought about by poor standards of environment, e.g. extremes of temperature, lighting and ventilation, the presence of dust, fumes and gases, noise. Thus, occupational health and safety law – e.g. Factories Act 1961, Offices, Shops and Railway Premises Act 1963, Health and Safety at Work, etc., Act 1974 – enshrines the employer's duty to provide a sound and healthy working environment, both in relation to the actual organisation of the environment and in the control of environmental stressors.

Environmental conditions have a direct effect on the way people behave at work, on the degree of risk of occupational disease and injury, and on morale, management/worker relations, labour turnover and profitability. This chapter examines the factors which are important in the organisation of the working environment, at the same time making recommendations for those involved in planning the environment and the enforcement of legal provisions relating to it.

Location of workplaces

Particularly with large undertakings, consideration should be given to the locality, density of surrounding buildings, availability of vehicle parking areas, access for employees and transport, including employees' own vehicles, and fire, ambulance and police vehicles. The need for a sound traffic control system, which does not expose pedestrians to risk of injury, must further be considered, together with the vulnerability of the general public to involvement in major incidents or disasters, e.g. from leaking gases or fumes, such as ammonia, explosions and/or large fires, contamination from toxic, corrosive or carcinogenic chemical substances, or heavy transport entering and leaving the premises.

Layout of workplaces

The term 'layout' refers to the space available for those employees working within a particular room or area, and the situation of plant, equipment, machinery, furnishings and stored goods in relation to the operative and the tasks performed. An efficient layout should make a material contribution to preventing or reducing overcrowding, minimising the physical and mental effort required to perform the operation, expediting the process in an orderly and sequential flow, and ensuring maximum safety and hygiene standards throughout. Moreover, the premises should be large enough and designed to allow for an orderly sequence of work without undue crossing of lanes and gangways, and without unnecessary manhandling of materials, but with easy movement between one part of the premises and another.

Overcrowding

In factories, the general requirement is that each person in a workroom shall be provided with 3.7 square metres of floor space, or 11.0 cubic metres where the ceiling is less than 3.3 metres high, heights over 4.2 metres being ignored in calculations. In premises registered under the Offices, Shops and Railway Premises Act 1963, the requirements are the same. This space is not in addition to the space taken up by a reasonable amount of equipment and/or furniture.

Allowance must be made for the existence of machinery and other fixed items of plant, furniture, etc., in assessing the potential for overcrowding. Conditions that may be prejudicial to health by overcrowding should also be considered, such as the risk of spreading minor infections.

Structural safety in relation to the worker

Floors, corridors and passages

Floors should be of sound construction, free from obstruction, sudden changes in level and of non-slip finish (Factories Act 1961, sec 28(1)). Where safety levels, production or the storage of goods are materially assisted, storage areas should be clearly marked by the use of yellow or white lines. 'No Go' areas should be cross-hatched with yellow lines. All openings in floors or significant differences in floor level should be fenced. Attention should be paid to ensure that floor loading does not produce structural instability. (*See Greaves & Co. (Contractors) Ltd* v.

Baynham Meikle & Partners [1975] 1 WLR 1095. This case concerned a badly designed floor which collapsed when heavy mobile machinery was installed. As a consequence, the structural engineering consultancy involved was held liable in negligence.)

Where a wet process is carried out, e.g. slaughterhouses, or where frequent floor washing is necessary, the floor should be laid to a fall to a drain. Floor channels incorporating metal gratings or covers can sometimes be used as an alternative, but this method may create hygiene risks.

Stairs, ladders and catwalks

For all stairs a handrail should be provided. If the staircase is open on both sides, a handrail should be provided on each side (Factories Act 1961, sec 28(2)). In the case of very wide staircases, further handrails may be necessary in addition to those at the sides. If necessary, the space between the handrail and the treads should be filled in, or an intermediate rail fitted. Fixed vertical ladders and catwalks, including bridges to them, should be securely fixed. Where practicable, back rings should be fitted to vertical ladders from a height of 2 metres upwards and spaced at 1 metre intervals. Catwalks and bridges should be adequately fenced by means of 1 metre high guard rails, 500 millimetres high intermediate rails and toe boards.

Underground rooms

An underground room is defined in the Factories Act 1961, sec 69, as 'any room or part of a room which is so situate that at least half its height, measured from the floor to the ceiling, is below the surface of the footway of the adjoining street or the ground adjoining or nearest the room'. Although decreasing in importance generally, there are special problems regarding the actual construction of such a room, its height and the system for lighting and ventilation. Means of escape in the event of fire presents a further special problem.

The occupier of any factory who proposes to use an underground room for purposes other than storage must, first, inform the HSE (Factories Inspector) of his intentions. The inspector may certify the room unsuitable for the reasons stated above or may forbid the use of the room for the purpose intended until the occupier has rendered it suitable. An occupier who is aggrieved by a decision by the Factories Inspector in this respect may appeal to a magistrates' court within 21 days of the date of issue of the certificate or the refusal of the consent, as the case may be (Factories Act 1961, sec 69(1) and (4)).

External areas and approach roads

To facilitate access to and egress from the premises by people and vehicles, external areas should have impervious and even surfaces and be adequately drained to a stormwater drain. The provision of water supply points and hoses, for washing down yards and approaches, is recommended.

Walls

Interior walls have a contribution to make to illuminance levels, colour schemes, maintenance of physical cleanliness, sound insulation and the prevention of fire spread. They should be substantial, durable, smooth, easily cleaned and reflect light. The use of hollow partitions and the practice of battening out of walls are not recommended.

Ceilings and inner roof surfaces

The ceilings or inner roof surfaces of workrooms should assist in the maintenance of satisfactory illuminance levels, heat insulation, sound insulation and physical cleanliness. The height of ceilings should be a minimum of 2.4 metres. If false or suspended ceilings are incorporated in the structure, provision should be made for safe access to the space created above the ceiling for maintenance and cleaning purposes.

Colour

Colour is an important factor in the maintenance of a sound working environment, and influences

(a) the extent to which the creation of a congenial environment is achieved;
(b) the amount of visual assistance afforded to employees by:
    (i) general and specific illuminance levels;
    (ii) drawing attention to specific parts of the workplace, e.g. fire escape routes;
    (iii) the control of glare;
(c) general safety performance, e.g. colour coding of safety signs and symbols as per the Safety Signs Regulations 1980, the use of 'tiger striping' to identify particular hazards.

Waste disposal

No waste material or refuse should be allowed to accumulate within a working area, and an adequate supply of containers should be provided at convenient points, together with an external storage and disposal area. Specifically, flammable wastes should be separated and stored in closed metal containers.

Good housekeeping requires that refuse and waste materials be removed not less than once daily and stored in a suitable enclosure. The use of refuse compactors in conjunction with an industrial side-loading waste container is recommended from a fire protection and hygiene viewpoint.

Traffic management

Many industrial accidents involve vehicles – fork lift trucks, lorries, tractors, vans and cars (see *Transport Kills* report by Health and Safety Executive, 1982). In most undertakings there is a need, therefore, for an efficient traffic control system. This assists in reducing internal traffic accidents and improves standards of security, particularly where employees and visitors are permitted to bring vehicles on to the premises. Effective traffic management embraces the following.

Segregation

There should be adequate segregation of pedestrians from vehicular traffic, of incoming from outgoing traffic, and of general parking areas from loading and unloading areas. In order to achieve this segregation, parking areas for commercial vehicles and cars must be clearly identified, properly marked out to indicate parking spaces, with directional signs showing the correct flow of traffic into, around and out of these areas. There is often a case for instigating a one-way system around the external parts of the premises, with separate entrance and exit to the highway. Road markings and signs should comply with the Road Traffic Regulation Act 1984 and BS 5378: 1980 'Safety Signs and Colours', e.g. road junction marking, 'No Entry' signs.

Vehicular traffic control

The system for traffic control should be effective and regularly reviewed. This should include designation of 'No Go' areas by yellow cross-hatched floor and road marking where there is extensive fork lift truck activity or in loading bays, or where pedestrians may be using a particular entrance to the premises. Moreover, speed control is most important in any system of traffic control. Apart from the standard speed limit signs (10 mph, 15 mph) there may be a need for the installation of 'sleeping policemen' or speed ramps, which have the effect of slowing down vehicles to an acceptable speed.

Pedestrian movement

Where there is extensive pedestrian movement at specific times of the day, it may be appropriate to install pedestrian crossings, with or without barriers, to ensure safe entry to and egress from the premises. The use of convex mirrors is recommended at obscured junctions or where vision of drivers coming from either direction is impaired. (Vehicles visiting work premises, and/or depositing goods there, are not 'machinery' for the purposes of the Factories Act 1961, sec 14. *Liptrot* v. *British Railways Board* [1967] 2 AER 1067.)

Control over drivers

Above all, there must be a system to control drivers whilst on the premises. Constant speeding, unsafe parking and bad driving should result in disciplinary action. In the case of fork lift and other types of truck, there is usually a case for a 'permit to drive' system, so that only those drivers who have passed an appropriate test are granted authority to drive trucks. The Factories Inspector generally requires documentary evidence of training and competence to handle fork lift trucks safely, as part of the general requirements of HSWA. Training undertaken by RoSPA is considered suitable (*see* Chapter 37). Fork lift truck 'cowboys' should be outlawed, followed by disciplinary action, including the cancellation of the permit to drive in extreme cases.

Environmental control

Lighting in external roadways, parking areas, loading points and pedestrian walkways must be sufficient to allow for safe vehicle movement. An illuminance level of 50 lux is recommended in these areas, together with spot lighting where specific hazards may exist or where there is a need to ensure handling at night. This is consistent with current best practice.

15

Temperature, lighting and ventilation

Any discussion on the working environment would be incomplete without consideration being given to temperature, lighting and ventilation. They are significant in the maintenance of comfort. Furthermore, poor standards of provision and control may result in stress on the part of the operator accompanied by gradual deterioration in health and, in some cases, the risk of heat stroke, heat stress, eyesight deficiencies and fume fevers.

Comfort

'Comfort' is a subjective assessment of the conditions in which an individual works, sleeps, relaxes, travels, etc. Sensations of comfort vary with a person's state of health, vitality and age. Despite the fact that comfort is a personal state, a degree of unanimity is usually found whenever a group of people are asked to assess a given atmospheric condition. Research indicates that there are four factors which are chiefly responsible for the production of the sensation of thermal comfort, namely air temperature, radiated heat, humidity and the amount of air movement. There are limits to the ability of the human body to adapt to achieve this state of comfort. Few people, for example, would choose to live in a greenhouse or a house without windows all the year round, yet in industry workers may be expected to do just that! The 'indoor climate' is of prime importance. Failure to recognise this fact can result in poor standards of performance and efficiency, discontent, increased labour turnover, increased accident rates and absenteeism.

Temperature

In order to understand why it is necessary to control the thermal environment, the important process of body temperature regulation, or 'thermoregulation', should be understood.

The chemical process for generating heat by food conversion is an important feature of a person's metabolism. Food is a source of energy and the body converts approximately 20 per cent of this energy to mechanical energy, the remaining 80 per cent being utilised as heat.

A healthy person has a body temperature of 36.9 °C which is kept remarkably constant, largely by the body continually varying the flow rate of blood. When body temperature increases, blood flows to the skin and dissipates its heat through the skin surface by thermal exchange. Conversely, when body heat is low, heat is conserved in the deep tissues to maintain what is commonly known as the 'core temperature'. If the air temperature is too high and the differential between the skin and the surrounding air is small, insufficient heat is lost through normal exchange. As a result, the body overheats and the sweat glands are activated. In very hot conditions as much as 1 litre of body fluid can be lost each hour. This reduces the body fluid level and salt deficiencies may be created.

Stress conditions

Although reference is made to heat stroke in Chapter 19, it is appropriate here to consider stress conditions associated with extremes of temperature.

Heat stress

Under most industrial working conditions operators tend to be self-limiting in their thermoregulatory control. The average worker will tend to withdraw from a hot environment or heat source before he becomes liable to heat stroke. Whilst there are no specific heat exposure limits in the UK, threshold limits for permissible heat exposure (indices of thermal stress) have been established in the USA. The most commonly used index of thermal stress is that based on physiological observations and related to wet bulb globe temperature shown with a whirling hygrometer. This index was developed for use in the desert under wartime conditions and is now incorporated in the American Conference of Governmental Industrial Hygienists' (1980) *Threshold Limit Values for Chemical Substances Physical Agents in the Workroom* as recommended practice. The following equations are used to calculate the wet bulb globe temperature (WBGT) values:

> Outdoor work with a solar load – WBGT = 0.7WB + 0.2GT + 0.1DB
>
> Indoor work, or outdoor work with no solar load – WBGT = 0.7WB + 0.3GT

where WB = natural wet bulb temperature
DB = dry bulb temperature
GT = globe thermometer temperature

The natural wet bulb temperature is that recorded from the sling hygrometer without any rotation of the sling.

After calculating the wet bulb globe temperature, the number in degrees Celsius is compared with recommended limits of work:rest schedules using either a table or a graph (*see* Table 4 and Fig. 15.1).

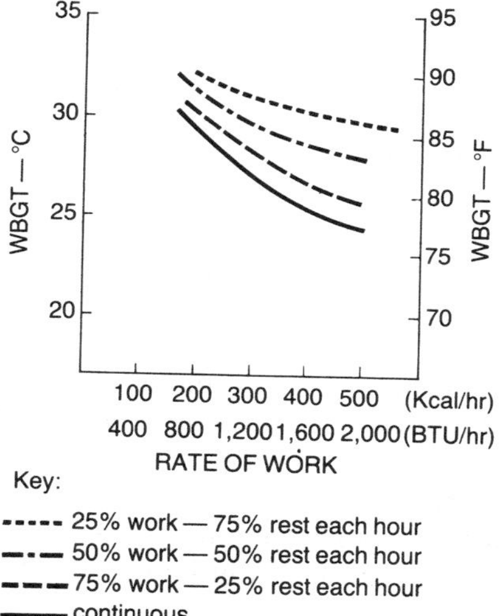

Fig. 15.1 WBGT values plotted against rate of work for various work:rest schedules

Table 4: Maximum permissible wet bulb globe temperature readings

	Work load		
Work:rest schedule (per hour)	*Light*	*Moderate*	*Heavy*
Continuous work	30.0 °C	26.7 °C	25.0 °C
75% work, 25% rest	30.6 °C	28.0 °C	25.9 °C
50% work, 50% rest	31.4 °C	29.4 °C	27.9 °C
25% work, 75% rest	32.2 °C	31.1 °C	30.0 °C

Workers should not be permitted to continue their work when their core temperature reaches 38 °C.

Cold stress

When outdoor clothing is worn, the limit of tolerance is as shown in Table 5. Whilst special protective clothing would be necessary for, say, cold store work, and work at −40 °C, some cooling is inevitable. Great attention should be paid in this case to protecting the extremities, i.e. hands, feet and head.

Table 5: Limit of cold stress tolerance

Air temperature	*Time*
−12 °C	6 hours
−23 °C	4 hours
−40 °C	1½ hours
−57 °C	½ hour

Ideal comfort conditions

Air temperature

This is the most important factor and depends upon the type of work being undertaken, e.g. relatively sedentary work such as office work, light work and heavy (manual) work. For each of these classifications, other thermal conditions notwithstanding, there is either an optimum air temperature or a fairly wide air temperature range (comfort range) within which the majority of workers will not feel any discomfort. It is apparent from the range of activities in Table 6, that as the activity increases so the optimum ambient temperature reduces. In any of these categories the air temperature should be reduced when operators are exposed to radiant heat.

Table 6: Optimum working temperatures

Sedentary/office work	
Comfort range	19.4 to 22.8 °C
Light Work	
Optimum temperature	18.3 °C
Comfort range	15.5 to 20 °C
Heavy Work	
Comfort range	12.8 to 15.6 °C

Radiant heat

Optimum temperature	18.3 °C
Comfort range	16.6 to 20 °C

It is important to regulate the worker's exposure to radiated heat. There should not be a temperature gradient between head and feet of more than 3 °C. In fact, any temperature gradient should be negative, i.e. cool head, warm feet.

Relative humidity

Relative humidity is defined as 'the actual amount of moisture present in air expressed as a percentage of that which would produce saturation'. It is generally accepted that relative humidity should be between 30 and 70 per cent. If the relative humidity is too low, a feeling of discomfort is produced due to the drying of the throat and nasal passages. Conversely, high relative humidity produces a feeling of stuffiness, and reduces the rate at which body moisture evaporates (sweat), thereby reducing the efficiency of the body's thermoregulatory system.

Air movement

Air movement is an important factor in the consideration of comfort conditions. Movement of air is just perceptible at about 9 metres per minute and complaints of draughts will be received when it exceeds 30 metres per minute. Below 6 metres per minute, a room could be considered airless. The sensation of air movement is directly related to air temperature and skin sensitivity. If the air is cool, even slight draughts are detectable, whereas if the air temperature is controlled then the draughts, although still present, may not be detected. Air movement assists in cooling and causes distress if excessive.

Temperature control in the workplace

In order to reduce stress associated with inadequate temperature control, a number of aspects need consideration at the design stage of projects and in the assessment of an existing thermal environment.

Space heating of the average workplace should be capable of reaching a minimum temperature of 16 °C within 1 hour of the commencement of working, and of maintaining this temperature throughout the working day. (A point to be noted here is that a maximum temperature is not specified in either the Factories Act 1961 or the Offices, Shops and Railway Premises Act 1963.) This temperature is only a minimum temperature and, in order to produce comfortable working conditions, the general aim must be to maintain temperatures more in line with those quoted earlier. (The legal requirements for heating in factories, offices and shops are laid down in FA, sec 3(2), and OSRPA, sec 6(2) respectively.)

In certain workplaces – e.g. warehouses, stores, depots – which are sparsely or spasmodically occupied, localised space heating points should be provided for use during cold periods. Conversely, where heat is produced by manufacturing processes, the adequacy of control and removal of surplus heat must be considered. Localised exhaust ventilation, in most cases, will resolve this problem.

Air temperature thermometers should be provided in all working areas (FA, sec 3(2), and OSRPA, sec 6(2)).

Central heating and other systems should operate independently of any hot water or steam installation, so that central heating can be reduced or turned off in summer months. Individual control of radiators and other heating appliances, together with installation of, where appropriate, thermostat control switches, should be provided where control of central heating is by electrical means.

Heating appliances with exposed electrical elements, and heaters producing combustion gases which vent to the workplace, should not be used. The use of privately owned heating appliances, particularly those of the open radiant type, should be strictly controlled or prohibited in view of the fire risk associated with them. In offices, wall-mounted convector heaters should be provided if it is necessary to supplement existing central heating during cold weather. Portable free-standing appliances, which are easily knocked over, create a greater fire hazard.

Lighting

Two specific aspects of health and safety are relevant in relation to lighting:

(a) a gradual deterioration in an individual's visual acuity and performance; and
(b) the increased likelihood of accident brought about by a worker's failing or incorrect perception.

The purpose of this section on lighting, therefore, is to consider lighting deficiencies which can result in the inability of people to perceive danger and cause deterioration in visual performance. In turn, this involves an examination of lighting in terms of

(a) the quantity and quality of light required for a given task as well as the relationship of lighting to the general environment of the workplace; and
(b) the basis for lighting design and specific applications, as in the case of visual display units (VDUs).

Present legal requirements

Current legislation provides little guidance about lighting in the workplace which is of significance today. Both the Factories Act 1961 and the Offices, Shops and Railway Premises Act 1963 refer to the duty to provide 'suitable and sufficient' lighting. However, the Health and Safety at Work etc., Act 1974 places a general duty on the employer to provide a safe working environment, and this duty has much broader implications for the provision and maintenance of sound standards of lighting in the workplace (HSWA, sec 2(2)(*e*)).

Quantitative aspects of lighting

The quantity of light flowing from a source such as a light bulb or fluorescent light (luminaire) is the luminous flux or light flow, which is generally termed 'illuminance'. The units of measurement of luminous flux were formerly foot candles or lumens per square foot, but more recently the unit has become the lux, which is the metric unit of measurement. Thus:

Foot candles	= lumens per square foot
Lux	= lumens per square metre
10.76 lux	= 1 lumen per square metre
1 lux	= 0.093 lumens per square metre

On this basis a conversion factor of 10 or 11 is used for converting from lumens per square foot to lux, i.e. 20 lumens per square foot = 200 lux.

The lux, therefore, is the unit of illuminance (not 'illumination'), and the value in lux, measured with a standard photometer or light meter, is an indication of the quantity of light present at a particular point.

Current legislation requires that 'suitable and sufficient' lighting be provided in every part of a factory or workplace (FA, sec 5, and OSRPA, sec 8). The current criteria for deciding what is sufficient lighting are the recommended 'standard service illuminances' published by the Illuminating Engineering Society (IES). The current *I.E.S. Code* (Illuminating Engineering Society, 1976) outlines a schedule of standard service illuminances in steps which range from 100 lux to 3,300 lux depending upon the task involved. The standard service illuminance is defined as 'the mean illumination through the life of the lighting system and averaged over the relevant area of the visual task and its immediate surrounds'. The values are related to visual performance and visual preference and also take into account other factors such as the influence of daylight in the interior, recent improvements in lamp efficacies and practical experience. Typical values are shown in Table 7. The recommended values are neither optima nor minima, but represent good current practice, and are generally used by enforcement authorities in the determination of what is 'sufficient' lighting.

Table 7: IES code for interior lighting – standard service illuminances

Task group	*Type of task or interior*	*Standard service illuminance (lux)*
—	Storage areas and plant rooms with no continuous work	150
Rough work	Rough machining and assembly	300
Routine work	Offices, control rooms, medium machining and assembly	500
Demanding work	Deep-plant drawing or business machine offices; inspection of medium machining	750
Fine work	Colour discrimination, textile processing, fine machining and assembly	1,000
Very fine work	Hand engraving, inspection of fine machining or assembly	1,500
Minute work	Inspection of very fine assembly	3,000

In high-risk areas, or where there is a high level of vehicular movement, or where dangerous chemical compounds are stored, it is recommended that the standard service illuminance be increased by one or more levels, e.g. from 500 to 750 lux, to take account of such factors. Furthermore, where the average age of workers is over 50 years, where eye protection is regularly worn, or where no natural lighting is available, the illuminance level should be increased by at least 50 per cent or more.

Qualitative aspects of lighting

The concept of standard service illuminances in the IES code relates only to the quantity of light, and in the design or assessment of lighting installations consideration must be given to the qualitative aspects. Factors which contribute to the quality of lighting include the presence or absence of glare in its various forms, the degree of brightness, the distribution of light, diffusion, colour rendition, contrast effects and the system for lighting maintenance.

Glare

This is the effect of light which causes discomfort or impaired vision, and is experienced when parts of the visual field are excessively bright compared with the general surroundings. This usually occurs when the light source is directly in line with the visual task or when light is reflected off a given surface or object. Glare is experienced in three different forms:

(a) Disability glare is the visually disabling effect caused by bright bare lamps directly in the line of sight. The resulting impaired vision (dazzle) may be hazardous if experienced when working in high-risk processes, at heights or when driving. It is seldom experienced in workplaces because most bright lamps, e.g. filament and mercury vapour, are usually partly surrounded by some form of fitting.

(b) Discomfort glare is caused mainly by too much contrast of brightness between an object and its background, and is associated with poor lighting design. It causes visual discomfort without necessarily impairing the ability to see detail, but over a period can cause eye strain, headaches and fatigue. Discomfort glare can be reduced by

   (i) careful design of shades which screen the lamp,
   (ii) keeping luminaires as high as practicable, and
   (iii) maintaining luminaires parallel to the main direction of lighting.

   The IES publishes a 'limiting glare index' for each of the above situations. This is an index representing the degree of discomfort glare which will be just tolerable in the process or location under consideration. If exceeded, occupants may suffer eye strain or headaches or both.

(c) Reflected glare is the reflection of bright light sources on shiny or wet work surfaces such as glass or plated metal, which can almost entirely conceal the detail in or behind the object which is glinting. Care is necessary in the use of light sources of low brightness and in the arrangement of the geometry of the installation, so that there is no glint at the particular viewing position.

Distribution

The distribution of light, or the way in which light is spread, is important in lighting design. The British Zonal Method classifies luminaires according to the way in which they distribute light from BZ1 (all light downwards in a narrow column) to BZ10 (light in all directions). A fitting with a low BZ number does not automatically mean less glare. Its positioning, the shape of the room and the reflective surfaces present are also significant. Poor lighting distribution may result in the formation of shadowed areas which can create dangerous situations, particularly at night. For good general lighting, regularly spaced luminaires are used to give evenly distributed illuminance. This evenness of illuminance depends upon the ratio between the height of the luminaire above the working position and the spacing of fittings. The IES spacing: height ratio provides a basic guide to such arrangements, in normal circumstances, this ratio being between $1\frac{1}{2}:1$ and $1:1$ depending upon the type of luminaire.

Colour rendition

This refers to the appearance of an object under a given light source, compared to its colour under a reference illuminant, e.g. natural light. Colour rendition enables the colour appearance to be correctly perceived. The colour-rendering properties of light fitments should not clash with those of natural light, and should be equally effective at night when there is no daylight contribution to the total illumination of the workplace.

Brightness

Brightness or, more correctly, 'luminosity', is essentially a subjective sensation and cannot be measured. It is possible, however, to consider a brightness ratio, which is the ratio of apparent luminosity between a task object and its surroundings. To achieve the recommended brightness ratio, the reflectance of all surfaces in the workplace should be carefully maintained and consideration given to reflectance values in the design of interiors. Given a task illuminance factor of 1, the effective reflectance values should be:

Ceilings — 0.6
Walls — 0.3 to 0.8
Floors — 0.2 to 0.3

Diffusion

This is the projection of light in many directions with no directional predominance. The directional effects of light are just as important as the quantity of light, however, as the directional flow of light can often determine the density of shadows, which may affect safety. Diffused lighting can soften the output from a particular source and so limit the amount of glare that may be encountered from bare fittings.

Lighting maintenance

A well-organised maintenance programme is necessary for permanently good illumination to be achieved. The programme should incorporate regular cleaning and replacement of lamp fittings as a basic consideration, together with regular assessment of illuminance levels with a standard photometer at predetermined points. Furthermore, the actual function of the lighting provided should be reviewed in line with changes that may be made in production, storage or office arrangements. To facilitate safe lamp cleaning and replacement, high-level luminaires should be fitted with raising and lowering gear, so that this work can be undertaken at floor level.

The design of lighting

In the design of lighting installations, many factors need consideration. These may include the following:

(a) General lighting requirements. Illuminance levels for the principal operations within the premises and for specific parts of the premises, both internally and externally, should be considered. Both general and task illuminance levels should be specified, bearing in mind the current IES code of recommended standard service illuminances listed above, and also the effects of lighting on worker performance and his potential for fatigue. Specific vision defects amongst workers and the hazards associated with incorrect or faulty perception must further be considered.
(b) Availability of natural lighting. Whilst natural lighting is the best form of illuminance, it must often be considered a secondary option in lighting design owing to its unreliability.
(c) Specific areas and processes. The type of lighting and lighting needs of specific areas and/or processes should be considered, e.g. access points, corridors, fine assembly work, catering, internal traffic lanes.
(d) Colour rendition aspects. These aspects need consideration to ensure correct perception of colour under both natural and artificial lighting. The positioning of safety signs and notices should take account of this factor.
(e) Glare. The potential for glare should be considered in the positioning of machinery, and for particular surfaces adjacent to machinery. The potential for dazzle should also be taken into account – extraneous light sources may produce it.
(f) Structural aspects. The effects of structural items such as screens, pillars and plant should be taken into account. Such items can obstruct light flow and reduce illuminance levels.
(g) Atmospheric influences. The presence of steam, fumes and mists should be considered, and illuminance levels upgraded where these influences may bring about a reduction in general lighting.
(h) Lamp and window cleaning. The need for frequent cleaning, replacement and maintenance of lamps will depend upon the types of process being undertaken in the area. Suitable access equipment must be provided, e.g. raising and lowering gear to permit lamp cleaning at floor level. Window cleaning should be incorporated in the cleaning schedule for the premises (*see* Chapter 17).
(i) High-risk areas. The potential for fire and explosion in certain

areas may indicate the need for sealed light fittings, e.g. petroleum installations.
(j) Emergency lighting. An emergency lighting system, using an independently operated emergency generator, battery-operated systems or hand lamps, is necessary in most activities. These systems should operate at least to between 5 and 10 per cent of usual operating illuminance.
(k) Energy considerations. The need for the use of time-switches or photo-electric switching devices should be considered.

Finally, the physiological effects of poor lighting, such as reduced acuity and performance, and the psychological effect on perception and attitudes of workers, must be considered. Lighting design has a direct effect on worker performance and accident potential, as do other environmental factors, such as temperature and ventilation.

Visual display units (VDUs)

In the last decade considerable attention has been given to the problem of stress associated with monitoring VDUs. This monitoring task may be combined with other tasks such as writing, undertaking calculations, operating calculating machines and answering a telephone. The increased use of computers, the majority of which incorporate a VDU, has intensified the problem still further. Typical health effects are outlined below.

(a) Eye strain is associated with glare from the display and the continual need to refocus from screen to paper and back again. The degree of individual eye strain will vary. Vision screening of staff on a regular basis, and as part of a pre-employment health screen, should be carried out.
(b) Fatigue can be brought about by poor environmental control, temperature variations, the sheer monotony of the task, inefficient machine response, work pressure, poor ergonomic design of controls and displays, and screen flicker.
(c) Operational stress may take many forms, and can include backache, neck and shoulder pains associated with poor chair and desk design and positioning in relation to controls and displays, insufficient leg room and the need regularly to adjust body position, noise from the unit and ancillary equipment, excessive heat and inadequate ventilation. The degree of operator stress will vary according to age, sex, physical build, attitude to the task, current level of visual acuity and general health.

Design aspects of VDUs

Complaints from operators of one or more of the above stress-related symptoms are common, calling for examination of the lighting arrangements for this type of task. Both ambient illuminance levels and specific light emission from the display should be considered. There must be adequate indirect local lighting within the range 150 to 500 lux, depending upon, first, the different tasks undertaken in addition to the monitoring task and, second, the actual illuminance level of the display. Readily adjustable luminosity contrasts, to achieve this balance between ambient lighting and display lighting, are most important. Furthermore, contrast between the screen background and the characters should be in the ratio of 1:3, and between ambient lighting and screen, between 1:3 and 1:5.

Screen flicker can cause severe eye strain. Flicker can be avoided by ensuring a sufficiently frequent 'refresh rate' for the image, e.g. 50 Hz. (Refresh rate is the rate at which phosphors return to luminosity after they have faded. This term is also known as the 'renewal rate' or 'critical frequency flicker'.) The use of phosphors – substances which emit light when struck by an electron beam – with adequate persistence is most important in the prevention of eye strain.

The above aspects are significant in any investigation following complaints from staff or prior to purchase of equipment. The careful design of controls and displays, together with better environmental control and application of basic ergonomic principles, are important factors in the reduction of operator stress (*see also* Chapter 39 which covers the ergonomic aspects of VDU operator stations).

Ventilation

In the control of health hazards from toxic fumes or airborne particulates, natural ventilation is rarely acceptable. (Natural ventilation is generally taken to mean ventilation produced without the aid of mechanically induced draught.) Mechanical ventilation systems take a number of forms and these are outlined below.

Extract ventilation

There are three principal forms of extract ventilation system, namely receptor systems, captor systems and low-volume high-velocity systems.

Receptor systems

In receptor systems the contaminant enters the system without inducement. The fan in the system is used to provide air flow to transport the contaminant from the hood through ducting to a collection system. The hood may form almost a total enclosure around the source, as with highly toxic contaminants, such as beryllium, or with radioactive sources; or it may form a partial enclosure, e.g. a spray booth in which all spraying takes place, or a laboratory fume cupboard. Generally, hoods which receive the contaminant air as it flows from its origin under the influence of thermal currents are receptors. (*See* Fig. 15.2(a).)

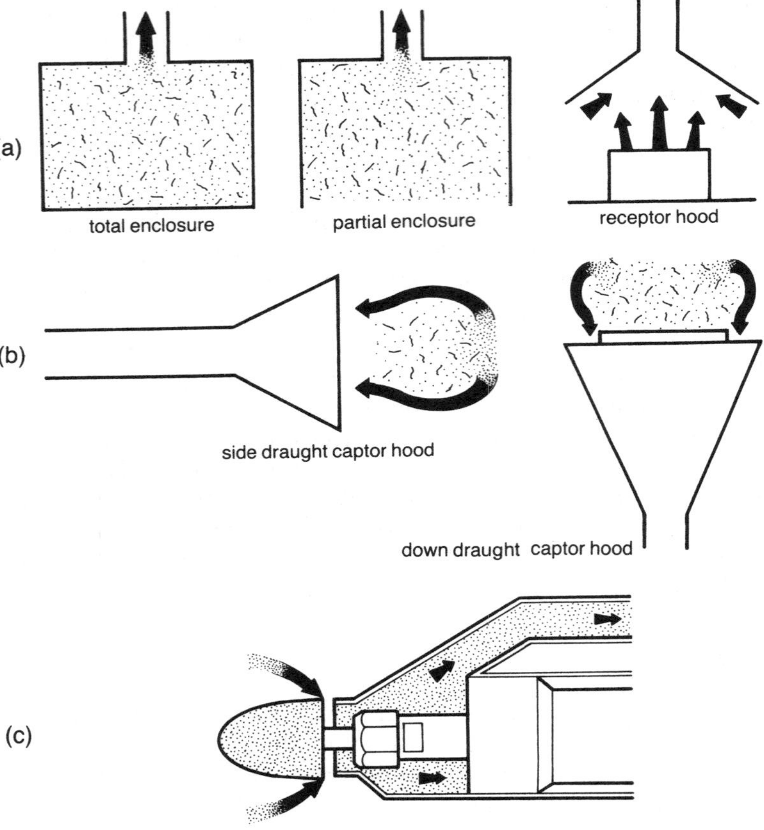

Fig. 15.2 Source: American Conference of Government Industrial Hygienists, 1980
(a) Receptor systems
(b) Captor systems
(c) Low-volume high-velocity system

Captor systems

With a captor system the moving air captures the contaminant at some point outside the hood and induces its flow into it. The rate of air flow into the hood must be sufficient to capture the contaminant at the furthest point of origin, and the air velocity induced at this point must be high enough to overcome any tendency the contaminant may have to go in any direction other than into the hood. Contaminants emitted with high energy (large particles with high velocity) will require high velocities in the capturing airstream. (*See* Fig. 15.2(b).)

Low-volume high-velocity (LVHV) systems

Dust particles emitted by high-speed grinding machines or pneumatic chipping tools require very high capture velocities. One method of achieving very high velocities at the source is to extract from small apertures very close to the source of the contaminant. (*See* Fig. 15.2(c).) The high velocities can be achieved with quite low air-flow rates. The following factors are essential in LVHV design:

(a) appropriate ergonomic design of the cowl and hoses,
(b) correct cowl adjustment,
(c) regular thorough maintenance, and
(d) training of operators.

Dilution ventilation

Occasionally it is not possible to extract a contaminant close to the point of origin. If the quantity of contaminant is small, uniformly evolved and of low toxicity, it may be possible to dilute the contaminant by inducing large volumes of air to flow through the contaminated region. Dilution ventilation is most successfully used to control vapours, e.g. organic vapours from low-toxicity solvents, but is seldom successfully applied to dust and fumes, as it will not prevent inhalation. In cold weather this method has self-evident implications for cost and thermal discomfort.

16

Welfare amenity provision

Welfare amenities include arrangements for sanitation (water closets, urinals), washing (wash-basins and showers), drinking water, storage for clothing, including protective clothing, taking meals (canteens, messrooms) and the provision of seats for certain work. First aid provision is also relevant here (*see* Chapter 29).

Sanitation and washing arrangements

Three factors are important, namely:

(a) the number of fitments in relation to the total number of employees, e.g. water closets, urinals, wash-basins, shower units;
(b) the arrangement of fitments in a correctly designed amenity area (*see later*), which should normally incorporate facilities for storing clothing; and
(c) the relative ease of maintenance and cleaning of the facilities.

General statutory requirements

Statutory requirements for amenities, as laid down in the Factories Act 1961, sec 7, and Offices, Shops and Railway Premises Act 1963, sec 9, prescribe that 'sufficient and/or adequate and suitable' sanitary accommodation and washing facilities should be provided and maintained. In calculating what is 'sufficient and/or adequate and suitable' sanitary accommodation and washing facilities for employees, reference should be made to Regulations made under these two Acts (*see below* 'Fitment Requirements'), and other Regulations and Orders for specific industries and processes.

A factory for these purposes is as defined in FA, sec 175(1). A shop, however, is not as defined in the Shops Act 1950. For health, safety and welfare purposes, a 'shop' has the extended meaning given to it by

OSRPA, sec 1(3). This includes not only retail premises, but restaurants, libraries, and bars and offices in hotels, though not hotels themselves.

Fitment requirements in factories, offices, shops, etc.

Fitment requirements are laid down in the following Regulations made under the above Acts:

(a) factories – Sanitary Accommodation Regulations 1938, as subsequently amended by the Sanitary Accommodation (Amendment) Regulations 1974;
(b) offices and shops – Sanitary Conveniences Regulations 1964 and Washing Facilities Regulations 1964.

NOTE. There are no general Regulations applicable to factories in respect of washing facilities; rather such requirements are frequently identified in special codes or regulations, e.g. Iron and Steel Foundries Regulations 1953, Control of Lead at Work Regulations 1980 and Approved Code of Practice, Construction (Health and Welfare) Regulations 1966.

Scale of provision of amenities

Sanitation

Factories:
Table 8: Water closet provision in factories

Number of persons of each sex regularly employed to work in the premises at any one time	*Number of water closets*
1–25	1
26–50	2
51–75	3
76–100	4

Table 8 indicates the number of water closets required for a factory of up to 100 employees. In the case of factories where the number of employed males exceeds 100 and sufficient urinal accommodation is also provided, it is sufficient if there is one water closet for every 25 males up to the first 100, and one for every 40 males thereafter. In the case of factories where the number of employed males exceeds 500, it is sufficient to provide one water closet as aforesaid for every 60 males after the first 100 if sufficient urinal accommodation is also provided.

Offices, shops and railway premises:

Table 9: Water closet provision in offices, shops and railway premises

Number of persons of each sex regularly employed to work in the premises at any one time	*Number of water closets*
1–15	1
16–30	2
31–50	3
51–75	4
76–100	5

Exceeding 100: five water closets, with the addition of one water closet for every unit of 25 persons by which the workforce exceeds 100 (any fraction of a unit of 25 persons being treated as one).

The standard in Table 9 applies to females, and males not provided with urinal accommodation. Where urinal accommodation is provided for males, the standard in Table 10 applies.

Table 10: Water closet and urinal provision in offices, shops and railway premises

Number of persons regularly employed to work in the premises at any one time	*Number of water closets*	*Units of urinal accommodation*
1–15	1	–
16–20	1	1
21–30	2	1
31–45	2	2
46–60	3	2
61–75	3	3
76–90	4	3
91–100	4	4

Exceeding 100: with the addition of one sanitary convenience (being either a water closet or a unit of urinal accommodation) for every unit of 25 persons by which the workforce exceeds 100 (any fraction of a unit of 25 persons being treated as one), of which additional number of sanitary conveniences not less than three-quarters shall be water closets (any fraction being treated as one).

For the purpose of the Regulations, the expression 'unit of urinal accommodation' means one stall of a urinal or, where stalls are not provided, 610 mm of space of a urinal.

Washing facilities

Factories: There are no general provisions as to the actual number of wash-basins and showers to be provided in a factory. However, it is normal practice to provide wash-basins on the same scale as water closets.

Offices and shops:

Table 11: Provision of washing facilities in offices and shops

Number of persons regularly employed to work in the premises at any one time (or where separate accommodation for the sexes is required to be provided, number of such persons of each sex)	*Number of wash-basins or units of trough or washing fountain accommodation*
1–15	1
16–30	2
31–50	3
51–75	4
76–100	5
Exceeding 100: with the addition of one 'washing unit' for every unit of 25 persons by which the workforce exceeds 100, any fraction of a unit of 25 persons being treated as one unit.	

Table 11 indicates the accommodation required. The expression 'unit of trough or washing fountain accommodation' means 610 mm of length of a trough or, in the case of circular or oval troughs and washing fountains, 610 mm of the circumference of the trough or fountain.

Drinking water

Factories

FA, sec 57, requires the provision and maintenance, at suitable points conveniently accessible to all persons employed, of an adequate supply of wholesome drinking water from a public main or some other approved source. Such water should be clearly marked DRINKING WATER. This requirement also broadly applies to 'building operations' and 'works of engineering construction' (see Construction (Health and Welfare) Regulations 1966).

Offices and shops

OSRPA, sec 11, lays down similar requirements. Wholesome drinking water must be provided and maintained at suitable places easily accessible to the workforce. If there is no piped supply, water should be stored in suitable vessels and renewed at least daily and, if necessary, steps taken to preserve the water and its container from contamination. If the water is not delivered by jet from which persons can drink, drinking vessels should be provided as well as facilities for rinsing them in clean water, unless such vessels are of the disposable type.

Clothing storage

Factories

FA, sec 59, requires that 'adequate and suitable accommodation for clothing not worn during working hours' must be provided and maintained for the use of employed persons, and arrangements made for the drying of such clothing. Depending upon the degree of soiling of protective clothing, separate accommodation for workwear and personal clothing may be necessary, e.g. for workers in the oil industry, sewer workers, abattoir workers or for those engaged in work involving lead. Civil action lies against a factory occupier in the event of personal clothing being stolen (*McCarthy* v. *Daily Mirror Newspapers Ltd* [1949] 1 AER 801). Broadly, the same requirements prevail under the Construction (Health and Welfare) Regulations 1966 as regards 'building operations' and 'works of engineering construction'.

Offices and shops

OSRPA, sec 12, requires that provision be made to enable workers' clothing, not worn by them during working hours, to be hung or otherwise accommodated and dried when necessary. If special protective clothing is required whilst at work, and that clothing is not taken home, facilities must similarly be provided for the storage and drying of such clothing. Presumably, as with breach of the FA, sec 59, breach of this section would give rise to civil liability, for instance, in the case of theft.

Sitting facilities

Factories

FA, sec 60, requires that where it is reasonable for employees to work, or do some part of it, in a sitting position, suitable facilities must be provided. Moreover, where the greater part of the work can properly be done in a sitting position, suitably designed and constructed seats, where necessary including a foot rest, must be provided. Presumably, by way of analogy with OSRPA, sec 14(1) (*see below*), improvement notices (*see* Chapter 3) may require additional modifications to chairs in the interests of the employee.

Offices and shops

Similar requirements in relation to sedentary work apply (OSRPA, secs 13 and 14). The scope of these statutory requirements has, however, been amplified by decisions of industrial tribunals adjudicating on improvement notices. Moreover, in parts of shops to which customers resort, there must be provided at least one seat for every three employees, and the employer must permit the use of such seats whenever this does not interfere with their work (OSRPA, sec 13(2) and (3)).

Facilities for taking meals

Factories

There is no general requirement under the Factories Act 1961 to provide facilities for taking meals, although in certain industries, such as chemical works, fruit-preserving and india-rubber processes, such facilities must be provided. In processes such as bronzing, enamelling and hide sorting, there is a positive prohibition on the taking of food due to the obvious risk of contamination.

Offices and shops

OSRPA, sec 15, states that where persons employed in a shop eat meals on the premises, suitable and sufficient facilities must be provided.

Amenity areas

Since statutory requirements relating to welfare amenities lay down *minimum* standards, prudent employers will endeavour to provide better standards for their employees. In factories and labour-intensive operations it is relevant to consider the provision of an amenity area. An amenity area includes all the general welfare provisions such as washing and sanitation, clothing storage, first aid and even catering, incorporated as one purpose-built unit, separate from the main activity, but with reasonable access to it. Much will depend upon existing layout, the needs of workers who may be separated from the main activity, e.g. engineers, and the degree of shift work. Sometimes smaller 'satellite' amenity areas, as distinct from one large central unit, may be more appropriate.

The design of amenity areas

The following factors should be taken into account in the design and use of amenity areas.

Sanitation

(a) The surfaces of the floors, walls, ceilings, doors and fittings should be capable of being readily cleaned and maintained.
(b) There should be total separation of sexes, except where fewer than three persons of one sex or the other are employed.
(c) There should be an intervening ventilated space between any sanitation area and a workroom, office, foodroom or store.
(d) Facilities for the disposal of sanitary dressings should be provided in female staff sanitation areas, e.g. incinerator, comminuter or chemical method.
(e) Adequate lighting and ventilation, by both natural and artificial means, should be provided.
(f) Walls, doors and fittings should be of vandal-proof design.

Hand washing and showers

(a) The above provisions relating to separation of the sexes, surfaces, lighting, ventilation and the use of vandal-proof fittings also apply here.
(b) Wash-basins and showers, where installed, should have adequate supplies of hot and cold water or of hot water at a suitably controlled temperature.
(c) Supplies of soap, clean towels and nail brushes should be provided. The use of wall-mounted liquid soap dispensers and disposable paper towels – or the continuous non-returnable type of roller towel cabinet – are recommended as opposed to tablet soap and the simple form of returnable roller towel. In food preparation and manufacture, the use of a bactericidal hand cleanser is recommended. Lidded containers should be installed for the storage of soiled paper towels.

Clothing storage

(a) The above provisions relating to separation of the sexes, surfaces, lighting, ventilation and the use of vandal-proof fittings apply here too.
(b) Suitable seats, preferably of the wall-mounted type, should be provided to permit easy changing of footwear.
(c) There must be effective means for drying clothing.

(d) Use of purpose-manufactured clothing storage units, as opposed to simple wall hooks, is recommended. Such units incorporate a fixed rail, with clothes hangers fixed to the rail, and banks of small personal lockers at each end of the unit for storage of personal items, such as handbags. This arrangement allows for effective drying of clothing, assisted by either wall-mounted fan heaters or floor-mounted tubular steel heaters.

Drinking water

(a) Provision of fountains, as opposed to the use of taps and cups, is recommended.
(b) Drinking water installations should be located outside any sanitation area.

Layout

(a) In activities requiring high standards of personal hygiene, such as food preparation and manufacture, layout should ensure that staff have separate access to clothing storage facilities, sanitation, hand cleansing and shower facilities, and are not required to pass through the working area in outdoor clothes.
(b) Where large numbers of staff use an amenity area, layout should ensure the operation of a sequential flow from outdoor clothing storage area to hand-washing and sanitation area and thence to protective clothing storage area, before entering the working area. The reverse process should take place on completion of work.
(c) The environmental health officer should be consulted at the design stage of new amenity provisions.

17

Cleaning and hygiene

Colin A. Stanley DSc, FRIPHH, FIEH, MIOSH

Hygiene has been defined as 'the science of health' or 'rules for health'. In factories and other workplaces it is concerned with the promotion of good health through the maintenance of satisfactory sanitary conditions and catering activities, and the prevention of contamination, in particular by pest infestation, which can create insanitary conditions and contaminate or damage food, raw materials, manufactured goods and the structure of the premises.

Legal requirements

Workplace legislation has always recognised the need for satisfactory levels of factory cleanliness with a view to the prevention of occupational ill-health associated with insanitary working conditions. The Factories Act 1961, sec 1, requires that every factory must be kept clean and free from effluvia (odours) arising from any drain, sanitary convenience or nuisance and:

(a) accumulations of dirt must be removed daily;
(b) the floor of every workroom must be cleaned at least once a week by washing, sweeping or other method; and
(c) inside walls and ceilings must be washed every 14 months, repainted every 7 years, or white- or colour-washed every 14 months.

The dates of whitewashing, painting, etc., must be entered in the Factories Act register.

Similar provisions apply to premises registered under the Offices, Shops and Railway Premises Act 1963, sec 4. Premises, and all furniture, furnishings and fittings therein, must be kept in a clean state. No dirt or refuse may accumulate in premises where work is done or through which workers pass, and steps must be cleansed not less than once a week, either by washing, sweeping or other method.

Requirements for the maintenance of sanitary working conditions are clearly identified in other statutes and subordinate legislation, e.g. Asbestos Regulations 1969, Rag Flock and Other Filling Materials Act 1951, Factories (Horsehair Processes) Regulations 1907, Construction (Health and Welfare) Regulations 1966.

Maintenance of sanitary conditions

The operation of satisfactory cleaning and housekeeping procedures is a prerequisite in the prevention of accidents and occupational ill-health. Indeed, poor housekeeping is a contributory factor in a large proportion of accidents.

Management of the cleaning operation is best undertaken by the use of a cleaning schedule or plan, produced after a hygiene survey of the premises, supported by frequent inspections to ensure effective implementation.

Cleaning schedules/plans

Schedules are most correctly produced in tabular form, identifying the following:

(a) what is to be cleaned, e.g. item of plant, area, room, surface;
(b) location;
(c) the nature and extent of soiling;
(d) frequency of cleaning necessary;
(e) method and materials to be used;
(f) responsibility for ensuring satisfactory completion of the cleaning task;
(g) monitoring procedure; and
(h) any precautions necessary, e.g. use of chemical-based cleaning agents.

Schedules should be reviewed annually, or more frequently if standards deteriorate.

A typical schedule for food-manufacturing premises or a large catering establishment is shown in Table 12. (This can be modified to suit other types of premises.)

The identification of management responsibility for implementation of schedules is the most important factor in ensuring sound levels of factory hygiene. Cleaning schedules must be linked with preventive maintenance systems, and cleaning staff must be trained in the correct and safe use of cleaning preparations.

Table 12: Cleaning schedule for food-manufacturing or catering establishment

Item	*Frequency*	*Responsibility*	*Equipment*	*Materials*	*Method*	*Special precautions*
Yard	Daily		Hose and broom		Sweep up all refuse. Hose and brush down yard surfaces	Keep drain gullies clear
Floor Stores Food preparation Kitchen Wash-up Servery Dining room Cloakroom Lavatory Washroom	Daily		Vacuum cleaner Suction polisher Polisher Floor scrubber Floor drier Sponge mop Plastic bucket	Detergent/ sanitiser Warm water	Vacuum clean Wash floor Dry floor Polish (where appropriate)	
Walls All rooms as above	Fortnightly		Vacuum cleaner (with attachment)		Vacuum clean	Ventilation fans should be included in the cleaning, but the electric supply to the fan must be switched off at the main
	Monthly		Mechanical wall washer or sponge and plastic bucket	Detergent/ sanitiser Warm water	Wash down	Include canopies over cooking equipment
Ceilings	Monthly		Vacuum cleaner (with attachment)		Vacuum clean	
	6-monthly		Sponge and plastic bucket	Detergent/ sanitiser Warm water	Wash ceilings	

Windows					
Interior Exterior	Fortnightly Monthly	Chamois leather Plastic bucket	Water	Wash	Safe working conditions must be ensured. Ladders must be sound and firmly placed
Electric fittings	Monthly	Drying cloth or vacuum cleaner			The electricity supply should be switched off at the main
WCs					
Pans	Daily	Nylon brush	Approved cleanser	Sprinkle cleanser around bowl at end of each day. Brush entire bowl surface following morning. Flush pan, holding brush under flush water	When an approved cleanser is used, no other cleansing agent must be mixed with it, or used at the same time
Seat Flushing handle Door Furniture	Daily	Disposable cloth Plastic bucket	Detergent/ sanitiser	Thoroughly wash the door, door furniture, flushing handle and pedestal seat. Dispose of the cloth via the WC pan	
Washbasins, Showers	Daily	Sponge	Approved cleanser	Thoroughly wash the basin	

Cleaning preparations

The type of preparation used will depend on the nature of the soiling. Cleaning preparations may be classified thus:

Acids

These are used to remove hard water scale and deposits on urinals formed by a combination of scale and urine salts. Commonly an inhibited hydrochloric acid preparation is used, although sulphamic acid preparations are less corrosive.

Alkalis

Caustic soda (sodium hydroxide) preparations will break down fat, grease and carbon deposits, but will seriously affect metals such as aluminium. Alkalis are neutralised by acids and in the presence of acids are ineffective as cleaning agents.

Detergents

These are mildly alkaline. Most detergents are manufactured in the form of washing powders and liquids for washing dishes and utensils. Detergents incorporate 'wetting agents' to increase surface contact, and added to acids, for example, provide a far greater degree of penetration, thereby ensuring quicker removal of soil.

Solvents

Solvent-based products are used to soften fats and greases. They may incorporate a detergent. Solvents incorporating methylene chloride require extreme caution in use as the vapour liberated in hot working conditions produces drowsiness.

Combined detergent/sanitisers

Sanitisers or bactericides are often combined with a detergent to achieve cleaning and sanitisation in one operation. The type of sanitiser used will depend on the soil to be removed and the necessity, if any, to ensure a sanitised surface on the item cleaned.

Disinfectants

A disinfectant is a chemical substance which will kill harmful organisms. Although most disinfectants incorporate detergents to improve wetting properties, some are manufactured to provide disinfection after the removal of soil. The choice of disinfectant will depend upon effectiveness, simplicity in use and cost. Hypochlorites release chlorine. They are inexpensive and effective but readily inactivated by organic matter. On no account should they be mixed with acids as chlorine gas can be liberated. Quarternary ammonium compounds

(QACs) tend to be more bacteriostatic than bactericidal. They are readily deactivated by a variety of materials including detergents. Iodophors resemble hypochlorites in action and incorporate a detergent. They are used extensively for sanitation area cleaning and disinfection and are usually acidified as the active ingredient, iodine, exerts maximum bactericidal action in the pH range 2–4. Phenolics are general purpose disinfectants, often emitting powerful odours. They should not be used in kitchens or canteens due to the risk of their tainting food.

PART V

Occupational health and hygiene

18 Toxicology and health

Toxicology

Toxicology is the quantitative study of the body's responses to toxic substances. In order to understand the subject and interpret toxicological data and information it is important to know the meaning of expressions and definitions commonly used.

Definitions

(a) *Toxicity* is the ability of a chemical substance to produce injury once it reaches a susceptible site in or on the body. The effects may be acute or chronic, local or systemic.
(b) *Acute effect* is a rapidly produced effect following a single exposure to an offending agent.
(c) *Chronic effect* is produced as a result of prolonged exposure or repeated exposures of long duration. Concentrations of the offending agent may be low in both cases. One single prolonged exposure can result in chronic effects, however.
(d) *Sub-acute effect* generally implies a reduced form of acute effect.
(e) *Progressive chronic effect* continues to develop after exposure ceases.
(f) *Local effect* is usually confined to the initial point of contact. The site may be the skin, mucous membranes of the eyes, nose or throat, liver, bladder, etc.
(g) *Systemic effects* occur in parts of the body other than at the point of initial contact, and are associated with a particular body system, e.g. respiratory system, central nervous system.
(h) *Dose* is the level of environmental contamination multiplied by the length of time (duration) of exposure to the contaminant.
(i) *Minimum lethal dose*, in experimental toxicology, is the minimum quantity of toxic substance per unit body of experimental animal

which will have a fatal effect. It is expressed in milligrams per kilogram of body weight.

(j) *LD_{50}*, a more commonly used term, is the amount of toxic material which will kill 50 per cent of the test animal population of an experimental group (lethal dose 50 per cent kill). This figure generally forms the basis for comparison between different chemical compounds.

(k) *LC_{50}* is the lethal concentration of a toxic substance in air which will kill 50 per cent of the test animal population of an experimental group (lethal concentration 50 per cent kill).

(l) *Toxic hazard* is a measure of the likelihood of toxic effects occurring.

Toxic substances

Routes of entry

Inhalation

Inhalation of toxic substances in the form of dust, fume, gas, vapour or mist, accounts for the majority of deaths and illnesses associated with toxic substances. The results may be acute (immediate) as in the case of many gassing accidents, e.g. chlorine, carbon monoxide (at high concentrations), hydrogen sulphide and nitric oxide; or chronic (prolonged and cumulative) as with exposure to, for example, chlorinated hydrocarbons, lead compounds, dusts which produce pneumoconiosis, mists and fogs, such as paint spray and oil mists, and fume, notably that from welding operations.

Absorption (pervasion)

The skin, if intact, is proof against most but not all inputs. There are certain substances and micro-organisms which are capable of passing straight through the intact skin into underlying tissue or even into the blood stream, without apparently causing any change in the skin itself (percutaneous effect). The resistance of the skin to external irritants varies with age, sex, race, colour and, to a certain extent, diet. Absorption, as a route of entry, is normally associated with occupational dermatitis, the causes of which may be broadly divided into two groups.

Primary irritants: These substances will cause dermatitis at the site of the contact if permitted to act for sufficient length of time in sufficient concentrations, e.g. strong acids, strong alkalis and solvents.

Secondary cutaneous sensitisers: These substances do not necessarily cause skin changes, but effect a specific sensitisation of the skin. If further contact occurs after an interval of approximately 7 or more days, a dermatitis will develop at the site of the second contact. Examples of secondary sensitisers are some rubber additives, nickel, certain wood dusts and proteolytic enzymes.

Ingestion

Certain substances are carried into the intestine from which some will pass into the body by pervasion through the intestinal wall. Like the lung, the intestine behaves as a selective filter which keeps out many, but not all, harmful agents presented to it.

Injection, inoculation and implantation

A forceful breach of the skin, perhaps as a result of injury, can carry harmful substances through the skin barrier.

Dose/response relationship

A basic principle of occupational disease prevention is the concept of threshold limits of exposure or dose, which normal people can tolerate without long-term or short-term damage to their health. For many chemical substances found in common industrial use, it is possible to discern a link between dose and the body's response, a characteristic known as the 'dose/response relationship'.

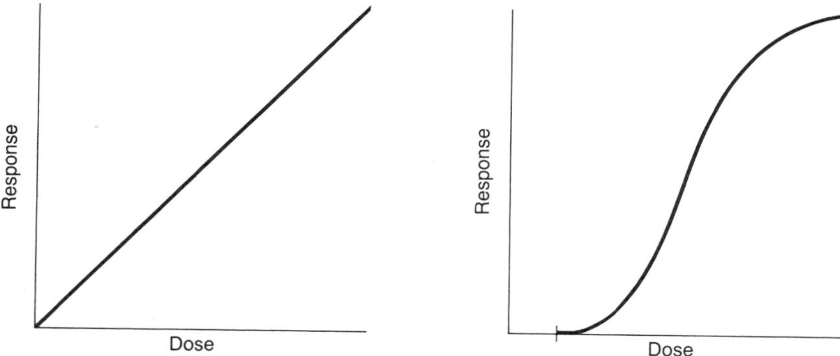

Fig. 18.1 (a) Response directly proportional to the dose received
(b) Identification of threshold dose

With many dusts, for instance, the body's reaction or response is directly proportional to the dose received over a period of time: the greater the dose, the more serious the resulting condition, and vice versa (*see* Fig. 18.1(a)). In the case of other substances, the dose/response curve remains at a level of no response at a point greater than zero on the dose axis, and this point of cut-off identifies the threshold dose (*see* Fig. 18.1(b)).

Exposure limits

Threshold limit values were values published by the American Conference of Governmental Industrial Hygienists in the USA (where, in effect, they are enforced through state inspectors as if they were minimum statutory standards) and adopted for use in the UK by the HSE. They refer to airborne concentrations of substances and represent conditions under which it is believed that nearly all workers may be repeatedly exposed, day after day, without adverse effects. Threshold limit values refer to time-weighted average concentrations for a 7- or 8-hour work day and a 40-hour working week. They have now been replaced by exposure limits (control limits and recommended limits).

Exposure limits – the new philosophy

Up to 1981 threshold limit values, the principal form of exposure limits, were published annually by the Health and Safety Executive in Guidance Note EH15. However, there has now been a move to phase out threshold limit values with the introduction of control limits which will establish tighter administrative and legal controls on occupational exposure to toxic substances. Guidance Note EH40/84 incorporates industrial hygiene information of greater relevance to the employer's duties under the Health and Safety at Work, etc., Act 1974, and this will be supported by the forthcoming Control of Substances Hazardous to Health Regulations. These Regulations will place general duties on employers wherever there is a potential risk of exposure to toxic substances or substances hazardous to health.

Occupational exposure limits are endorsed by the Health and Safety Commission and by the Advisory Committee on Toxic Substances (ACTS). (ACTS comprises representatives from the Health and Safety Executive, scientific groups concerned with the assessment of risks and hazards, employers and employees.) These limits take two forms.

Control limits

Control limits are described in the new document as 'those exposure limits which are contained in Regulations, Approved Codes of Practice and EEC Directives or those which have been agreed by the Health and Safety Commission'. A *control limit* is defined as the limit which is 'judged, after detailed consideration of the available evidence, to be "reasonably practicable" for the whole spectrum of work activities in Great Britain'. Control limits are characterised by:

(a) having been set at a level which it would be reasonably practicable for all relevant sectors of industry to achieve;
(b) providing a clear indication of what the law requires as a maximum so that when they are exceeded employers know they are in breach of HSWA; and
(c) being based on a full review of medical and scientific evidence carried out by the Health and Safety Executive and having been agreed by both employer and employee representatives on the Health and Safety Commission as being acceptable.

In the case of asbestos, the Advisory Committee on Asbestos confirmed that the concept of the control limit is intended to represent a realistic level of airborne concentration of dust, closely associated with the relevant legislation, above which no person should be occupationally exposed. However, there is also a general requirement to reduce exposure further and the established control limits represent the upper limit of permitted exposure, not a 'safe' level such that, once attained, no further improvement in dust control would be necessary. This same principle, namely that of aiming for further reductions in control limits over a period of time, applies in other cases, e.g. styrene, trichlorethylene.

To summarise, the most important feature of the control limit concept, which sets it apart from both the recommended limit (*see below*) and the threshold limit value, is that generally it represents the lowest exposure technically and economically possible. Recommended limits or threshold limit values, on the other hand, indicate the highest tolerable level of exposure.

Recommended limits

Recommended limits have replaced threshold limit values. In most cases, they are still numerically equivalent to the original threshold limit values. They are 'recommended' by the Advisory Committee on Toxic Substances. A large proportion of these limits, however, have not yet been individually considered by the committee or the Health and Safety Commission, as has been the case with control limits.

Toxicological assessment

Toxicological assessment refers to the collection, assembly and evaluation of data on a potentially toxic substance and the conditions of its use, in order to determine the danger to human health, systems for controlling the danger, the detection and treatment of over-exposure and, where such information is insufficient, the need for further investigation. It is closely related to the duties of manufacturers and importers of substances used at work, under HSWA, sec 6, to ensure the safety of their products, to undertake testing and examination and to provide adequate information for the user to ensure safe working (*see* Chapter 3). These duties are further extended in the Notification of New Substances Regulations 1982 and the approved codes of practice.

In assessing toxic hazards, the following basic information is required:

(a) the name of the substance, including any synonyms;
(b) a physical or chemical description of the substance;
(c) information on potential exposure situations;
(d) details of exposure limits;
(e) general toxicological aspects, such as:
  (i) the route of entry into the body,
  (ii) the mode of action in or on the body,
  (iii) signs and symptoms,
  (iv) diagnostic tests,
  (v) treatment, and
  (vi) the disability potential.

Moreover, under the Notification of New Substances Regulations 1982 specific duties are placed on the manufacturers and importers of new substances with regard to testing and notification, announcement procedures, submission of information to the 'competent authority', the form, content and time of notification and procedures for further notification.

Protection against toxic substances

Although the various control strategies are considered in Chapter 26, 'Control Strategies in Occupational Hygiene', reference, nevertheless, should be made to some of the more common methods of protecting workers against toxic substances. Such methods of protection include the following:

Substitution

The best solution, in many cases, is to substitute a harmless substance for a toxic substance – or, perhaps, one that is less harmful. Benzene, which is an extremely hazardous substance, has been replaced with safer solvents in the rubber industry, leadless glazes can be substituted in the pottery industry, and sesqui-sulphide has been used to replace white phosphorus.

If substitution is not possible, then the following alternatives should be considered.

Mechanical handling

The objective here is to eliminate completely physical contact with the offending agent, or to keep it at a safe distance or enclose it so that it cannot be inhaled. This may take the form of circulating the agent by the use of pumps and pipework or, as in the case of radioactive materials, remote control handling systems.

Total enclosure

This involves the use of a closed container and exhaust ventilation, e.g. in the extraction of benzene, in dry cleaning plants using trichlorethylene, or in seed dressing, where dangerous mercury-based fungicides are used.

Exhaust ventilation

Much will depend on whether a system of total or partial enclosure is used. However, good design of the system is of the utmost significance. Typical examples of where exhaust ventilation is used are with lead processes in the accumulator and pottery industries, in chrome-plating plants and in luminising rooms.

Wet methods

Wet methods prevent the formation of dust in that the dust particles are entrained in the very fine water spray or mist and settle as a sludge at the bottom of the spray chamber. Wet methods are used in the manufacture of lead paint, in the suppression of cotton dust and in asbestos weaving.

Personal protection

Personal protective equipment in the form of overalls, respirators, gloves and eye protection has a significant part to play in the protection of workers against contact with toxic substances. Careful selection and acceptability to the user are key factors here (*see* Chapter 24).

19

Occupational diseases and conditions

Occupational diseases are those diseases contracted as a result of a particular employment. This chapter considers the wide range of occupational diseases and conditions, their causes and symptoms. Many occupational diseases are prescribed, in which case benefit is payable under the Social Security Act 1975.

Test of prescription

A disease may be prescribed if

(a) it ought to be treated, having regard to its causes and incidence and other relevant considerations, as a risk of occupation and not as a risk common to all persons; and
(b) it is such that, in the absence of special circumstances, the attribution of particular cases to the nature of the employment can be established with reasonable certainty (Social Security Act 1975, sec 76(2)).

Current law relating to prescribed occupational diseases is to be found in the Social Security (Industrial Injuries) (Prescribed Diseases) Regulations 1985, S.I. 967.

Classification of the causes of occupational disease

Physical causes

Examples include:

(a) Heat – heat cataract, heat stroke (prescribed disease A2).
(b) Lighting – miner's nystagmus (prescribed disease A9).

(c) Noise – noise-induced hearing loss (occupational deafness) (prescribed disease A10).
(d) Vibration – vibration-induced white finger (prescribed disease A11).
(e) Radiation – radiation sickness (at ionising wavelengths), burns, arc eye.
(f) Dust – silicosis, coal worker's pneumoconiosis (prescribed disease D1).
(g) Pressure – decompression sickness (prescribed disease A3).

Chemical causes

Examples include:

(a) Acids and alkalis – dermatitis (non-infective dermatitis is prescribed disease D5).
(b) Metals – lead and mercury poisoning (prescribed diseases C1 and C5).
(c) Non-metals – arsenic and phosphorus poisoning (prescribed diseases C4 and C3).
(d) Gases – carbon monoxide poisoning, arsine poisoning (prescribed disease C4).
(e) Organic compounds – occupational cancers, e.g. bladder cancer (prescribed disease C23).
(f) Dusts – mercury poisoning (prescribed disease C5).

Biological causes

Examples include:

(a) Animal-borne – anthrax, brucellosis, glanders fever (prescribed diseases B1, B2 and B7).
(b) Human-borne – viral hepatitis (prescribed disease B8).
(c) Vegetable-borne – aspergillosis (farmer's lung) (prescribed disease B6).

Ergonomic causes

Examples include:

(a) Job movements – cramp (in relation to handwriting or typewriting) (prescribed disease A4).
(b) Friction and pressure – bursitis, cellulitis, i.e. beat hand, traumatic inflammation of the tendons or associated tendon sheaths of the hand or forearm, i.e. tenosynovitis (prescribed diseases A5 and A8).

The physical causes

Heat

Heat cataract

Cataracts of the eye, caused by excessive exposure to heat and microwaves, have been common in many industries, e.g. glass blowing, chain making and others requiring the operation of furnaces. Continuous exposure to radiant heat results in the opacity of the lens of the eye. Such radiations, it is thought, disturb the nutrition of the lens and cause localised coagulation of the protein. (Heat cataract is included in prescribed disease A2.)

Heat stroke

Heat stroke is occasionally encountered in workers in hot processes. The symptoms are due to a defect in thermoregulation – the ability of the body to vary its temperature according to external factors. The onset is usually abrupt: the patient falls unconscious and could have a temperature of 40.6 °C or more. Emergency treatment is aimed at reducing the body temperature to 40.0 °C within 1 hour by all possible means, thus minimising the risk of damage to the central nervous system. (Heat stroke is included in prescribed disease A2.)

Heat cramps

Such cramps may be encountered by workers in the heat treatment of metals, e.g. forging or casting, or as a result of heat from microwave radiation. Most cases occur during summer months. Cramps take the form of pain in the muscles beginning in the calves and spreading to the arms and abdomen. The pains are of an intermittent nature, occurring with increasing severity every few minutes. Generally, taking a drink containing common salt (saline) is the only treatment necessary, and it is normal in many industries to have stocks of salt tablets available.

Lighting

Headaches, vertigo, insomnia and 'eye strain' (visual fatigue) are common in many work situations. They are associated with poor lighting and the level of visual performance of the operator (*see* Chapter 15). There is one occupational disease prescribed in relation to lighting (or the lack of it), i.e. miner's nystagmus (prescribed disease A9).

Miner's nystagmus

This disease is associated with poor lighting conditions in underground working operations, and is a complex psychological malady. It is thought to be primarily the result of poor lighting. However, exposure to toxic gas, the adoption of unusually awkward working postures or the onset of a state of anxiety have often been precipitating factors. The disease is associated with the more or less rhythmic oscillation of the eyeballs often coupled with persistent headaches, vertigo and insomnia. It may be accompanied by contraction of the fields of vision, poor visual acuity and photophobia, nervous symptoms and tremor, as well as nuchal rigidity (a condition of the brain) with a characteristic posture in walking. Generally, complete recovery takes place after cessation of underground work and a return to exposure to good illuminance levels.

Noise

The most common condition associated with exposure to noise is occupational deafness. Under the provisions of the Social Security (Industrial Injuries) (Prescribed Diseases) Regulations 1985 the condition is described as follows: 'Substantial sensorineural hearing loss amounting to at least 50 dB in each ear, being due in the case of at least one ear to occupational noise, and being the average of pure tone losses measured by audiometry over the 1, 2 and 3 KHz frequencies.'

Noise may affect hearing in three ways.

(a) Temporary threshold shift is the short-term effect (i.e. a temporary reduction in hearing acuity) which may follow exposure to noise. The condition is reversible. The effect depends upon individual susceptibility.
(b) Permanent threshold shift takes place where the limit of tolerance is exceeded in terms of time, level of noise and individual susceptibility. Recovery from permanent threshold shift will not proceed to completion, but will effectively cease at some particular point in time after the end of the exposure. ('Persistent threshold shift' is used to denote the degree of hearing impairment remaining after at least 40 hours.) The term 'permanent' is reserved for conditions which may be reasonably supposed to have no possibility of further recovery. Some recovery of hearing may be found after 2 days away from noise, and even longer.
(c) Acoustic trauma is quite a different condition from occupational deafness (noise-induced hearing loss). It involves sudden aural damage resulting from short-term intense exposure or even from one single exposure. Explosive pressure rises are often responsible, such as exposure to gunfire, major explosions or even fireworks.

For most steady types of industrial noise, intensity and duration of exposure are the principal factors in the degree of noise-induced hearing loss. Hearing ability also deteriorates with age (presbyacusis), and it is sometimes difficult to distinguish between the effects of noise and normal age deterioration in hearing. Research by the UK Medical Research Council and the National Physical Laboratory has shown that the risk of noise-induced hearing loss can be related to the total amount of noise energy that is taken in by the ears over a working lifetime.

The Department of Employment's *Code of Practice for Reducing the Exposure of Employed Persons to Noise* (1972) seeks to limit the amount of noise energy that is taken in by the ears during each working day. (Although not a legal instrument and therefore not enforceable, this code is the industrial standard in the UK and, to some extent, forms the basis of the draft Protection of Hearing Regulations. A key feature of both the code and the draft regulations is the 'requirement' that employees should not be exposed to the equivalent of a continuous sound level of more than 90 dBA over the duration of an 8-hour day. Significantly, proposed EEC legislation opts for 85 dBA as the control limit. This is also the North American standard.)

NOTE. It is necessary to be aware of the current instructions by the HSE to Factory Inspectors to enforce the code of practice and HSWA, sec 2(2)(*b*), which can require safe 'arrangements' to be made to reduce noise exposure, even if under 90 dBA leq, if this can be done by 'reasonably practicable' means.

Symptoms of noise-induced hearing loss

Mild form of noise-induced hearing loss: There is sometimes difficulty in conversing with people, the wrong answers may be given occasionally, and speech on television and radio seems indistinct. Moreover, there is difficulty in hearing normal domestic sounds, such as a clock ticking.

Severe form of noise-induced hearing loss: With a severe degree of deafness, there is difficulty in conversing, even when face to face with people, as well as hearing what is said at public meetings, unless sitting right at the front. Generally, people seem to be speaking indistinctly, even on radio and television, and there is an inability to hear the normal sounds of home and street. It is often impossible to tell the direction from which a sound is coming, and to assess the distance from the sound. (This last-mentioned feature is a contributory factor in accidents.) In most severe cases, there is a sensation of whistling or ringing in the ears (tinnitus). This condition can give rise to liability at common law in an action against an employer, even though the resultant deafness is quite insignificant (*O'Shea* v. *Kimberley-Clark Ltd*, reported in the *Guardian*, 8 October 1982). Moreover, it has recently been decided that it is legitimate to apportion an employer's liability for an employee's occupational deafness according to the length of time the employer can be shown to have been in breach of his duty of care (*Thompson, Gray, Nicholson* v. *Smiths Ship Repairers (North Shields) Ltd* [1984] IRLR 93–116). This is contrary to the earlier decision in *Heslop* v. *Metalock (Great Britain) Ltd, Observer*, 29 November 1981.

In order to understand the mechanism of noise-induced hearing loss, see the description later in this chapter.

Hygiene standards for noise-induced hearing loss

Standards are based on noise-induced deafness, age-based deafness, and speech range at the frequencies of interest, i.e. 500 Hz, 1 kHz, 2 kHz and 3 kHz. The various standards are as follows:

(a) National Insurance (Industrial Injuries) Commission: 50 dB hearing loss averaged through 1, 2 and 3 KHz in the ear which hears best (Social Security (Industrial Injuries) (Prescribed Diseases) Regulations 1985, A10 Part 1, Schedule 1).
(b) American Academy of Ophthalmologists and Otolaryngologists (AAOO): 25 dB hearing loss averaged through 0.5, 1 and 2 kHz in both ears.
(c) British Association of Ophthalmologists (BAO): 40 dB hearing loss averaged through 1, 2 and 3 kHz in both ears.

Cause of noise-induced hearing loss

In order to ascertain how noise-induced hearing loss takes place, it is necessary to understand the physiology of the human hearing system. The ear is composed of three specific parts, the outer, middle and inner ears (*see* Fig. 19.1). The outer ear comprises the pinna, with the auditory canal (meatus) leading to the ear-drum (tympanic membrane). The middle ear is a chamber containing three linked bones or ossicles, the malleus (hammer), incus (anvil) and stapes (stirrup). The function of the ossicles is to transform the vibration caused by sound waves impinging on the tympanic membrane into mechanical movements. These are transmitted to the fluid of the inner ear by the stapes bone, which fits into one of the two holes connecting the middle and inner ears, the fenestra ovalis (oval window).

The inner ear contains the important organ of hearing, the cochlea, which comprises a coiled fluid-filled tube, similar in appearance to a snail's shell. The cochlea has a basilar membrane, an auditory nerve and frequency-responsive hair cells incorporated along its coil. The hair cells run along the length of the basilar membrane. A sound entering the cochlea causes vibration of fluid resulting in the hair cells also

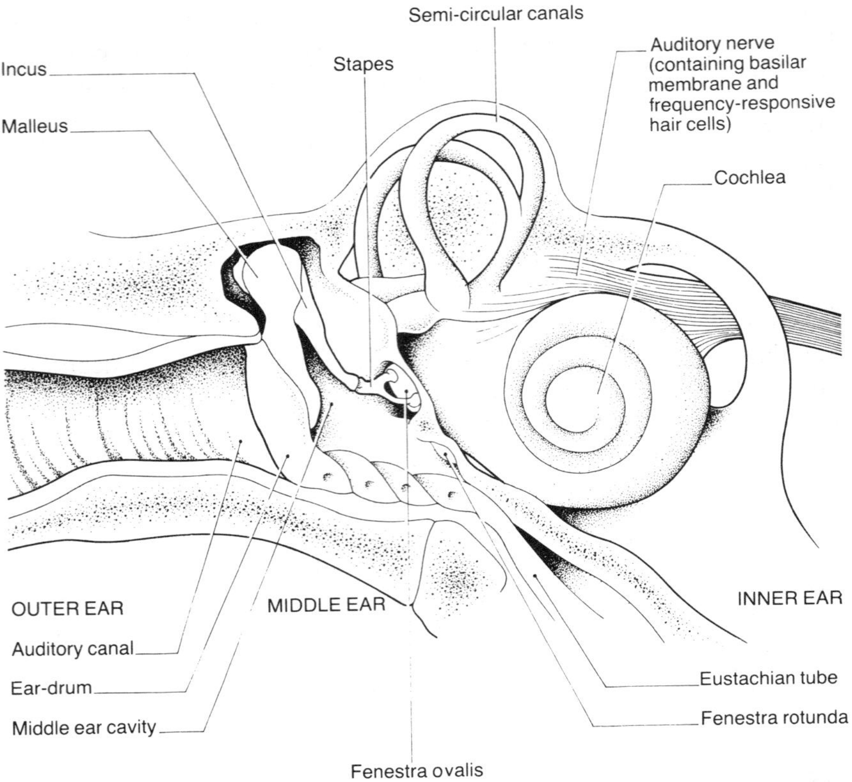

Fig. 19.1 The human hearing system

being vibrated. At the beginning of the cochlean coil the hair cells detect the lower frequencies whilst progressively higher frequencies are detected by the hair cells located towards the centre of the coil. The hair cells effectively turn mechanical energy into electrical impulses which they send to the brain by means of the auditory nerve.

When the ear-drum is vibrated, this vibration is amplified by the ossicles and transmitted to the cochlea. The cochlea transforms the vibrations into nerve impulses which are sent to the brain via the auditory nerve. If the ear-drum is vibrated between 20 and 20,000 times per second a sound will be heard. Normally the hair cells to the cochlea respond well to vibration, and they normally recover after periods of excessive vibration from noise. However, noise can so fatigue one of these cells that it no longer revives and actually dies; thus the row of cells gradually thins out. In cases of noise-induced hearing loss, the projecting cells can be compared with a cornfield that has been subjected to storm or people walking through it. Some of the hair cells will be standing, others will be partly flattened, some will be totally flattened and many will be broken off at their base. This is the effect of excessive noise on the fine hair cells of the cochlea, resulting in varying degrees of noise-induced hearing loss, and variable ability to hear sound at different frequencies.

Measuring hearing loss – audiometry

Hearing loss is measured by audiometry, the most widely used technique being pure tone audiometry. This involves the subject sitting in a sound-proof booth and listening through earphones to a series of pure tone sounds. Each sound is gradually increased in intensity until the subject can hear it, whereupon the subject presses a button to indicate that he has perceived that sound. In this way, the hearing threshold, or lowest level at which the sound can be heard, is established over a range of frequencies. At the end of the audiometric test, an audiogram is produced which records the hearing of the subject over these frequencies. An audiogram is produced for each ear.

The audiogram is then compared to an audiogram which, notionally, would be produced by perfect hearing. No one has perfect hearing and the audiogram for a subject with normal hearing is shown in Fig. 19.2(a). In 'normal' hearing the audiograms for both ears will be virtually identical. An audiogram is used to assess the degree of hearing loss across the frequencies of interest, which are particularly those at which normal speech takes place, i.e. 0.5, 1 and 2 kHz. In Fig. 19.2(b) there is substantial hearing loss at 3, 4 and 6 kHz, but not predominantly at the frequencies of interest. This would be described as a moderate degree of hearing damage.

State benefit for occupational deafness

Certain key changes in the law relating to state benefit for occupational deafness were introduced by the Social Security (Industrial Injuries) (Prescribed Diseases) Amendment No. 2 Regulations 1983 (SI 1983 No. 1094) which came into effect on 3 October 1983. These changes are now consolidated in the current Social Security (Industrial Injuries) (Prescribed Diseases) Regulations 1985 (SI 1985 No. 967) (hereafter cited in this section as the 1985 Regulations), and the present law relating to claims for occupational deafness may be summarised as follows:

(a) Hearing loss need not be permanent (1985 Regulations, A 10 Part 1, Schedule 1).
(b) A person must have been employed for at least 10 years in prescribed occupation(s) in order to claim benefit (previously 20 years) (1985 Regulations, Reg 25(2)(*a*)).

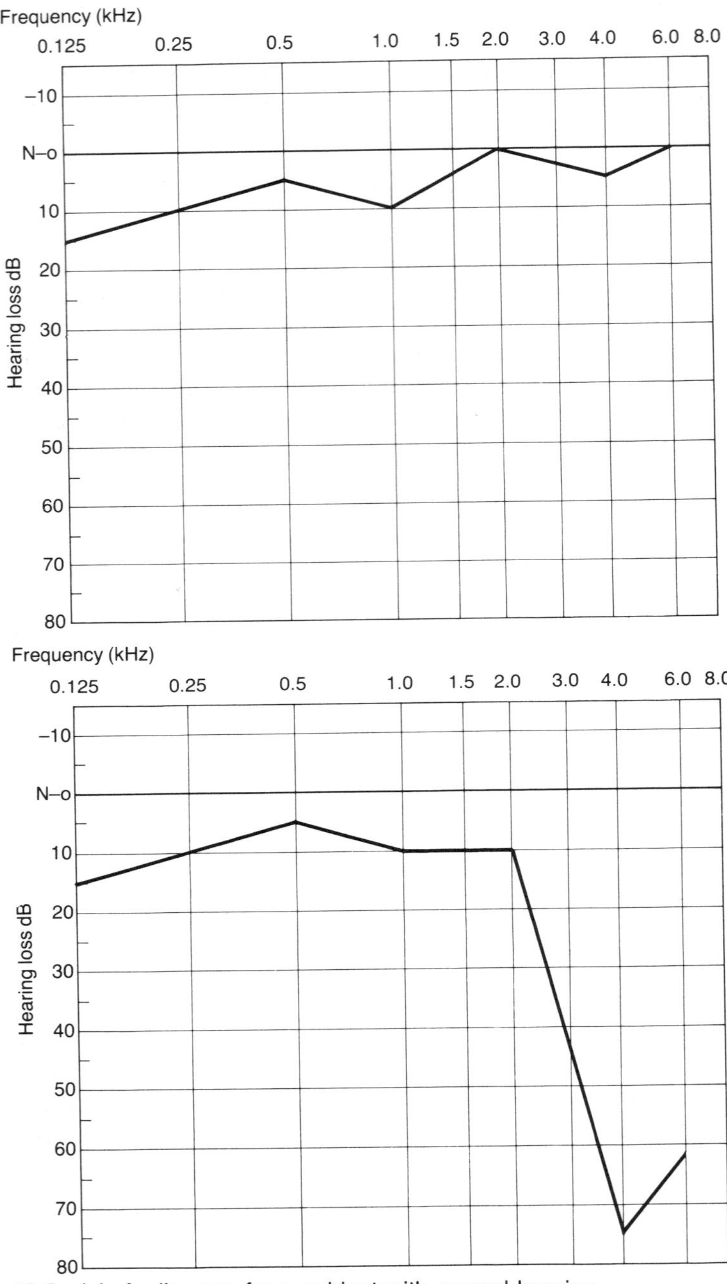

Fig. 19.2 (a) Audiogram for a subject with normal hearing
(b) Audiogram for a subject with a moderate degree of hearing damage

(c) A claim for benefit must be made within 5 years of the last date when the claimant worked in an occupation prescribed for occupational deafness (1985 Regulations, Reg 25(2)).
(d) Occupational deafness is presumed to be due to the nature of the employment (1985 Regulations, Reg 4(5)).
(e) Although not specifically mentioned in the 1985 Regulations (it was Regulation 10 of the Social Security (Industrial Injuries) (Prescribed Diseases) Amendment No. 2 Regulations 1983), it can confidently be assumed that age-related hearing loss (presbyacusis) no longer has to be set off in assessing hearing loss.
(f) Any assessment of disablement at less than 20 per cent is final (1985 Regulations, Reg 33).

Vibration

The principal condition related to vibration is 'vibration-induced white finger' (VWF), which is associated with the use of vibrating hand tools, such as compressed air pneumatic hammers, electrically operated rotary tools and chain-saws. Prolonged exposure to local vibration causes this condition. VWF is now a prescribed occupational disease, and benefit is payable as from 1 April 1985. People suffering from the similar condition, Raynaud's syndrome, are likely to have the condition dramatically worsened by exposure to vibration.

Vibration-induced white finger

The condition is defined as

episodic blanching, occurring throughout the year, affecting the middle or proximal phalanges or in the case of a thumb the proximal phalanx, of

(a) in the case of a person with five fingers (including thumb) on one hand, any three of those fingers; or
(b) in the case of a person with only four such fingers, any two of those fingers; or
(c) in the case of a person with less than four such fingers, any one of those fingers or ... the one remaining finger. (Social Security (Industrial Injuries) (Prescribed Diseases) Regulations 1985, Schedule 4.)

Raynaud's syndrome: This may be caused by a number of conditions unassociated with vibration. In fact, research indicates that vibration is not the primary cause. It was originally seen as a manifestation of Raynaud's disease (or 'constitutional white finger') which is thought to be of a hereditary nature. The symptoms may also be caused by diseases of the connective tissue, such as rheumatoid arthritis, trauma, thrombotic conditions, blood disorders and certain neurological diseases. In order to put a specific label on a characteristic set of symptoms caused by exposure to vibration, the Industrial Injuries Advisory Committee has favoured the term 'vibration-induced white finger'.

Symptoms of VWF: The first signs of VWF, which often pass unnoticed or are not attributed to vibration, are mild tingling and numbness of the fingers, similar to 'pins and needles'. Later, the tips of the fingers which are most exposed to vibration become blanched, typically early in the morning or in cold weather. On further exposure, the affected area increases, sometimes to the base of the fingers, sensitivity during attacks is reduced and the characteristic reddening of the areas affected marks the end of an attack causing severe pain. Prolonged and intense exposure may cause further advancement of the condition with the fingers sometimes taking on a blue-black appearance. In severe cases, gangrene and necrosis (death of living tissue) have been reported. Table 13 shows a classification of the severity of VWF developed by Taylor and Pelmear in 1975.

Table 13: Stages of vibration-induced white finger

Stage	*Condition of digits*	*Work and social interference*
O	No blanching of digits	No complaints
O_T	Intermittent tingling	No interference with activities
O_N	Intermittent numbness	No interference with activities
1	Blanching of one or more finger tips with or without tingling and numbness	No interference with activities
2	Blanching of one or more fingers with numbness; usually confined to winter	Slight interference with home and social activities. No interference at work
3	Extensive blanching; frequent episodes, summer as well as winter	Definite interference at work, at home and with social activities; restriction of hobbies
4	Extensive blanching; most fingers; frequent episodes, summer and winter	Occupation changed to avoid further vibration exposures because of severity of signs and symptoms

Note: Complications are not considered in this grading
Source: Taylor and Pelmear, 1975

There is a latent or symptom-free period from the commencement of regular exposure to the onset of ill-effects, the length of which is thought to be related to the intensity of the vibration. In people subjected to very high intensity levels, stages 2 and 3 may be reached within a few months. Usually the condition progresses more slowly, and a typical latent period is around 5 years. In general, the shorter the latent period, the more severe the condition will become as exposure increases.

Other vibration-related conditions

These include:

(a) Osteoarthritis of the arm joints: this condition is encountered most commonly in the elbow joints, but also in the wrist and shoulder joints.
(b) Injury to the soft tissues of the hand: this is mainly injury to the palm of the hand (Dupuytren's contracture) and bursitis; atrophy (shrinkage or wasting) of the palmar muscles and injury to the ulnar nerve are less common.
(c) Decalcification of the carpus: this condition in the main bone at the base of the hand has been noted in the hands of workers using pneumatic tools, but it does not deteriorate.

Vibratory hand tools

With hand tools the energy level at particular frequencies is significant in the prevention of VWF. Percussive action tools in the range 2,000–3,000 'beats per minute', equal to a frequency range of 33–50 Hz, are the worst. With rotary tools, the range 40–125 Hz is common and promotes similar damage. Many vibratory hand tools are used in industry, including pneumatic tools (for riveting, caulking, fettling, rock drilling and hammering), combustion engine operated tools (for chain-sawing, drilling, vehicle operation, the operation of flex-driven machinery) and electrically powered tools (for grinding, concrete levelling, swaging, drilling and burring).

Reduction of vibration injuries

Vibration is best reduced either by redesign of the tool or by introducing more automation to isolate the operator's hand from the source of vibration. Alternatively, it may be possible to introduce a shock-absorbing mechanism between the vibration source and the handles of the tool. If this is impracticable, the following procedures should be carried out:

(a) pre-employment health screening of potentially exposed workers to assess susceptibility to VWF or manifestation of Raynaud's syndrome;

(b) ensuring body warmth before the start of work in order to achieve good circulation to the extremities;
(c) ensuring that the temperature in the workplace maintains body warmth throughout the working day;
(d) in the case of outside workers, the supply of wind-resistant clothing and gloves together with replacements for wet clothing;
(e) minimising smoking because of its effect on circulation;
(f) where workers are reaching or have already reached the irreversible stage, i.e. stage 4, preclusion from further exposure;
(g) regular health examinations;
(h) redesign of portable hand tools at reduced frequencies;
(i) mechanisation of grinding methods;
(j) provision and use of cotton gloves with rubber inserts or padded with absorbent material;
(k) use of specific working methods to reduce exposure time, such as job rotation;
(l) proper maintenance of tools, such as sharpening of cutters, tuning of engines and renewal of vibration isolators; and
(m) training in correct work techniques to minimise exposure.

Whole body vibration

Whilst VWF tends to be the principal problem associated with vibration, the effects of vibration on the body generally should not be ignored. Whole body vibration, associated, for instance, with driving heavy lorries long distances, can cause blurred vision, loss of balance and loss of concentration, the latter being a causative factor in accidents. In 1974 the International Standards Organisation published recommendations concerned with vibration and the human body (ISO 2631–1974). The recommendations cover cases where the human body is subjected to vibration on one of three supporting surfaces, i.e. the feet of a standing person, the buttocks of a person whilst sitting down and the areas supporting a lying person. Three severity criteria are specified:

(a) a boundary of reduced comfort, applying to fields such as passenger transportation;
(b) a boundary of fatigue-decreased efficiency that is relevant to drivers of vehicles and to certain machine operators; and
(c) an exposure limit boundary, which indicates danger to health.

Research shows that in the longitudinal direction, i.e. head to feet, the human body is most sensitive to vibration in the frequency range 4–8 Hz, whilst in the transverse direction, i.e. finger tip to finger tip, the body is most sensitive in the range 1–2 Hz (*see* Chapter 21).

Radiation

Electromagnetic radiations are those radiations by which energy is transmitted without the necessity of a material medium. The spectrum of electromagnetic radiation extends from the very short X or gamma rays to long radio waves and includes X-rays, ultraviolet, visible light, infrared and short radio waves. Ionising particles can be the corpuscular products of atomic disintegration and the result of high-energy electron beams. The bodily effects of radiation across the electromagnetic spectrum are developed in Chapter 23.

Dust

The group of lung diseases of a chronic fibrotic nature due to the inhalation of dust are generally classified as pneumoconiosis (*see* Chapter 22).

Pneumoconiosis

This disease is defined by the International Labour Organisation (ILO) as 'the accumulation of dust in the lungs and the tissue reactions to its presence'. It is divided by the ILO into the collagenous and non-collagenous forms. (Collagen is a protein-based substance which forms the principal component of connective tissue. Its molecules are assembled like three-strand ropes. The collagen diseases or connective tissue diseases have as their common factor a disorganisation of collagen strands. In all collagen diseases there is inflammation without infection.) Non-collagenous pneumoconiosis is caused by non-fibrogenic dust and has the following characteristics: intact alveolar architecture, minimal supporting tissue reaction and potentially reversible effects. Collagenous pneumoconiosis, on the other hand, may be caused by fibrogenic dusts or an altered tissue response to a non-fibrogenic dust. It has the following characteristics: authenticated damage to alveolar architecture, appreciable supporting tissue reaction and permanent (irreversible) scarring of the lung. The following types of collagenous pneumoconiosis may occur following inhalation of dust: anthracosis (coal dust), silicosis (free silica particles in gold, tin, zinc, iron and coal mining, sand blasting, metal grinding, slate quarrying, granite, sandstone and pottery work), siderosis (iron particles), lithosis (stone particles), asbestosis (asbestos) and byssinosis (cotton). Specific aspects of these diseases are outlined below.

Coal worker's pneumoconiosis: This disease takes two forms, simple and complicated. Simple coal worker's pneumoconiosis is a relatively harmless condition. There are nodular lesions with little fibrosis. Emphysema, the abnormally distended condition of the lungs, is slight and there is little distortion of the lung architecture. This condition does not progress in the absence of further dust exposure. Neither does it regress, however.

Complicated coal worker's pneumoconiosis (progressive massive fibrosis) is a different matter, however. Dust collections are embedded in the diseased areas of fibrous tissue, and there is considerable distortion of lung architecture and elasticity producing interference with lung function. There is still considerable argument as to whether the simple form progresses to the complicated form or whether they are two separate disease entities.

Asbestosis: This is a fibrotic condition of the lung, resulting in scarring and thickening of the lung tissue, which may occur after many years of exposure to high concentrations of asbestos dust. The disease may manifest itself some years after occupational exposure has terminated. The risk of contracting asbestosis appears to be related to the duration and level of exposure to asbestos dust. The characteristic symptoms are a progressive breathlessness and unproductive cough. Lung damage takes the form of a diffuse fibrosis or scarring throughout the lungs accompanied by emphysema and collagenous thickening of the pleural lining. The skin may have a bluish discoloration due to cyanosis and sputum may contain asbestos bodies. Other features include the presence of pleural placques (small patches attached to the pleura and peritoneum), asbestos bodies in the lung tissue and asbestos warts on the hand where the fibres penetrate the skin. A characteristic feature is also finger clubbing, i.e. thickening of the fingers. Evidence so far suggests that asbestosis usually has a long induction period (10 to 20 years) and there is abundant evidence that those who smoke suffer both a greatly enhanced risk of contracting the disease and the prospect of a much worse overall lung condition. There is increasing confidence among researchers that a dose–response relationship exists between the amount of dust inhaled and the emergence of asbestosis.

Asbestosis, which is included in occupational disease D8, is prescribed in relation to

(a) the working or handling of asbestos or any admixture of asbestos; or
(b) the manufacture or repair of asbestos textiles or other articles containing or composed of asbestos; or
(c) the cleaning of any machinery or plant used in any of the foregoing operations and of any chambers, fixtures and appliances for the collection of asbestos dust; or
(d) substantial exposure to the dust arising from any of the foregoing operations (Social Security (Industrial Injuries) (Prescribed Diseases) Regulations 1985).

Research indicates that around 50 per cent of asbestosis sufferers develop lung cancer and/or cancer of the bronchus, and that smoking and asbestos act synergistically, thereby producing a far greater risk (some say more than 20 times) of bronchogenic lung cancer.

Mesothelioma, also included in occupational disease D8, is prescribed in relation to the same occupations as asbestosis. Moreover, bilateral diffuse pleural thickening has also been made a prescribed occupational disease (D9) in relation to the same occupations as asbestosis, both, as from 1 April 1985, entitling the sufferer to compensation under the Social Security (Industrial Injuries) (Prescribed Diseases) Regulations 1985.

Silicosis

This is a condition resulting in fibrosis of the lung. Nodular lesions are formed which ultimately destroy the lung structure. It is caused by the inhalation of respirable sized particles of free silica. There is a strong predisposition to tuberculosis as a result of contracting silicosis. Silica takes a number of forms in both the crystalline and the amorphous state:

(a) crystalline – tridymite, cristobalite, quartz;
(b) amorphous (after heating) – vitreous silica, diatomite, silica fume and dried silica gel.

Sources of silicosis are

(a) potteries, tile making – the drying out process produces silica dust;
(b) masonry industry – granite polishing, cutting, chipping, quarrying;
(c) furnaces – cutting of refractory bricks, stripping of furnaces;
(d) ceramics – manufacture of insulators;
(e) mining – coal-face working, coal washing;
(f) steel foundries – foundry sand, parting powders; and
(g) sand-blasting processes – use of sandstone wheels.

Byssinosis

This disease is predominantly associated with the textile industry. It is a chronic respiratory disease which progresses to bronchitis and emphysema. No physical change is noted in the lung before bronchitis develops. It is characterised by tightness of the chest and increased breathlessness and leads to respiratory disability. Typical is the 'Monday feeling' or 'Monday fever' which occurs when the individual has been away from cotton dust for some days and then returns.

Byssinosis is a response to a substance or substances found in cotton. It appears to occur either as a result of a direct action on the bronchi or broncheoles or through a histamine release mechanism. The severity of the pattern of symptoms is related to the actual tasks carried out by the individual. Textile manufacturing follows some ten or eleven different stages. 'Ginning', the coarse sorting of cotton balls from bracts, leaves and soil, is the first stage and it takes place overseas. Bales are opened by machine after which 'carding' takes place. Here the cotton is separated by a carding engine producing 'slub', a coarse, loosely wound rope of cotton fibres. 'Spinning' results in the strands becoming thinner as the fibres are pulled out. The strand is strengthened by 'twisting' and 'doubling' where more than one thread may be brought together. Workers involved in the early stages of the process, i.e. ginning, opening, carding and spinning, tend to contract byssinosis more than workers involved in the later stages, e.g. twisting, doubling, winding, beaming and weaving.

Symptoms are as follows:

Grade 0 – No chest tightness or difficulty in breathing.
Grade ½ – Occasional chest tightness or difficulty in breathing on the first day of a working week.
Grade 1 – Chest tightness or difficulty in breathing on the first day of every working week.
Grade 2 – Chest tightness or difficulty in breathing on the first and other days of every working week.
Grade 3 – Chest tightness or difficulty in breathing on the first and other days of every working week, accompanied by permanent incapacity with diminished effort tolerance or reduced ventilatory capacity.

It is necessary to distinguish between the term 'byssinosis' as defined above and that used for the purpose of assessing benefit under the Social Security (Industrial Injuries) (Prescribed Diseases) Regulations. For the latter purpose, the existence of Grade 2 or more would normally be expected in the absence of other complications.

Normally the condition does not progress after removal from exposure, except when emphysema has developed or chronic bronchitis is present. In the early stages the symptoms may remit or disappear.

Pressure

The most commonly encountered condition associated with exposure to pressure is the decompression sickness syndrome (prescribed disease A3).

Decompression sickness

Work in compressed air is undertaken during civil engineering excavations in water-bearing strata or under water, as well as in occupations involving diving. The work is effected either by single divers using diving suits or by a group of workers in a caisson or a diving bell. A caisson consists of a working chamber and shaft communicating at the surface with an air-lock. This, in turn, communicates with the outer air. Caissons are pressurised with cool compressed air from a pipeline. Within the caisson proper, in which the men work, and in the shaft, the air pressure must be equal to the pressure exerted by the water outside, and so must be raised in proportion to the depth at which the work is being carried out, i.e. raised approximately 1 atmosphere for each 10 metres of depth (see Diving Operations at Work Regulations 1981).

Decompression sickness is associated with the release within the blood and tissues, when the air pressure is reduced, of gases driven into solution when the air pressure was higher. The gases concerned are oxygen, carbon dioxide and nitrogen. Oxygen is removed very rapidly by reabsorption and carbon dioxide by exhalation from the lungs. Nitrogen, however, is relatively insoluble in the body fluids and collects as minute bubbles of gas which coalesce to form emboli. Nitrogen is, however, five or six times as soluble in fats and lipoids as in the body fluids, and tissues such as the nervous system and bone marrow hold proportionately more of the gas than others, releasing it in bulk when the pressure is dropped.

The symptoms of decompression sickness usually appear within the first few hours following decompression, but may not develop for 12 hours or longer. They depend, in general, on the location of the emboli formed, and may therefore simulate many other diseases. The most common symptom is pain in the limbs which when mild is known as the 'niggles' and when severe, the 'bends'. Generalised itching, vertigo, nausea, vomiting, epigastric pain and dyspnoea ('the chokes') may also occur at this stage. In some cases there is involvement of the central nervous system, and symptoms such as paralysis of the skeletal muscles or of the bladder may occur. Emboli in the blood vessels of the lungs, brain or heart may be fatal.

Electricity

Electric shock

This is the principal hazard and has been the cause of many fatalities. A number of factors affect the severity of electric shock. The actual harm depends on the current flowing through the body and particularly the heart. This is affected, however, by voltage, the resistance of the skin and internal organs (dry skin – high; organs – low), the type of current (a.c. or d.c.), the current pathway through the body, the duration of the current flow and the surface area of contact. The concept of 'let-go currents' is important here. *Let-go current* is defined as 'the maximum d.c. current a person can tolerate when holding an electrode and still let go using muscles stimulated by the shock'. Average let-go currents are 16.0 mA for men and 10.5 mA for women. A current of only 10 mA passing through the heart can have a serious effect on it depending on the duration of the flow. At higher currents, ventricular fibrillation (heart 'flutter') can set in, until at 100 mA cessation of the heart beat altogether is the likely result.

Other effects of electricity

Other bodily effects of electricity include burns, 'arc eye' and broken bones through muscular spasm.

The chemical causes

The effects on the body of exposure to chemical substances are many and varied. They can, however, be split into a number of well-defined areas to include the dermatoses, the various forms of poisoning, occupational cancers, the dust-borne diseases and gassing situations or gassing accidents.

Dermatoses

This group includes the range of skin conditions referred to as 'eczema', an inflammation of the skin. Dermatitis is by far the most common occupational disease, and prevention is largely aimed at or associated with improvements in personal hygiene. Only non-infective dermatitis is classified as a prescribed disease (D5), in relation to exposure to dust, liquid, vapour or other skin irritant (Social Security (Industrial Injuries) (Prescribed Diseases) Regulations 1985).

Most cases of dermatitis are either:

(a) endogenous – controlled by factors within the person, and mainly a matter of medical concern; or
(b) exogenous – controlled by factors from outside the person, which is very common and preventable.

With an endogenous dermatitis, withdrawal of the affected person from any future contact with the offending factor or agent may be the only solution. Most cases of occupational dermatitis are, however, exogenous in nature, being associated with contact with a specific factor or agent. Agents which produce the typical skin lesions can be classified thus:

(a) mechanical factors – friction, pressure and trauma;
(b) physical factors – heat, cold, electricity, sunlight, radiation;

(c) chemical agents – organic and inorganic substances;
(d) plants and their products, resins and lacquers; and
(e) other biological agents such as insects and mites.

Chemical agents are by far the greatest cause of occupational skin disorders, but the other factors mentioned above will be briefly commented upon.

Mechanical factors

These give rise to cuts, abrasions and skin lesions which may become secondarily infected.

Physical factors

Heat may affect the skin, causing excessive perspiration which softens the protective horny layers. When this is combined with frictional stress, a heat rash can develop. This is common in people working on hot processes, e.g. metal workers, furnacemen. Cold injuries to the skin include chilblains and, in extreme cases, frostbite. The secondary effects of burns at work should also be considered, together with possible exposure to ionising radiations.

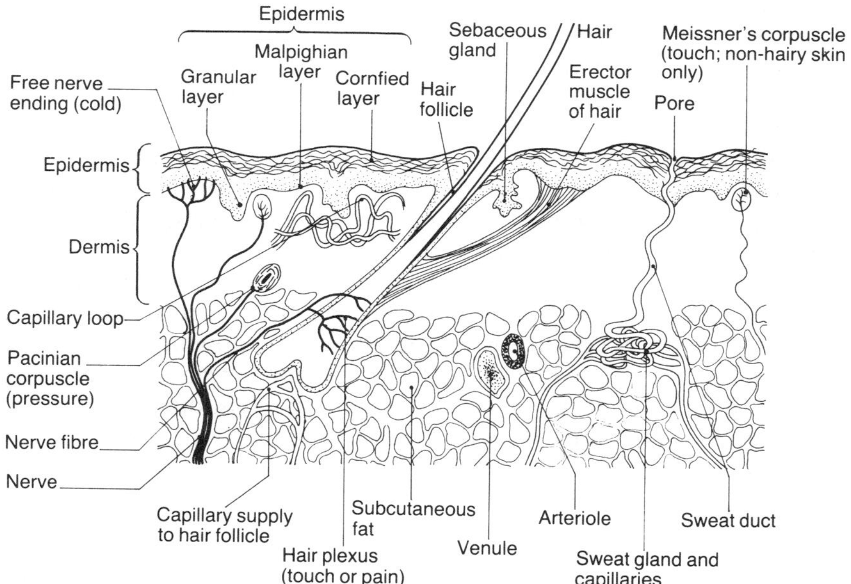

Fig. 19.3 Section through human skin

Chemical agents

The main defences of the skin against external irritants are the cornified layer of the epidermis (*see* Fig. 19.3) and the glandular secretions (sebum). The epidermis may, to some small extent, withstand the action of fairly strong acids, but it is particularly damaged by acids and sulphides. The glandular secretions normally form a fatty and slightly acid protective coating against water soluble irritants, but maceration of the epidermis, by friction, heat and excessive sweating may lead to an inflammatory response to external irritants. Similarly, the openings of the sebaceous glands and hair follicles provide entry for irritants, particularly when the irritant is fat soluble, and inflammatory changes may result. Oil folliculitis and chlor-acne are examples of such changes. The resistance of the skin to external irritants varies with age, sex, race, colour, diet and state of health.

Plants and their products

Certain plants can cause dermatitis by virtue of the chemical compounds contained within them, e.g. members of the *Liliaceae* and *Primulaceae*. There may be some degree of risk to nurserymen, gardeners and florists. Dermatitis from certain woods is common amongst carpenters, wood machinists and cabinet makers, the sawdust, sap, polishings or oil in the wood being the principal causative agents. Such woods usually produce a 'sensitivity' and a worker may become affected several days after beginning work with a new wood. Most of those affected become desensitised, but a small minority may remain sensitised, and will need medical treatment for the rash formed on the hands and arm. Where an employer either actually knew or ought to have known of the harmful properties of wood dust, an action against him will lie at the suit of the affected employee (*Ebbs* v. *James Whitson & Co. Ltd* [1952] 2 QB 877, where the action was unsuccessful).

In some cases more symptoms may be produced. For instance, *Gonioma kamassi*, known as Kamassi boxwood or African boxwood, causes systemic effects in susceptible individuals, owing to the liberation of an alkaloid which has effects similar to curare, i.e. languor, mental dullness and influenza-like symptoms. Skin disorders associated with occupations involving the manufacture of articles from *Gonioma kamassi* are prescribed occupational disease C16.

Other biological agents

Grain itch, barley itch, grocer's itch and copra itch are varieties of dermatitis caused by mites amongst workers involved in agriculture, in the handling of cargoes of grain or in agricultural mills. Scabies, commonly associated with bad hygiene in camps and similar settings, can be contracted by veterinary practitioners and animal breeders and handlers.

The causes of occupational dermatitis

The causes may be broadly divided into two groups of substances:

(a) Primary irritants will cause dermatitis at the site of contact if permitted to act for sufficient length of time in sufficient concentration, e.g. solvents, strong acids and alkalis. Some agents, such as fibreglass, can also cause dermatitis by straight mechanical (abrasive) action.
(b) Secondary sensitisers – e.g. plants, rubber, nickel and many chemical compounds – do not necessarily cause skin changes on first contact, but effect a specific sensitisation. If further contact occurs after 7 days or more, dermatitis will develop at the site of the second contact.

A primary irritant may also be a sensitiser in that an initial exposure may so condition the skin that subsequent exposures result in dermatitis.

Most cases of occupational dermatitis go through a number of distinct stages – redness of the skin, swelling, blistering, cracking, scaling and crusting. The principal causes are the use of poor or totally unsuitable hand-cleansing agents, such as paint stripper, paraffin, petrol and proprietary substances which defat the skin, thereby removing the normal defences provided by the cornified layer of the epidermis and the glandular secretions of the skin. Unrefined neat mineral cutting oils and certain coal tar derivatives have promoted dermatitis and can also cause skin cancer in the longer term. The backs of hands are invariably worse affected than the palms, due to the greater degree of softness. Dermatitis is also sometimes the first indication of an unsatisfactory degree of exposure to toxic materials.

Occupational cancers

A tumour or neoplasm (new growth) consists of a mass of cells which have undergone some fundamental and irreversible change in their physiology and structure which leads to a continuous and unrestrained proliferation. The word ‘tumour’ strictly means ‘lump’, but is often used to describe a solid neoplasm. Any cell type within the body can give rise to a neoplasm, although this occurs more frequently with some cell types than with others. Cells which do not undergo regeneration or replacement, nerve cells or voluntary muscle cells, are the ones least likely to give rise to tumours. The rate of growth of neoplasms varies greatly. Some may take many years to develop, whilst others may show an increase within a few days and extend far beyond their point of origin. The variation in growth behaviour and rate forms the basis of a broad classification of tumours into the benign and malignant classes. Benign tumours are those which grow slowly and less expansively, and unless they occur in some vital site, e.g. the brain, or interfere with an important organ, are well tolerated and do not necessarily interfere with a person's wellbeing or shorten his life. They are composed of well-differentiated and mature types of cells. The cells of the neoplasm resemble the cells of the original tissue. Malignant tumours, on the other hand, grow more rapidly, will infiltrate and extend into normal tissue and structures and, unless effectively treated, interfere with health and eventually cause death. They are often composed of more embryonic (primitive) or poorly differentiated cell types, resembling less the cells of origin. They spread by means of secondary deposits or 'metastases' to other sites in the body. (*See* comparison in Table 14.)

Table 14: Characteristics of tumours

Benign	*Malignant*
Remain localised	Can form secondary bodies – metastases
Slow growth	Rapid growth
Often encapsulated	Encapsulation rare and incomplete
Very similar to cells of origin	Less similar and, in some cases, totally undifferentiated
Cells of uniform size and appearance	Cells and nuclei vary in size and structure – nuclei often hyperchromatic
Degenerative changes relatively uncommon	Degenerative changes relatively common

There are three main ways in which tumours spread to form metastases – by the lymphatic system, through the bloodstream or through transcoelomic spread, i.e. from the pleural or peritoneal cavities.

Some cancer-promoting agents or 'carcinogens' have a 10–40-year latent period. This is the time between first exposure and the actual diagnosis of the tumour. This could mean that a new chemical substance introduced to industry, and which is later identified as a bladder carcinogen, may result in a tumour after, say, 12 years following the initial exposure (induction period). Even if the use of this compound were immediately prohibited, there would still be the problem of workers exposed during the 12-year period and there could be chemically induced tumours recorded up to 40 years after the last recorded exposure. This was the situation with β-naphthylamine.

Although exposure was prohibited many years ago, bladder cancer cases are still coming to light.

Classic examples of the carcinogens discovered in the last 65 years are shown in Table 15.

Table 15: Carcinogenic hazards discovered

Occupation	*Agent*	*Site*
Chimney sweeps Distillers of brown coal Makers of patent fuels Manufacturers of coal gas Road workers, boat builders and others exposed to tar and pitch Cotton mule spinners	Combustion products of coal, shale oil (polycyclic hydrocarbons)	Scrotum and other parts of skin; bronchus
Dye manufacturers, rubber workers, manufacturers of coal gas	α- and β-naphthylamine, benzidine and methylene bis-orthochloro-aniline (MBA)	Bladder
Radiologists, radiographers	Ionising radiation and X-rays	Skin
Chemical workers	4-aminodiphenol	Bladder
PVC manufacturers	Vinyl chloride monomer	Liver
Haematite miners	Radon	Bronchus
Asbestos workers, insulation workers, dock workers	Asbestos	Bronchus, pleura and peritoneum
Chromate workers	Chrome ore and pigments	Bronchus
Workers with glues and varnishes	Benzene	Marrow (myeloid and erythro-leukaemia)

Chemical poisoning

The effects on the body of exposure to chemical compounds are many and varied. Some of the more common chemical substances and their effects on humans are detailed below.

Lead

Lead is a microconstituent of many foodstuffs, and is normally found in human tissues and fluids in small amounts, although it is not thought to be an essential element. It may enter the body by inhalation of the fume or dust, by ingestion of contaminated food or through pervasion of the unbroken skin in the form of organic compounds such as tetra-ethyl lead. Exposure to lead or a lead compound is a prescribed occupational disease (C1).

When absorbed, lead rapidly becomes widely distributed. (Its degree of toxicity depends largely on the ratio between the rate of absorption and the rate of excretion.) When absorption is slow and continuous over a long period of time, the storage factor is significant. Lead is a cumulative poison which, in cases of chronic absorption, is deposited in the calcareous portion of the bones as an insoluble and harmless triple phosphate. In certain circumstances, lead may be released from the bones into the blood stream, producing symptoms similar to those of acute poisoning.

Many processes may result in lead poisoning, the most common being lead smelting, melting and burning; vitreous enamelling on glass and metal; the glazing of pottery; the manufacture of lead compounds, such as red and white lead, and lead colours; the manufacture of lead accumulators; shipbuilding and ship breaking; painting; plumbing and soldering operations, and the manufacture of rubber. (All these processes are controlled by specific Regulations, including the Control of Lead at Work Regulations 1980, together with the approved code of practice.)

Lead poisoning occurs in two distinct forms, namely by inorganic lead, and by lead in the organic form, mainly tetra-ethyl lead and tetra-methyl lead, tetra-ethyl lead being the more common. In acute cases, usually caused by exposure to fume, the initial symptoms are a sweetish taste in the mouth, especially on smoking, with anorexia, nausea, vomiting and headache, sometimes persistent constipation and intermittent colic. Acute poisoning is often fatal, although exposure may have been of only a few days' duration. In severe cases the effect on the nervous system is startling – restlessness, talkativeness, excitement, muscular twitchings accompanied by insomnia, delusions, hallucinations and even acute and violent mania. It is typically accompanied by a fall in blood pressure and body temperature.

In more chronic cases the classical symptoms and signs are headache, pallor, a blue line around the gums, anaemia, palsy (drop wrist) and encephalopathy, a form of mental disorder characterised by mental dullness, inability to concentrate, faulty memory, tremors, deafness, convulsion and coma. The great majority of lead-poisoning cases are, in fact, occasioned by inhalation of fume containing lead due to heating the metal, for various reasons, above a temperature of 500 °C.

Tetra-ethyl lead is volatile at room temperature. It is readily inhaled and, on absorption, exercises a focal effect on the central nervous system.

Mercury

Mercury and its compounds enter the body in dangerous amounts via the alimentary tract, through unbroken skin or mucous membranes, or by inhalation of the vapour or dust. Poisoning occurs commonly in the following occupations:

(a) mercury mining and the recovery of the metal from the ore;
(b) use of metallic mercury in the manufacture of thermometers, barometers and electric meters;
(c) associated mercury distillation processes;
(d) manufacture of salts of mercury;
(e) manufacture and use of organic compounds of mercury as fungicides in seed dressing;
(f) manufacture and use of disinfectants; and
(g) use as a carroting agent in the treatment of animal skins in the manufacture of fur felts.

Mercury poisoning is prescribed occupational disease C5.

Mercury is used in the form of metallic mercury and inorganic mercury compounds. Generally, mercury poisoning results from exposure to metallic mercury or the dust of its compounds. Chronic poisoning produces the characteristic tremors which are noticeable from a simple handwriting test, and drowsiness by day coupled with insomnia at night. Often there are symptoms similar to paranoia or persecution complex, which were very common in the hatting industry a century ago. (The Mad Hatter in *Alice in Wonderland* was not a figment of Lewis Carroll's imagination, but like real people commonly found in the hatting trade!)

There are important differences in the effects of exposure to metallic mercury and the different forms of mercurial compound. With metallic mercury, its oxides and inorganic salts, early symptoms include nausea, frequent headaches, tiredness and chronic diarrhoea. The characteristic features are stomatitis (inflammation of the mucous membranes of the mouth), muscular tremors and psychic disturbances. Effects on the mouth may vary from a mere metallic taste to salivation, bleeding of the gums, ulceration and loosening of the teeth. Muscular tremors appear early, often starting in the fingers and spreading to the tongue, lips, eyes and lower limbs. The psychic disturbance of mercurial erethism manifests itself in abnormal shyness and loss of confidence, coupled with irritability, vague fears and depression, often leading to loss of memory, hallucinations and deterioration of intellect. Metallic mercury has a dangerously high vapour pressure and tends to release dangerous levels of fume at normal room temperature. Most cases of inorganic mercury poisoning occur due to inhalation of the vapour in such circumstances.

In poisoning by methyl and ethyl (alkyl) organo-mercury compounds, the symptoms are more pronounced. Early stages may be no more than tiredness, followed by sensations of tingling or numbness in the fingers and toes. In the later stages, however, loss of co-ordination of movement (ataxia), tremors, difficulty in speaking clearly (dysarthria) and constriction of the visual field, in extreme cases amounting to 'tunnel vision', may occur.

Chromium

Chromium is a hard, steel-grey, brittle metal. It forms two series of salts, the trivalent and the hexavalent, the latter being of great industrial importance, for instance, in chromium plating. It also forms an acid oxide, chromium trioxide (chromic acid), from which chromates and dichromates are formed.

Chromium comes within the group of external irritants responsible for occupational dermatitis. The common symptom with chromium, however, is the formation of chromium ulcers or chromium holes on the hands and forearms due to direct contact. These are also common on the eyelids or, if chromium is inhaled, in the nostrils, and a hole can be formed right through the nasal septum. Chromic ulceration is included in prescribed occupational disease D5.

Chromic ulceration of the skin may be caused by chromic acid, the alkali chromates and dichromates, and zinc chromate. The penetration of these substances through a minute break in the skin may cause a raised hard lump which breaks down at the centre revealing a deep ulcer with rounded and thickened edges and a slough-covered base. (Slough is a portion of dead tissue cast off from living tissue.) The risk of contracting this form of occupational dermatitis is associated with the following uses of chromium:

(a) as metallic chromium in the formation of alloys; and
(b) as chromium compounds in chromium plating and anodising, in metal treatment processes, as tanning agents in the leather industry, in the impregnation of timber for preservation, as a constituent of anti-corrosion paints, as sensitisers in the photographic industry and in the manufacture of dyestuffs.

The benzene family

Included in this family are benzene (benzole), nitrobenzene and aniline. Benzene is produced from coal tar distillation and as a by-product of petrochemical processes. Until recently it was the starting point for many processes in the chemical industry, and was used in the manufacture of paints, plastics, lacquers, rubber and adhesives. Benzene has virtually been banned from industry and replaced by the safer toluene, but may still be found in research situations, where its use is strictly controlled. Toluene and xylene are structurally similar to benzene, but much less toxic than benzene in its pure state. The commercial forms, Toluol and Xylol, however, may contain significant concentrations of benzene and are thus rendered much more hazardous, and should be regarded as potential carcinogens. Benzene poisoning is prescribed occupational disease C7.

In acute poisoning cases where there may have been accidental exposure, the early symptoms include euphoria, giddiness, headache and vomiting. Unconsciousness and death from respiratory failure can follow. Chronic benzene poisoning has its principal effect on the bone marrow, leading to leukaemia, which can be delayed for some years after cessation of exposure. There are usually no symptoms in the early stages, but if any *are* present they tend to be vague and non-specific. The first symptoms are tiredness, mild gastro-intestinal disturbance and giddiness, followed by haemorrhages from mucous membranes and the development of skin rashes. Anaemia is commonly encountered and, in serious cases, leukaemia may develop.

Xylene and toluene are metabolised in a similar way to benzene. They have narcotic properties and produce symptoms ranging from drowsiness, fatigue and headache, to unconsciousness and death. Toluene is less powerful a narcotic than benzene.

Nitrobenzene is used in perfumery and in the manufacture of aniline, and is readily absorbed through the skin. Aniline is used in the rubber industry, in dyeing and in resin extraction. Contact may be through inhalation of aniline-contaminated dust or aniline fumes, together with absorption through the skin.

Trichlorethylene and other chlorinated hydrocarbons

Within this group are included carbon tetrachloride, methyl chloride, tetrachlorethane, methyl bromide and perchlorethylene, all solvents with varying degrees of toxicity.

Trichlorethylene, commonly known as 'Trike', 'Triklone' and 'Trilene', has widespread use, either in the pure state as an anaesthetic or mixed with other solvents. Its main uses are as a degreasing agent for metals, as a dry-cleaning agent and as a refrigerant. Inhalation can produce drowsiness, giddiness, unconsciousness and death. If the fumes are drawn through the lighted tip of a cigarette, the danger is greatly increased due to the formation of acidic products, including phosgene.

Carbon tetrachloride has similar properties to trichlorethylene. It is used as a fat and rubber solvent and in dry cleaning, but principally as a refrigerant, where it is used in the manufacture of 'Freon' (trade name of a group of ICI fluorocarbons). As with other solvents, the main hazard is from the vapour. This solvent should only be used in a well-ventilated room.

Carbon tetrachloride has a narcotic effect which produces unconsciousness. This may be preceded by signs of central nervous disturbance. Nowadays, severe cases are rare; the symptoms are predominantly those of liver or renal damage, the renal symptoms being more evident. Initially the patient will complain of persistent headaches, nausea and vomiting, colic and diarrhoea, and hepatic tenderness. Renal and hepatic damage appear after a variable latent period.

Tetrachlorethane is one of the most toxic chlorinated hydrocarbons. It is between eight and ten times more toxic than carbon tetrachloride and four times as toxic as chloroform, with a smell similar to that of chloroform. The vapour constitutes the main hazard, and it should only be used where the ventilation is adequate. Tetrachlorethane principally affects the liver and central nervous system. The effects on the liver, or hepatic syndrome, occur in four specific stages, commencing with persistent headache, lassitude, anorexia and vomiting. There may be an unpleasant taste in the mouth, together with stomach pain. Then follows the jaundice stage, closely followed by the typical toxaemic stage, with enlargement of the liver and deepening jaundice. Vomiting is severe and there may be signs of liver damage. There may be delirium, stupor, rashes and oedema. In the final stage of the disease the patient may develop ascites – a swelling of the abdomen due to fluid exuded from the blood vessels – but he may die before reaching this stage. Tetrachlorethane poisoning is prescribed occupational disease C10.

The neurological symptoms of tetrachlorethane poisoning include numbness and tingling of the fingers and toes. There may be tremor and twitching of the face muscles. At a later stage, power in the hands and feet is lost and this weakness can spread to the rest of the body.

Tetrachlorethane has many industrial uses as a general purpose solvent, and as an intermediary in the manufacture of tetrachlorethylene and trichlorethylene.

Methyl bromide is an extremely volatile liquid in gaseous form at a temperature above 4.5 °C. It is used as a refrigerant, insecticide and fumigant. Past occupational exposures have largely been associated with leakage of the gas from pipework and storage vessels where, because of its high volatility, even a minute crack or pin hole will permit large quantities of the gas to be liberated. Methyl bromide poisoning is prescribed occupational disease C12.

Whilst methyl bromide is highly toxic, there is a latent period of up to 48 hours before bodily symptoms are apparent. After the latent period initial effects are irritation of the respiratory tract, followed by nausea, vomiting, headache, cough, watering of the eyes and abdominal pain. Vision becomes blurred, then double vision occurs. At this stage an affected person will appear drunk, with a staggering walk, slurred speech and loss of balance. In severe cases, pulmonary oedema, an excess of tissue fluid, may be present, together with convulsions.

The symptoms are directly related to the length of exposure and the concentration of the gas.

Direct splashing onto the skin of methyl bromide results initially in a tingling sensation followed by burning. The skin becomes inflamed and, after several hours, small vesicles (blisters) appear. The vesicles become distended with straw-coloured fluid but, if punctured, they do not refill. Healing takes place after a few days. If the degree of exposure is insufficient to produce vesicles, a form of dry eczema may be produced.

Methyl chloride is less toxic than methyl bromide, but has a greater narcotic action. It is used as a refrigerant, in the manufacture of chloroform and in the dyestuffs industry. Typical poisoning symptoms are similar to those of methyl bromide, but there are several important differences. Ocular symptoms are more frequent a day or so following exposure, but symptoms such as headache and dizziness follow immediately upon exposure. Anorexia and vomiting are common within 24 hours. Generally, mild cases recover, but this may take 6–9 months, depending on the duration of exposure and the concentration of the gas.

Isocyanates

A range of isocyanates is used in industry, principally in the manufacture of urethane foams and resins, for instance toluene di-isocyanate (TDI) and methylene bisphenyl di-isocyanate (MDI). TDI is an extremely volatile compound and should only be used under closely controlled conditions in an enclosed system or with well-controlled ventilation. The vapour can be evolved during the manufacture of foams, and also during cutting of the finished product with a hot wire. A dust hazard may arise from the use of 1:5 napthalene di-isocyanate (NDI) which is sometimes used in powder form. In the latter case there is a potential hazard from the spray when NDI in solid form is being sprayed with polyurethane lacquers. This practice is common in the furniture and allied industries. The spraying of urethane foams is a particularly hazardous operation which requires a high degree of environmental and personal protection.

TDI is the most volatile of the isocyanates and one of the most toxic. Symptoms are usually reduced when the patient is removed from contact, but a severe respiratory reaction, as with MDI, may follow on second or subsequent exposures, even if the exposure is to extremely low concentrations of the vapour. Vapour pressure, i.e. the percentage gas by volume in air, is particularly important in controlling the hazards associated with isocyanates. Vapour pressure increases very rapidly with temperature (see Fig. 19.4).

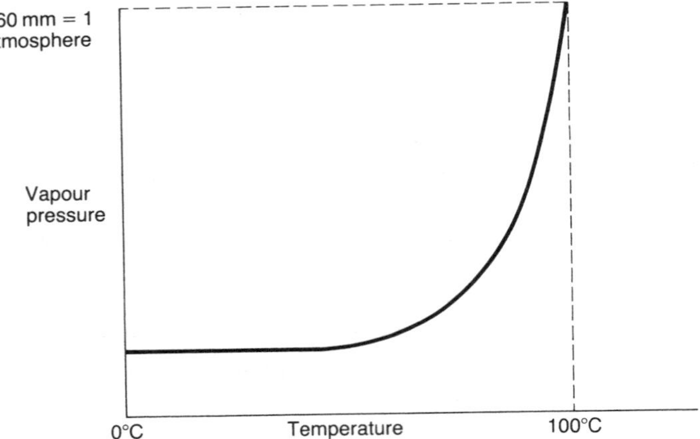

Fig. 19.4 The relationship between vapour pressure and temperature

The degree of volatility of a vapour affects the degree of inhalation and therefore the risk associated with a particular substance. The vapour pressure of a liquid at room temperature can be estimated from the boiling point, i.e. the temperature at which the vapour pressure equals the pressure of the atmosphere; the lower the boiling point, the greater the vapour pressure at room temperature. (7.6 mm mercury vapour pressure, 10,000 ppm or 1 per cent concentration is the concentration at which most solvents will produce narcosis. All solvents have a greater vapour pressure than 7.6 mm of mercury.) TDI has a vapour pressure at 25 °C of 0.025 mm of mercury, and is very volatile. MDI has a vapour pressure of 0.00009 mm of mercury.

Most isocyanates can produce varying degrees of dermatitis, and exposure can result in skin sensitisation effects in rare cases. The main consideration, however, is that isocyanates are a potent primary irritant to the respiratory tract and, in some cases, cause dramatic sensitisation, i.e. asthmatic effects once an individual has become sensitised. Eye splashes may cause severe chemical conjunctivitis. Handling in open vessels should, therefore, be prohibited, any transference being undertaken in fully enclosed systems. Spillages should be cleared up immediately and decontaminants should be readily available, e.g. 5 per cent ammonia in sawdust. Health supervision should include pre-employment and routine periodic health examinations for all operators and other staff coming into contact with isocyanates. Asthma due to exposure to (*inter alia*) isocyanates is prescribed occupational disease D7(a).

Alcohols

Any of the simple alcohols, e.g. amyl, ethyl, butyl, methyl and propyl alcohols, will produce intoxication if an excess of vapour is inhaled. In rare cases, contact can cause temporary or even permanent blindness. Where an alcohol is combined with chlorine, a highly poisonous solvent can be formed, e.g. ethylene chlorohydrin, a solvent used in lacquers. Where poisoning has occurred, the symptoms of vomiting, headache, shortage of breath and unconsciousness may precede death, with evidence of damage to internal organs. In most cases, poisoning takes place through inhalation or absorption through the skin.

Acetates

The principal acetates used in industry are ethyl, methyl and amyl acetate. They are closely related to solvents and are highly flammable. There is little toxic risk, exposure typically causing running eyes and smarting.

Ethers

Diethyl ether is a commonly used industrial solvent. Toxic effects are usually limited to loss of consciousness and, in most cases of exposure, a good recovery is made. Diethyl ether is highly flammable. Diethylene dioxide, or 'Dioxan', another member of the ether family, is both poisonous and highly flammable. It may be inhaled as a vapour or absorbed through the skin.

Carbon disulphide

This is an extremely toxic solvent with one of the lowest flashpoints. It can be ignited by the heat from a radiator or an electric light bulb. It is used extensively in the production of rayon and paper. As with other solvents, bodily effects rest on the degree and length of exposure. Symptoms include headache, fainting, vomiting, breathlessness, hallucinations, degrees of blindness and mental disorders. Death commonly follows cases of severe exposure.

Carbon monoxide

This gas is produced as a result of combustion. It causes death by poisoning due to its ability to deprive the body tissues of oxygen. Its propensity to combine with the haemoglobin in the blood is at least 200 times greater than that of oxygen, and the victim of carbon monoxide gassing dies from asphyxiation.

Cyanides

The use of cyanide-based substances has been reduced considerably in the last two decades. Cyanides are used in heat treatment and electroplating processes. Cyanide is renowned for the fact that it kills swiftly through inhalation of cyanide fume, ingestion of cyanide contaminated food or absorption through the skin. Contact between cyanides and other substances, notably acids, causes the evolution of hydrocyanic acid which is lethal.

Arsenic

Arsenic poisoning in industry occurs in two distinct forms, with totally different symptoms. The first form, an acute and serious type, arises from inhalation of arseniuretted hydrogen (arsine) gas. The second, which is the more common and chronic type, results from absorption into the body, usually by inhalation over a long period, of dusts of arsenical compounds.

Arsine is produced when nascent hydrogen is accidentally released in the presence of arsenic. This type of accident can occur wherever dilute sulphuric or hydrochloric acids are used in the processing of ores or residues, while 'pickling' (acid cleaning of metals), while clearing acid tanks of sludge, or in the manufacture of electric accumulators. Arsine can be produced accidentally in laboratories. Solid arsenical compounds are encountered in smelting and other industrial processes. More commonly, they are used as weed killers and insecticides, in the preservation of hides, skins and furs, and in glass making.

With arsenic poisoning, 25–30 per cent of all cases die in a relatively short period of time. Mild cases, after a latent period of several hours to a day or more, show varying degrees of nausea, headache, shivering, exhaustion, giddiness, stomach pain and vomiting, all of which are of sudden onset. In more severe cases, the latent period may be reduced to 6 hours or less, after which haemoglobinuria appears. Within 24 hours, jaundice develops followed by anaemia and severe kidney damage. If treatment is not rapid, the patient drifts into a 'typhoid' state with death from anuria.

Poisoning from solid compounds is usually through inhalation of the dust. There may also be local irritation of the mucous membranes of the nose and mouth together with skin inflammation and ulceration, resulting in localised dermatitis, conjunctivitis and ulceration of the nasal septum.

Phosphorus

This element occurs as either red phosphorus or yellow (white) phosphorus. Red phosphorus is relatively non-toxic, being used in the manufacture of safety matches, and as a starting point for other preparations. Yellow phosphorus is a waxy solid which ignites spontaneously on contact with air, emitting poisonous fumes. The handling of yellow phosphorus can cause severe burns. Yellow phosphorus was once widely used in the manufacture of matches, but the practice was banned in 1906 owing to the necrotic condition of the jaw bone or mandible ('phossy jaw') produced in workers dipping matches. Yellow phosphorus has limited industrial use as a rodenticide and in the production of non-ferrous alloys. The chronic poisoning, typified by phossy jaw, is now rarely encountered, but there is a need to consider the results of acute poisoning. This follows the ingestion of yellow phosphorus, where the symptoms are delayed. The main symptoms are abdominal pain, vomiting, depression and general weakness followed, after an interval of days or weeks, by toxic jaundice and possibly haemorrhages of the mucous membranes. In fatal cases, the principal cause of death is atrophy, i.e. wastage and shrinking, of the liver.

Phosphine, a gas with the odour of decaying fish, may be evolved during the preparation and use of calcium phosphide, in the manufacture of acetylene from impure calcium carbide and when zinc phosphide, a grain fumigant constituent, is accidentally wetted. Quenching metal alloys with water may also produce the gas, as may the manufacture of certain forms of graphite.

Symptoms of phosphine poisoning include abdominal pain, nausea and vomiting. Ataxia (loss of muscle co-ordination), convulsions, coma and death may follow within 24 hours. In milder cases, the gas may produce some degree of respiratory irritation but recovery could be complete. Chronic poisoning, with resulting effects on the central nervous system, may occur in persons regularly exposed to low concentrations of phosphine.

Organo-phosphorus compounds are being used increasingly as insecticides. The principal route of entry is through the skin with minor local irritation, but entry may also be through inhalation and ingestion. The effect of these chemical substances is to inhibit the action of the enzyme cholinesterase present in red blood cells and motor nerve end plates. The action is cumulative and a toxic concentration may be built up by repeated slight exposure. Early symptoms of organo-phosphorus poisoning are non-specific, but may include anorexia and nausea (the latter characteristically increased by taking food and smoking), giddiness, drowsiness, diarrhoea and fatigue. Within a few hours, muscular twitchings, cramps, incontinence, coma, convulsions, paralyses and signs of pulmonary oedema may develop. The severity of symptoms is directly related to the dose.

The biological causes

Several occupational diseases are transmissible from animal to Man. These are the 'zoonoses' and include such diseases as anthrax, leptospirosis, orf (contagious pustular dermatitis), glanders fever and brucellosis. Whilst the incidence of such diseases is low, there is always some degree of risk to anyone working with animals, especially veterinary surgeons, meat inspectors, pet shop workers, people working in zoos, artificial inseminators and farmers. Anthrax, glanders, leptospirosis and brucellosis are all prescribed occupational diseases (B1, B7, B3 and B2).

Anthrax

This is a disease which may occur in Man and certain animals, e.g. cattle and sheep, as a result of infection by *Bacillus anthracis*, a spore-forming organism which, although killed by boiling for 10 minutes, may survive for years in the soil and in animal remains. Cattle are the main source of the infection, and infection in Man may occur through contact with fresh infective material containing the bacillus; people at risk include agricultural workers, veterinary surgeons, knackers, slaughtermen, and those working with dried animal products such as hides, skins, hair, wool, hooves, bone-meal and contaminated implements. Infection in Man may be of the cutaneous type (malignant pustule) or internal, e.g. the pulmonary form (wool sorter's disease). The disease manifests itself in almost every case as a grave toxaemia, with headache, shivering, muscle and joint pains, nausea, vomiting and collapse, together with additional symptoms depending on the site and type of infection.

Malignant pustule is the more common form of anthrax. Infection takes place through cuts and abrasions on the skin. After an incubation period of 1–4 days an irritant pimple develops. The pimple rapidly enlarges and breaks down with a black necrotic centre. The lesion may be ringed with small vesicles and inflammatory swelling. Local lymph nodes may be slightly enlarged. In 90 per cent of cases the pustule is situated on some exposed part of the body such as the face or neck, and in such cases the intense oedema may be fatal.

Internal anthrax takes place through ingestion or inhalation of the bacilli. In these cases, even more than in external cases, the general intense toxaemia, with sudden vertigo, somnolence, dyspnoea (difficulty in breathing), croup and marked prostration, is prevalent, and death may ensue. In typical pulmonary cases there is widespread congestion and oedema or an atypical pneumonia with frothy blood-stained sputum. If untreated, death occurs from septicaemia in the first few days.

Glanders fever

Glanders fever or 'farcy' is a disease of horses, mules and donkeys. The infecting organism is *Bacillus mallei* or *Pfeifferella mallei*. Infection in Man is now rare, but is always caused by contact with an infected animal. The disease occurs in both acute and chronic forms. In the acute form there is an incubation period of 2 to 3 days before general malaise is experienced, together with headaches, anorexia and joint pains. The site of infection becomes ulcerated and there is marked lymphangitis (inflammation of the lymph vessels). Nodular abscesses form along the lymphatic vessels and these break down to form painful ulcers. There is a marked fever, highest between the sixth and twelfth days, after which time eruptions appear on the face and on the nasal, palatal and pharyngeal mucosae. The lesions typically begin as patches which eventually enlarge and form pustules. The pustules ulcerate with the destruction of bone and cartilage or produce a thick blood-stained purulent discharge. A form of arthritis may also occur with the development of abscesses in the muscles.

The chronic form is more rare than the acute form, but is again characterised by the formation of abscesses, which break down to form painful ulcers. The lungs may be involved in terms of pneumonia, pleural effusion, lung abscesses and empyema (a collection of pus in a natural body cavity, e.g. in the space between the lung and outer wall of the chest). The disease runs a long course and an acute phase may supervene at any time.

Leptospirosis

This disease is also known as 'leptospiral jaundice', 'spirochaetal jaundice', 'spirochaetosis icterohaemorrhagica' and 'Weil's disease'. It is a feverish condition caused by the organism *Leptospira icterohaemorrhagica*, commonly found in rats, which are the source of human infection. Infection may be due to ingestion of food or water contaminated with the urine of infected rats; alternatively, it may enter the skin or through the mucous membranes of the eyes, nose and mouth. The disease sometimes occurs amongst men who work in rat-infested locations such as mines, slaughterhouses and fish docks.

After an incubation period of 6–12 days there is an abrupt onset of high fever, rigors, headache, muscular pain and vomiting, accompanied by prostration. At this time, the leptospires multiply in the blood and may be carried to and affect any organ. Conjunctival haemorrhages are common together with a body rash, often accompanied by petechial (pin-point sized) haemorrhages in the skin. There may be mild liver damage and jaundice is common 2–5 days after onset of the fever. There is usually a steady improvement after the second week of the illness and mild cases recover completely without specific treatment. Fatalities are rare.

Brucellosis

Brucellosis in Man is caused by contact with infected animals. Three species of the organism account for most human disease. These species show an affinity for particular animal hosts, so that *Brucella abortus* is found in cattle, *Brucella melitensis* in sheep and goats, and *Brucella suis* in pigs. The disease may be contracted by persons working in slaughterhouses or among those handling meat, meat products or the by-products and waste from slaughtering. Veterinary surgeons and meat inspectors are an outstanding high-risk group.

The routes of infection can be through inhalation, ingestion and direct contact with infected material, e.g. the uterus of an infected animal, direct contact being the most important. In the latter case, this occurs usually through handling the placenta or foetal parts during the delivery of a calf or in post mortem examinations. The organism gains access through cuts and abrasions in the skin or through the mucous membranes, including the conjunctivae.

Brucellosis takes two forms, the acute attack and the chronic condition. In acute cases, onset may be gradual with non-specific signs such as headache, joint pains, fever, insomnia and low back pain, or it may be abrupt with fever, rigors and prostration. Usually the disease subsides within 2 weeks and the patient makes a complete recovery. Some patients will continue, however, to have intermittent bouts of fever, back pain, a feeling of lethargy and depression which may last for several months or years.

Chronic brucellosis has all the symptoms of an acute attack, i.e. lassitude, malaise, joint pains and prolonged depression. There is not always a history of an acute attack and, in many cases, the occupation of the patient may be the only clue in diagnosis, e.g. a stockman on a farm. In chronic brucellosis there may be complications including endocarditis (inflammation of the heart lining) and spondylitis (inflammation of the vertebrae).

Q Fever

This is an infection caused by an organism, *Rickettsia burneti*. The infection is found most frequently in farm workers who contract the disease from sheep and cows by the inhalation of infected dust or by drinking infected raw milk. Veterinary surgeons, meat inspectors and abattoir workers are particularly high-risk groups in this case. The symptoms are very similar to those of influenza and it is common for cases of Q fever to be diagnosed as such. Typically, the illness begins with fever accompanied by shivering, sweating and backache, inflammation of the throat and suffused conjunctivae. In many cases, the patient has an unproductive cough, photophobia and muscular pains.

Orf (contagious pustular dermatitis)

Orf is a viral infection of sheep and goats which is transmitted occasionally to abattoir workers and animal handlers. The disease takes the form of a mild skin rash occurring at the site of infection. Clinical signs appear 4–12 days after infection, with the development of a red macule (a spot level with the surface of the surrounding skin) or papule (a raised spot on the surface of the skin). This enlarges until it becomes 1–4 cm in diameter containing first clear fluid and then pus. There may be some local tenderness and lymphadenitis (inflammation of the lymph nodes), and the lesion is sometimes painful. Healing is usually complete within 4–6 weeks.

Viral hepatitis

Hepatitis (inflammation of the liver) is most commonly ascribed to various infections. Hepatitis B (serum hepatitis) occurs more frequently amongst members of the medical and allied professions than among the general public, the risk being greatest among those who handle blood or blood products, and who work in renal dialysis units. The symptoms of the disease include malaise, myalgia (muscle pain), headache, nausea, vomiting, anorexia, abdominal pain and pruritis (itching). The patient becomes jaundiced and the liver is enlarged. Generally the disease runs a mild course, although some cases may turn to chronic hepatitis.

Hepatitis A, on the other hand, is a form of epidemic jaundice spread through human contact or through contaminated food and water supplies. Viral hepatitis is prescribed occupational disease B8.

Aspergillosis (farmer's lung)

Exposure to the dust of mouldy hay or other mouldy vegetable produce can result in pulmonary disease. It is characterised, along with many other similar conditions such as mushroom picker's lung and malt worker's lung, by an influenza-like illness, during which the person feels generally unwell, has pain in the limbs and is feverish. The patient will also have a dry cough and dyspnoea. Farmer's lung is one form of extrinsic allergic alveolitis, an inflammatory condition of the lung tissue associated with hypersensitivity to the spores of mouldy hay. It is usually a transitory condition where the symptoms abate after 3–4 days. It is prescribed occupational disease B6.

The ergonomic causes

A number of occupational conditions are associated with repetitive job movements, e.g. cramp, or with friction and pressure on limbs and joints. Whilst they have not attracted great attention from the medical world, they are of significance in any consideration of occupational conditions.

Cramp

This disability, known as 'writer's cramp', 'twister's cramp', 'occupational cramp' or 'craft palsy', is characterised by attacks of spasm, tremor and pain in the hand or forearm caused by attempts to perform a familiar act involving frequently repeated muscular action. Muscular co-ordination necessary for the performance of the repetitive movements breaks down and the continuation of the movements becomes impossible. The causative factors in this condition are unknown, but may be attributed to a combination of physical fatigue of muscles and nerves and an underlying psychoneurosis. It is prescribed occupational disease A4.

Beat hand

Referred to as 'subcutaneous cellulitis of the hand', this condition or disability, prescribed occupational disease A5, is the result primarily of the bruising of the skin and the underlying tissues and the implantation there, by friction or pressure, of 'dirt' and particles. The condition is liable to follow frequent jarring of the hand in the use of pick and shovel, and is more likely to occur in wet conditions. It is principally found in the hand of people unaccustomed to manual labour or who have been away from such activity for a long time. When accompanied by local infection, it may become acutely disabling. This condition is encountered in the palm of the hand and takes the form of, first, an acute inflammation, followed in many cases by a suppurative condition, i.e. broken skin and the presence of pus, due to infection.

Beat knee

Officially described as 'bursitis or subcutaneous cellulitis arising at or about the knee due to severe or prolonged external friction or pressure at or about the knee', this condition, prescribed occupational disease A6, is similar in aetiology to beat hand. It occurs in those unaccustomed to working in a kneeling position or on returning to such work after a prolonged absence, and is more likely to occur if the skin is wet and sodden. Repeated or lengthy pressure, together with regular pivotting on the knee, as in the case of roof tilers or carpet fitters who persistently kneel, is a potential cause.

Cellulitis of the skin generally proceeds to the suppuration stage and may involve the bursa of the knee. In bursitis, the enlargement of the knee joint may be due to acute effusion (leakage of fluid into a body cavity) or to infection of a chronic enlargement. Depending on the severity of the condition, incapacity may last only a few weeks or surgery may be necessary to remedy the condition.

Beat elbow

This condition is similar in aetiology to beat hand and beat knee, but with the elbow a single, although perhaps sustained, injury during work is more easily identified as the cause. Here again there are the classical signs of acute inflammation. The elbow is swollen and painful, signs of deep inflammation set in, and the swelling rapidly extends down the back of the forearm. The prognosis, as with other 'beat' conditions, depends on the degree of severity of the condition.

20

Occupational health practice

Occupational health is essentially a branch of preventive medicine which examines the relationship between work and health and the effects of work on the worker. Occupational health practitioners include the occupational health nurse, occupational physician, occupational hygienist, the health and safety specialist and the trained first aider, all of whom have a specific contribution to make in the provision and maintenance of healthy conditions at work. The principal areas of occupational health practice are outlined below.

Placing people in suitable work

As industry becomes more sophisticated it is of vital significance that workers should be physically and mentally suited for the tasks they are required to undertake. The pre-employment medical examination for restricted groups of people has been common practice for many years, but over the last quarter of a century the more prudent employer has extended this form of examination to all grades of staff. In many cases the examination is undertaken by a registered medical practitioner paid on a retainer basis, or by an appointed factory doctor. However, in recent years the concept of health screening by a trained occupational health nurse has found favour with many organisations, and such a pre-employment health screen for prospective employees is a standard feature of their recruitment policies. This is particularly appropriate in the food and catering industries where not only the health of the worker is important but the potential for his contaminating the product must be given considerable prominence.

Pre-employment screening activities now include not only an assessment of general fitness for the job but specific aspects of it such as vision screening of drivers, VDU operators and people engaged in fine assembly work, the assessment of disability levels where heavy work is involved, certain tests for suitability as food handlers and aptitude testing for a wide range of tasks.

Health surveillance

Health surveillance concentrates on two main groups of workers:

(a) those at risk of developing further ill-health or disability by virtue of their present state of health, e.g. people exposed to excessive noise levels; and
(b) those actually or potentially at risk by virtue of the type of work they undertake during their employment, e.g. radiation workers.

Health surveillance of such groups usually takes the form of on-going health examinations at predetermined intervals of, say, 6 months or 12 months according to the degree of risk involved. Such a system allows for early detection of evidence of occupational disease and for its early treatment.

Providing a treatment service

This activity has for many years been the principal function of some occupational health services. However, with the greater emphasis on prevention, there has been a tendency to reduce the importance of this activity. Nevertheless, the efficient and speedy treatment of injuries, acute poisonings and minor ailments is important because it prevents complications and aids rehabilitation. Such a service does have an important role to play in keeping people at work, thereby reducing lost time associated with attendance at casualty departments or doctors' surgeries.

Yet another important feature of a treatment service is that of detecting trends in accidents and injuries, with a view to improving preventive measures, and assisting injured persons, through counselling, in their rehabilitation after an accident. A joint approach between occupational health practitioners and safety practitioners can be effective here.

Primary and secondary monitoring

Primary monitoring is concerned largely with the clinical observation of sick people who may seek treatment or advice on their condition. Such observation will identify new risks which were previously not considered. For instance, there may be a sudden increase in the number of workers reporting signs of dermatitis, which could subsequently, through investigation, indicate the total unsuitability of a new adhesive or similar solvent-based product being used for the first time.

Secondary monitoring, on the other hand, is directed at controlling the hazards to health which have already been recognised. Audiometry is a classic form of secondary monitoring whereby the hearing levels of workers are tested on a 6-monthly or annual basis to assess whether there has been any further hearing loss due to exposure to noise. Similar secondary monitoring may be carried out for workers using vibratory hand tools in order to assess early stages of vibration-induced white finger.

Avoiding potential risks

This is an important feature of occupational health practice with the principal emphasis on prevention, in preference to treatment, for a known condition. The occupational health practitioner can make a significant contribution to the planning and design of work layouts, and to considering the ergonomic aspects of jobs and the potential for fatigue amongst workers. The effects of shift working, long hours of work and the physical and mental effects of repetitive tasks would be taken into account in any assessment of risks involved.

Supervision of vulnerable groups

There is no doubt that certain groups are more vulnerable to accidents and occupational disease than others. Included in this grouping of 'vulnerable' workers are young persons, the aged, the disabled and people generally who may have long periods of health-related absence. Special attention must be given to such persons in terms of counselling on a wide range of matters, assistance with rehabilitation in the workplace and, possibly, assistance in the reorganisation of their tasks to remove harmful factors. Routine health examinations to assess their continuing fitness for work should be a standard feature here.

Monitoring for early evidence of non-occupational disease

Many industries are associated with specific occupational diseases. For instance, the pottery industry has long been associated with silicosis, the mining industry with coal worker's pneumoconiosis and the cotton industry with byssinosis. Whilst improvements in environmental working conditions have greatly reduced the incidence of such diseases, routine monitoring of workers not exposed to such conditions is an important feature of occupational health practice. Here the principal objective is that of controlling diseases prevalent in industrial populations with a view to their eventual eradication. Such monitoring also makes a great contribution to the control of the stress-related diseases and conditions such as mental illness and heart disease.

Counselling

Counselling, carried out by a trained occupational physician or occupational health nurse is, perhaps, the most significant component of occupational health practice. This may take two forms, viz. counselling on health-related matters and counselling on personal, social and emotional problems. There is no doubt that, in the second case, many people would benefit from a sound counselling session with an occupational health nurse. Most people, at some time in their lives, have social and emotional problems. In many cases, for a variety of reasons, they are unable or unwilling to consult their spouse or their family or general practitioner and, over a period of time, develop a high state of stress. This results in an inability to concentrate for long periods, fatigue, frustration and absence from work. It may be associated with an inability to cope with problems or, perhaps, a feeling of injustice brought about by certain events. The availability of a sympathetic ear, independent of organisational controls, can assist the individual to come to terms with such problems more easily.

Health education

This is a particularly broad area of occupational health practice. It is primarily concerned with the education of employees towards healthier modes of living, but can also include training of management and staff in their respective responsibilities for health and safety at work, in healthy working techniques and in the avoidance of health hazards. In the food industry, where the purity of the product is of utmost significance, it can include the training of production staff and catering staff in food hygiene. It can incorporate feedback from other areas of occupational health practice, such as the reasons for certain aspects of health surveillance or the reinforcement of the need for the wearing of personal protective equipment.

Clearly, any health education, as with other areas of education, must be related to the health risks present and must be directed at bringing about an improvement in attitudes in individual areas of health care.

First aid and emergency services

Included in this area are the supervision of first aid facilities and ancillary equipment such as emergency showers, eye wash stations and emergency breathing apparatus, together with the preparation of contingency plans to cover major disasters such as fire, explosion or gassing accidents. This would entail the training of first aiders, rescue staff and key members of the management team in preparation for such disasters.

Welfare amenity provisions

Occupational health practice can include procedures for advising management on legal requirements for sanitation, hand-washing facilities, showers, arrangements for storing and drying clothing and the provision of drinking water. Routine surveillance of such installations and other amenities such as kitchens, canteens, rest rooms and day nurseries feature strongly in the maintenance of sound health standards.

Environmental control and occupational hygiene

Control of the working environment and the environment outside the workplace are important components of occupational health and hygiene practice. The employer must provide a safe working environment by recognition, measurement, evaluation and control of long-term health hazards. He must also ensure that he does not expose people living in the vicinity of the workplace to health risks or public health nuisances from pollution of the air, land, water, drainage system, watercourse or surrounding land.

Liaison

Staff of occupational health services liaise with a wide range of enforcement officers, such as medical and nursing advisers of the Medical Branch of the HSE, Factories Inspectors, environmental health officers, planning officers and staff of the Area Health Authority.

The importance of the relationship between members of the occupational health team and general medical practitioners must not be overlooked in planning and implementing any programme of health supervision and care. It is important that the general practitioner, who has primary responsibility for the health of individual workers registered with him, is kept informed of any health matters of significance and is involved in the care of the patient while at work. Similarly, the occupational physician or nurse should always be involved in cases where management receive a communication from a general practitioner about the health of an individual employee.

Health records

The maintenance of suitable records relating to the health state of individual employees features significantly in occupational health practice. The purpose of such records is to:

(a) assist occupational health staff to provide efficient health surveillance, emergency attention, health care and continuity of such care;
(b) enable staff to undertake epidemiological studies to identify general health and safety problems and trends arising amongst employees and to identify problem areas and specific risks;
(c) establish, maintain and keep up to date written information relating to people, hazards and current monitoring activities; and
(d) facilitate assessment of problems, decision making, recommendations and the writing of reports.

The following records on individual employees, although not required by law, are desirable in an occupational health department:

(a) initial and subsequent health questionnaire, interview, examination and screening test results;
(b) relevant medical and occupational history, smoking habits, disabilities and handicaps;
(c) attendance in the department for first aid, treatment, re-treatment, general health care and counselling;
(d) injuries resulting from occupational and non-occupational accidents;
(e) illness occurring at work or on the way to or from work;
(f) sickness absences;
(g) occupational conditions and diseases;
(h) care and treatment provided;
(i) advice given, recommendations and work limitations imposed;
(j) referrals made to other specialists or agencies;
(k) correspondence relating to the health of employees;
(l) dispersal of cases following emergencies and treatment;
(m) communications between occupational health staff and others, including written reports.

The following information should be included in occupational health records:

(a) Personal identification details. Personal records are necessary for identifying and tracing individual employees and groups of employees exposed to particular risks. Identification details which are of particular value are:
    (i) National Health Service number;

(ii) National Insurance number;
(iii) surname and forenames (maiden name, where applicable);
(iv) sex;
(v) date of birth, country of birth and place of birth; and
(vi) usual address and date of taking up residence there.

Some of these items are useful for tracing individuals who are no longer employed by the organisation.

(b) Job history. Before he commences work with a new employer, an occupational history should be taken from the prospective employee. Details of the occupations in the current employment should appear on the individual record including transfers to alternative work with dates and duration in each job.

Other records which should be maintained include accident records, the results of work area visits, a daily attendance record of employees visiting the occupational health department and information relating to such matters as potential health hazards, drugs, medical equipment and departmental procedures.

Specific aspects of occupational health practice

In addition to the areas detailed in the earlier part of this chapter, occupational health practice includes a number of specific areas which have come into prominence, largely as a result of medical research, over the last 20 years. Included in this group are, for instance, the problem of drug taking, hearing and eyesight defects, the relationship of social habits to work – e.g. smoking and the taking of alcohol – and the relationship of physical defects to the safety of the employee. These various aspects are discussed below.

Drug addiction

Here we must consider the problem of addiction to drugs such as opium, cocaine, morphine, heroin, etc., which is common amongst certain age groups and ethnic groups. Addiction, in its broadest sense, implies that the individual has developed a need for the particular drug in order to stay both physically and mentally normal. Once access to the drug is prevented or removed, certain physical and/or mental symptoms become apparent in the addict. With the increased publicity that has been given to the problem of drug addiction, most people would be aware of the weakness and depression of the cocaine taker, the persistent diarrhoea of the morphine addict or the excessive excitement of the marijuana smoker. It is possible to become addicted to the strangest drugs, for instance to chloroform and ether, the benzedrene in nasal inhalers, and opium in the form of chlorodyne in certain cough medicines.

In most cases addiction to a particular drug will bring about some changes in behaviour or bouts of abnormal behaviour and, whilst the health of the individual addict needs careful attention from the occupational health practitioner and his doctor, attention must also be given to the safety of individuals with whom the addict may come into contact whilst at work. Drug addicts do represent a serious threat to safety and, therefore, must be carefully controlled in terms of the tasks they undertake. Health surveillance and primary monitoring of such persons on a regular basis feature strongly in good occupational health practice.

Hearing and eyesight defects

It is a fact of life that as people get older so their ability to see and hear reduces. This is part of the normal ageing process, so that where workers are exposed to high noise levels or need to undertake close visual tasks a form of secondary monitoring is necessary. In the first case, this may be undertaken by annual audiometric testing and the comparison of audiograms from previous tests carried out for the individual. Such examination should indicate the current level of hearing ability and identify whether there is a need for, perhaps, a change of job to a less noisy part of the factory, increased emphasis on the wearing of hearing protection or further assistance from a medical specialist. The main objective is, of course, to prevent further deterioration in hearing whether this be associated purely with ageing (presbyacusis) or exposure to excessive noise (sociocusis) or both.

Vision screening now features prominently in both pre-employment screening and secondary monitoring activities. Here again the problem of ageing must be taken into account, together with the visual demands of certain tasks. With advancing age the human eye gradually loses its ability to adapt for near and/or distance vision, so that frequently objects tend to be held further from the eyes in order to bring them into focus, unless corrective spectacles are worn.

One indicator of deteriorating focusing ability is the distance of the 'nearpoint', which is the shortest distance at which an object can be brought into sharp focus. Conversely, the 'far point' is the furthest distance at which an object can be focused.

Colour-blindness in men is another difficulty which increases with age. One in ten young adults has some degree of colour-blindness but many more lose some power of colour differentiation as they get older.

As with defects in hearing, defects in visual acuity and performance can be a cause of or contributory factor in accidents. Specialist groups to whom particular attention should be paid include drivers of all types of vehicle, including fork lift trucks; crane drivers; machinery operators; VDU operators; laboratory staff, who may use optical equipment such as microscopes; and most clerical workers.

Smoking and alcoholism

The relationship of cigarette smoking in particular with various forms of cancer is now well established. Many experts would argue that smoking is not a true form of addiction due to the fact that many people give up smoking quite easily without the usual symptoms of true addiction such as trembling, loss of appetite or a high excitement level. However, there is no doubt that smoking has a direct effect on a high proportion of people in terms of reduced lung function and an increased potential for lung conditions such as bronchitis. The synergistic effect of smoking and, say, asbestos, producing a vastly increased risk of lung cancer, should receive careful consideration.

Alcoholism, on the other hand, is a true addiction, and the alcoholic must be encouraged to obtain medical help and advice. There is no doubt that the abuse of alcohol leads to broken homes, broken marriages, lost jobs, a certain amount of crime and unhappiness generally for all those who may come into contact with the alcoholic, together with varying degrees of physical and mental disease. On the other hand, it is a fact that many people can consume very large quantities of alcohol throughout a long life without showing any apparent ill-effects whatever, and that in most cases alcoholism is a symptom rather than a disease in itself.

The general, although by no means universally accepted, belief today is that the physical diseases brought about by the excessive consumption of alcohol are the result of its indirect effect in producing malnutrition rather than its direct toxic one. The repeated consumption of strong spirits, especially on an empty stomach, can lead to chronic gastritis, and possible inflammation of the intestines which interferes with the absorption of food substances, notably those in the vitamin B group. This, in turn, damages the nerve cells causing alcoholic neuritis, injury to the brain cells leading to certain forms of insanity and, in some cases, cirrhosis of the liver.

The alcoholic is not necessarily the person who becomes obviously drunk on frequent occasions but is more commonly the man or woman who drinks steadily throughout the day, often without any immediate effect being apparent to others. Later, however, symptoms which are partly due to physical effects, partly to the underlying neurosis which is at the root of the trouble in most cases, and partly social, begin to show themselves. The individual eats less and drinks more, often begins the day with vomiting or nausea which necessitates taking the first drink before he can face the public, his appearance tends to become bloated and the eyes are often red and congested. His work suffers, he forgets to keep appointments and he becomes indifferent to his social responsibilities. His craving for drink becomes insatiable, and when he is unable to get it he becomes shaky, irritable and tense. Since he is ashamed of his condition, he tries to hide it and often, instead of drinking openly, hides his bottles about the house and perhaps his office. His emotions are less controlled and he gets angry or tearful readily, tells facile lies, and a minor illness or cessation of the supply may lead to an attack of 'DTs' (delirium tremens).

In severe cases the alcoholic may die from cirrhosis of the liver; or an attack of pneumonia or some other infection, not generally fatal to healthy people, may be so in his case. No matter how alcoholism manifests itself, the alcoholic needs help, particularly if his condition is prejudicing the safety of his fellow workers. In most cases, this implies complete abstention for a period of time under controlled conditions away from the normal temptations of the home and the workplace, perhaps psychotherapy to assess any psychological causes of the condition, and the general building up of impaired physical health.

It is in cases of alcoholism that the occupational health practitioner can be of considerable support and assistance in bringing about the gradual rehabilitation necessary, perhaps through advising on the various social and therapeutic treatments available. The occupational health practitioner is also trained in the early detection of cases of alcohol abuse and, through counselling and routine surveillance, can prevent the situation from deteriorating further.

Conclusion

This chapter has endeavoured to cover the very broad field of occupational health practice. It should be appreciated that only the more general aspects of this discipline have been mentioned, and that many more aspects could be added. Fundamentally, as stated at the beginning of the chapter, occupational health is concerned with prevention of accidents and ill-health at work, the treatment, in certain cases, of injuries and illness sustained at work, and the promotion, maintenance and restoration of health. Many people are directly involved in the promotion of sound occupational health standards but, as with safety, everyone at work must consider his own health and potential health hazards and, where possible, take preventive action. The training of staff in avoiding hazards to health is, therefore, vitally important if the toll of occupational disease and conditions affecting health is to be reduced.

21
Noise and vibration

Sound and noise

Sound

Sound is defined as 'any pressure variation in air, water or some other medium that the human ear can detect'. Sound, within the physical sense, is a vibration of particles in a gas, liquid or solid.

Noise

Noise is generally defined as 'unwanted sound'. It is a problem to Man for many reasons. First, environmentally it can be a nuisance, resulting in disturbance and loss of enjoyment of life, loss of sleep and fatigue. Its nuisance effect, whether as noise from a factory, motorway or discothèque, varies from person to person. Second, it can distract attention and concentration, mask audible warning signals or interfere with work, thereby becoming a causative factor in accidents. Finally, exposure to excessive noise can result in hearing impairment. However, provided the exposure period is of sufficient duration, even 'wanted sound', such as loud music, can lead to hearing impairment.

The nature of sound

Sound is a series of pressure waves or fluctuations impinging on the ear-drum (sound waves). The sounds of everyday life are composed of a mixture of many simple sound waves. Sound is generated from any energy source which sets up rapid pressure variations in the surrounding air. The rate at which variations occur ('frequency' or 'pitch') is expressed in hertz (Hz) (cycles per second, i.e. the number of complete air waves passing a fixed point per second). The normal human ear is sensitive to frequencies between about 20 and 20,000 Hz, being particularly sensitive in the range 2,000 to 6,000 Hz (with maximum sensitivity at 4,000 Hz), and is progressively less sensitive at higher and lower frequencies. This fact is very important when measuring sound, since two sounds of equal intensity, but of different frequency, may appear, subjectively, to be of different loudness.

Characteristics of sound waves

Sound may be 'pure tone', that is of one frequency only, such as the sound produced by a tuning fork (*see* Fig. 21.1(a)). Some industrial noise is of this type, but most is highly complex, with components distributed over a wide range of frequencies. Noise of this type is referred to as 'broad band' (*see* Fig. 21.1(b)), common examples being noise produced by looms, an air jet or printing presses.

Industrial noise is often produced by impact between metal parts. If there are many impacts per second, as in a rivetting machine, the noise produced is usually treated as broad band noise, but if the noise is produced by widely spaced impacts, as from a drop hammer or cartridge-operated hand tool, then the noise produced is termed 'impulse noise' (*see* Fig. 21.1(c)). Impulse noise can present special difficulties in measurement and in assessing the risk to hearing.

Wavelength

This is the physical distance in air from one peak of a sound wave to the next. It equals the ratio of the speed of sound in the medium to the fundamental frequency.

Amplitude

The amplitude of a sound wave is the maximum displacement of a particle from its rest position. For practical purposes, this means the sound wave size and, in turn, therefore, the amount of sound energy involved. The amplitude of a sound wave determines loudness, although the two are not directly related.

Sources of noise and vibration

Noise and vibration in the working environment can include the following:

(a) noise produced as a result of vibration in machines;
(b) noise taking a structure-borne pathway;
(c) radiation of structural vibration into the air;
(d) turbulence created by air or gas flow;
(e) noise taking an airborne pathway;
(f) noise produced from vibratory hand tools, e.g. chain-saws.

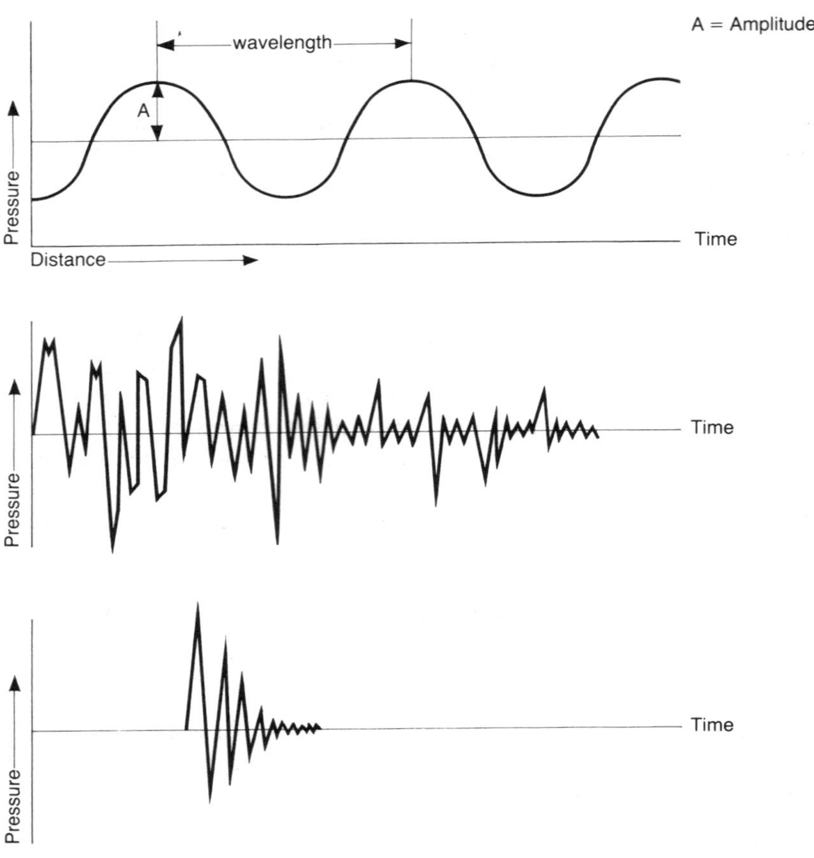

Fig. 21.1 (a) Pure tone sound
(b) Broad band noise
(c) Impulse noise

The effect on hearing

All the above sources of noise result in vibration of the ear-drum. This vibration is amplified by the ossicles (malleus, incus and stapes) in the middle ear, and transmitted to the cochlea. In the cochlea, the vibrations are transformed into nerve impulses which are sent to the brain. It is in this way that a sound is heard. (*See* Chapter 19, which deals with noise-induced hearing loss.)

Important aspects of sound and noise

Sound intensity

Sound intensity describes the particular power of a sound or the level of sound energy with which it confronts the ear. Intensity thus describes the rate of flow of sound energy. High-intensity sound has more energy than low-intensity sound.

Sound pressure level

Sound intensity is difficult to measure directly, but the passage of sound energy through air is accompanied by fluctuations in atmospheric pressure. These fluctuations can be measured and related to the amount of sound energy that is flowing. Therefore, it is usual to measure sound pressure level, which is a measurement of the magnitude of the air pressure variations or fluctuations which make up sound. The root mean square value of the pressure variations is used and expressed in decibels (dB).

Frequency

Frequency is the number of complete pressure variations passing a fixed point per second. It is measured in Hertz (Hz), i.e. 1 Hz = 1 cycle per second; 1 kHz = 1,000 cycles per second. The frequency of a sound gives it its distinguishing character. For instance, high-frequency sound, such as a train whistle, will sound high pitched, whereas a low-frequency sound, such as that from a double bass, will sound low pitched. The more rapidly the vibrations occur, the higher is the frequency and vice versa.

Pitch

This is the subjective quality of a sound which determines its position in the musical scale. It is determined by frequency.

Tone

The tone and quality of a note depend upon the particular overtones or harmonics which are sounding together with the fundamental note.

Loudness

The loudness of a sound depends upon its intensity and the amplitude of the sound waves involved. However, since the human ear is less sensitive to high and low frequencies, it also depends upon frequency and the subjective perception of sound by human beings. (*See also* 'phons' and 'sones' later in this chapter.)

Basic theory of noise measurement

A sound pressure level meter measures sound intensity on a comparative basis. The range of intensities to which the ear responds, however, is enormous, from the threshold of hearing to the threshold of pain.

For example, at 1,000 Hz the threshold of pain is 100,000,000,000,000 (10^{14}) times more intense than the threshold of hearing, where sound is just discernible. It is clearly difficult to express such ratios on a simple arithmetic scale, so a logarithmic scale is used. The ratio would therefore be expressed as

$$\log_{10}\frac{10^{14}}{1} \text{ or } 14, \text{ rather than}$$

$$\frac{10^{14}}{1}.$$

The unit used is the bel. Thus 1 bel is $\log_{10}10^1$ (a tenfold change in intensity), 2 bel is $\log_{10}10^2$ (a hundred-fold change in intensity) and so on. The bel, however, is a very large unit, so it is further split into tenths, called decibels (dB); 1 bel equals 10 decibels. For example, $10 \log_{10}10^{14}$ equals 140 dB. Thus 1 decibel equals a change of intensity of 1.26 times, since $10^{1/10}$ is 1.26 (or 1.26^{10} is 10). Also, a change of intensity of 3 dB $= 1.26^3 = 2$, so that doubling the intensity of a sound gives an increase of 3 dB.

If there are two sounds of intensities I_1 and I_2 and they differ by n dB, then

$$n = 10 \log_{10}\frac{I_1}{I_2}$$

It is normal practice to relate intensity to a standard reference level, so that

$$n = 10 \log_{10}\frac{I_1}{I_0}$$

and I_0 is taken as 10^{-12} watts per square metre.

However, as intensity is proportional to pressure squared,

$$n = 10 \log_{10}\frac{P^2}{P_0^{\,2}}$$

$$= 10 \log_{10}\left[\frac{P}{P_0}\right]^2$$

$$\text{or} \quad n = 20 \log\frac{P}{P_0}\,\text{dB}$$

where P is the standard reference level of 2×10^{-5} newtons per square metre (pascals) and n is sound pressure level in dB. Pressure is the easiest quantity to measure, hence the use of dB sound pressure level.

The standard reference level of 2×10^{-5} N/m^2 is chosen since it is the average threshold of audibility at 1,000 Hz (i.e. it is 0 dB).

NOTE. Under the SI system, sound pressure is expressed in pascals. A pascal is a unit of pressure corresponding to a force of one newton acting uniformly upon an area of 1 square metre. Hence 1 Pa = 1 N/m^2.

The use of a logarithmic scale in sound measurement has a further advantage, because the evaluation of intensities is simplified by the replacement of multiplication with addition and of division with subtraction. Furthermore, the response of the ear tends to follow a logarithmic scale.

The addition of decibels is carried out on a ratio basis, rather than an arithmetic one, and Table 16 may be used to simplify the procedure. To add two sound pressure levels, take the difference between the two levels and add the corresponding figure in the right-hand column to the higher sound pressure level.

Table 16: Addition of decibels

Difference (dB)	*Add to higher (dB)*
0.0–0.5	3.0
1.0–1.5	2.5
2.0–3.0	2.0
3.5–4.5	1.5
5.0–7.0	1.0
7.5–12.0	0.5
Over 12.0	0.0

Other units used in noise measurement

Phons

The human ear does not respond equally to all frequencies. Sounds of different frequency at a constant sound pressure level do not evoke equal loudness sensations. This phenomenon is linear with neither amplitude nor frequency, and 'loudness level' is measured in phons, the sound being compared again to a standard reference signal of 1,000 Hz. The loudness level in phons of any sound is taken as that which is subjectively as loud as a 1,000 Hz tone of known level. 0 phon is 0 dB at 1,000 Hz. 50 phon is the loudness of any tone which is as loud as a 1,000 Hz tone of 50 dB. This can be demonstrated by equal loudness curves for pure tones shown in Fig. 21.2. Maximum sensitivity occurs between 1 and 5 kHz. The curves are obtained by finding the sound levels at different frequencies which seem equally loud to the listener in comparison with a reference sound at 1 kHz.

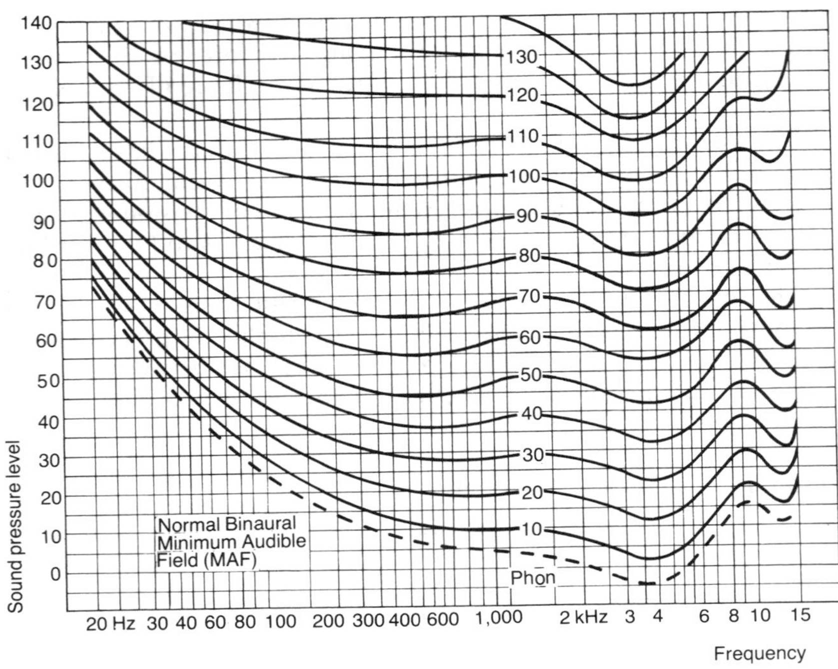

Fig. 21.2 Equal loudness curves

This is a linear unit of loudness on a scale designed to give scale numbers approximately proportional to loudness. The scale is precisely defined by its relation to the phon scale.

Octave bands and octave band analysis

It is possible to make a single measurement of the overall sound pressure of the entire range of audible frequencies but this measurement, if taken in linear decibels, is of limited use since the ear is more sensitive to some frequencies than others. Use of the 'A' weighted decibel scale (*see* page 260) provides a reasonable means of assessing likely risk to hearing but a knowledge of the way in which the sound is distributed throughout the frequency spectrum provides a much more accurate picture. This can be obtained by dividing the noise into octave bands and measuring the sound pressure level at the centre frequency of each band. (An octave represents a doubling of frequency, so that the range 90–180 Hz is one octave, as is the range 1,400–2,800 Hz.)

The octave bands are usually identified by their geometric centre frequencies. For example, the geometric centre frequency of the octave 90–180 Hz is approximately 125 Hz. The standard range of octave bands has the geometric centre frequencies shown in Table 17. Octave band analysis is used for assessing risk of noise-induced hearing loss and in the specification of certain forms and types of hearing protection. It is also used in the diagnosis of machinery noise and in the selection of noise attenuation methods.

Table 17: Standard range of octave bands

Limits of band (*Hz*)	*Geometric centre frequency* (*Hz*)
45–90	63
90–180	125
180–355	250
355–710	500
710–1,400	1,000
1,400–2,800	2,000
2,800–5,600	4,000
5,600–11,200	8,000

The sound pressure level meter

A sound pressure level meter is an instrument which measures linear sound pressure level in the human audiofrequency range unless provided with and set to various weighting networks. The 'A' weighted network gives objective measurements of sound pressure level in accordance with the manner of response of the human ear. A typical mode of operation is shown in Fig. 21.3. The microphone senses the air pressure fluctuations and converts mechanical vibration to an electrical signal containing amplitude and frequency components. The amplifier increases the weak signal from the microphone and incorporates gain adjustment, which enables the instrument to cope with the very wide range of pressure amplitudes which the ear can sense. The sound signal is also available as an output socket so that it may be fed to external instruments such as recorders or noise dosemeters.

Since an accurate response from the sound level meter is necessary, provision is made to calibrate it for accurate results. This is best done by the use of a portable acoustic calibrator placed directly over the microphone. The calibrator is basically a miniature audible signal generator giving a precisely defined sound pressure level to which the sound level meter can be calibrated. Electronic oscillators are most commonly used.

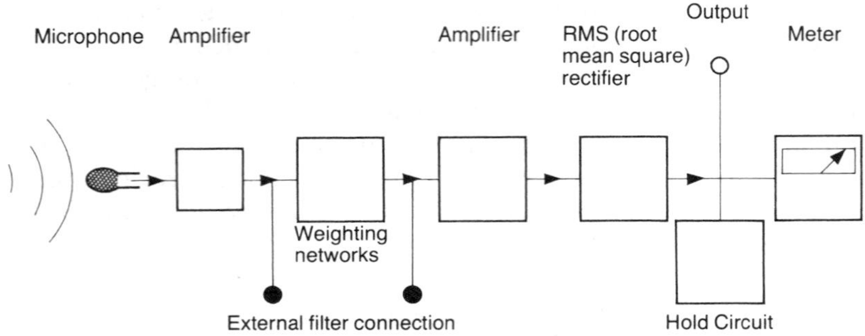

Fig. 21.3 Measurement of sound pressure level in accordance with the manner of response of the human ear

When the sound level fluctuates, the meter needle should follow these variations. However, if the level fluctuates too rapidly, the meter needle may move so erratically that it is impossible to obtain a meaningful reading. For this reason, two meter response characteristics are used:

(a) Fast: this gives a fast reacting indicator response which enables the user to follow and measure noise levels which are not fluctuating too rapidly.
(b) Slow: this gives a damped response and helps average out meter fluctuations which would otherwise be impossible to read.

Weighting networks

The sound level meter incorporates electrical circuits known as weighting networks. These provide for various sensitivities to sounds of different frequencies, the original object being to simulate the response characteristics of the human ear at different frequencies. These weighting networks are known as 'A', 'B', 'C' or 'D' weighted decibel scale operating conditions and can be selected on a sound level meter.

'A' scale

The 'A' scale is normally used for industrial noise measurement. This scale makes the instrument more sensitive to the middle range of frequencies, and less sensitive to high and low frequencies, and is the one which most closely approximates to the response of the human ear. Measurements of the sound pressure level using this scale are designated 'dBA'.

'B' scale

This scale was intended for the measurement of middle range sound pressure levels, between 55 and 85 dB. It is not commonly used as it does not give good correlation to subjective tests of hearing perception.

'C' scale

This scale gives most sensitivity in low frequencies and is, therefore, of limited use. As with the 'B' scale, it does not give good correlation to subjective tests.

'D' scale

This scale is generally limited to the measurement of aircraft noise and has little or no application in the measurement of industrial noise.

Noise control

In any strategy to reduce noise two factors must be considered: first, the source of the noise, and second, the actual pathway taken by the noise to the recipient. Personal protective equipment, e.g. ear-plugs, ear defenders or acoustic wool, may go some way towards preventing people from going deaf at work, but such a strategy should be regarded as secondary since it relies too heavily upon the exposed person wearing potentially uncomfortable and inconvenient protection for the correct amount of time. The better and primary way of preventing noise and, therefore, the risk of persons sustaining noise-induced hear-

Table 18: Methods of noise control

Sources and pathways	*Control measures*
Vibration produced through machinery operation	Reduction at source, e.g. substitution of nylon components for metal, tapered tools on presses
Structure-borne noise (vibration)	Vibration isolation, e.g. resilient mounts and connections, anti-vibration mounts
Radiation of structural vibration	Vibration damping to prevent resonance
Turbulence created by air or gas flow	Reduction at source or use of silencers
Airborne noise pathway	Noise insulation – reflection; heavy barriers Noise absorption – no reflection; porous lightweight barriers

ing loss is, if practicable, to tackle the potential problem at the design stage, rather than endeavouring to control noise once the machinery or noise-emitting item is installed and has become operational.

Different methods of noise control are suitable for dealing with different sources and for the different possible stages in the pathway to the recipient. These may be summarised as in Table 18. The sequence does not necessarily apply in all cases, and is reversible or interchangeable. Control of the main or primary noise pathway is the most important factor in noise control. For instance, the noise pathway for a vibration-induced noise has three distinct stages:

(a) structure-borne noise emission;
(b) radiation of the noise from the structure into the air; and
(c) the actual airborne noise pathway.

In this case, the way to reduce structure-borne noise is to isolate the noise-generating parts of the machine from the radiating surface with vibration isolators (resilient mounts). Isolators consist of steel springs or flexible materials such as rubber or cork. The amount of noise radiated from machine surfaces will be increased substantially if the surfaces resonate or oscillate. In this case it would be appropriate to apply a damping treatment using a spray-on, stick-on or magnetic damping compound. Panel-damping materials can be extremely effective in a wide range of applications, and the application of damping treatments can result in noise reductions of as much as 10 dBA if the material is initially poorly damped.

Once the noise has been radiated into the air, two completely different methods of control are possible. The recipient can be insulated from the noise with a heavy limp airtight screen, which simply acts as an impervious barrier to prevent noise transmission. Alternatively, noise can be absorbed in porous materials mounted on walls or suspended from a ceiling. Absorption of noise will only be helpful if most of the noise which reaches the subject has been reflected off walls and ceilings.

Vibration

A body is said to vibrate when it describes an oscillating motion about a fixed position. As with sound, the number of times a complete motion cycle takes place during the period of one second is referred to as the 'frequency', which is measured in hertz (Hz). The motion can consist of a single component occurring at a single frequency, as with a tuning fork, or of several components occurring at different frequencies simultaneously, e.g. with the piston motion of an internal combustion engine.

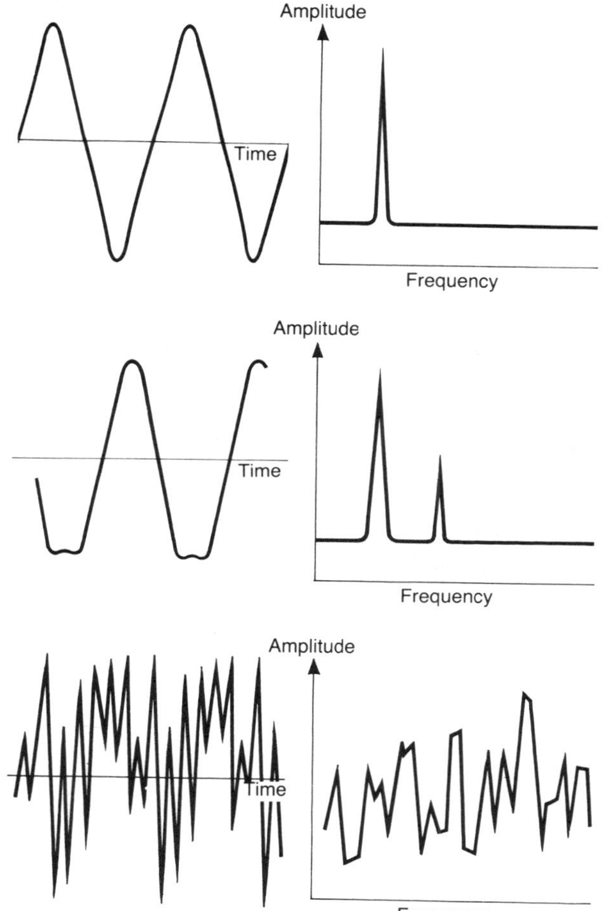

Fig. 21.4 Vibratory motion
Tuning fork – a single component vibrating at a single frequency
Internal combustion engine – several components vibrating at different frequencies simultaneously
Factory machinery – a large number of components vibrating at different frequencies simultaneously

Vibration signals in practice usually consist of very many frequencies occurring simultaneously, so that it is not possible to see immediately, just by examination of the amplitude–time pattern, how many components there are and at what frequencies they occur. These components can be revealed by plotting vibration amplitude against frequency, the process being known, as in the case of sound, as 'frequency analysis'. The graph showing the vibration level as a function of frequency is known as a 'frequency spectrogram', and the vibration amplitude is the characteristic which describes the severity of the vibration. Typical frequency analyses and spectrograms are shown in Fig. 21.4.

Frequency ranges of significance

The principal hazards associated with vibration are whole body vibration and the condition known as vibration-induced white finger (VWF), the physiological aspects of which are discussed in Chapter 19. The human body is most sensitive to vibration in the frequency range 1–80 Hz and is principally subjected to vibration in three supporting surfaces, viz. the feet of a person while standing, the buttocks of a seated person and the supporting areas of a person lying down. In the longitudinal direction, i.e. feet to head, the human body is most sensitive to vibration in the frequency range 4–8 Hz. In the transverse direction, however, it is most sensitive to the frequency range 1–2 Hz.

Vibration-induced white finger is a condition generally associated with the use of vibratory hand tools, the frequency of the hand tool being the significant factor.

22

Dust and fumes

Dust

Dust is defined by the International Labour Organisation (ILO) as 'an aerosol composed of solid inanimate particles'. The term *aerosol* implies that airborne particles are carried in or contained in air, which may be inhaled. An aerosol can embrace liquid droplets as well as solid particles.

Some dusts are fibrogenic, i.e. they cause fibrotic changes to lung tissue, or toxic, in that they eventually poison the body systems. Examples of fibrogenic dusts are silica, cement dust and certain metals, whereas toxic dusts may include arsenic, mercury, beryllium, phosphorus and lead. Some toxic dusts, such as arsenic, have an acute effect. Others, such as mercury, may have a chronic effect. A number of dusts, although not harmful to health, can have a nuisance effect, e.g. dust from the combustion of solid fuels.

Definitions relevant to dust and fumes

Particulate – a collection of solid particles, each of which is an aggregation of many molecules.

Mist – airborne liquid droplets, e.g. oil mist.

Fume – airborne fine solid particulates formed from the gaseous state usually by vaporisation or oxidation of metals, e.g. lead fume.

Vapour – airborne liquid droplets given off from the surface of a volatile liquid, e.g. trichlorethylene.

The behaviour of dusts

All dusts are potential aerosols and the behaviour of particles is influenced by

(a) the rate of air movement;

(b) Brownian motion, that is the 'joggling' movement or effect imparted to submicron particles by molecular bombardment; and
(c) the size, density and shape of the particle.

The unit of particle size is the micron, which equals one thousandth of a millimetre, designated μm.

When a particle falls in air it does not accelerate indefinitely. Eventually it reaches a speed at which air resistance equals its weight, and thereafter it falls at constant speed, its 'terminal velocity'. This depends to a great extent upon its size and density.

Physiology of the human lung

The lungs are enclosed in the thoracic cavity and have a sponge-like elastic texture. They are expanded or compressed by movements of the thorax in such a way that air is repeatedly taken in and expelled. They communicate with the atmosphere through the trachea or windpipe, which opens into the pharynx. In the lungs, gaseous exchange takes place. Some of the atmospheric oxygen is absorbed and carbon dioxide from the blood is released into the lung cavities. The trachea divides into two bronchi which enter the lungs and divide into smaller branches. These divide further into bronchioles which terminate in a mass of minute thin-walled, pouch-like air sacs or alveoli (*see* Figs. 22.1 and 22.2).

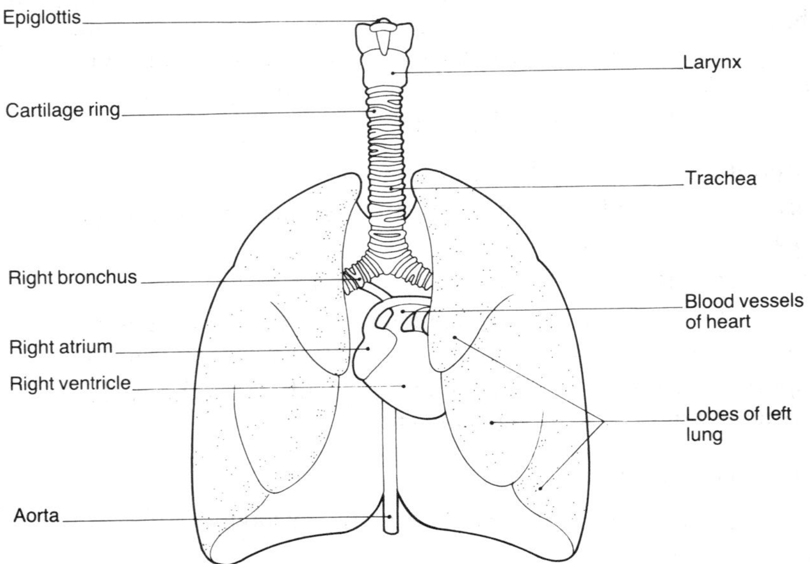

Fig. 22.1 Diagram of lungs

Physiological mechanisms of dust movement

The mechanisms which induce a particle to move through a particular air pathway into the lung and subsequently be deposited in the lung tissue are the following.

Sedimentation

Dust particles settle under the influence of gravity. The terminal velocity of the sedimenting aerosol is related to the density of the aerosol and to the square of the diameter of the aerosol for those aerosols in the diameter range 1–20 μm. Many industrial aerosols are not spheres of uniform shape, however. They may be clumps (aggregates) of particles. The terminal velocity of aggregated aerosols cannot be determined by the above relationship; instead, the aerodynamic diameter must be considered. This is the diameter of a uniform sphere which has the same terminal velocity as the aggregate of other irregular particles. Where the uniform sphere has unit density, the aerodynamic diameter is expressed as the diameter of an equivalent unit density sphere, but where the uniform sphere has the same density as the irregular sphere the diameter is expressed as the Stokes diameter. Both are expressed in microns.

Interception

This is the process whereby irregular particles such as asbestos fibres become caught on the walls of small airways. The length and size of the fibres in relation to the dimensions of the airway are important.

Impaction

Impaction takes place through curving in the airstream. Suspended aerosols continue under momentum and collide with the wall of the airway. Impaction is related to the velocity of aerosol movement and angular change of direction.

Diffusion

This is the process whereby small aerosols behave like molecules and move freely throughout an air space. It is brought about by the random bombardment of the aerosols by the molecules of the gas in which they are suspended.

The body's protective mechanisms

There are a number of mechanisms by which the body endeavours to prevent dust entering the lungs. The operation of a particular mechanism depends upon the shape and size of particles. The principal protective mechanisms are the following.

The nose

The very coarse hairs lining the nostrils have a filtering effect and trap the larger particles. The cyclonic effect caused by the sudden changes in direction of the nasal passages also causes dust to impinge on the mucous membranes of the nose. In many cases the particle may be expelled by sneezing or blowing the nose.

Ciliary escalator

The surface of the respiratory tract (trachea and bronchi) is lined with special cells, each of which has a cilium growing from its head. The mucuous membrane contains mucous glands which secrete a tacky fluid. This forms a sticky film bound up with the cilia. The cilia exhibit a wave-like motion and a particle falling on to the cilia is carried by this motion back to the pharynx, after which it may be swallowed or expectorated. This mechanism is assisted by mucus which causes particles to adhere to the cilia.

Dust deposition locations in the respiratory tract (*see* Fig. 22.2) can be broadly classified as follows:

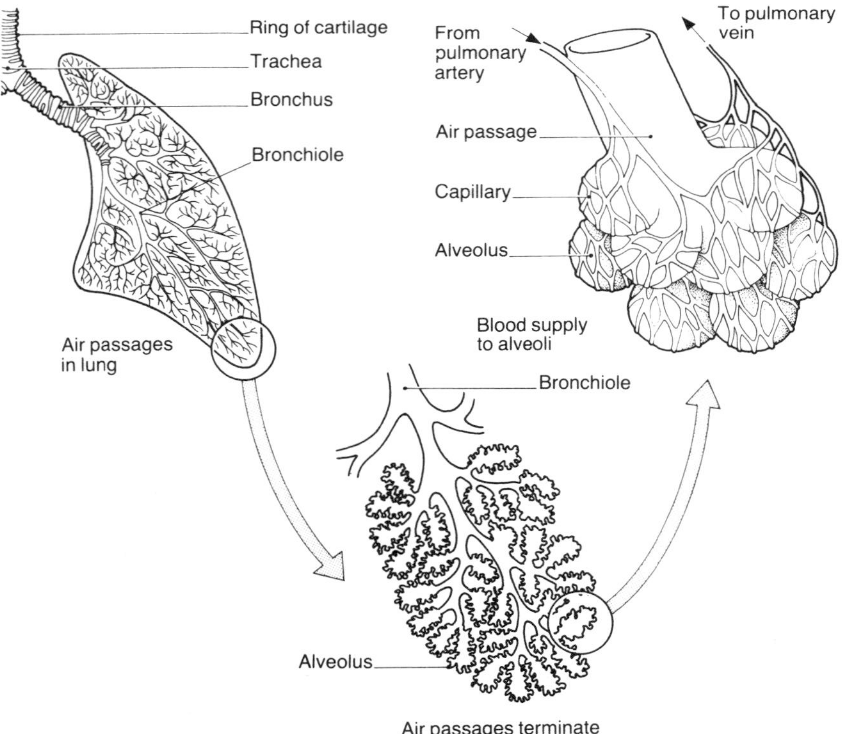

Fig. 22.2 The respiratory tract

Above 7 microns	– mouth and throat only
4.7 to 7.0 microns	– pharynx
3.3 to 4.7 microns	– trachea and bronchi
2.1 to 3.3 microns	– bronchioles
1.1 to 2.1 microns	– terminal bronchi
0.43 to 1.1 microns	– alveoli

Particles less than 0.43 microns tend to remain airborne and are exhaled.

'Respirable range' particles are, therefore, those particles in the size range 0.43 to 7.0 microns which enter the various parts of the respiratory tract, those entering the respiratory bronchioles, terminal bronchi and alveoli being the most significant. Consequently, control over particles in this size range is important.

Fibres have different deposition characteristics from uniform density spheres. Broadly, asbestos and man-made mineral fibres having a diameter less than 3.5 microns may be regarded as aerodynamically respirable.

Macrophages (phagocytes)

These are wandering scavenger cells with a large nucleus and irregular outline. They move freely through tissue, engulfing bacteria and dust particles in the process. They secrete hydrolytic enzymes which attack the foreign body, neutralising its activity to some extent. They are found in the alveoli where, after carrying out this scavenging action, they migrate back along the respiratory pathway. At the terminal bronchioles they meet the lowest reaches of the ciliary escalator on which they are carried, ultimately to be swallowed or expectorated. In this way, macrophage action supplements respiratory filtration processes.

Lymphatic system

The lymphatic system acts as a form of drainage system throughout the body for the removal of foreign bodies. Lymphatic glands or nodes at specific points in the lymphatic system act as selective filters preventing infection from entering the bloodstream. In many cases a localised inflammation occurs in the node.

Sources of dust

There are many industrial sources of dust, and they may be classified thus:

(a) dust produced in the cleaning and preliminary treatment of raw materials, e.g. dust resulting from sand-blasting operations in foundries, abrasive treatments for the removal of rust;
(b) dust produced in processes such as refining, grinding, milling and other size reduction processes;
(c) manufactured dusts for specific treatments or dressings, e.g. in the dressing of seed corn with powdered mercury-based fungicides; and
(d) environmental or background dusts, such as those produced by routine sweeping of factory floors, combustion of fuels, the use of packaging materials or road dust.

Dust control measures

The following aspects are important in the selection of dust control measures:

(a) the type of dust in terms of particle size, weight, density, air velocity and toxicity;
(b) the source of dust in a particular process;
(c) the number of personnel exposed, the duration of exposure (continuous or intermittent) per day, and the number of days per week this emission takes place;
(d) methods of monitoring emissions, e.g. static sampling, personal dosemeters, and the results of past monitoring activities;
(e) the efficiency of cleaning procedures; manual methods should be replaced by the use of industrial vacuum cleaners; and
(f) the efficiency of dust arrestment plant, including the system for the maintenance of, and testing, the efficiency of such plant.

Emphasis should always be placed on control at source by means of dust arrestment plant, in preference to the provision and use of respiratory and other protection.

Control strategies

Replacement or substitution

Replacement or substitution of the hazardous dust-producing process or material by a suitable alternative should always be considered first. For instance, the use of a liquid mercury-based dressing for seed corn instead of the powder form, or the replacement of toxic dust-producing materials by non-toxic materials, is an effective control strategy.

Suppression

In many cases, the use of a wet process, as opposed to a dry process, will be sufficient to reduce the dust hazard. A typical example is in the pottery industry where flint is ground under water due to the danger of fibrogenic dust emission in a dry process.

Isolation

Isolation entails enclosure of the complete process or the actual point of dust production, for instance the total enclosure of large grinding processes or of tipping points for certain dust-producing materials, such as coal, to the total exclusion of the workforce. Tipping points should be provided with efficient dust arrestment plant to prevent dust nuisance to people living in the immediate vicinity.

Ventilation

Local exhaust ventilation points linked to collection and filtration plant must be considered. In most cases it is necessary to install a system of total or partial enclosure in conjunction with cyclone arrestors, dry deduster units, wet arrestors or electrostatic precipitators. It is vital that factors such as particle size, weight and density, together with efflux velocity, are evaluated prior to the selection of a particular form of dust arrestment.

Cleaning and housekeeping

High standards of cleaning and housekeeping should be maintained wherever workers are exposed to a dusty process. Failure to do so can lead to an action for breach of statutory duty and/or common law duty. Whilst dust suppression plant, depending upon its efficiency, will remove the majority of dust from the working environment, small quantities may escape as a result of handling, plant defects or plant malfunction. Hand sweeping, using brushes or brooms, should be replaced by mechanical vacuum-cleaning equipment. Operators should be trained in the correct use of the equipment, which should be serviced and maintained on a regular basis. Such activities should form part of a general cleaning schedule for the area. In recent years *in situ* vacuum systems (ring mains) have been introduced to facilitate the removal of dust from process and storage areas. With this system dust is removed to a central collection point through fixed pipework connected via hosing to hand-held suction devices.

Personal protection

This aspect subdivides into the following areas:

(a) medical supervision of exposed personnel for early detection of respiratory conditions, supported by annual health screening by occupational health nurses, with referral to the occupational physician where appropriate;

(b) the supply, maintenance and use of personal protective equipment, which implies the provision of the correct type of respiratory protection according to the dust hazard involved, and which the operator should use all the time that he may be exposed to dust; also he should wear a one-piece boiler suit, cap and gloves;

(c) the provision of a high standard of welfare amenities, in particular showering and separate workwear and personal clothing storage facilities; and

(d) the frequent training of management and operators in these procedures.

Dust explosions

Many solid particulates, particularly organic materials, in the right combination with air, will form an explosive mixture. Some particulates are relatively harmless in their traditional form, but when reduced to dust by grinding, sanding or other forms of size reduction or refining they can become highly explosive. In fact, some of the most serious dust explosions have been associated with dusts created during the processing of tea, sugar, starch and potato as well as metals such as zinc and aluminium. Other materials such as coal, wood, cork, grain and many plastics can form explosive dust clouds.

Although an intimate mixture of flammable dust and air may burn with explosive violence, not all mixtures will do so. There is a range of concentrations of the dust and air within which the mixture can explode, but above or below this range an explosion will not take place. The lowest concentration of dust capable of exploding is referred to as the lower explosive limit and the concentration above which an explosion will not take place as the upper explosive limit. Furthermore, the range of the explosive concentrations of a dust cloud is not solely a function of the chemical composition of the dust. The limits vary, inter alia, with the size and shape of the particles in the dust cloud.

For an explosion to take place there must be some form of ignition source available. This can be a hot surface, electrical spark, frictional spark or direct flame. The ignition temperature for sugar is 350 °C, coal 610 °C, wood 430 °C, zinc 600 °C, polystyrene 490 °C and magnesium 520 °C. The lower explosive concentration for sugar is 350 mg/m^3, coal 550 mg/m^3, wood 400 mg/m^3, zinc 4,800 mg/m^3, polystyrene 150 mg/m^3 and magnesium 200 mg/m^3.

There are several clearly defined stages of a typical factory dust explosion. The preliminary stage, similar to the situation where fine coal dust is thrown onto an open fire, is the typical 'flare up', where there is a sudden release of flame for an instant. This can, however, be sufficient to raise locally deposited dust into suspension in air and cause a localised explosion. This primary explosion stage may not result in a great degree of damage but is sufficient to send pressure waves in all directions, causing further liberation into the air of deposited dust. The secondary explosion stage, which is much more devastating than the primary stage, follows quickly, resulting in extensive damage and often loss of life. Depending upon the layout of the premises and the presence of walls, which may act as temporary baffles, the secondary stage may take place as one great explosion or a series of lesser explosions in different part of the premises.

Most dust explosions take place, however, in specific items of plant such as spray driers, cyclones, settling chambers, powder silos, pneumatic conveying equipment, grinding plant, disintegrators, milling plant and dust collection systems.

Precautions against dust explosions

The frequent removal of deposited dust by industrial vacuum cleaners is one of the most important strategies in preventing dust explosions. Moreover, dust-producing plant should be checked frequently for leakages. Items of plant such as evaporator driers, storage silos and bins, grain elevators, fluid beds and cyclones should be fitted with explosion reliefs, which minimise the devastation by relieving the explosive pressure to a safe area or to atmosphere. Explosion reliefs (vents) may take the form of lightweight panels installed at the top of evaporator driers, elevators and silos. The size of the explosion relief is related to the volume of the installation and its mechanical strength. There are several methods for calculating the size of explosion relief according to the type of installation and particulate under consideration.

In general, any explosion of a flammable mixture, whether dust or gaseous, which, when ignited in a confined space, reaches its maximum pressure in not less than 40 milliseconds, can be brought under control by methods which include suppression, venting, advance inerting, isolation and automatic plant shutdown.

As a dust explosion is not an instantaneous occurrence but requires a definite time for the development of maximum pressure, it is possible, by the introduction of a suppressant, to arrest the rise of pressure before it reaches dangerous levels. The explosion suppression system in its simplest form consists of a detector, an electrical power unit and a number of suppressors (*see* Fig. 22.3).

An explosion detector and the associated electrical equipment may also be used to open detonator-operated bursting discs, to close high-

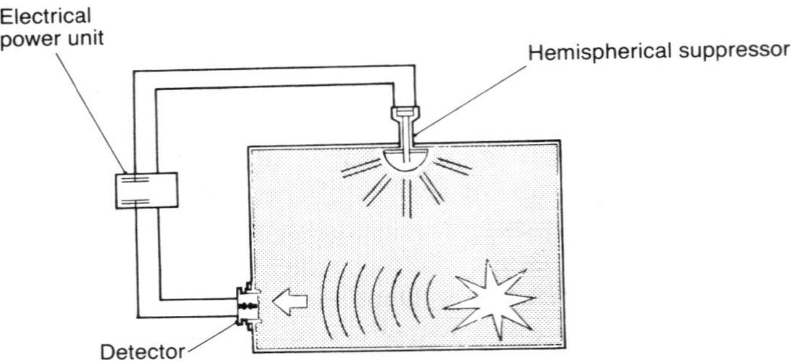

Fig. 22.3 Explosion suppression using an explosion detector, electrical power unit and a hemispherical suppressor

speed isolation valves, to inert automatically parts of the plant remote from the seat of the explosion and to shut down the plant immediately an explosion occurs. These methods may be used individually but more often are used in combination, depending upon the type and construction of plant and its operating conditions. (*See* Fig. 22.4.)

Although the fitting of explosion reliefs may prevent devastation of plant by an explosion this may not be sufficient to stop flame or smouldering material from spreading elsewhere through rotary valves, worms, conveyors or other inlets or outlets for the plant. The use of an explosion detector to initiate inerting and isolating arrangements coupled with automatic plant shutdown, therefore, offers an important additional degree of safety which it is often difficult, if not impossible, to achieve in any other way.

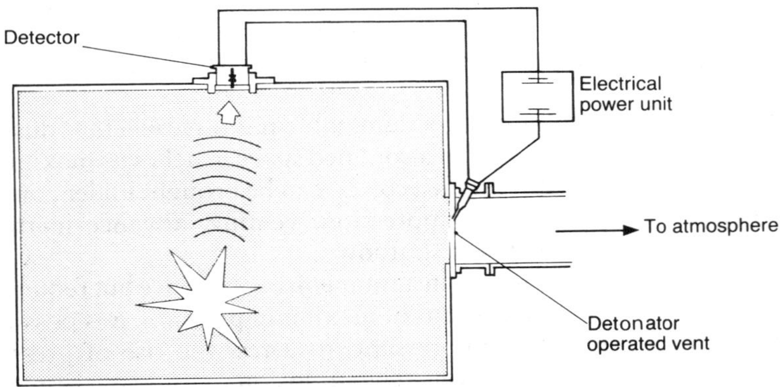

Fig. 22.4 Explosion venting using a detonator operated bursting disc

Other precautions include the installation of baffle walls in processing areas to prevent the spread of explosion, regular damping down of dusty areas, enclosure of processes and the use of dust arrestment plant appropriate to the type of dust produced.

Fumes

Fume is formed by the vaporisation or oxidation of metals. Typical metallic fumes encountered in industry are lead fume and welding fume, each of which creates ill-effects following inhalation.

Lead fume

Environmental control of fume should include damping of process and raw materials, the control of molten lead well below 500 °C – the temperature at which fume is produced – and the use of dust and fume control equipment. Any lead process which emits dust and fume should be enclosed and maintained under negative pressure by an enclosing hood, or a hood fitted as close as possible to the source of emission with a capture velocity not less than 1.0 m/s. Fume must be treated before discharge to atmosphere. Dust and fume arrestment plant should incorporate cyclone dust arrestors for the removal of coarse particles, and fabric filters or high-efficiency wet scrubbers for fine dust and fume produced.

Control measures should be supported by meticulous levels of cleaning and housekeeping, environmental and biological monitoring, strict control over personal hygiene and welfare amenities, and personal protection measures to prevent the contamination of the body and clothing worn by process workers. The degree of respiratory protection necessary is directly related to concentrations in air of lead fume. This may vary from an approved dust respirator for atmospheres containing up to ten times the threshold limit value (TLV) to compressed air line constant-flow breathing apparatus to ensure 100 per cent protection.

Welding fume

During welding a wide range of airborne particulates are produced according to the base metals and electrodes used. Inhalation of these fumes, gases and dusts may lead to the condition known as 'welder's lung'. Metallic fumes in the form of oxides are the main constituent of welding fume, together with dust and fumes from flux coatings and metals being welded. The action of heat and ultraviolet light during the process can lead to the evolution of ozone, carbon monoxide and oxides of nitrogen. These gases are harmful. Heavier particulate matter is also produced as smoke and metal spatter. Most spasmodic welding operations are relatively safe because the fumes are readily diluted by fresh air in the workshop. A serious situation can develop, however, where welding is carried out in confined or unventilated areas.

The following control measures are recommended wherever welding is to be undertaken regularly. Welding workshops should be provided with mechanical ventilation capable of achieving six to ten air changes per hour. Local exhaust ventilation should be provided at the point of fume production to supplement general ventilation. Portable extraction and filtration units should be used when welding is undertaken *in situ* on production plant. Where welding is carried out in confined spaces, a permit to work system should be operated, together with a system for environmental monitoring. Welders should know the composition of different welding materials in use and any new materials introduced, together with fumes, dusts and gases which could be evolved during the welding process. They must also understand the need for different forms of respiratory protection. As a broad guide, where unknown toxic metals, fluxing, etc., are involved, a TLV or recommended limit of 5 mg/m^3 total particulate matter should be applied.

23

Radiation and radiological protection

The structure of matter

All matter is composed of elements such as hydrogen, lithium, carbon, iron, lead and oxygen. Elements consist of characteristic atoms, which contain a relatively small nucleus and a number of electrons. The nucleus contains protons, which carry positive electric charges, and neutrons, which carry no charge. The electrons are negatively charged and may be imagined as encircling the nucleus, most frequently within shells with indefinite boundaries. Atoms are relatively empty structures and symbolic diagrams, such as Fig. 23.1, cannot fully convey this.

An atom contains equal numbers of protons and electrons and is electrically neutral. It is the number of protons, called the atomic number, that characterises an element. The atomic number of lithium, for instance, is 3, and of oxygen, 8. Atoms of the same or different elements combine to form uncharged entities called molecules. Thus 1 atom of oxygen combines with 2 atoms of hydrogen to form a molecule of water. In the same way, 2 atoms of oxygen combine to form one molecule of oxygen.

The mass of an atom is concentrated in the nucleus and the number of protons plus neutrons is called the mass number. Most species of atom can be characterised by the atomic number and mass number, or simply by the name of the element and the mass number. Thus characterised, they are called nuclides. Lithium-7, as the diagram shows, is a nuclide with 3 protons, the unique atomic number of the element, lithium, plus 4 neutrons. Carbon-12 is a nuclide with 6 protons plus 6 neutrons. Lead-208 is a nuclide with 82 protons plus 126 neutrons.

Nuclides of an element that have different numbers of neutrons are called isotopes of that element. Hydrogen, for instance, has three isotopes – hydrogen-1, hydrogen-2, called deuterium, and hydrogen-3, called tritium. Iron has ten isotopes from iron-52 to iron-61.

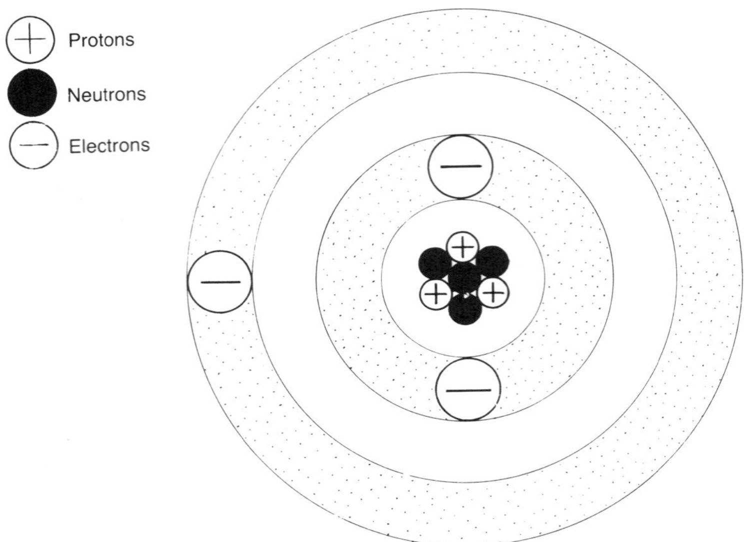

Fig. 23.1 Diagram of a lithium atom

Radioactivity and radiation

Radiation is a form of energy, and the basic energy equation applies:

E	=	mc^2
Energy	=	mass × constant^2
Joules	=	kg × 3 × 10^8 (numerical value of the velocity of light)

Tremendous forces are involved in holding together even the simplest atom of hydrogen, and when such an atom is 'split', these forces can be released, the energy contained in the atom, which held it together, being transformed into heat, light and other forms of radiation. These effects which are created – e.g. visible light, infrared radiation, ultraviolet, microwaves – are all forms of released energy.

To understand radiation, imagine that the energy released from an atom is released in the form of waves. The length and frequency of these waves depends upon how much energy the atom is releasing. It is the length and frequency of the waves that control the form of energy and the effect it can have on the human body, and it is possible to list these energy types in a table indicating increasing wavelength. This is called the electromagnetic spectrum; *see* Table 19.

The most important division in this spectrum is between ionising and non-ionising radiation. (An *ion* is defined as a charged atom or group of atoms.) Ionising radiation can produce chemical changes as a

Table 19: The electromagnetic spectrum

Radiation	*Frequency (Hz)*	*Wavelength*	*Energy*	*Radiation sources*
Gamma	10^{21}	Short ↑	High ↓	Cosmic sources
X-ray	10^{18}			Atoms struck by high-energy particles
Ultraviolet light				Excited gases
Visible light	10^{15}			Hot bodies
Infrared	10^{12}–10^{14}			Hot bodies
Microwaves	10^{9}			Microwave generator
Radio waves	-10^{6}	Long	Low	Radio transmitter

result of ionising molecules upon which it is incident. Non-ionising radiation, however, does not have this effect and is usually absorbed by the molecules on which it is incident, with the result that the material will heat up, as in the case of microwaves.

To assess the hazard associated with radiation, it is necessary to consider the type of radiation, the energy, the extent of penetration of tissue, and the duration of exposure. This is particularly so with particulate radiation which involves the emission of streams of particles, such as protons, neutrons and electrons. These kinds of particulate radiation are often involved in spontaneous emissions from radioactive materials.

Forms of radiation

Alpha particles

An alpha particle may be said to consist of two protons and two neutrons bound together. It is therefore heavy and double charged. These are helium nuclei, i.e. helium atoms that have lost their two orbiting electrons and are, therefore, positively charged. Though they are ejected from the nucleus of the radioactive substance with considerable energy, they are relatively large particles and are easily absorbed by matter.

A nucleus that ejects an alpha particle will form a new nucleus with a mass number reduced by 4 and an atomic number reduced by 2. For example, radium ejects an alpha particle and becomes an inert gas, radon, as follows:

$$^{226}_{88}\mathrm{Ra} \rightarrow {}^{222}_{86}\mathrm{Rn} + {}^{4}_{2}\mathrm{He}$$

(In this equation the subscript denotes the atomic number of the nucleus while the superscript denotes the mass number.)

Beta particles

These are electrons, not from the orbiting electrons of the atom but from within the nucleus. They are ejected with great speed and have a range of up to 15 cm in air. A nucleus that ejects a beta particle will form a new particle with the same mass number but with 1 added to its atomic number. For example, thorium ejects a beta particle and becomes proactinium, thus:

$$^{234}_{90}\mathrm{Th} \rightarrow {}^{234}_{91}\mathrm{Th} + {}^{0}_{-1}\mathrm{e}$$

Gamma rays

These are very high-energy electromagnetic waves that are emitted at the same time as the alpha and beta particles. They are similar in nature to light but of very much shorter wavelength. They are very highly penetrating, being capable of passing through several centimetres of lead.

X-rays

Similar to gamma rays, X-rays are emitted from metals when bombarded with high-energy electrons. They are produced by changes in the energy state of planetary electrons (e^-). As with gamma rays, X-rays are a discrete quantity of energy, without mass or charge, that are propagated as a wave.

Neutrons

A neutron is an elementary particle with unit atomic mass and no electric charge. The most powerful source of neutrons is the nuclear reactor.

Bremsstrahlung

These are weak X-rays, produced by negative beta particles impinging on heavy materials, i.e. those with a high atomic number.

Cosmic rays

These are fundamentally high-energy ionising radiations from outer space. They have a complex composition at the surface of the Earth.

Radiation energy

It is customary to express the energy with which some radiations are produced in units of electron volt (symbol eV). This is equivalent to the energy gained by an electron passing through a potential difference of 1 volt. Multiples of this unit are frequently employed, especially 1 million or 10^6 electron volts (symbol MeV).

Sources of radiation

These sources can be split into non-ionising and ionising radiation sources.

Sources of non-ionising radiation

New processes and developments in industry continue to increase the uses of non-ionising radiation. Lasers are being used in industry and medicine more and more. (The word 'laser' broadly implies light amplification by stimulated emission of radiation.) These very high-energy beams of light are used widely in the construction industry for reference lines, since the beam is straight and does not spread like a torch beam. Lasers are also used for welding and cutting, and in surgery for the sealing of fine blood vessels. The organ most vulnerable to all sources of non-ionising radiation is the eye. A laser beam can destroy the retina, causing blindness. Use of the appropriate goggles can, in most cases, protect the operator from this danger, however.

Ultraviolet radiation is produced in arc welding and exposure may cause the condition known as 'arc eye'. As with lasers, protection may be obtained by the use of goggles. Ultraviolet radiation also burns the skin and may cause cataracts and inflammation of the cornea. All workers exposed to ultraviolet radiation must wear the correct type of protective glasses.

Infrared radiation is emitted by all hot bodies, particularly radiant fires. Long-term exposure to even low doses of infrared radiation may damage the eyes, burning the lens and causing heat cataracts. Shields which reflect the heat may be installed as a form of protection. Personnel in frequent contact should wear the correct type of protective glasses.

Microwaves are emitted at extremely high radio frequencies. Typical examples of use are radar in military installations, certain drying processes and medical diathermy. It is relatively simple to shield such sources since microwaves cannot penetrate even thin metal. Microwave ovens have caused public concern. It is vital to ensure that the door fits perfectly and that the appliance is regularly maintained.

Sources of ionising radiation

Radioactive sources producing ionising radiation vary considerably. They include radioactive gases, certain rocks and dust, and X-ray machines. Small doses of radiation are received by wearers of luminised watches, though the watch face acts as a filter. Radioactive materials and X-rays are used mainly in medicine. X-rays are used increasingly in industry, for example in thickness gauges and in checking welded joints. The treatment of various types of cancer frequently involves radium therapy which may expose hospital staff. Workers in the nuclear power industry may be exposed to radiation, especially during the mining of uranium ore and in the reprocessing of spent fuel.

Radioactive decay

The quantity of a radionuclide is described by its activity, the rate at which spontaneous decay occurs in it, expressed in becquerels (Bq). 1 becquerel corresponds to the decay of one radionuclide per second. (Activity was formerly expressed in curies, i.e. the radioactivity of 1 gram of radium, namely 3.7×10^{10} disintegrations or nuclear transformations per second.) Thus 1 curie = 3.7×10^{10} becquerels.

The time taken for the radioactivity of a radionuclide to lose half its value by decay is called the half-life (symbol $t_{\frac{1}{2}}$). Each radionuclide has a unique and unalterable half-life. For carbon-14 it is 5,730 years, for barium-140, 12.8 days. Values for radionuclides range from fractions of a second to millions of years. In successive half-lives, the activity of a radionuclide is reduced by decay to $\frac{1}{2}$, $\frac{1}{4}$, $\frac{1}{8}$, etc., so that it is possible to predict the activity remaining at any future time.

Units of measurement

Rontgen (R) is the unit of measurement of a material's absorption of gamma or X-radiation.

Rad is 'radiation absorbed dose', and is the quantity of ionising radiation energy absorbed per unit mass. The unit for absorbed dose has undergone various changes in definition and numerical value over the years. Whilst the rontgen and rad are actually different in concept and magnitude, they may be considered to be equivalent to 100 ergs/gram of water. The modern unit of absorbed dose is the Gray, which corresponds to 1 J/kg, abbreviated Gy.

Rem means 'radiation equivalent man' and is a unit of biological damage to living tissue per unit weight. It is generally taken to mean the degree of damage due to 1 rad of alpha, beta or X-radiation. Each type of radioactive particle has its own 'relative biological effectiveness' (rbe) to destroy tissue by ionisation. The rem is equal to the number of rads multiplied by the relative biological effectiveness. The use of the rem for this purpose is being overtaken by that of the sievert (Sv). 1 rem is 1 rad multiplied by 1 for gamma or beta rays, by 10 for alpha rays or neutrons, and by other factors for some other radiations, e.g. 'heavy recoil nuclei'. The sievert is similar, but is based on the gray rather than the rad.

1 Sv = 100 rems; 1 rem = 10 mSv

Definitions associated with radiation

Dose is a general term to indicate the quantity of radiation in relation to the duration of exposure.

Dose equivalent is the quantity obtained by multiplying the absorbed dose by a factor to allow for the different effectiveness of the various ionising radiations in causing harm to tissue, as discussed under 'rem' above. The unit is the sievert. For gamma rays, X-rays and beta particles, the factor is 1, and the gray (Gy) and sievert are numerically equal. For alpha particles, the factor is 20, so that 1 Gy of alpha radiation corresponds to a dose equivalent of 20 Sv. The dose equivalent thus provides an index of risk of harm from exposure of a particular tissue to various radiations.

Effective dose equivalent (EDE) is the quantity obtained by multiplying the dose equivalents to various tissues and organs by a risk weighting factor appropriate to each and adding the various fractions. The sum of the weighted dose equivalents is the dose equivalent to the whole body that would yield the same overall risk. Typical risk weighting factors are testes and ovaries – 0.25, thyroid – 0.03, breast – 0.15 and red bone marrow – 0.12. For instance, if a radionuclide causes irradiation of the liver and lungs the following calculation would apply. If the dose equivalents to the liver and lungs are respectively 70 mSv and 100 mSv, the effective dose equivalent is calculated thus:

$$(70 \times 0.06) + (100 \times 0.12) = 4.2 + 12.0 = 16.2 \text{ mSv}$$

The effective dose equivalent is, therefore, the dose equivalent weighted for the susceptibility to harm of different tissues.

Collective dose equivalent is the quantity obtained by multiplying the average effective dose equivalent by the number of persons exposed to a given source of radiation. It is expressed in man-sieverts (symbol man-Sv).

Maximum permissible dose is the strict limit on the effective dose equivalent that a person may receive. For a radiation worker this is 50 mSv, and for a member of the public, 5 mSv. These values must be observed without regard to cost, and are designed to control the incidence of effects, such as cancer, that involve an element of probability.

The type, energy, radioactive half-life, relative biological effectiveness and any concentration in particular tissues or organs are all combined to give maximum permissible body burdens, which also take into account the differing radiosensitivities of the different body tissues.

Radiological protection

In considering radiological protection strategies it is necessary to distinguish between sealed and unsealed sources of radiation.

Sealed sources

As the term suggests, the source is contained in such a way that the radioactive material cannot be released, e.g. X-ray machines. The source of radiation can be a piece of radioactive metal, such as cobalt, which is sealed in a container or held in another material which is not radioactive. It is usually solid and the container and any bonding material are regarded as the source.

Unsealed sources

Unsealed sources may take a variety of forms – gases, liquids and particulates. Because they are unsealed, entry into the body is comparatively easy.

Criteria for radiological protection

The basic criteria for radiological protection rest on three specific considerations – *time*, *distance* and *shielding*. The principle is to ensure that no one receives a harmful dose of radiation.

(a) Radiation workers may be protected on a time basis by limiting the duration of exposure to certain predetermined limits.
(b) Alternatively, they may be protected by ensuring that they do not come within certain distances of radiation sources. This may be achieved by the use of restricted areas, barriers and similar controls. The Inverse Square Law applies in this case.
(c) They may be shielded by the use of absorbing material, such as lead or concrete, between themselves and the source to reduce the level of radiation to below the maximum dose level. The quality and quantity (thickness) of shielding varies for the radiation type and energy level and varies from no shielding through lightweight shielding (e.g. 1 cm thick Perspex) to heavy shielding (e.g. centimetres of lead or metres of concrete).

'Half thickness' is the thickness of shielding required to reduce incident ionising radiation to half intensity.

Statutory radiological protection procedures

Statutory protection procedures from radiation are laid down in the Ionising Radiations Regulations 1985.

The main statutory requirements are:

(a) (i) no radioactive substance (in the form of a sealed source) is to be held in the hand or manipulated directly by hand, unless the instantaneous dose rate to the skin of the hand does not exceed 7.5 μSvh^{-1}; and
(ii) no unsealed radioactive substance, or article containing radioactive substance, is held in the hand or directly manipulated by hand;

[Regulation 6]

(b) Employees and other persons must not be exposed to ionising radiation beyond specified dose limits, i.e.
(i) 50 μSv for employees aged 18 or more,
(ii) 15 μSv for trainees under 18, and
(iii) 5 μSv for any other person;

[Regulation 7]

(c) employers must designate as controlled areas any area where doses are likely to exceed 30 per cent of any dose limit for employees of 18 or more;

[Regulation 8]

(d) employers must designate as supervised areas any area (not a controlled area) in which any person is likely to be exposed to more than 30 per cent of ionising radiation to which he would be exposed in a controlled area;

[Regulation 8]

(e) employers must designate as classified persons employees likely to receive a dose of ionising radiation exceeding 30 per cent of the relevant dose limit;

[Regulation 9]

(f) employers must appoint qualified persons as radiation protection advisers in cases where
(i) any employee is exposed to an instantaneous dose rate exceeding 7.5 μSvh^{-1}; or
(ii) the employer has designated a controlled area which persons enter;

[Regulation 10]

(g) in the case of classified persons, employers must ensure that all significant doses of ionising radiation received are assessed, preferably by use of personal dosemeters;

[Regulation 13]

(h) health records of classified persons and employees who have been overexposed must be kept for, at least, 50 years;

[Regulation 13]

(i) radioactive substances used as source of ionising radiation must be in the form of a sealed source;

[Regulation 18]

(j) the design, construction and maintenance of articles containing or embodying radioactive substances must prevent leakage;
[Regulation 18]

(k) employers must account for and keep records, for at least two years, of the quantity and location of radioactive substance(s);
[Regulation 19]

(l) radioactive substances are to be kept in suitable receptacles in a suitable store;
[Regulation 20]

(m) during transportation, radioactive substances are to be kept in a suitable labelled receptacle;
[Regulation 21]

(n) work is not to be carried out with ionising radiation unless an assessment is made identifying the nature and magnitude of the radiation hazard to employees and the general public;
[Regulation 25]

(o) where assessment shows that employees or the general public are likely to receive a dose of ionising radiation above the relevant dose limit, the employer must prepare a contingency plan to restrict exposure.
[Regulation 27]

Current extension of statutory controls to all workplaces means that more than 50,000 medical and 10,000 dental workers, as well as 10,000 university researchers, are now covered by law.

Radiological emergencies

With any process involving unsealed sources of radiation, a suitable emergency or contingency plan is needed (*see* Chapter 9). There is a special scheme called NAIR (National Arrangements for Incidents involving Radioactivity) which can be implemented via the police if there is a risk to the public following an incident, such as the loss of a source. The principal radiological emergency is a major release of radioactivity from a nuclear reactor. Following such accidental release, the radioactivity would be dispersed from the power station in a spreading plume or cloud, and in a manner determined by the characteristics of the release coupled with the prevailing weather conditions.

Emergency plans are required by law and exist for each station in the UK. They depend upon co-operation from the licensee, local authorities and emergency services. The administration of plans is facilitated by local liaison committees. Essentially the plans require:

(a) an early assessment of the magnitude and nature of the release,
(b) its dispersion in the environment, and

(c) the doses that might arise.

Measurement and detection of radioactivity

Geiger-Muller counter

The operation of this instrument is based on the fact that ionising radiations produce electrical charges which can be detected. One 'click' of a Geiger counter corresponds to one atom of radioactivity being detected. The Geiger counter (Fig. 23.2) is an extremely sensitive instrument and can be used for monitoring background radiation to the extent that a dose of one-fiftieth (background) of the maximum permissible dose can be detected.

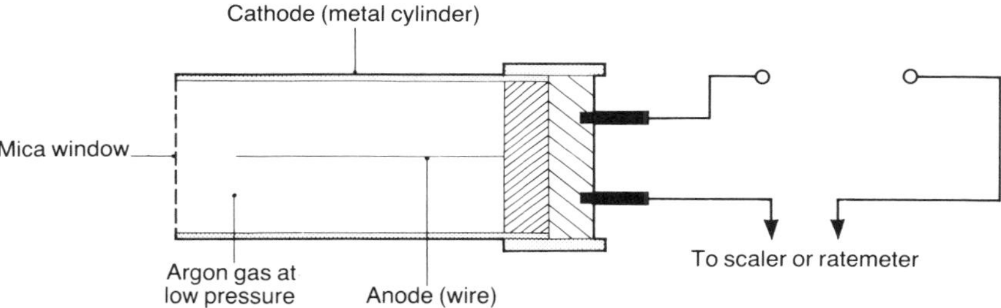

Fig. 23.2 Geiger counter

When radiation enters the tube, either through a thin window made of mica, or, if it is very penetrating, through the wall, it creates argon ions and electrons. These are accelerated towards the electrodes and cause more ionisation by colliding with other argon atoms. On reaching the electrodes, the ions produce a current pulse which is amplified and fed either to a scaler or a ratemeter. A scaler counts the pulses and shows the total received in a certain time. A ratemeter has a meter marked in counts per second (or minute) from which the average pulse rate can be read. It usually incorporates a loudspeaker which gives the characteristic click for each pulse. This instrument cannot deal with count rates in excess of 1,000 to 2,000 counts per second. It is very useful, however, for measuring low levels of radiation. It will not generally detect the presence of beta particles due to the relative thickness of the window.

Scintillation counter

This instrument measures radiation intensity and uses a screen of material which emits flashes of light when bombarded with alpha, beta, gamma and/or slow neutron radiation. These light flashes are converted to an electric current which increases as the bombardment increases. The current is amplified and indicated in the same way as with a Geiger-Muller counter.

Airborne sampler

As with airborne dust, certain radiations can be sampled on a filter paper using a high-volume air sampler. A known volume of air is drawn through a filter which is removed at the end of the sampling period and scanned for its radioactivity, using a counter.

Film badges

A film sensitive to radiation is housed in a specially designed plastic casing containing windows of various materials which shield certain kinds of radiation, but which allow others to pass through. This allows assessment of the various types of radiation. The device is worn during periods of exposure, one badge lasting a week. The film is developed and analysed for the accumulated dose of the various types of radiation, and a permanent record of the worker's personal exposure is produced.

Thermoluminescent personal dosemeter (TLD)

Some materials, such as lithium fluoride, can convert to an 'excited' state when bombarded with ionising radiation. This state is reversed only on the application of heat when the crystals return to normal, but with a measurable emission of light. Thus, a small badge containing these crystals can be used as a dosemeter, since the degree of irradiation can be related to the amount of light produced on heating. An advantage with this type of dosemeter is that it is small and its analysis can be quickly and automatically performed.

Quartz fibre detector (packet electrometer)

This detector consists of a metal cylinder with a loop of quartz fibre in the middle which is charged up to approximately 200 volts, electrical attraction or repulsion taking place between the fibre and the outside case. Ionising radiation will allow the charge to leak away slowly, permitting the loop to move over a scale back to the centre of the cylinder. This instrument will measure down to 5 millirems of dose and is ideal for use in short-term exposure situations, e.g. 1–2 weeks.

Assessment of information

Wherever radioactive sources or radio isotopes are under consideration for future use, as part of the assessment to ensure maximum safety, the following information/data must be known.

(a) The quantity of radiation, i.e. the activity in becquerels.
(b) The concentration of radioactivity in becquerels per gram.
(c) The types of radiation emitted – alpha, beta or gamma.
(d) The energy of each type of radiation in MeV.
(e) The penetrating power of the radiations, i.e. half-thicknesses or range in air, living tissue and the appropriate shielding materials (concrete, lead, etc.), though these depend upon (c) and (d) above.
(f) The radioactive half-life.
(g) The biological half-life, i.e. the time taken for the original level of radioactivity in the body to fall to exactly half.
(h) The relative biological effectiveness, which depends on (c) and (d) above.
(i) Any concentrations of the substance in particular tissues or organs after uptake in the body.
(j) The physical nature of the radioactive substance, i.e. solid, liquid or gas. (If solid, the degree of solubility is important, and if in liquid form, the vapour pressure.) Volatile liquids, gases and particulate solids are especially dangerous because of the inhalation risk. Where the substance can be absorbed through the skin, this fact should be known.
(k) The most appropriate monitoring devices for detecting the radiation, which will depend upon the types of radiation and energies involved.
(l) Maximum permissible body burdens and maximum permissible concentrations should be clear. Maximum permissible concentrations are listed, for instance, by the International Commission on Radiological Protection (ICRP) for air and water – i.e. air for breathing and drinking water – which are also derived from maximum permissible body burdens.
(m) The exact location, quantity and nature of all radioactive materials to be stored and used.
(n) The procedure for training personnel and the maintenance of dose records.
(o) The complete procedures in the event of accidental release together with safety drills necessary. These should include decontamination measures, warning systems and evacuation procedures.

The effects of exposure to radiation

The effects of a dose of ionising radiation vary according to the type of exposure, for instance, whether the dose was local, affecting only a part of the body surface, or general, affecting the whole body. Furthermore, the actual duration or length of time of exposure determines the severity of the outcome of such exposure.

Local exposure, which is the most common form of exposure, may result in reddening of the skin with ulceration in serious cases. Where exposure is local and the dose small, but of long duration, loss of hair, atrophy and fibrosis of the skin is known to occur.

The effects of acute general exposure range from mild nausea to severe illness, with vomiting, diarrhoea, collapse and eventual death. General exposure to small doses may result in chronic anaemia and leukaemia. The ovaries and testes are particularly vulnerable and there is evidence that exposure to radiation reduces fertility and causes sterility.

Apart from the danger of increased susceptibility to cancer, radiation can damage the genetic structure of reproductive cells, causing increases in the number of stillbirths and malformations. It is a maxim of radiological protection that all exposures must be the absolute minimum allowable. Dose equivalent limits for workers are:

(a) 0.5 Sv (50 rem) in a year for all tissues except the lens of the eye;
(b) 0.15 Sv (15 rem) in a year for the lens of the eye; and
(c) 0.05 Sv (5 rem) in a year for uniform irradiation of the whole body or its equivalent if the body is not uniformly irradiated.

The limits of 0.5 and 0.15 Sv in a year are to prevent those effects which only occur above relatively high doses, e.g. erythema (reddening/inflammation of the skin) together with increased cancer and genetic damage risks.

Dose equivalent limits for members of the public are:

(a) 0.05 Sv (5 rem) in a year for all tissues; and
(b) 0.005 Sv (0.5 rem) in a year for uniform irradiation of the whole body or its equivalent if the body is not uniformly irradiated.

Personal protective equipment

One-piece overalls or chemical grade suits are necessary when dealing with unsealed sources, together with respiratory protection in the form of breathing apparatus. However, thick overclothing will generally protect the individual from alpha and beta radiation provided dust respirators are worn and proper decontamination is carried out afterwards.

Disposal of radioactive wastes

Under the Radioactive Substances Act 1960, no person may dispose of, or accumulate for disposal, radioactive wastes except in accordance with an authorisation issued by the Department of the Environment. Where such disposal can safely be carried out, the conventional methods of waste disposal should be followed, i.e. discharge into sewers or disposal on refuse tips. In the case of refuse tips, the waste should be taken direct to the tip, without passing through any preliminary processing or handling, and immediately buried under at least 1.5 metres of refuse or refuse ash.

Radiological protection agencies in the UK

The International Commission on Radiological Protection (ICRP)

The ICRP was established in 1928. Today its activities, which are mainly concerned with setting dosage standards, cover all aspects from individual exposure to population exposure.

Health and Safety Commission and Health and Safety Executive

The Health and Safety Commission has overall responsibility for matters of public health and safety arising from industrial activities, and this includes radiation. The Health and Safety Executive enforces current legal requirements relating to ionising radiations in the workplace.

Nuclear Installations Inspectorate

Specific responsibility for nuclear installations rests with the Nuclear Installations Inspectorate, whose approval of any nuclear installation is a prerequisite for the granting of an operating licence. The Advisory Committee on Nuclear Installations advises the HSC on the siting, design, operation, etc., of nuclear installations.

National Radiological Protection Board (NRPB)

This board was set up in 1970 with the following functions:

(a) by means of research and otherwise, to advance the acquisition of knowledge about the protection of mankind from radiation hazards; and
(b) to provide information and advice to persons, including Government Departments, with responsibilities in the UK in relation to the protection from radiation hazards either of the community as a whole or particular sections of the community.

The board maintains a register of all radiation workers, except those employed by the Ministry of Defence. In fulfilment of its statutory functions, the board produces reports from time to time reviewing the radiation exposure of the population.

24

Personal protection

Reference was made earlier, in Chapter 12, to the twin strategies of 'safe place' and 'safe person'. Safe place strategies characterise much legislation, particularly provisions relating to access and egress, machinery and plant, environmental factors and the structural safety of premises. Wherever possible, a safe place strategy is preferred to a safe person strategy.

Personal protection, implying the provision and use of various items of personal protective equipment – e.g. safety boots, ear defenders – should be considered as a last resort when all other measures have failed, or purely as an interim form of protection until the hazard can be eliminated at source or by a form of safe place strategy. As a form of protection it relies too heavily on, first, the individual wearing the equipment, and second, wearing it correctly and for the full length of time that he may be exposed to the hazard, such as dust or noise. Above all, many forms of personal protection are uncomfortable and/or inconvenient to wear, particularly over long periods. It is, therefore, an imperfect solution for preventing occupational ill-health or personal injury. However, total safety can rarely be achieved. The technology for ensuring total protection may not have been developed, the cost of such protection may be out of proportion to the risks involved or – particularly in situations where workers frequently move from one location to another, as with welding operations – total protection may be impracticable. There is, therefore, a need for personal protective equipment with certain tasks, which is recognised in statutes and specific regulations.

The choice and use of personal protective equipment

A systematic approach is needed to ensure that workers at risk are properly protected. The main components of this approach are choice, introduction and use, maintenance, and the system for monitoring the effectiveness of personal protective equipment.

Choice

When considering the type and form of equipment to be provided, the following factors are relevant:

(a) the needs of the user in terms of comfort, ease of movement, convenience in putting on, use and removal, and individual suitability;
(b) the number of personnel exposed to a particular hazard, e.g. noise;
(c) the type of hazard, e.g. fume, dust, molten metal splashes, etc.;
(d) the scale of the hazard;
(e) standards representing recognised 'safe limits' for the hazard, e.g. British Standards, HSE guidance notes or codes of practice, in-house codes of practice (here, it should be understood, a standard, code of practice, or guidance note is not a legal instrument and cannot be enforced by the enforcing authorities. Their recommendations can, however, have legal consequences, particularly in criminal cases. *See* Chapter 4);
(f) specific Regulations currently in force, e.g. the Protection of Eyes Regulations 1974 (as subsequently amended);
(g) specific job restrictions or requirements, e.g. work in confined spaces, roof work;
(h) the presence of environmental stressors such as extremes of temperature, inadequate lighting and ventilation, background noise; and
(i) ease of cleaning, sanitisation, maintenance and replacement of equipment and/or its component parts.

Introduction and use

Users must be educated as to the reasons for personal protection, the nature of the protection provided and the correct way to wear the equipment. Moreover, where hazards are assessed on the basis of exposure over a period of time, e.g. noise and airborne particulates, the level of protection afforded will reduce dramatically with only partial use. This is particularly true in the case of exposure to noise levels in excess of 90 dBA, and workers must appreciate this fact. Other ways of promoting and reinforcing positive attitudes to the wearing of personal protective equipment are:

(a) involving workers in the choice and selection of equipment;
(b) requiring management and visitors to wear/use the personal protection in a hazardous environment or situation (it should be

remembered that the General Duties of the Health and Safety at Work etc., Act 1974 apply to all levels of management and, therefore, failure to observe them, e.g. not wearing eye protection in a designated eye protection area, can result in a criminal offence. Moreover, any injury suffered in consequence by such a person, or a visitor, might well mean loss of part or even all compensation. (*See* Chapter 2); and

(c) the use of safety propaganda such as safety posters, displays and demonstrations of the equipment to be used.

Maintenance

An effective maintenance system should ensure the routine repair and maintenance of personal protective equipment where this may be required, e.g. breathing apparatus. It may also be necessary to provide a sanitisation facility for some equipment, e.g. safety spectacles, ear muffs. (Provision and maintenance of personal protective equipment is both a common law and a statutory requirement, giving rise to both civil and criminal liability.)

Monitoring

There should be a permanent system for assessing the effectiveness, use and maintenance of equipment. Users should be encouraged to report any difficulties or problems.

Types of personal protective equipment

The following are the main categories of personal protective equipment.

Head, face and neck protection

Helmets: These protect the head from falling objects or overhead hazards. They should meet the British Standard BS 5240:1975 'Specification for General Purpose Industrial Safety Helmets'. Helmets should be strong but light. If they are too heavy, they will cause discomfort, particularly if worn for long periods. Individual head protection should be identified by means of a helmet numbering system or by the use of name tabs on helmets. In certain construction work, by trade union agreement, safety helmets must be worn on site unless there is 'no foreseeable risk of head injury' (Building Industry National Working Rule No. 12 – August 1981. This rule seems to relate to the position in common law negligence, where liability depends upon proof of foreseeable injury. *See* Chapter 2.)

Caps and hair nets: These prevent the hair coming into contact with moving machinery, e.g. the terrible 'scalping' accidents when long hair becomes entangled in the bits and chucks of vertical drilling machines. Long-haired workers, both male and female, should, where circumstances demand, be provided with a form of snood attachment, which completely encloses the hair. To refuse to wear such protection is a dismissible offence (*Marsh* v. *Judge International Housewares Ltd* [1976] COIT No. 511/57, Case No. 23119/76).

Face shields: These protect the area from the forehead to the neck against flying particles and splashes, i.e. metal dusts and chips, molten metal, glass splinters and chemicals. They are also used in spot welding. Manufactured in clear or tinted plastic or polycarbonate, they can be provided with chin guards to provide protection from upward splashing of molten metals or chemicals.

Eye protection

The Protection of Eyes Regulations 1974, as amended in 1975, place a specific duty on the employer to provide eye protection for employees, the type of protection varying according to the circumstances of the job (*see* Schedule 1 to the Regulations). Eye protection which is damaged, lost or destroyed must be replaced by the employer. In certain cases, 'persons at risk', i.e. employees not involved in the specific process, must be protected by a fixed shield or provided with eye protection as well. All eye protectors provided to comply with the Regulations must be manufactured in conformity with the appropriate approved specification. It is not necessary that they be BS 'kite marked', but they must be marked to indicate the purpose for which they are designed to be used, as follows:

General purpose	BS 2092
Chemical	BS 2092 + 'C'
Dust	BS 2092 + 'D'
Gas	BS 2092 + 'G'
Impact – Grade 1	BS 2092 + '1'
– Grade 2	BS 2092 + '2'
Molten metal	BS 2092 + 'M'
Glare	BS 1542/679

Devices conforming to more than one type can be marked with all the appropriate letters or figures. Attention is drawn to Schedule 1 of the Regulations which outlines the 'specified processes' for which a particular form of eye protection is needed.

Eye protection takes a number of forms:

Safety spectacles: These may have toughened glass or plastic lenses with plastic or metal frames. Lenses should not be removable as they could fall out. Spectacles can be supplied with side shields and should be fitted for the individual concerned, particularly if he has prescription lenses.

Safety goggles: These are generally cheaper and more versatile than spectacles. Users can experience discomfort when they are worn for long periods, however. Some designs can be worn over prescription lenses but this, too, may cause discomfort. Cup-type goggles protect against flying particles, welding glare or radiation, whereas wide-vision goggles (specific to purpose) give protection against flying particles, welding glare, radiation, dust, fumes and splashes.

Shields: Face shields, which can be hand-held, fixed to the helmet or strapped to the head, protect the face and eyes. The shield can also be fixed between the operator's head and his job.

Hearing protection

Any person working in an area where the equivalent continuous sound level (leq) exceeds 90 dBA for an 8-hour working shift should be provided with hearing protection. When selecting it, it is important to ensure that the form of hearing protection – acoustic wool, ear plugs, ear muffs – will produce the necessary attenuation (sound pressure reduction) at the operator's ear. (*See* Chapter 21.)

The need for workers to wear hearing protection for long periods can be reduced by job rotation and reorganisation of tasks, so that part of the work may be done without exposure to noise, and short breaks during which exposed workers can relax in a quiet environment, perhaps in a sound haven. The principle should always be, however, to reduce noise at source, and the wearing of hearing protection regarded as an unavoidable last resort.

Problems associated with hearing protection

The wearing of hearing protection incurs the risk that accidents could occur if audible warning signals or human speech are not heard, or if audible malfunction of machinery or equipment is not noticed. This situation can easily arise, particularly with intermittent noise and, unless this hazard can be eliminated, the use of hearing protection may introduce dangers far worse than those of impaired hearing. The problem of disorientation, through wearing hearing protection for long periods, is a further risk which management must consider.

Forms of hearing protection

Hearing protection takes three principal forms:

Ear plugs: There are fitted into the auditory canal. They tend to move out of place with jaw movements. Ear plugs are manufactured in plastic, rubber, glass down or combinations of these materials.

Ear defenders, muffs and pads: These cover the whole ear and can reduce exposure by up to 50 dBA at certain frequencies. They can be uncomfortable in hot conditions and difficult to wear with safety spectacles or goggles. Many safety helmets incorporate a fitting for attaching ear defenders.

Ear valves: These are inserted into the auditory canal and, theoretically, allow ordinary conversation to continue while preventing harmful noise reaching the ear.

Respiratory protection

Use of respiratory protection (*see* Fig. 24.1) is essential wherever workers are exposed to dangerous concentrations of toxic or fibrogenic dusts, or fumes – e.g. from paint spraying – or where they may work in unventilated spaces. The correct selection and use of respiratory protection is absolutely vital and a guide to the use of different forms of protection is shown at pages 297–301. Management should decide on the respiratory protection required in individual circumstances. The use of face masks (*see below*) is definitely not recommended as a means of protection against anything other than low concentrations of nuisance particulates and atomised liquids. Reference should be made to BS 4275:1974 'Recommendations for the Selection, Use and Maintenance of Respiratory Protective Equipment' and to the quoted nominal protection factor for the equipment.

Nominal protection factor

BS 4275:1974 refers to the selection of respiratory equipment and lists nominal protection factors for different forms of equipment. The nominal protection factor (NPF) measures the theoretical capability of respiratory protection and is calculated thus:

$$\text{NPF} = \frac{\text{Concentration of contaminant in the atmosphere}}{\text{Concentration of contaminant in the face-piece}}$$

Forms of respiratory protection

Face masks: These are a simple device for holding filtering media against the nose and mouth to remove coarse nuisance dust particles or

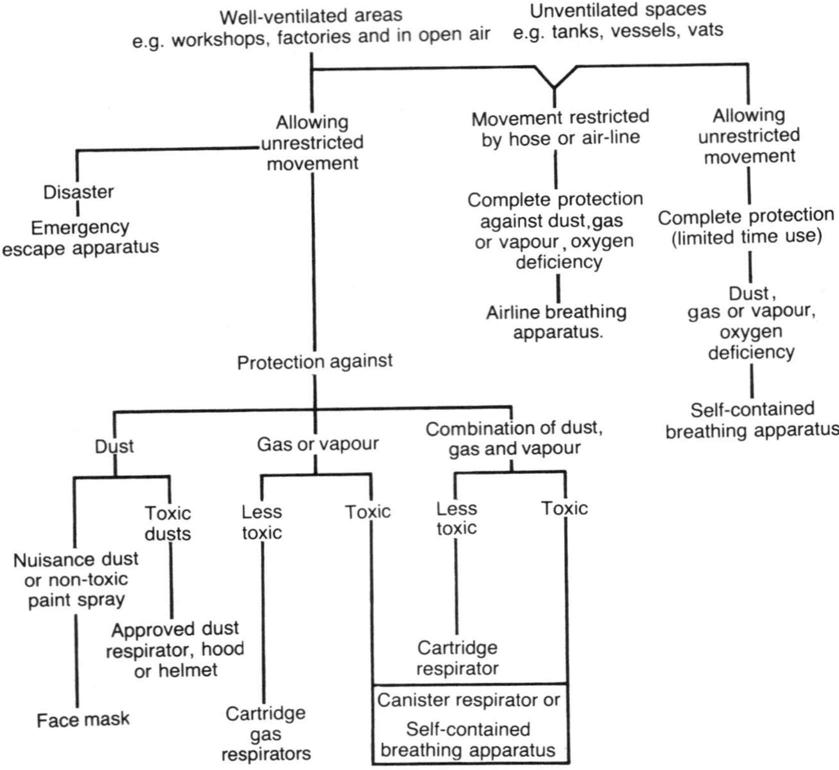

Fig. 24.1 Selection of respiratory protection

non-toxic paint sprays. They should *not* be used for protection against dangerous or toxic substances.

General purpose dust respirators: These take the form of an ori-nasal face mask and a particulate filter to trap finely divided solids or liquid particles. BS 2091:1969 'Specification for Respirators for Protection against Harmful Dusts, Gases and Scheduled Agricultural Chemicals' provides a classification and specification for such forms of general purpose respiratory protection. In addition, the HSE specify 'approved' types for certain industries. For industries involved in work with substances subject to specific legislation, e.g. asbestos, the HSE has instituted an approval scheme for respirators suitable for compliance with the hygiene provisions of that legislation. There are three groups, which are listed on forms available from HMSO, namely:

F2486: 'Dust Respirators of All Sorts Suitable for Work with Asbestos, Lead and Other Dangerous Dusts'

F2500: 'Blasting Helmets (for Operations Involving Shot Blasting and Allied Operations)'
F2506: 'Chemical Works Respirators'

An approval scheme is dependent on a respirator manufacturer applying to the HSE and paying for the testing.

Positive pressure powered dust respirators: These comprise an ori-nasal face mask fitted to a power-driven pack carried on the individual and connected by a flexible hose. They are more efficient than the simple form of dust respirator, as they utilise a much more efficient filtering medium and operate with positive pressure in the face-piece. Their construction is specified in BS 4558:1970 'Specification for Positive Pressure Powered Dust Respirators'.

Helmet-contained positive pressure respirators: This device provides head, eye, face and lung protection together with a high degree of comfort (*see* Fig. 24.2). It incorporates a helmet and visor with a high-efficiency axial fan mounted at the rear of the helmet, which draws the dust-laden air through a coarse filter. The partially filtered air is then passed through a fine filter bag. The filtered air provides a cool pleasant airstream over the entire facial area, and is finally

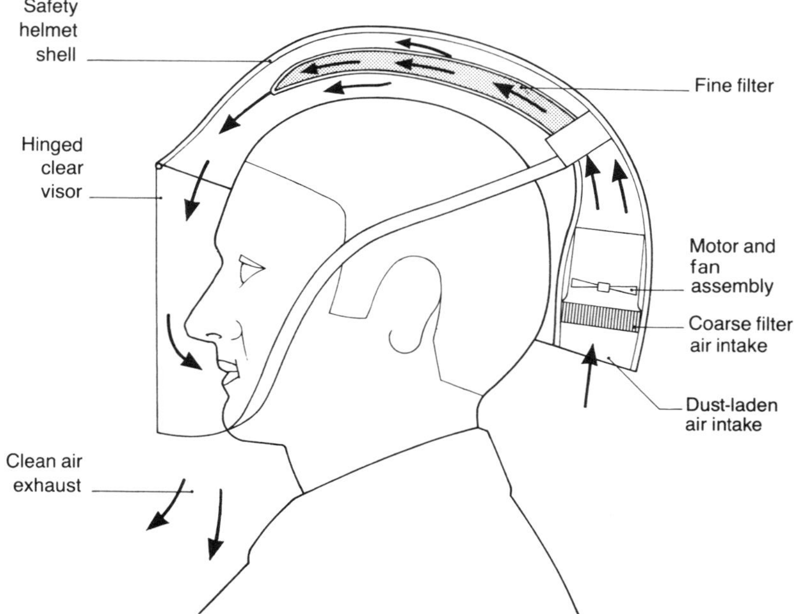

Fig. 24.2 Helmet-contained positive pressure respirator

exhausted at the bottom of the visor at a flow rate sufficient to prevent dust entering the mouth or nose. The low voltage electrical power is supplied by a lightweight rechargeable battery pack, connected to the helmet by means of a flexible cable. This portable battery pack may be clipped to a belt or carried in an overall pocket.

Gas respirators: This respirator takes two forms, cartridge and canister. The cartridge respirator is similar to the dust respirator. It uses a chemical cartridge filter and is effective against low concentrations of relatively non-toxic gases or vapours which have an acceptable level of concentration exceeding 100 ppm. Canister respirators, on the other hand, are normally of the full face-piece type with exhalation valves, incorporating goggles and visor. They are connected to a chemical canister filter for protection against low concentrations of designated toxic gases or vapours. The manufacturer's instructions on the avoidance of cartridge/canister saturation, maximum periods of use in relation to concentrations of gas in air, shelf-life, etc., must in all cases be carefully followed. They are effective against toxic gases and vapours in limited concentrations. A particulate filter can be incorporated to remove dust particles.

Emergency escape respirators: These are specially designed respirators using a chemical filter which will enable persons to escape from dangerous atmospheres in an emergency. They are intended for very short-term use and should never be used for normal industrial protection.

Air-line breathing apparatus: This apparatus consists of a full face mask or half mask connected by flexible hose either to a source of uncontaminated air (short distance) or to a compressed air-line via a filter and demand valve. The apparatus is usually safe for use in any contaminated atmosphere (see manufacturer's stated nominal protection factor) but is limited by the length of the air-line, which also places some restriction on movement. When using a fresh-air hose, a pump is necessary for lengths over 10 metres. Reference should be made to BS 4667: 1974 Part 3 'Specification for Breathing Apparatus: Fresh Air Hose and Compressed Air Line Breathing Apparatus'.

Self-contained breathing apparatus: This may be of the open or closed circuit type. The open circuit type supplies air by a lung-governed demand valve or pressure reducer connected to a full face-piece via a hose supply. The hose is connected to its own compressed air or oxygen supply which is carried by the wearer in a harness. The closed circuit type incorporates a purifier to absorb exhaled carbon dioxide. The purified air is fed back to the respirator after mixing with pure oxygen. Both types of apparatus may be used in dangerous atmospheres or where there is a deficiency of oxygen, or for rescue purposes from confined spaces. The following British Standards are relevant in the case of self-contained breathing apparatus:

BS 4667:1974 'Specification for Breathing Apparatus':
Part 1 – Closed Circuit Breathing Apparatus
Part 2 – Open Circuit Breathing Apparatus

NOTE. The UK is a multiracial society, yet many respirators are designed for the European face. Negroid and Asiatic faces are not normally catered for, and this can leave gaps in the fit between face and mask. Beards, moustaches and sideburns can also create gaps in the fit, or reduce the efficiency of fit. Thus, in certain cases, it may be necessary to provide certain people with positive pressure powered dust respirators as opposed to general purpose dust respirators.

Skin protection

Where industrial dermatitis develops it is often due to failure by the individual to wash off immediately any chemicals from the skin. Personal cleanliness is of utmost significance in many processes. For instance, cotton waste or rag, if used to wipe off oils from the skin, should not be kept in the trouser pocket owing to the risk of scrotal cancer. In *Stokes* v. *GKN Sankey Ltd* [1968] 1 WLR 1776, the defendant employer was held vicariously liable for the failure of the company doctor to warn the plaintiff employee of the danger arising from rubbing oil on his overalls, i.e. scrotal cancer. The plaintiff later contracted cancer and brought a successful suit. (For 'vicarious liability' *see* Chapter 2.)

Chemical substances causing dermatitis include strong acids and alkalis, chromates and bichromates, formaldehyde, organic solvents, resins, certain adhesives, suds, degreasing compounds and lubricants. Paraffin and trichlorethylene remove the natural fats from the skin and render it liable to damage by other substances. Where dermatitis is identified, medical aid should be sought. The principal cause of dermatitis is poor personal hygiene. The presence, however, of dermatitis is often a first indication of exposure to dangerous substances, in particular primary irritants and secondary cutaneous sensitisers (*see* Chapter 19). As an additional precaution, therefore, the use of barrier creams is recommended.

A range of barrier creams is available to meet varying work conditions. They provide skin protection in wet conditions, and for workers handling acids, alkalis and other potentially dangerous substances. The barrier cream must be applied to the hands and forearms before work commences. Failure on the part of employees to use a barrier cream may well mean that, if they contract dermatitis, they are not entitled to damages against their employer (*Clifford* v. *Challen & Sons Ltd* [1951] 1 AER 72).

Barrier creams should be used only as an *aid* to protection and should not be regarded as a protection against powerful skin damage agents. The greatest care should be taken to avoid contact with corrosive chemicals. The use of barrier creams before work generally dispenses with the need to use skin cleansers other than soap. Where skin cleansers are used, these should be as weak as possible, consistent with effective cleansing, and should be completely removed from the skin by washing with soap and water. The use of perfumed barrier creams in catering and food preparation can result in taint in the foods under preparation.

Body protection

This classification includes one-piece and two-piece overalls, donkey jackets, aprons, warehouse coats, etc., which can be of the washable, disposable or semi-disposable (short life) type. In selecting the correct body protection, the following factors are relevant:

(a) the degree of personal contamination from the task or process, e.g. dust, oil, general soiling;
(b) the level of hygiene control necessary for the product, e.g. food manufacture;
(c) whether a wet or dry process is involved;
(d) the ease and cost of washing or dry cleaning;
(e) individual preferences shown for specific types of protection (*see above* and Chapter 5);
(f) the degree of exposure to temperature and humidity variations;
(g) possible discomfort produced by moisture/sweating when wearing impervious garments; and
(h) ease of storage.

There is a general statutory requirement (HSWA, sec 9) for employers to provide the accommodation for safety equipment, protection and appliances, detailed in the Factories Act 1961, sec 59(1), free of charge. A civil action for breach of section 59, e.g. loss of clothing, will lie against employers. The same provisions apply under legislation relating to ionising radiations.

It is now common practice for employers to provide overalls, donkey jackets, foul weather clothing, wellington boots, etc., for the use of employees whilst at work. Company rules should prohibit employees returning home in such equipment due to the risk of contamination from processes, dangerous substances and other agents being taken into public transport and the home. Moreover, this would reduce the losses of protective garments and increase the life of such garments.

Hand and arm protection

A wide variety of hand and arm protection is available, from general purpose fibre gloves to PVC fabric gauntlets and sleeves, depending upon the hazards. Persons exposed to risk of injury through handling operations, or exposure to dangerous substances, or through the use of hand tools, such as knives, chisels, hammers and strapping equipment, should be provided with protection. A recent development has been a range of chain mail protective wear for personnel using knives, particularly in abattoirs, meat-packing establishments and butchers' shops.

A chart outlining the principal hazards to hands, the typical operations involved, suitable protective materials and suggested glove types is incorporated in *The Hand Book* published by RoSPA (Hamilton, 1983).

Leg and foot protection

Many injuries are caused as a result of poor standards of leg and foot protection; others are caused because management fail to provide protection or workers fail to wear it. Foot protection should be waterproof, resistant to acids, alkalis, oils and other substances, and incorporate steel toecaps where workers handle items such as drums, crates or other heavy containers. Safety footwear should incorporate a safety toecap to either Grade 1 or Grade 2 standard under BS 1870:1976–81 'Safety Footwear'. Where safety boots are provided, e.g. for drivers and maintenance fitters, the toecap should be to Grade 1 standard. With wet processes, wellington boots provided should incorporate protective fins for ankle, instep and leg protection, a deep tread patterned outsole and internal steel toecap. Moreover, the provision of gaiters for workers exposed to flying sparks and molten metal during casting operations is well established in law and practice in the UK (Foundries (Protective Footwear and Gaiters) Regulations 1971). Where, on construction sites, workers are likely to tread on sharp objects, such as nails projecting through timber, consideration should be given to safety footwear incorporating steel sole inserts in addition to safety toecaps.

Safety belts, harnesses and lanyards

All three items must conform to BS 1397:1979 'Industrial Safety Belts, Harnesses and Safety Lanyards'. A safety harness must incorporate simply fitted quick action buckles and fixed rings positioned in a manner which avoids body contact. Harnesses should be adjustable over the range of body sizes, and should incorporate quickly adjustable waist and shoulder straps, fixed leg straps, a safety line and two canvas pockets for carrying tools and other items. This requirement is particularly relevant in the case of self-employed or contract window cleaners working on high-rise buildings, e.g. office blocks. The design, construction and materials used should minimise adverse effects on the body in the event of a fall. The safety line should not exceed 1.83 metres in length and should be of double thickness tubular-woven high-elasticity nylon cord with a minimum breaking strength of 35 kg/cm^2, attached to a belt by a 'D' ring and with a steel Karabinier safety hook at the anchorage end. Safety harnesses are recommended in preference to safety belts.

Safety belts should only be considered as a safeguard when it is impracticable to wear the full harness. Belts should carry a record card indicating the date of the last inspection by a responsible employee.

Safety lanyards are used when workers may be moving within a fixed area above ground level, e.g. on a mobile access tower or loading stage. They incorporate a 2 metre length of webbing contained in a spring-loaded drum. One end of the webbing is hooked to a fixed anchorage point, the other end to the worker's belt. The webbing extends from and retracts to the fixed drum as the worker moves. In the event of a fall, the belt locks, the nylon webbing stretching slightly to cushion the operator as the fall is arrested.

Eye and face washes and emergency showers

Wherever workers are exposed to contact with strong acids and alkalis, an emergency eye and face wash facility is necessary. This can be an emergency eye and face irrigation bottle, a permanently installed eye and face wash point, particularly in laboratories, or a larger combined emergency shower unit and eye wash station adjacent to a bulk chemical storage area. A safety shower can be stationed in an internal or external location. It delivers a large quantity of water quickly in order to prevent chemical burns.

25

Occupational hygiene practice

Occupational hygiene

Hygiene

One definition of *hygiene* is 'the science of the preservation of health' (*see* Chapter 17 on this subject). People need to protect their health in terms of the food they eat (food hygiene) and the air they breathe (atmospheric hygiene). Occupational hygiene, therefore, is concerned with the preservation of health whilst at work.

Occupational hygiene

Occupational hygiene has been defined as 'the identification, measurement and control of contaminants and other phenomena, such as noise and radiation, which would otherwise have unacceptable adverse effects on the health of people exposed to them' (Annual Report of HM Chief Inspector of Factories, 1973). It is concerned with the monitoring and control of the working environment to ensure that contaminants are kept to as low a level as is reasonably practicable and, in all cases, to a level that is above the appropriate hygiene standard, i.e. below the exposure limit. The provision of a safe working environment forms part of the legal duty of all employers (Health and Safety at Work etc., Act 1974, sec 2). (*See* Chapter 3.)

Principles and practice of occupational hygiene

Wherever environmental contamination is present, or suspected to be present, the following sequence of operations is necessary.

Recognition and identification

The recognition and subsequent identification of the specific contaminant – e.g. dust, fume, gas, vapour, mist, virus, sound pressure level – is the first stage in the sequence. A number of spot check devices are used such as detector stain tubes for gases, coated slides for dust or, in the case of noise, a sound pressure level meter.

Measurement

Once the contaminant has been identified, it is necessary to measure the extent of the contamination. A wide range of equipment is available for the accurate measurement of environmental contamination (*see* Gill and Ashton, 1982).

Evaluation

Evaluation is an important part of the procedure. Measured levels of contamination must be compared with existing hygiene standards (always assuming there is such a standard applicable to the material in question), such as exposure limits (control limits and recommended limits). (*See* Chapter 18.) In addition, the duration and frequency of exposure to the contaminant must be taken into account. Following a comprehensive evaluation, a decision must be made as to the actual degree of risk to workers involved. This degree of risk will determine the control strategy to be applied (*see* Chapter 26).

Control

The implementation of a specific control strategy is the last of the four stages of occupational hygiene practice. In extreme cases it may be necessary to implement a total prohibition strategy; in less severe situations the risk to the health of workers may be eliminated by the installation of a system of exhaust ventilation.

Measurement techniques

Stress in the working environment can be created by the presence of dust, gases, fumes and vapours, extremes of lighting, temperature, ventilation and humidity or by the presence of high sound pressure levels, radiation or vibration. Whatever the cause of the stress, there must be a system of control to ensure adequate protection for the worker. Whilst systems for the measurement of noise and radiation are dealt with in Chapters 21 and 23, this chapter is principally concerned with the measurement of airborne particulates, a process which involves the taking of air samples for measurement purposes.

Air sampling

Air sampling can be undertaken on either a short-term or a long-term basis.

Short-term sampling techniques (grab sampling, snap sampling)

Grab sampling implies taking an immediate sample of air and, in most cases, passing it through a particular chemical reagent which responds to the contaminant being monitored.

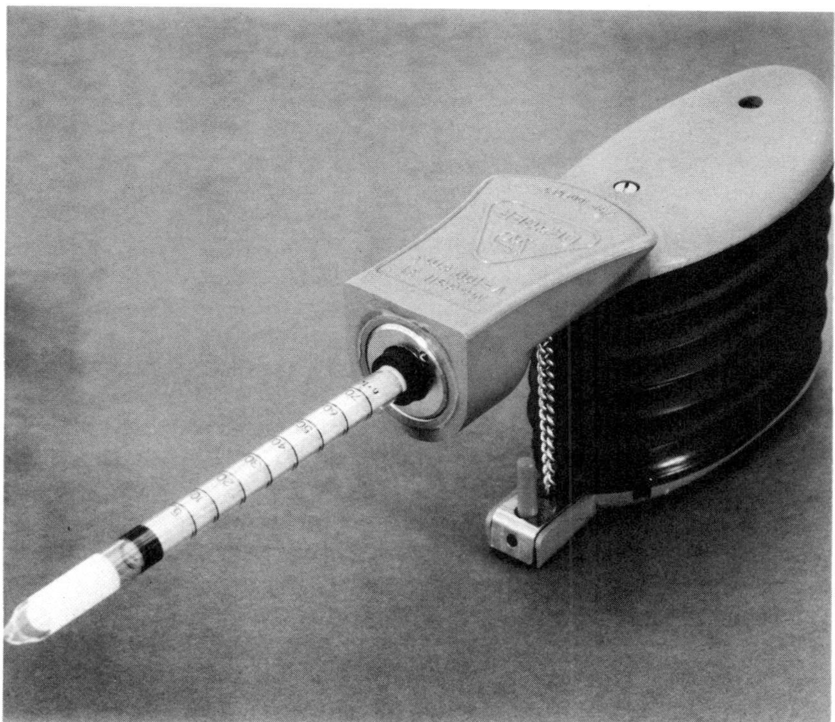

Fig. 25.1 Multi-gas detector
Reproduced by courtesy of Draeger Safety

The simplest device for the measurement of concentrations of gases and vapours is the hand pump and bellows device (multi-gas detector – *see* Fig. 25.1) which incorporates a specific detector tube. The detector tube is a glass tube, sealed at both ends, and filled with porous granules of an inert material, such as silica gel. The granules are impregnated with a chemical reagent which changes colour in the presence of the contaminant gas. In order to detect and measure this gas, the ends are broken off the tube and the tube inserted into the tube holder of the sampling pump. The correct volume of air is drawn through the tube (*see* Fig. 25.2), according to the number of times the bellows are depressed, and the resultant colour stain indicates the presence of the gas.

The actual concentration can be determined either by the length of the stain, which increases proportionally with the concentration, or by comparing the intensity of the colour with a prepared standard. The sampling pump is small, light and hand-operated. The combination of pump and detector tube provides a convenient method of on-the-spot evaluation of atmospheric contamination.

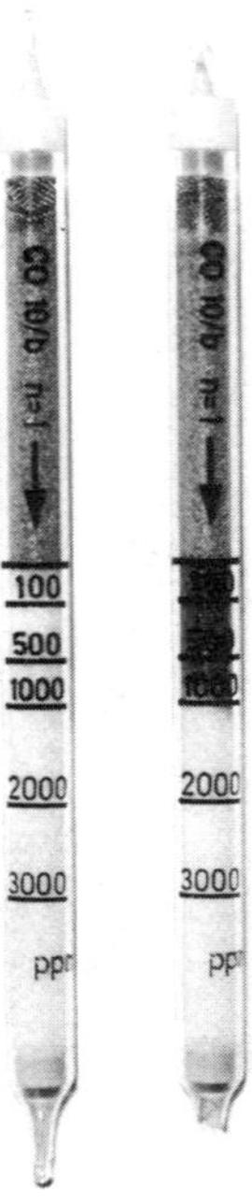

Fig. 25.2 Gas and vapour detector tubes
Reproduced by courtesy of Draeger Safety

The hand pump and bellows device is a useful instrument for the early detection of atmospheric contamination. Users do not require extensive training and it can be used relatively cheaply in random sampling exercises or routine day-to-day monitoring. However, its accuracy must always be suspect owing to the problems of cross-sensitivity of detector tubes, tubes being used that have gone past the expiry date or even the operator failing to give the appropriate number of pump strokes when operating the bellows. Therefore, when frequent monitoring must be undertaken, an automatic system should be provided. Furthermore, normal stain tubes will only give 'point in time' results and, dependent on circumstances, may not give an adequate picture of major fluctuations in concentration across a working shift.

Long-term sampling techniques

Instruments which carry out long-term sampling are, broadly, of two types, personal samplers and static samplers.

Personal sampling instruments: There are several kinds of personal sampling instruments, e.g. gas monitoring badges, filtration devices and impingers. With gas monitoring badges, the worker wears a badge containing a solid sorbent or a chemically impregnated carrier and the air sample comes into contact with the badge by diffusion. The results can be read directly by a colour change or determined by analytical instruments.

Filtration devices comprise a low-flow or constant-flow sample pump, which is motor-operated from a rechargeable battery, and a sampling head, which incorporates a specific filter, attached close to the operator's breathing zone. Many dusts, mists, etc., can be collected by passing a known volume of air through a filter, the pore diameter of which is selected to remove the chemical hazard completely. The quantity of dangerous material collected may be determined gravimetrically (weighing the filter before and after collection) or by solvent extraction and analysis by gas chromatography, atomic absorption, etc. Filtration methods are particularly useful in the sampling of large particles or aggregates of particles.

The impinger method is used for collecting such chemical compounds as acetic anhydride, hydrogen chloride, etc. The impinger is a specially designed glass bubble tube. A known volume of air is bubbled through the impinger containing a liquid medium chosen to react chemically to, or physically to dissolve, the contaminant. The liquid is then analysed by gas chromatography, spectrophotometry, etc. An impinger operates in conjunction with a constant-flow sample pump. It may be mounted on the side of the sampling pump, which is worn on the operator's belt, or in a holster near the breathing zone.

Another method of personal sampling is with the aid of a sorbent tube, which is a method for collecting a large percentage of the hazardous chemical vapours in a work environment. A glass sample tube is used, normally filled with two layers of a solid adsorbent capable of completely removing chemicals from the air. The tube has breakable end tips. To collect a sample, the end tips are broken and a known volume of air is drawn through the tube. Airborne chemicals are trapped by the first adsorbent layer, with the back-up layer assuring removal of all the chemicals from the air. The tube is then sealed with a push-on cap prior to analysis. The tube may be inserted into a tube holder, located in the breathing zone of the operator, which is connected to a constant-flow pump, or direct into the pump by means of a short extension piece.

Static samplers: These are devices stationed in the working area. They sample continuously over the length of a shift, or longer period if necessary. Mains or battery operated pumps are used. They can sample contaminants which may be present in the general atmosphere in very small quantities but which nevertheless may be dangerous. Such pumps can handle large or small quantities of air per minute and pass it through a variety of sampling devices. For obtaining samples of harmful dusts such as asbestos or silica, filters of various ranges of porosity are used. Where the particle size of the dust is significant, size-selective filters are used. Moreover, when the substance to be sampled is volatile, e.g. a solvent vapour, or must be analysed in solution, the contaminant must be trapped onto a suitable medium, such as activated charcoal, or in an absorbing liquid, for subsequent laboratory analysis.

Long-term stain detector tubes are now available for this purpose. The device is connected to a constant-flow pump and air is drawn through the tube at a steady rate. Examination of the detector tube at the termination of the sampling period will indicate the amount of contaminant absorbed, which is directly related to the average level of contamination present over the period.

A number of direct monitoring devices are also available for the detection and measurement of gases and vapours. They operate on several different principles, e.g. infrared absorption, and give an instant read-out on a chart, meter or display. In many cases they can be linked to an alarm device which sounds once a particular concentration of gas or vapour reaches a predetermined level.

26

Control strategies in occupational hygiene

Occupational health practice and occupational hygiene are closely related, their basic objective being the prevention or reduction of stress in the working environment, the outcome of which can be occupational ill-health and disease.

Principles of control

The Health and Safety at Work etc., Act 1974 clearly identifies the duty of the employer to provide a safe working environment (HSWA, sec 2(2)(*e*); *see* Chapter 3). Control strategies must be directly related to this duty. In the control of occupational health hazards, many approaches are available, depending upon the severity and nature of the stress. The principal control strategies and support strategies are outlined below.

Prohibition

This is the most extreme form of control applicable and forms the basis for the prohibition notice (*see* Chapter 4). As a strategy, prohibition characterises much of the legislation relating to known carcinogens, as well as other hazards where there is no known form of protection for the operator. Prohibition, therefore, implies a total ban on a particular system, the use of a dangerous chemical substance or the operation of a practice where the danger level is unacceptable.

Substitution

The substitution of a less toxic material in place of a more highly toxic one, e.g. toluene for benzene, is a frequently used control strategy. A further example is the substitution of trichloroethane 1,1,1 in place of carbon tetrachloride.

Segregation

Segregation is a method of controlling the risks from toxic materials or physical hazards such as noise and radiation. It can take a number of forms, thus:

Segregation by distance (separation)

This is the relatively simple process where a person separates himself from the source of the danger. This is appropriate in the case of noise where, as the distance from the noise source increases, the risk of occupational deafness reduces. Similar principles apply to radiation. Segregation by distance protects those at secondary risk, if those at primary risk are protected by other forms of control.

Segregation by age

The need for protection of young workers has reduced over the last 50 years but, where the risk is marginal, it may be necessary to exclude young persons, particularly females, from an activity. An example of such segregation occurs in the Control of Lead at Work Regulations 1980, which exclude the employment of young persons in lead processes.

Segregation by time

This refers to the restriction of certain hazardous operations to periods when the number of workers present is small, for instance at night or during weekends, and when the only workers at risk are those involved in the operation. An example of such an operation is examination by radiation of very large castings.

Segregation by sex

There is always the possibility of sex-linked vulnerability to certain toxic materials, particularly in the case of pregnant women, where there can be damage to the foetus, e.g. in certain processes involving lead.

Change of process

Improved design or process engineering can bring about changes to provide better operator protection. This is appropriate in the case of machinery noise or dusty processes. A typical example is the dressing of seed corn with mercury-based fungicides. Traditionally, this was carried out in a seed-dressing machine in which the fungicidal powder was brushed onto the seed corn as it passed along a conveyor inside a dressing chamber. The fungicide escaped through apertures in the construction of the chamber, contaminating the atmosphere and surrounding structural items. A change to liquid seed dressing using a sealed spray chamber has eliminated this toxic dust hazard.

Controlled operation

Controlled operation is closely related to the duty under HSWA, sec 2(2)(*c*), to provide a safe system of work. It is particularly appropriate where there is a high degree of foreseeable risk. It implies the need for high standards of supervision and control, and may take the following forms:

(a) isolation of processes in which dangerous substances are used or where there may be a risk of heat stroke;
(b) the use of mechanical or remote control handling systems, e.g. with radioactive substances;
(c) the use of permit to work systems, e.g. entry into confined spaces such as closed vessels, tanks and silos, or fumigation processes using dangerous substances such as methyl bromide; and
(d) restriction of certain activities to highly trained and supervised staff, e.g. authorised persons working in high-voltage switchrooms.

Enclosure

This strategy is based on the containment of an offending agent or environmental stressor to prevent its liberation into the working environment. Enclosure may take a number of forms, e.g. acoustic enclosures for noisy machinery, dust enclosures, paint spray booths, laboratory fume cupboards (*see* Chapters 15 and 22).

Reduced time exposure (limitation)

Risks to health from dangerous substances or physical phenomena such as noise can be reduced by limiting the exposure of workers to certain predetermined maxima. This strategy forms the basis for the establishment of occupational exposure limits, i.e. long-term exposure limits (8-hour time-weighted average value) and short-term exposure limits (10-minute time-weighted average value). (*See* Chapter 18.)

This strategy is encompassed in the Department of Employment's (1972) *Code of Practice for Reducing the Exposure of Employed Persons to Noise*, whereby the total noise dose over an 8-hour day, 5-day week must not exceed 90 dBA.

Dilution

There is always some danger in handling chemical compounds in concentrated form. Handling and transport in dilute form reduce the risk. This strategy is appropriate where it is necessary to feed strong chemicals into processing plant regularly or carry quantities of dangerous substances for short distances in open containers. Generally, such practices should be discouraged and, wherever possible, eliminated by process change. Dilution is a poor form of control strategy.

Neutralisation

This is the process of adding a neutralising compound to another strong chemical compound, e.g. acid or alkali, thereby reducing the immediate danger. This strategy is practised commonly in the transportation of strong liquid waste chemical substances, e.g. acid-based wastes, where a neutralising compound is added prior to transportation, and in the treatment of factory effluents prior to their passing to a public sewer.

Ventilation

Ventilation may be by natural or mechanical means. The former refers to ventilation produced as a result of natural leakage of air into a building through doors, windows and other openings in the fabric. It is subject to variable weather conditions and the direction of the prevailing wind and, in the control of toxic fumes or airborne particulates, is unacceptable as a control strategy. Mechanical ventilation systems take a number of forms:

(a) extract ventilation – receptor systems, captor systems, local exhaust ventilation, low-volume high-velocity systems; and
(b) dilution ventilation.

Extract ventilation is an important control strategy in the prevention of occupational disease from exposure to dusts, fumes, vapours, gases and mists (*see* Chapter 15).

Support strategies

Reference was made in Chapter 12 to the twin concepts of 'safe place' and 'safe person'. The above control strategies are essentially 'safe place' strategies, where there is a duty upon the employer to provide a safe working environment to protect the health of workers. In order to comply fully with these duties, the following support strategies should also be noted.

Cleaning, housekeeping and preventive maintenance

Cleaning and housekeeping is an important support strategy in the prevention of accidents and occupational disease. Emphasis should be placed, where appropriate, on the use of portable mechanical cleaning equipment rather than on manual methods of cleaning. Moreover, housekeeping inspections should feature in any general safety inspection system. Within the field of preventive maintenance, the potential for leakage of dangerous substances from pipework, ducting and processing plant is considerable. Maintenance schedules, therefore, should include parts of the premises and plant where there is a high degree of risk, e.g. pressure vessels, bulk chemical stores (*see also* Chapter 16).

Welfare amenity provisions and personal hygiene

Good standards of sanitation, hand cleansing, showers and clothing storage facilities are a prerequisite to personal hygiene. Welfare facilities should cater for the direct needs of workers and the elimination of the health hazards to which they may be exposed, e.g. the risk of dermatitis (*see* Chapter 16).

Personal hygiene control measures include the following:

(a) strict control over decontamination procedures, particularly before eating, drinking, smoking or leaving the premises at termination of work;
(b) a prohibition on eating, drinking and smoking wherever there may be a risk of hand-to-mouth contamination, e.g. handling dangerous substances;
(c) use of barrier creams and other forms of skin protection directly related to the risks;
(d) procedures for sanitisation of eye, face and hearing protection, or the use of disposable forms of protection;
(e) total prohibition of workers returning home whilst wearing contaminated protective clothing;
(f) training at induction and on a regular basis in the principles of personal hygiene and its relationship to existing health risks;
(g) linking personal hygiene requirements with current industrial relations policy; and
(h) formulation and formalisation of a company hygiene policy accompanied by strict enforcement.

(For the legal consequences of failure by employers and employees to comply with safety and hygiene policies, resulting in breach of contract of employment, *see* Chapter 5.)

Personal protection

Although HSWA, sec 2, generally requires the provision of personal protective equipment by employers and the wearing of it by employees, this strategy must be considered a last resort or a short-term strategy until control can be achieved by more permanent means. Clearly, it is also wrong to expect employees to wear potentially uncomfortable and inconvenient protective equipment if alternative control strategies can be employed. (*See* Chapter 24; also Chapter 5 for the legal position concerning failure to make use of protective measures.)

Health screening and first aid

There is now increasing emphasis on occupational health, including health screening, as a support strategy, together with first aid and other services (*see* Chapters 20 and 29).

Training, propaganda and joint consultation

The training of staff to identify health risks and measures to avert them should feature in every company training programme. Operators must be made aware of the potential hazards, understand management actions and directives, and appreciate that their co-operation is needed to make the environment a safe and healthy one for themselves and fellow workers. Co-operation by employees is a legal requirement under HSWA, sec 7, and is also an implied condition of an employment contract at common law.

The use of various forms of health and safety propaganda, with a view to drawing the attention of workers to health risks, is a continuing process, and a wide range of posters, films and other forms of propaganda is available.

Joint consultation between employers and employees, through safety representatives, by the work of a health and safety committee or by the use of in-company working parties is an important tool in the prevention of health risks. The hazards must be identified and systems established to reduce, or preferably eliminate, the risks.

27 Ergonomics

The scope of ergonomics

Ergonomics is the scientific study of the interrelationships between people and their work. Ergonomics, or 'human factors engineering' or 'the scientific study of work', seeks to create working environments in which people receive prime consideration. It is a multidisciplinary study which incorporates the expertise of engineers, occupational physicians, occupational health nurses, occupational hygienists, health and safety specialists, organisation and method study people and research scientists in a team approach to the examination of numerous aspects of the working environment.

Egonomics is also sometimes narrowly referred to as the study of the 'man–machine interface'. This interface is significant in the design of working layouts and safe systems of work and in setting work rates. Ergonomics covers four main areas:

The human system

This is the study of the principal characteristics of people, in particular the physical elements of body dimensions, strength and stamina, coupled with the psychological elements of learning, perception, and reaction to given situations.

Environmental factors

This area examines the effects on the human system of the working environment, in particular the effects of temperature, light, ventilation, humidity, sound and vibration (*see* Chapters 15 and 21).

The man–machine interface

This is the study of displays, controls and design features of machinery, automation and communication systems, with a view to reducing operator error.

Total working system

Here consideration is given to fatigue, stress, work rate, productivity, systems effectiveness and the related aspects of health and safety. This area would cover, for instance, the aspect of working posture, in particular the need to ensure a correct and comfortable stance, in order to avoid long-term bad posture effects.

These areas of study may be summarised as in Table 20.

Table 20: The total working system – areas of study

Human characteristics	*Environmental factors*
Body dimensions Strength Physical and mental limitations Stamina Learning Perception Reaction	Temperature Humidity Light Ventilation Noise Vibration
Man–machine interface	*Total working system*
Displays Controls Communications Automation	Fatigue Work rate Posture Stress Productivity Accidents Safety

Ergonomic design

Important features in the design of the interface include the following.

Layout

Layout of working areas and operating positions should allow for free movement, safe access and egress, and unhindered visual and oral communication. Congested, badly planned layouts result in operator fatigue and increased potential for accidents.

Vision

The operator should be able to set and read easily control switches, dials and displays. This reduces fatigue and accidents arising from inadequate or faulty perception.

Posture

The more abnormal the working posture, the greater the potential for fatigue and long-term injury. Work processes and systems should be designed to permit a comfortable posture which reduces excessive job movements. This must be considered in the siting of controls and displays on machinery, plant and vehicles, and in the organisation of working systems, e.g. assembly work.

Work rate

Rates should be set to suit the operator. They need constant reassessment and revision. Movements which are too fast or too slow cause fatigue.

Comfort

The comfort of the operator, whether he is driving a vehicle or operating machinery, is essential for his physical and mental well-being. Environmental factors directly affecting comfort – e.g. lighting, temperature, ventilation and humidity levels – should be given priority.

Anthropometry

A key feature of ergonomic design is matching people to their equipment. Anthropometry is the study and measurement of body dimensions, the orderly treatment of resulting data and the application of those data in the design of workspace layouts and equipment. Few workstations are 'made to measure' owing to the wide range of human dimensions and the sheer cost of designing individual workstations and machines to conform with individual body measurements. The fact that this is not done creates many problems, best demonstrated by research undertaken at the Cranfield Institute of Technology, who created 'Cranfield Man'. Using a horizontal lathe, researchers examined the positions of controls and compared the locations of these controls with the physical dimensions of the average operator. Table 21 shows the wide differences between the two. The ideal operator would be 1.35 m tall with a 2.44 m arm span (*see* Fig. 27.1). Clearly, no effort had been made to design the machine even remotely within the bodily limitations of the average operator. During the last 10 years, however, greater attention has been paid to this aspect, particularly in the design of machinery. This can be seen in the improved design of controls and displays on motor vehicles, cranes, aircraft, computer terminals and processing machinery, the objective being to reduce operator fatigue and error, which lower productivity and contribute to accidents.

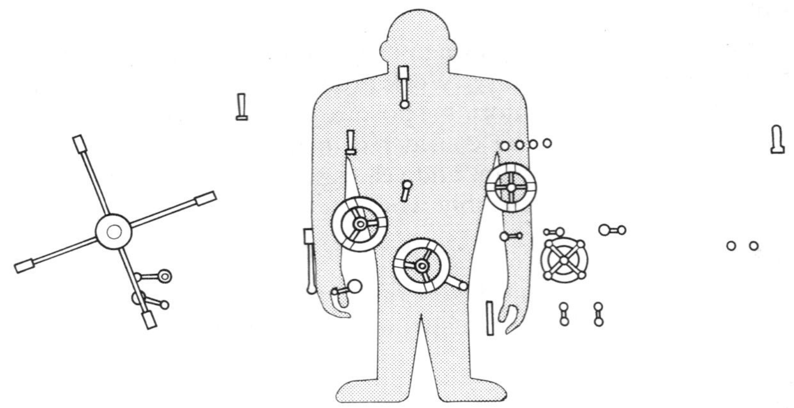

Fig. 27.1 'Cranfield Man' – 1.35 m tall with a 2.44 m arm span

Table 21: Physical dimensions of an average operator compared with those of 'Cranfield Man'

Average operator	*Dimension*	*Operator who would suit these controls*
1.75 m	Height	1.35 m
0.48 m	Shoulder width	0.61 m
1.83 m	Arm span	2.44 m
1.07 m	Elbow height	0.76 m

Interface design

The principal objective of interface design is to minimise the potential for error in the operation of plant and equipment. Equipment can include anything from a horizontal lathe to a jet aircraft. Design is concerned with two aspects, namely controls and displays. Controls take many forms, e.g. the steering wheel of a fork lift truck, the lever on a crane, an electrically operated stop–start button on a vertical drill.

Displays supply specific information to the operator. They are either static or dynamic. Dynamic displays, such as gauges, give an instant indication of variations, e.g. in pressure and temperature. (The most obvious form of dynamic display is a clock.) Static displays include instruction labels on plant and machinery, wiring diagrams and specific data relating to dangerous substances or emergency fire procedures.

In the design of controls and displays, it is necessary to consider the potential for error. This has been most apparent in the motor vehicle industry with its standardisation of gear-change routines, signalling and the layout of speedometer, fuel gauge and other gauges.

Principles of interface design

Separation

Physical controls should be separated from displays. The safest routine is achieved where there is no relationship between them.

Comfort

If separation cannot be achieved, control and display elements should be mixed to produce a system which can be operated with ease.

Order of use

Controls and displays can be set in the order in which they are used, e.g. left to right for start-up and the reverse direction for closedown of plant.

Priority

Where there is no competition for space, controls most frequently used should be sited in key positions. Controls such as emergency stop buttons should be sited in the most easily seen and reached position.

Function

With large consoles, controls can be divided according to functions. This division is commonly found in power stations. The layout relies heavily on the ability of the operator and speed of reaction. A well-trained operator, however, benefits from such functional division and the potential for error is reduced.

Fatigue

Convenient siting of controls is paramount. In designing a layout, the hand movements and body positions of the operator should be observed and studied.

28

Manual handling

Douglas A. Payne and Jeremy Stranks

More than a quarter of all industrial injuries result from manual handling activities. Statistics from the last 60 years indicate that in almost every year the number of people injured in this way has increased. As a result, more than 70,000 workers are off work for variable periods of time. This amounts to nearly 30 per cent of all reportable accidents. Even more surprising is the fact that, during this period, there have been greater advances in the technology and engineering aspects of mechanical handling than ever before. Certainly workers today perform fewer manual handling tasks than their grandfathers, and it would be reasonable, therefore, to expect a comparable reduction in injuries associated with manual handling.

Not only manual workers contribute to the handling injuries statistics, however. Those in sedentary occupations are similarly at risk, e.g. office workers, library staff, catering staff, hospital workers and people working in shops.

Current legal requirements

The Factories Act 1961, sec 72(1), requires that a person shall not be employed to lift, carry or move any load so heavy as to be likely to cause injury. Similar provisions are contained in the Offices, Shops and Railway Premises Act 1963 (sec 23). The Agriculture (Lifting of Heavy Weights) Regulations, 1959 indicate the maximum weight of a sack or bag which a worker employed in agriculture may lift or carry unaided as 81.648 kg. Other legal provisions dealing with lifting, particularly in the case of women and young persons, are covered in the Jute (Safety, Health and Welfare) Regulations, 1948 (Reg 4), the Pottery (Health and Welfare) Special Regulations, 1950 (Reg 6) and the Woollen and Worsted Textiles (Lifting of Heavy Weights) Regulations, 1926 (Schedule to Regulations).

Whilst the law has endeavoured to provide both general and specific requirements relating to manual handling of loads, their enforcement and the setting of standards has always been extremely difficult, particularly FA, sec 72, due to the fact that what constitutes an excessive load varies enormously from person to person by virtue of variations in the physique and strength of individuals. Levels of training, past experience and individual lifting technique also vary considerably.

Manual handling injuries and conditions

Typical injuries and conditions associated with manual handling can be both external and internal. External injuries include cuts, bruises, crush injuries and lacerations to fingers, hands, forearms, ankles and feet. Generally, such injuries are not as serious as the internal forms of injury which include muscle and ligamental tears, hernias (ruptures), prolapsed intervertebral discs and damage to knee, ankle, shoulder and elbow joints. One of the most significant injuries, and the one which results in frequent incapacity and even permanent crippling, is the prolapsed intervertebral disc. The various features of internal handling injuries are discussed below, together with certain conditions resulting from manual handling.

Muscle and ligamental strain

Muscle is the most abundant tissue in the body, and accounts for some two-fifths of the body weight. The specialised component is the muscle fibre, a long slender cell or agglomeration of cells which becomes shorter and thicker in response to a stimulus. These fibres are supported and bound by ordinary connective tissue, and are well supplied with blood vessels and nerves. When muscles are utilised for manual handling purposes, they are subjected to varying degrees of stress. Carrying generally imposes a pronounced static strain on many groups of muscles, especially those of the arms and trunk. This is a particularly unsuitable form of labour for human beings because the blood vessels in the contracted muscles are compressed and the flow of blood, and with it the oxygen and sugar supply, is thereby impeded. As a result, fatigue very soon sets in, with pains in the back muscles, which perform static work only, occurring sooner than in the arm muscles, which perform essentially dynamic work.

Ligaments are fibrous bands occurring between two bones at a joint. They are flexible but inelastic, come into play only at the extremes of movement, and cannot be stretched when they are taut. Ligaments set the limits beyond which no movement is possible in a joint. A joint can be forced beyond its normal range only by tearing a ligament: this is a sprain. Fibrous tissue heals reluctantly, and a severe sprain can be as incapacitating as a fracture. There are many causes of torn ligaments, in particular jerky handling movements which place stress on the joint, unco-ordinated team lifting, and dropping a load half-way through a lift, often caused by failing to assess the load prior to lifting.

Hernia

A hernia is a protrusion of an organ from one compartment of the body into another, e.g. of a loop of intestine into the groin or through the frontal abdominal wall. Both these forms of hernia can result from incorrect handling techniques and particularly from the adoption of bent back stances, which produce compression of the abdomen and lower intestines.

The most common form of hernia or 'rupture' associated with manual handling is the inguinal hernia. The weak point is the small gap in the abdominal muscles where the testis descends to the scrotum. Its vessels pass through the gap, which therefore cannot be sealed. Excessive straining, and even coughing, may cause a bulge at the gap and a loop of intestine or other abdominal structure easily slips into it. An inguinal hernia sometimes causes little trouble, but it can, without warning, become strangulated, whereby the loop of intestine is pinched at the entrance to the hernia. Its contents are obstructed and fresh blood no longer reaches the area. Prompt attention is needed to preserve the patient's health, and even his life will be at risk if the condition does not receive swift attention. The defect, in most cases, must be repaired surgically.

'Prolapsed' disc

The spine consists of a number of small interlocking bones or vertebrae (*see* Fig. 28.1). There are seven neck or cervical vertebrae, twelve thoracic vertebrae, five lumbar vertebrae, five sacral vertebrae and four caudal vertebrae. The sacral vertebrae are united, as are the caudal vertebrae, the others being capable of independent but co-ordinating articulating movement. Each vertebrae is separated from the next by a pad of gristle-like material (intervertebral disc). These discs act as shock absorbers and help to protect the spine. A prolapsed or 'slipped' disc occurs when one of these intervertebral discs is displaced from its normal position and is no longer performing its function properly. In other cases, there may be squashing or compression of a disc. This results in a painful condition, sometimes leading to partial paralysis, which may be caused when the back is bent while lifting, as a result of falling awkwardly, getting up out of a low chair or even through over-energetic dancing.

Rheumatism

Rheumatism is a painful disorder of joints or muscles not directly due

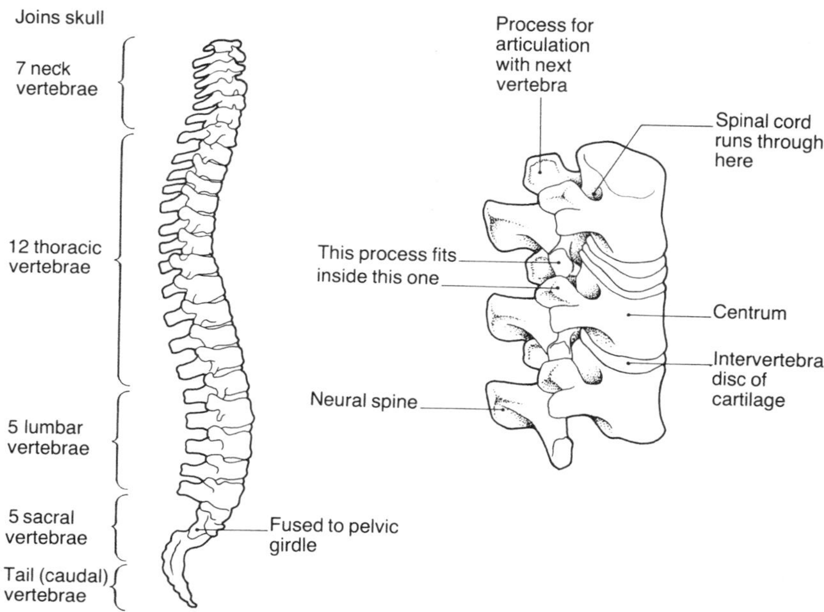

Fig. 28.1 The human spine

to infection or injury. This rather ill-defined group includes rheumatic fever, rheumatoid arthritis, osteoarthritis, gout and 'fibrositis', itself an ill-defined group of disorders in which muscular and/or joint pain are common factors. There is much evidence to support the fact that stress on the spine, muscles, joints and ligaments during manual handling activities in early life results in rheumatic disorders as people get older.

In industrial handling situations, therefore, there is an urgent need to instruct operators in correct techniques of movement and posture. Above all, they must be made aware of the importance of the correct assessment and planning of a task such as moving a particular load prior to tackling it.

Assessment prior to handling

Before examining the various problems of handling, the first important rule must be recognised, namely: 'If you think you can't manage to move the load, get help.' This may be help from another person or the use of a mechanical handling aid. The decision must ultimately be left to the person who is doing the job. There will rarely be a single deciding factor, however. The size, shape, weight, degree of rigidity, outside surface of the load, conditions such as the height of the load, state of the ground surface, headroom and temperature and, most important of all, the physical and temperamental characteristics of the individual concerned, must be considered. These factors are discussed below.

Size

Sizes of loads vary in terms of their actual volume. For instance, a sack of cement weighing 50 kg needs a totally different lifting technique from a box of feathers, measuring 1 m × 1 m ×1 m but of the same weight. The centre of gravity of the load should be as near to the body as possible (as with any lifting machine). Moreover, the wider the arms are stretched and the further the hands are in front of the body, the greater the tension on the shoulders, chest and back muscles. Often the use of straps, hooks and other handling aids will assist when moving large loads. There is also a considerable difference between handling indoors and outdoors, where wind velocity can affect individual lifting ability, especially where the handling of sheet materials or large light-weight loads is concerned.

Shape

It is essential to carry a load at the point of balance. Many loads are carried off balance and, in the case of a moving load in a container – e.g. liquids, loose items – the point of balance constantly changes.

Where more than one person is moving a large object, it is essential that the weight be evenly distributed among the people concerned, and that the contents of any container, box, drum, packing case or sack are known.

Weight

Many organisations and individuals have attempted to identify a maximum weight that people of different sexes and ages could handle safely. Indeed, this concept was embodied in several sets of Regulations already mentioned in this chapter. However, such a philosophy is not practicable for a number of reasons:

(a) all people are different in terms of physical strength, height, degree of physical fitness and body weight;
(b) if statute stipulated a maximum weight, the implication would be that the handling of a weight in excess of that figure was illegal and vice versa; this philosophy is suspect, since many strain injuries occur when moving the lightest of loads; and
(c) the weight of an object is only one factor in determining whether or not to move a load. For instance, reducing the overall weight of a load might be considered salutary, but a person is likely to take greater care when moving a large heavy load than a light one, and

he can abuse his body more easily with small light loads than with large heavy ones.

Lack of rigidity

A load likely to change its overall shape during handling can create difficulties in terms of grip and hold. Many materials are packed in sacks or bags. When these are pressure-filled, the 'floppy' nature of the load can pull a person off balance. A typical example here is in the nursing profession. Lifting patients, who may be totally or partially incapable of assisting, is the principal reason why this profession has such a bad record of muscular strain injuries. The fact that the load is live aggravates the problem, coupled with the need to provide careful support not only to the torso but to individual limbs. The difficulty in obtaining a satisfactory grip without harming the patient, who may have been injured, compounds the problem.

Outside surfaces

The material in which a load is packed can directly affect the ease with which it is handled. In the days of hessian sacks the handler used hooks, such as the docker's hook, and the roughness of the material enabled him to acquire a better grip and hold on the load. The increasing use of plastics has reduced this ability for obtaining a good hold. Moreover, the practice of shrink wrapping of goods has created its own handling problems in terms of gripping the load properly. The use of purpose-designed gloves can help in overcoming many of these problems. Such gloves are useful for moving smooth-surfaced loads, whether plastic-sacked goods, domestic appliances or even glass sheets.

Height

The location of a load and the positioning of the person's hands will affect the ease with which the load is moved. Hands can only perform a task efficiently when they are placed directly in front of the body, and close to it, in an area between the chest and thigh levels. Handling loads below the feet or above the head is inadvisable, but there are times when this is unavoidable. The use of hooks and other aids can assist when the load is below feet level. A typical example is keys used to lift manhole tops. Handling loads above head level is made the more hazardous because the handler cannot see the top of the load. This exposes him to the risk of other items falling on his head. The weight of a load should always be known when it is to be taken from a shelf, so that the person is not 'taken off guard' when he initially receives it. Here the use of staging or steps to permit the load to be at waist level is advantageous.

Ground or floor surface

Balance depends upon the stability of the base. If a person stands or moves on an unstable base, muscles will automatically be tensed to safeguard balance. Icy or wet surfaces also create this stiffening. When a person walks over a loose surface, this creates tension in the legs and lower parts of the body, e.g. walking over sand dunes. Suitable footwear should, therefore, be worn. When selecting footwear there is a tendency to consider the protection afforded to the toes only. However, on certain surfaces, the sole of the boot or shoe can stabilise the body. The use of safety shoes, with high-grip soles, generally improves body stability.

Headroom

Whenever a person needs to lower his head, he tends to adopt a top-heavy bending action. Many tasks are performed with restricted headroom, e.g. mining, and loading and unloading vans and other forms of transport. The removal of unconscious passengers from window seats of many airliners creates almost insurmountable problems for airline staff. Acquiring the ability to perform instinctively good 'base movements' as distinct from 'top-heavy bending' will reduce the risk of strain in such cases.

Temperature and humidity

Temperature and humidity affect the way and speed with which a person moves. If it is too cold, muscles tend to stiffen; a 'warming up' period should be allowed – not, however, using movements that cause 'stiffening up' but rather using gentle movements to stretch and shorten muscles by relaxing and tightening. An advantage of working in high temperatures is that the worker tends to move more slowly, reducing the discomfort of perspiring, and the tendency to employ sudden or snatching movements. Injury statistics for tropical climates indicate fewer strain injuries. Moreover, use of the correct clothing is important. Clothing should not be tight yet should be sufficiently close fitting to give freedom of movement. Gaps, especially around the waist, should be avoided when working outdoors.

Physical and psychological characteristics

It is not only the physical shape and size of a person that is important but posture and muscular condition. There are quite heavy jobs which can be undertaken successfully by small people. What they lack in body bulk, they may compensate for in dexterity, suppleness and timing. Age is also relevant, particularly the inevitable stiffening which accompanies the ageing process. So, too, is the temperament of an individual and the degree of mental stress which can affect muscular tension. The more placid the individual, the more likely he is to be a relaxed mover, making more fluid and 'segmental' movements than the jerky staccato-type movements associated with a tense person. Equally, a person's own physical performance will often vary from day to day, depending upon factors such as general state of health, food intake, amount of sleep, tasks performed the day before and general mental state.

All the above factors must be considered when assessing handling procedures. No single factor should be considered in isolation. It is incorrect to adopt a black-or-white approach to every situation, and frequently a compromise must be reached. Often, the really awkward job does not create difficulties when extra care and thought are given, but the simple everyday job, apparently with few risks, in some cases leads to severe injuries being sustained.

Handling techniques

General rules for safe lifting

(a) No one should ever attempt to lift anything beyond his capacity. If in doubt, get help.
(b) Where mechanical lifting aids are provided, they should be used.
(c) Extra care should be taken when lifting awkwardly shaped objects.
(d) In the analysis of individual posture and movement considerable observation of the operator is necessary. The following should occur at the moment the force is exerted on the load:
  (i) Position the feet correctly. The feet should be placed hip-width apart to provide a large base. One foot should be put forward and to the side of the object, which gives better balance.
  (ii) Bend or 'unlock' the knees and crouch to the load. The weight will then be safely taken down the spine and the strong leg muscles will do the work.
  (iii) Get a firm grip. The load should be gripped by the roots of the fingers and the palm of the hand. This keeps the load under control and permits it to be distributed more evenly up the arms. Use of the finger tips only can produce excessive tension in the forearms and possible loss of grip.
  (iv) Extend the neck upwards by tucking in the chin. This will automatically straighten the back as the load is taken. This does not mean in a vertical position, but inclined at an angle of approximately 15°. This prevents pressure on the

abdomen, reduces the risk of hernia and ensures an even pressure on the intervertebral discs.

(v) Keep the arms close to the body. This reduces muscle fatigue in the arms and shoulders and the effort required by the arms. It ensures that the load moves with the body and becomes, in effect, part of the body.

(vi) Use the leg muscles. Lifting should utilise the strong thigh muscles. Lifting should proceed by straightening the legs, lifting in one smooth and progressive movement from floor to carrying position. Push off with the rear foot.

NOTE. The above points should be considered as features of an overall smooth lifting movement and not a sole means of instruction.

(e) Hand protection, and arm protection where appropriate, should always be used, particularly when lifting rough loads, or loads with sharp edges or projections.

Specific handling activities

Some of these are illustrated in Figs. 28.2–28.6.

Human kinetics

This section examines the concepts of kinetics, first by observing the human being as a handling machine and, second, by relating these observations to the problems involved in handling which were discussed earlier, e.g. size, shape, weight, lack of rigidity. Correct and incorrect methods of movement are also considered.

Human kinetics follows from the detailed study of body reactions, and may be defined as 'the study of mechanical, nervous and psychological factors which influence the functions and structure of the human body as a means of producing higher standards of skill and reducing cumulative strain'. A simpler definition might be 'a technique of moving in a more relaxed and efficient way'.

Physiology of kinetics

Many injuries and disabilities arise from a common cause, namely cumulative strain, or stiffening of the body structures. When body structures are unduly tense their adaptability is reduced, and they are more easily injured and tired. Body structures are elastic, given to stiffening and relaxing, shortening and lengthening. If they are maintained in either state over a period of time, they will lose their elasticity. Indeed, one of the inevitable effects of growing old is the loss of suppleness accompanied by general stiffening throughout the body.

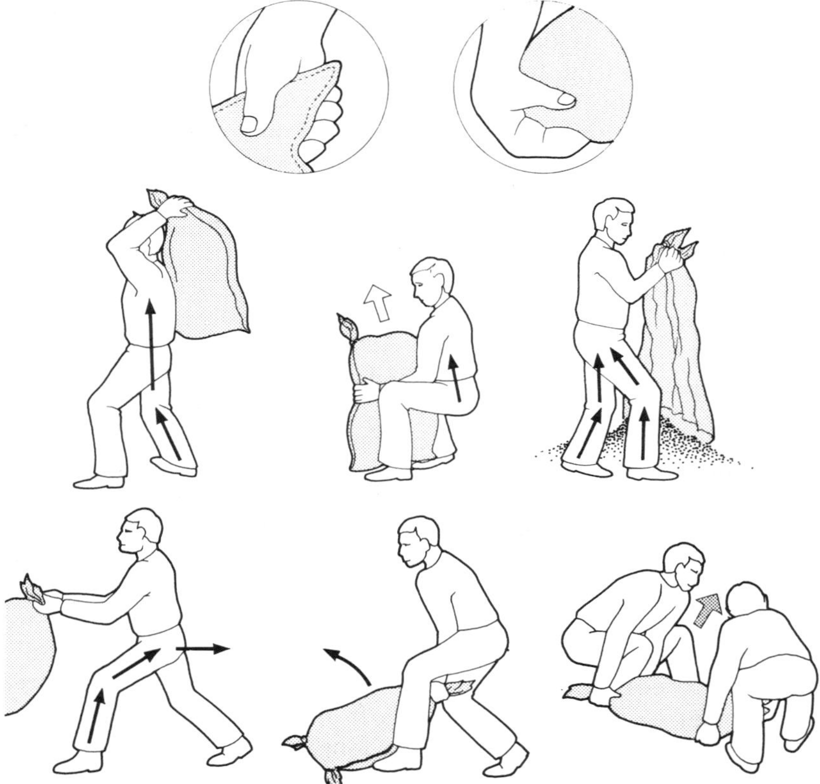

Fig. 28.2 Bag and sack handling
Gripping Take hold from below. Grip with the palms and the roots of the fingers
Carrying Relax the knees, arms in, and forward foot pointing in the direction of travel. Straighten knees to lift the load clear. Thrust strongly with rear foot to pivot and move off
Lifting Raise the head and straighten the back. Correct feet positioning enables the handler to swing the load forward then upwards. The leg muscles then do the work
Emptying Relax the knees. Keep the elbows tucked into the body
Laying a sack down Use front foot straight forward to thrust, with knee bent to let body move back as far as possible. Stretch rear foot well out to improve balance. Tuck the chin in to keep the shoulders stable. Keep the arms straight
Standing a sack up Lower the hands by relaxing the knees. Take a proper hold and position the feet correctly, one between the lugs, and one forward alongside the sack. Move forward and upwards in one rhythmic movement
Team lifting The same principles apply as for single lifting. The lift must be co-ordinated by the team leader
Source: Creber, 1967

Human tissues undergo structural changes as a result of reasonable activity regularly performed. Moreover, structural adjustment of tissue can be beneficial. It enables people to perform a particular task more easily, thereby developing a skill or 'knack' in the job, especially if the working method is related to sound kinetic principles. The kinetic method of movement depends upon good balance adjustment and tissue elasticity. In this case structural changes produced by regular, but not excessive, use of the tissues tend to be healthy and beneficial. In contrast, where the actions are carried out by sheer muscular effort and brute force, this increases the risk of strain and expedites development of other harmful conditions, such as rheumatism and fibrositis.

Rhythmic muscle contraction and relaxation has a salutary effect on body tissues whether movements are carried out performing a task or as a specific exercise. Sustained tension in the muscles inhibits their nourishment, restricts absorption of muscle waste products and causes fatigue, thereby undermining efficiency of effort. Where tension is sustained in a muscle, a 'muscle-bound' condition develops. The connective tissue which binds the muscle fibres becomes contracted so that it tends to resist expansion of muscle fibres and makes proper relaxation of the muscles impossible. Conversely, when the muscles are relaxed, the connective tissue will become sufficiently loose to allow the blood to circulate freely in the small blood vessels which carry nourishment to and waste materials from the muscle fibres. If the connective tissue is contracted for too long, the muscle fibres begin to lack vitality, become slower in action and more easily tired.

When a muscle contracts or tightens, it does not lose bulk. What it

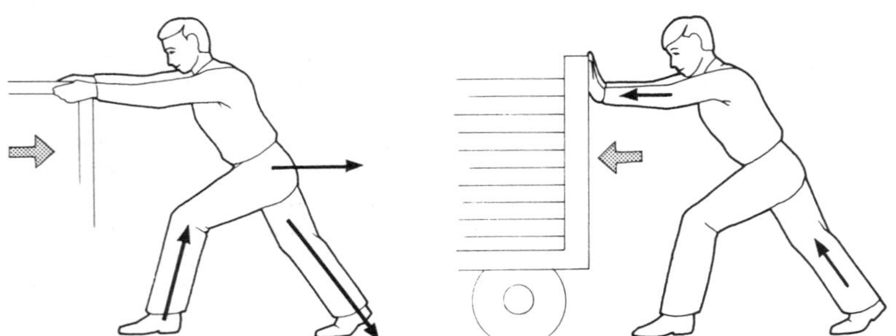

Fig. 28.3 Pulling and pushing
Tuck the chin in, keeping the back and arms straight. In pushing, the front foot should balance the body, while the rear foot, pointing forward, gives the thrust. In pulling, the back foot safeguards balance while the front leg, with knee bent to allow the body to move back, does the thrusting
Source: Creber, 1967

loses in length, it gains in breadth. Connective tissue is important to the economy of body movement, and sustained tension, which causes connective tissue to shorten, undermines the health and efficiency of the body. A good muscle is one that reacts quickly and accurately to the demands imposed by retaining or reacquiring elasticity in the connective tissue.

A large percentage of strains occur in experienced operators who have been doing a particular job for years prior to injury. It is sometimes cynically suggested that this problem arises as a result of carelessness brought about by overfamiliarity. Such suggestions are fallacious, however. The most common cause of injury in experienced workers is cumulative strain, usually arising from incorrect methods of working. Most strains and injuries arise as a result of repetitive incorrect body usage, contributed to by poor workplace design, systems of work or environmental factors. Additionally, however, body conditions dictate the way the body is used. Muscles are powerful in relation to their size, and the natural tendency to be proud of physical strength leads to muscle abuse. To use the body intelligently, individuals must learn to employ skill instead of brute force, thereby cultivating sensitivity rather than muscle bulk.

This can be illustrated by the two methods of pulling on a rope (*see* Fig. 28.8, *page* 337). If a 'doubled-up' position is adopted, brute force and sheer muscular effort are used, thereby explaining why there are so many strains and ruptures throughout industry. In a 'top-heavy' movement, the initial head-bending action causes concentration of pressure on the toes, simultaneously stimulating a chain of stiffening reactions throughout the body. Similarly, the doubled-up position puts a needless load on the abdominal and lower back muscles, causing congestion in the lower abdomen and pelvis, and leading to rupture or hernia. However, in the correct 'skilful' position the feet are so placed that the maximum amount of body weight is deployed and arm muscles, which

Fig. 28.4 Stowing and stacking
When stacking to high level, make the legs do the work. Relax both knees when approaching the stack and thrust upwards with a swinging movement, one foot following through
Source: Creber, 1967

are strongly contracted in the 'brute force' method, are under less strain when the arms are kept straight.

The character and effects of a movement are determined by how the movement begins. For example, if the position in a pushing action has been assumed by leaning forward in a top-heavy manner, the operator will increase resistance by pushing the load into the ground. There would also be excessive tension throughout the body. On the other hand, if the action had first started by unlocking the knees, the feet would adjust and the operator could push the load over the ground, thereby reducing resistance and requiring less muscular effort with correspondingly more effective use of body weight.

The human being is like a puppet on a string. Any task that requires lowering of the head or hands starts by unlocking the knees and the feet and works progressively upwards. Any upward movement starts by raising the head and works progressively downwards. This principle applies irrespective of the movement to be performed, e.g. lifting, pulling, pushing, thrusting, down pulling or just sitting or kneeling down. All movements start by relaxing or unlocking the knees to allow the feet to adjust to safeguard balance.

The correct and the incorrect way of moving

Good movement

Good movement is that which fulfils its function efficiently with the minimum of effort and cumulative strain. The key to this is co-ordination of muscular action, i.e. reciprocation between:

(a) muscles which contract to produce movement and those which elongate to allow it to take place;
(b) muscles concerned with maintaining and readjusting balance throughout the movement; and
(c) muscles which stabilise the spinal joints and the bases of the limbs during movement.

The most 'expensive' form of muscle work, in terms of energy expended and cumulative strain, is that involving sustained contraction of muscles. Housewives find that the most tiring jobs are working at the sink and ironing, which involve standing up with the feet side by side and bending the upper trunk, resulting in gradual build up of excessive tension and stiffening of body tissues, i.e. cumulative strain.

Body balance

Good balance is a prerequisite of most physical activities, from maintaining stationary positions to balance readjustment whilst performing movements. The slightest limb movement can change the centre of gravity, requiring balance readjustment. There are two ways of maintaining balance:

(a) by simply stiffening the legs; or
(b) by relaxing or unlocking the legs so that the feet can readjust to safeguard balance.

All movements performed in an upright position are either top-heavy or base movements. Top-heavy movements are those which begin by bending the head, upper trunk and arms, so that the legs and back stiffen to prevent the body falling. This leads to a staccato-type movement which concentrates stresses in the shoulders, neck and lower back. Sustained tension in the legs leads to circulatory deficiency, loss of resilience and predisposition to injury in the legs and back.

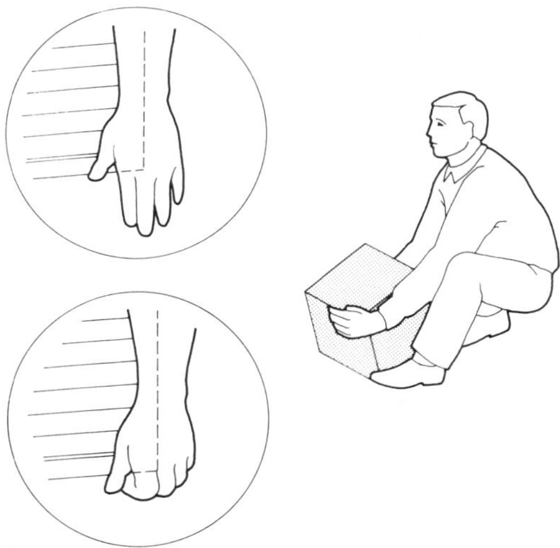

Fig. 28.5 Box handling
Grip with the palms to reduce finger strain. Position the feet as shown to maintain balance and give a strong thrust forward and upwards off the back foot. The arms should be close to the sides and the hands placed diagonally. The legs will then do the lifting
Source: Creber, 1967

A good movement (*see* Fig. 28.9) always begins as a base movement and is segmental. In contrast to the initial stiffening of the legs in a top-heavy movement, it begins by relaxation of the legs so that one foot can move automatically to safeguard balance. Simply bending the knees, however, is not necessarily relaxing to the legs. People tend to bend their knees excessively, leading to awkwardness in movement. In

Fig. 28.6 Spool handling
The head is raised, the chin tucked in and the back straight. To lift or lower, relax the knees, keep the arms into the body, stabilising one forearm inside the thigh, feet apart, with one foot forward, pointing in direction of travel. Grip with the palms and the roots of the fingers
Source: Creber, 1967

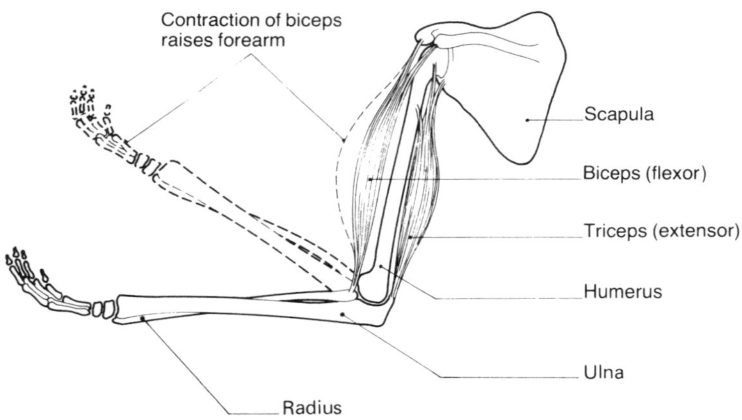

Fig. 28.7 Contraction of bicep muscle

a good movement, action in the knees is rather a 'giving' or unlocking of the joints.

Conclusion

Human kinetics is not simply a new type of drill routine to be employed in performing certain tasks, but a method of thinking which involves fundamental changes in attitude and physical habits. First, the problem itself must be clarified before deciding on the methods to be employed in dealing with that problem. Much confusion arises

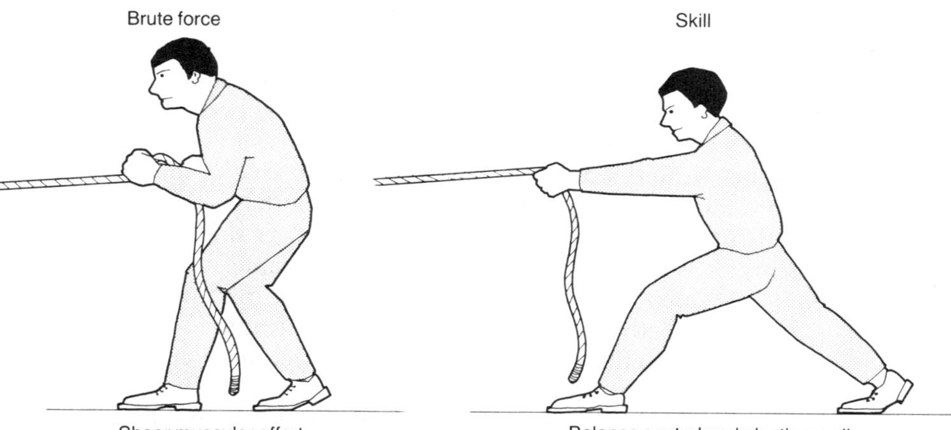

Fig. 28.8 Conflicting ideas of movement. Real strength depends upon skilful use of body weight, good balance adjustment and elasticity of body structures

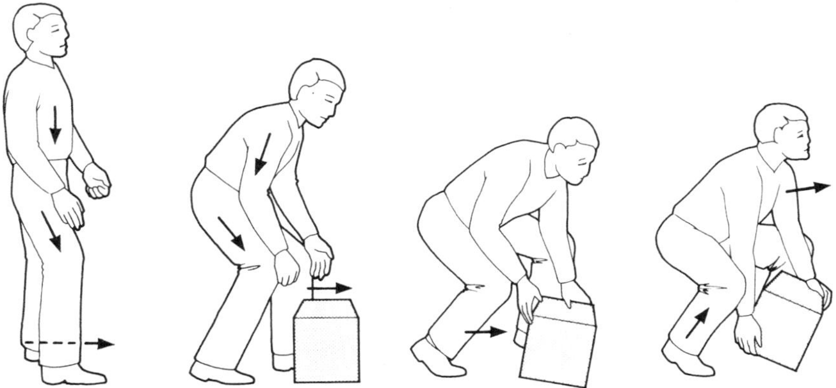

Fig. 28.9 Healthful movement
Progressive relaxation results from unlocking both knees as hands are lowered
Raising the head as hand takes the load automatically

when body movements are discussed because of different interpretations of the terms employed. For instance, if twelve people in a class were asked to 'arch' their backs, half would bend forwards and the other half backwards.

Whilst some people have a natural sense of good movement, in most instances individuals must be encouraged to change long-established physical habits and to acquire a new way of thinking regarding the mechanical use of their bodies. Instructors themselves must learn to feel reactions in their own bodies and acquire skill in getting others to do the same. Teaching should concentrate on practical experiments which make clear the basic principles of good movement, followed by explanations of how and why they influence the body structures. Practical demonstrations speak louder than words!

Even when trainees are fully convinced that kinetic methods of moving are more beneficial, there is a likelihood that old habits will reassert themselves when the individual ceases to think about his movements. It is for this reason that the main emphasis in teaching should be on cultivating good base movements, so that when movements begin correctly the correct movements will follow.

No matter how efficiently the primary instruction is carried out, long-established habits cannot be changed overnight. There should always be some form of follow-up. The role of immediate supervision is essential. The man who supervises the job has the most influence on how the individual carries out that job. Because of this, all supervisors should have an understanding of the basic aspects of good movement.

Human kinetics is a way of life and should be taught at a very early age. Waiting until people reach adulthood, before introducing them to the subject, may be too late.

29

First aid

Lawrence Bamber, BSc, DIS, MBIM, MIOSH, and Jeremy Stranks

First aid is a post-accident strategy vital to prevent loss of life and future deterioration in health following accidental injury or sudden illness. *First aid* is defined as 'the skilled application of accepted principles of treatment on the occurrence of an accident or in the case of sudden illness, using facilities and materials available at the time'. It is given:

(a) to sustain life;
(b) to prevent deterioration in an existing condition; and
(c) to promote recovery.

The most important areas of first aid treatment are:

(a) restoration of breathing (resuscitation);
(b) control of bleeding; and
(c) prevention of collapse.

These various areas are discussed later in this chapter.

General legal requirements

The practice of first aid within the UK needs to take account of the Health and Safety (First Aid) Regulations 1981. These Regulations provide that all employers should make first aid arrangements for all employees, and ensure that all employees are informed of such arrangements. The Regulations further require that a self-employed person provide his own first aid equipment. An approved code of practice gives practical guidance to employers and self-employed persons on how they may meet the requirements of the Regulations. The HSE has produced guidance notes, which supplement the Regulations and approved code of practice, and give advice on such matters as equipment and training. Within the Regulations, 'first aid' means:

(a) in cases where a person will need help from a medical practitioner or nurse, treatment for the purpose of preserving life and minimising the consequences of injury or illness until such help is obtained; and
(b) treatment of minor injuries which would otherwise receive no treatment or which do not need treatment by a medical practitioner or nurse.

First aid equipment and first aid rooms

The criteria for deciding on the scale and type of first aid equipment and rooms necessary within an organisation depend upon a range of factors including the number of employees, the nature of the undertaking, the size of the establishment, the geographical distribution of employees, the location of the establishment and the locations to which employees go in the course of their work.

First aid equipment

Every first aider should have access to first aid equipment and, in all establishments, employees should have reasonably rapid access to first aid. Thus all establishments need at least one first aid box, which should be clearly identified and readily accessible.

All first aid boxes and travelling first aid kits should contain a sufficient quantity of suitable first aid materials and nothing else. (Detailed information relating to the contents of first aid boxes and travelling first aid kits is given in the guidance notes.) The contents of first aid boxes should be replenished as soon as possible after use to ensure that there is always an adequate supply of materials available. It is therefore essential that first aid boxes and kits are checked frequently, to make sure they are fully equipped, and that all items are usable. Records of checks should be maintained. Other equipment needed may include carrying equipment, such as stretchers, blankets and protective equipment and clothing if there is a risk of the first aider becoming a casualty himself, whilst administering first aid.

First aid rooms

A first aid room should be provided in all establishments with 400 or more employees, and in all establishments which present special or unusual hazards. Where these circumstances do not apply, but where there is dispersed working, or where the location of the establishment makes access to places of treatment outside it difficult, the employer should consider whether a first aid room may be needed.

Where a first aid room is appropriate for an establishment, the following criteria should be adhered to:

(a) A suitably qualified person should be made responsible for the room and its contents.
(b) A first aider should be nearby or on call at all times when employees are at work.

(c) The first aid room should be made available at all times when employees are at work.
(d) The room should be located as near as possible to a point of access for transport to hospital.
(e) The room should contain suitable facilities and equipment, and should be effectively ventilated, heated, lighted and maintained.
(f) The room should be cleaned daily.
(g) The room should be large enough to accommodate a couch.
(h) The doorway should be wide enough to allow access for a stretcher, wheelchair, etc.
(i) A waiting room should be provided close to the first aid room.
(j) The room should be clearly identified as the first aid room and used solely for that purpose.
(k) A list of the names of qualified first aiders (or appointed persons), together with their work locations and the times at which they are available for first aid treatment, should be posted at the entrance to the first aid room, and elsewhere in prominent positions, e.g. notice boards, within the workplace.
(l) It is essential that, in the event of an injury, accident or sudden illness, immediate contact can be made with the first aider on call.
(m) In certain cases, workers should carry emergency aid cards (*see* Fig. 29.1).

The following facilities and equipment should be provided in first aid rooms:

(a) a sink with hot and cold running water, soap, nailbrush and paper towels;
(b) drinking water and suitable vessels;
(c) smooth-topped working surfaces;
(d) a couch with pillow and blankets;
(e) an adequate supply of sterile dressings;
(f) a clinical thermometer;
(g) clean garments for use by first aiders;
(h) a suitable store for first aid materials; and
(i) a lidded refuse container.

Simple first aid procedures

As many employees as possible should be trained in simple first aid procedures, namely resuscitation, control of bleeding and treatment of the unconscious patient, so as to ensure that casualties receive prompt attention. It may also be appropriate to train employees in other aspects of first aid, such as treatment for burns, scalds, broken bones and electric shock and in the event of gassing. A number of simple first aid procedures are outlined on pages 343–5.

EMERGENCY AID

Name ....

Address ....

....

Telephone number ....

In case of accident or illness, please inform next of kin

Name ....

Relationship..

Address ....

....

Telephone number ....

For emergency medical information, see below.

Height..................... Weight.................. Date of birth ....

Blood Group .... Religion ....

Allergic to..

....

Date of last tetanus injection..

Medical condition (tick ☑ where applicable)

☐ Heart condition	☐ Pacemaker	☐ Asthma
☐ Contact lenses	☐ Deaf	☐ Epilepsy
☐ Diabetic	☐ Hypertension	☐ Haemophilia
☐	☐	☐

(enter other conditions in spaces above)

RESCUE BREATHING AND HEART COMPRESSION INSTRUCTIONS INSIDE

Cannon House, The Priory Queensway, Birmingham B4 6BS IS222

Fig. 29.1 RoSPA emergency card

Resuscitation

Resuscitation (artificial respiration) may be required where the victim has suffered electric shock, gassing, suffocation or drowning. In each case, certain preliminary action is necessary as follows:

(a) Electric shock. Switch off the current if possible, otherwise pull victim from contact, using heavy-duty insulating gloves (to BS 697:1977) if available, rubber sheet, piece of dry timber, cloth, a folded newspaper, rope, the victim's own clothing if dry or other dry non-conducting material. Extreme care must be taken not to touch the victim's skin before the current is switched off.
(b) Gassing. Remove the victim to the fresh air or a gas-free atmosphere as quickly as possible, ensuring that the rescuer is wearing suitable respiratory protection, e.g. breathing apparatus.
(c) Suffocation. If the victim has been buried in loose materials, e.g. earth, immediately and quickly clear any debris from his mouth and nose. It may be desirable in this case to begin mouth-to-mouth resuscitation immediately the victim's head has been uncovered.
(d) Drowning. Remove the victim from water with all speed. Clear any debris from his mouth. If rescue is by boat, begin resuscitation in the boat.

Once the victim is clear of danger, resuscitation should be commenced immediately as the first minutes are vital, and should be continued without interruption until breathing is restored or until a doctor certifies that life is extinct. Resuscitation procedure is described in Fig. 29.2.

Bleeding

If bleeding is more than minimal, control it by direct pressure. Apply a pad of sterilised dressing or, if necessary, direct pressure with the fingers or thumb on the bleeding point. Raising a limb, if the bleeding is sited there, will help reduce the flow of blood (unless the limb is fractured).

Unconsciousness

Where the patient is unconscious, care must be taken to keep the airways open. This is done by clearing the mouth and ensuring that the tongue does not block the back of the throat. Where possible, the patient should be placed in the 'recovery position' (*see* Fig. 29.3).

Broken bones

Unless he is in a position which exposes him to further danger, no attempt should be made to move a casualty with suspected broken

1 RECOGNISE A LACK OF OXYGEN

Arising from
ELECTRIC SHOCK
DROWNING
POISONING
HEAD INJURY
GASSING etc

May be causing
UNCONSCIOUSNESS
NOISY OR
NO BREATHING
ABNORMAL COLOUR

2 ACT AT ONCE

SWITCH OFF ELECTRICITY, GAS, etc.,
REMOVE CASUALTY FROM DANGER
SEND SOMEBODY FOR HELP

GET A CLEAR AIRWAY ...
REMOVE ANY OBSTRUCTION ... then

BREATHING MAY RESTART ... IF NOT ...

3 APPLY RESCUE BREATHING

START WITH FOUR QUICK DEEP BREATHS

SEAL NOSE AND BLOW INTO MOUTH

or

SEAL MOUTH AND BLOW INTO NOSE

KEEP FINGERS ON JAW BUT CLEAR OF THROAT

MAINTAIN HEAD POSITION

AFTER BLOWING INTO MOUTH or NOSE, WATCH CASUALTY'S CHEST FALL AS YOU BREATHE IN

REPEAT EVERY 5 SECS

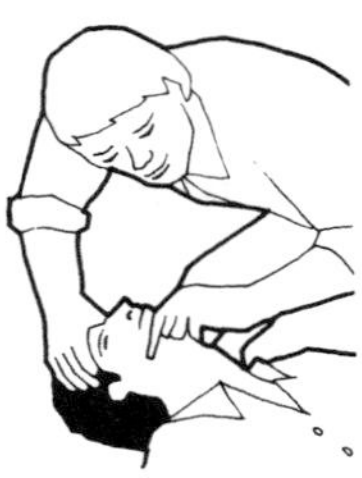

AFTER FIRST FOUR BREATHS TEST FOR RECOVERY SIGNS

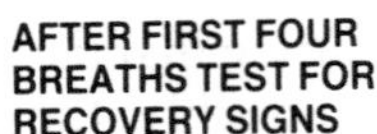

1. PULSE PRESENT?
2. PUPILS LESS LARGE?
3. COLOUR IMPROVED?

PULSE POINTS

4 IF NONE, COMBINE RESCUE BREATHING & HEART COMPRESSION

PLACE CASUALTY ON A FIRM SURFACE

COMMENCE HEART COMPRESSION

HEEL OF HAND ONLY ON LOWER HALF OF BREASTBONE
OTHER HAND ON TOP, FINGERS OFF CHEST

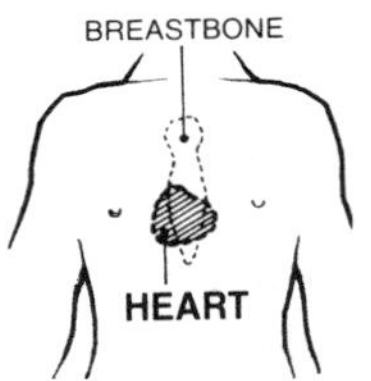

KEEP ARMS STRAIGHT AND ROCK FORWARD TO DEPRESS CHEST 1½ INCHES (4 cm)

APPLY 15 COMPRESSIONS ONE PER SECOND ... then GIVE TWO BREATHS

RE-CHECK PULSE ... IF STILL ABSENT CONTINUE WITH 15 COMPRESSIONS TO TWO BREATHS

IF PULSE RETURNS CEASE COMPRESSIONS BUT CONTINUE RESCUE BREATHING

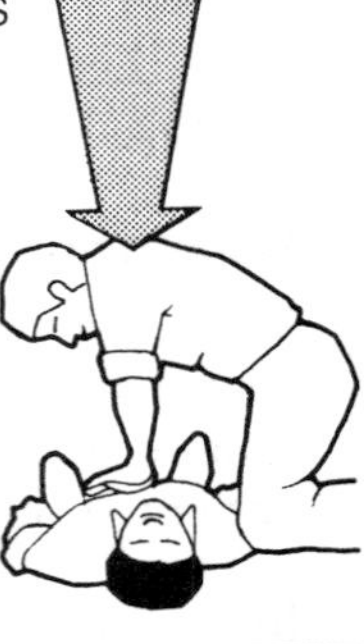

Fig. 29.2 Resuscitation procedure
Source: RoSPA

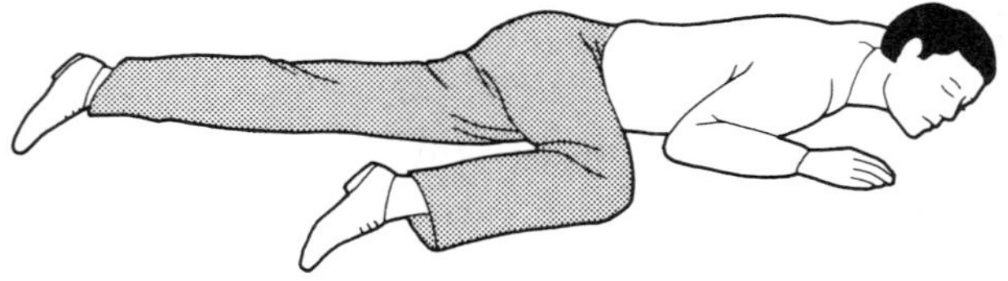

Fig. 29.3 Recovery position

bones or injured joints until the injured parts have been supported to such an extent that they cannot move or be moved separately.

Burns and scalds

Small burns and scalds should be treated by flushing the affected area with plenty of clean cool water before applying a sterilised dressing or a clean towel. Where the burn is large or deep, a sterilised dressing should be applied. It is most important that blisters do not burst and that no attempt is made to remove clothing which may be sticking to burns or scalds. In the case of chemical burns, any contaminated clothing which shows no signs of sticking to the skin should be removed, and all affected parts of the body flushed with plenty of clean cool water, ensuring that all the chemical substance is so diluted as to be rendered harmless. A sterilised dressing should be applied to exposed damaged skin and clean towels to damaged areas where the clothing cannot be removed. Care should be taken when treating such a casualty to avoid personal contamination.

Foreign bodies in the eye

Unless the object can be removed easily with a clean piece of moist material, no attempt should be made to remove the object. The eye should be irrigated with clean cool water. People with eye injuries, or foreign bodies in the eye which cannot be removed in a simple fashion, should always be sent to hospital immediately, with the eye covered by a sterilised eye pad dressing.

NOTE. It is now well-established medical opinion that no first aider should attempt to remove any form of foreign body from the eye of an injured person.

Chemical substances in the eye

The open eye should be flushed at once with clean cool water, the treatment continuing for 5–10 minutes or even longer. If the contamination is more than minimal, the casualty should be taken to hospital.

Basic first aid training

Classes of persons involved in first aid

The approved code of practice identifies three classes of suitable persons to be involved in the provision of first aid. These are as follows.

(a) An *appointed person* is a person provided by the employer to take charge of the situation, e.g. to call an ambulance, if a serious injury, accident or major illness occurs and there is no first aider available. The appointed person will also take charge of the first aid equipment. No training is required for appointed persons, although knowledge of simple first aid procedures outlined above is highly desirable. However, such persons should be appointed in writing by the employer, and their names brought to the attention of all employees.
(b) A *first aider* is a person who has been trained and holds a current first aid certificate. The training requirements for first aiders are given below.
(c) An *occupational first aider* is a person who has been trained and holds a current occupational first aid certificate, and who has received specialised instruction concerning the particular first aid requirements of his employer's undertaking. The training requirements for occupational first aiders are outlined below.

For the purpose of the approved code, the training and qualifications of medical practitioners and State Registered, Registered General, State Enrolled and Enrolled Nurses count as qualifications for first aiders or occupational first aiders.

Training requirements

The guidance notes associated with the approved code of practice outline the subjects that should be included in a training course for first aiders. These are

(a) resuscitation,
(b) control of bleeding,
(c) treatment of shock,
(d) treatment of the unconscious patient,
(e) dressing and immobilisation of injured parts,
(f) the contents of first aid boxes and their use,
(g) transport of sick and injured patients,
(h) recognition of illness,
(i) treatment of injuries,
(j) treatment of burns and scalds,

(k) simple record keeping,
(l) poisons and substances capable of causing poisoning,
(m) personal hygiene in dealing with wounds, and
(n) communication and delegation in an emergency.

The duration of a course, including examinations, should normally be at least 4 days. The examination should cover both theory and practice, and every trainee should be required to demonstrate proficiency in resuscitation, control of bleeding and treatment of the unconscious patient.

Certificates of qualification in first aid are valid for 3 years only. A refresher course, followed by re-examination, is required before re-certification.

Occupational first aiders should have completed training in the subjects listed above for the first aider's training course. In addition, the following should be included:

(a) safety and hygiene in treating the patient;
(b) detailed record keeping;
(c) detailed training on particular aspects of first aid relevant to the undertaking, e.g. treatment of eye injuries, rescue techniques, use of protective equipment and emergency procedures; and
(d) chemical hazards and their treatment specific to the place of work, e.g. use of cyanide, platinum salts, acids and alkalis.

All such training must be undertaken by an organisation approved by the HSE under the Regulations.

30 Stress

The meaning of stress

'Stress' is a word which is rarely clearly understood. It means different things to different people. Indeed, almost anything one can think of, pleasant or unpleasant, has been described as a source of stress, e.g. getting married, being made redundant, getting older, getting a job, too much or too little work, solitary confinement or excessive noise. A number of definitions of 'stress' are shown below.

Definitions

(a) Any influence that disturbs the natural equilibrium of the living body.
(b) The common response to attack (Hans Selye, 1936).
(c) Some taxation of the body's resources in order to respond to some environmental circumstance.
(d) The common response to environmental change.
(e) A psychological response which follows failure to cope with problems.
(f) A feeling of sustained anxiety which, over a period of time, leads to disease.
(g) The non-specific response of the body to any demands made upon it.

Stress could be defined simply as the rate of wear and tear of the body systems caused by life. The acknowledged father of stress research, Dr Hans Selye, a Vienna-born endocrinologist of the University of Montreal, comments thus: 'It is important that people understand what they are talking about when they speak about stress. Whenever anyone experiences something unpleasant, for lack of a better word they say they are under stress.' In his classic book *The Stress of Life*, Selye (1936) corrects several notions relating to stress, in particular:

(a) Stress is not nervous tension.
(b) Stress is not the discharge of hormones from the adrenal glands; the common association of adrenalin with stress is not totally false, but the two are only indirectly associated.
(c) Stress is not simply the influence of some negative occurrence; stress can be caused by quite ordinary and even positive events, such as a passionate kiss.
(d) Stress is not an entirely bad event; we all need a certain amount of stimulation in life and most people can thrive on some forms of stress.
(e) Stress does not cause the body's alarm reaction, which is the most common misuse of the expression; what causes a stress reaction is a stressor.

Whilst (a) to (e) above eliminate virtually everything that people associate with stress, a number of common factors emerge from these definitions and comments. Stress is a state manifested by a specific syndrome of biological events. Specific changes occur in the biological system, but they are caused by such a variety of agents that stress is, of necessity, non-specifically induced. The key to understanding the nature of this overall biological impact lies in the fact that some stress response, however slight, will result from any stimulus.

Quite simply, a 'stressor' produces stress. First, the stressors may be extremes of temperature, lighting or ventilation, or the emission of noise, dust or fume from a process (environmental stressors). Second stress may be induced by isolation, rejection or the feeling that one has been badly treated (social stress). Third, stress can be viewed as a general overloading of the body systems (distress). Stress has a direct association with the autonomic system which controls an individual's physiological and psychological responses. This is the 'flight or fight' system, characterised by two sets of nerves, the sympathetic and parasympathetic, which are responsible for the automatic and unconscious regulation of body function. The sympathetic system is concerned with answering the body's call to fight, i.e. increased heart rate, more blood to organs, stimulation of sweat glands and the tiny muscles at the roots of the hairs, dilation of the pupils, suppression of the digestive organs, accompanied by the release of adrenalin and noradrenalin. The parasympathetic system is responsible for emotions and protection of the body, which have their physical expression in reflexes, such as widening of the pupils, sweating, quickened pulse, blushing, blanching, digestive disturbance, etc.

The general adaptation syndrome

Stress response is a mobilisation of the body's defences, an ancient biochemical survival mechanism perfected during the evolutionary process, allowing human beings to adapt to threatening circumstances. In 1936, in *The Stress of Life*, Selye defined the 'general adaptation syndrome', recognised as a major advance in biological research. It comprises three stages:

(a) The alarm reaction stage. This is typified by receiving a shock, at which time the body's defences are down, followed by a counter shock when the defences are raised. In physiological terms, once a stressor is recognised, the brain sends forth a biochemical 'messenger' to the pituitary gland which secretes adrenocortitrophic hormone (ACTH). ACTH causes the adrenal glands to secrete corticoids, such as adrenalin. The result is a general 'call to arms' of the body's systems.

(b) The resistance stage. This stage is concerned with two responses. The body will either resist the stressor or adapt to the effects of the stressor. It is the opposite of the alarm reaction stage, whose characteristic physiology fades and disperses as the organism adapts to the derangement caused by the stressor.

(c) The exhaustion stage. If the stressor continues to act on the body, however, this acquired adaptation is eventually lost and a state of overloading is reached. The symptoms of the initial alarm reaction stage return and, if the stress is unduly prolonged, the wear and tear will result in damage to a local area or death of the organism as a whole. (*See* Fig. 30.1.)

The causes of stress

The causes of stress are diverse. They are classified thus:

Environmental stressors

Stress in the working environment is caused by extremes of temperature, inadequate lighting and ventilation, presence of dust, fumes, vapours and gases, noise and vibration and poor amenity provision. Noise, with its attendant risk of occupational deafness, is one of the greatest environmental stressors.

Occupational stressors

Stressful conditions at work can lead to accidents or health deterioration. Typical conditions include:

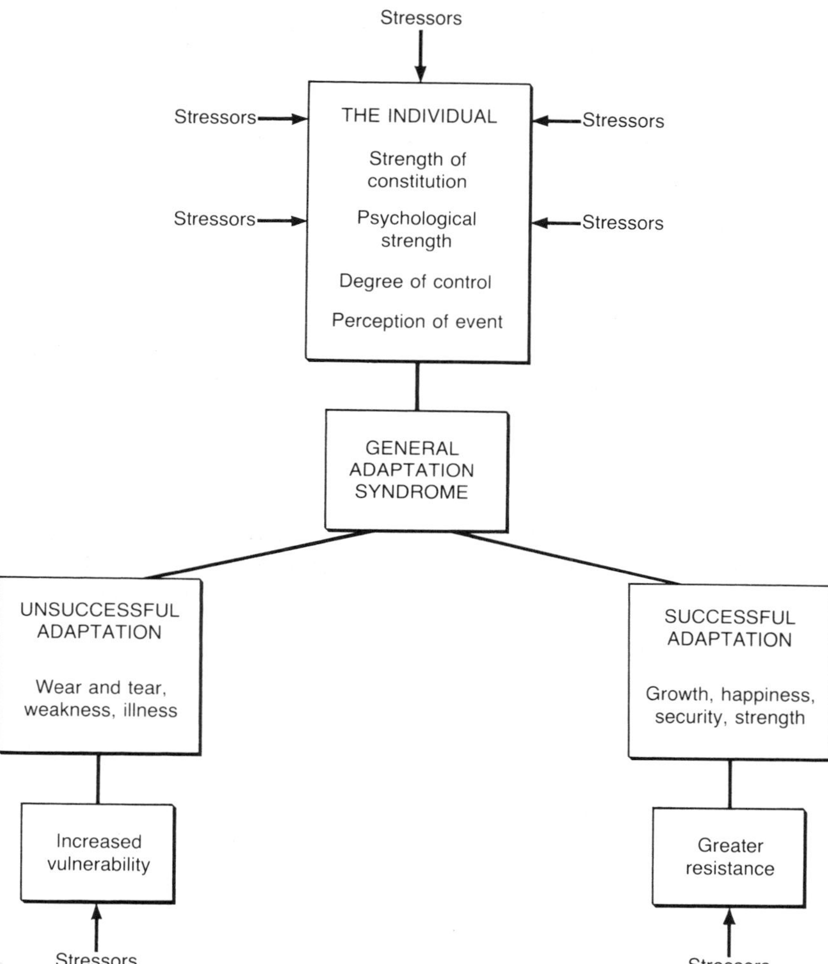

Fig. 30.1 Summary of effects of stress on the individual

(a) too heavy or too light a workload;
(b) a job which is too difficult or too easy;
(c) working excessive hours, e.g. 60 or more hours per week;
(d) conflicting job demands – the 'servant of two masters' situation;
(e) too much or too little responsibility;
(f) poor human relationships;
(g) incompetent superiors, in terms of their ability to make decisions, their level of performance and their job knowledge;
(h) lack of participation in decision making and other activities where a joint approach would be beneficial;

(i) middle-age vulnerability associated with reduced career prospects or the need to change career, the threat of redundancy or premature retirement;
(j) overpromotion or underpromotion;
(k) interaction between work and family commitments; and
(l) deficiencies in interpersonal skills.

Social stressors

Social stress is associated with family life, marital relationships, bereavement – the everyday problems of coping with life. Typical examples are the death of a husband or wife, parent or child, moving house, maintaining repayments on a large mortgage, trouble with the neighbours and changes in social activities. These situations result in worry and anxiety and no two people cope or adapt in the same way.

'Role' Theory

Role Theory views large organisations as systems of interlocking roles. These roles relate to what people do, and what others expect of them, rather than their individual identities. An individual's thoughts and actions are influenced by identification with a role and with the duties and rights associated with that role. Everyone in a role has contact with people – superiors, subordinates, external contacts or contractors who communicate their expectations of the role holder, trying to influence his behaviour and subjecting him to feedback. The individual, therefore, has certain expectations about how people should behave according to their status, age, function and responsibility. These expectations form the basis for a standard by which individual behaviour is evaluated, as well as a guide for reward. Stress arises in this framework due to role ambiguity, role conflict and role overload.

Role ambiguity

This is the situation where the role holder has insufficient information for adequate performance of his role, or where the information is open to more than one interpretation. Potentially ambiguous situations are in jobs where there is a time lag between action taken and visible results, or where the role holder is unable to see the results of his actions.

Role conflict

Role conflict arises where members of the organisation, who exchange information with the role holder, have different expectations of his role. Each may exert pressure on the role holder. Satisfying one expectation could make compliance with other expectations difficult.

Role overload

This results generally from a combination of role ambiguity and role conflict. The role holder works harder to clarify normal expectations or to satisfy conflicting priorities which are impossible to achieve within the time limits specified.

Research has shown that when experience of role conflict, ambiguity and overload is high, then job satisfaction is low. This may well be coupled with worry and anxiety. These factors may add to the onset of stress-related diseases such as peptic ulcers, coronary heart disease and nervous breakdowns.

Evaluation of stress

Major changes in people's lives – such as marital separation, changes in responsibility at work, job loss and even getting married – can be stressful. Research by Dr Holmes and Dr Rahe of the School of Medicine, University of Washington, USA, into the clinical effects of major life changes has identified the concept of the 'life change unit' (LCU), a unit of individual stress measurement in terms of the impact of stress on health. Over a period of 20 years Holmes and Rahe were able to assign a numerical value to a range of 'life events', such as a son or daughter leaving home, change in residence or the death of a family member, and rank them according to their magnitude and importance. Then they compared the LCU scores of some 5,000 individuals with their respective medical histories. They concluded that those with a high rating on the life change index were more likely to contract illness.

The 'schedule of recent events', based on the total number of LCUs received in a year, has since been applied to many groups, confirming the notion that the higher the degree of life change within a period of time, the greater the risk of subsequent illness, regardless of whether the change is perceived as desirable or undesirable. According to Holmes and Rahe, if an individual's LCUs total 150–99, he stands a mild chance of illness in the following year. If the total is in the range 200–99, then he stands a moderate risk. Over 300 LCUs puts him in the group very likely to suffer serious physical or emotional illness.

The lesson to be learnt from this theory is that people should try to regulate the changes in their lives, most of which are under their control, and endeavour to stagger their incidence and intensity. Table 22 shows life change events and LCU ratings. The values assigned to the Holmes–Rahe scale are, of course, averages.

Effects of stress

The signs and symptoms of stress disorders vary. They can include

Table 22: Holmes–Rahe scale of life change units

Event	*LCUs*	*Event*	*LCUs*
Death of a spouse	100	Change in work responsibilities	30
Marital separation	65	Son or daughter leaving home	29
Death of a close family member	63	Trouble with in-laws	29
Personal injury or illness	53	Outstanding personal achievement	29
Marriage	50	Wife beginning or stopping work	29
Loss of job	47	Revision of personal habits	24
Marital reconciliation	45	Trouble with business superior	23
Retirement	45	Change in work hours or conditions	20
Change in health of a family member	44	Change in residence	20
Wife's pregnancy	40	Change in schools	20
Sex difficulties	39	Change in recreation	19
Gain of a new family member	39	Change in social activities	18
Change in financial status	38	Taking out a small mortgage on your home	17
Death of a close friend	37	Change in sleeping habits	16
Change to a different kind of work	36	Change in number of family get-togethers	15
Increase or decrease in arguments with spouse	35	Change in eating habits	15
Taking out a bigger mortgage on home	31	Vacation	13
Foreclosure of mortgage or loan	30	Minor violations of law	11

headaches, inability to sleep, fatigue, over-eating, constipation, lower back pain, allergies, nervousness, nightmares, high blood pressure, alcohol abuse, indigestion, dermatitis, menstrual distress, nausea, irritability, loss of appetite, asthma attacks, depression, arthritis, minor accidents, peptic ulcers, heart palpitations, sexual problems, feelings of anger and many others. Typical signs of this 'flight or fight' response include rapid pulse, increased perspiration, pounding heart, tightened stomach, tensing of limb muscles, shortness of breath, gritting the teeth, clenching the jaw, an inability to sit still, racing thoughts and gripping emotions. No two people react in the same way to a stressful occurrence; one may become withdrawn and depressed, whilst another is hyperactive, compulsive or abnormally gregarious. One loses his appetite, while another becomes gluttonous; one sleeps incessantly, another gets insomnia.

The common psychological effects of stress are anxiety and depression. Anxiety is a state of tension coupled with apprehension, worry, guilt, insecurity and a constant need for reassurance. It is accompanied by a number of psychosomatic symptoms, such as profuse perspiration, difficulty in breathing, gastric disturbances, rapid heartbeat, frequent urination, muscle tension or high blood pressure. Insomnia is a reliable indicator of a state of anxiety. On the other hand, depression is much more a mood, characterised by feelings of dejection and gloom, and other permutations such as feelings of hopelessness, futility and guilt. The well-known American psychiatrist, David Viscott, described depression as 'a sadness which has lost its relationship to the logical progression of events'. It may be mild or severe. Its milder form may be a direct result of a crisis in work relationships. Severe forms may exhibit biochemical disturbances, and the extreme form may lead to suicide.

Stress-related diseases and conditions

Research indicates that many diseases and conditions incorporate a stress element. Whilst stress is not the sole cause, it can play a key role in the promotion of the disease or condition. Some of the more common stress-related diseases are cardiovascular disease, arteriosclerosis including stroke, angina pectoris and heart attack, hypertension, duodenal and stomach ulcers, diabetes, migraine and disorders of the immune system – e.g. allergies, infections (viruses, influenza, colds) – rheumatoid arthritis and ulcerative colitis. There is a correlation with the incidence of certain forms of cancer, e.g. breast cancer.

Smoking, alcohol and drugs

Stress can result in increased addiction to smoking and alcohol consumption and, occasionally, drug addiction (*see* Chapter 20).

Drugs and drug addiction

The expression 'drug' is popularly identified with a narcotic or habit-forming substance. Technically, however, a drug is a substance taken medicinally to assist recovery from sickness or relieve symptoms, or to modify any natural body process. Consequently, many people see drug taking as the panacea for stress, relying on tranquillisers to reduce anxiety and amphetamines (pep pills) to counter fatigue. Such drug taking represents a major health menace, particularly if the individual consumes alcohol. The prescription of drugs should be seen, in most cases, as a stop-gap measure not a permanent one.

PART VI

Safety technology

31
Machinery safety

Machinery – general aspects

Any analysis of machinery safety involves an examination of the first principles of design. By definition, a *machine* is an 'apparatus for applying power, having fixed and moving parts, each with definite functions' (BS 5304:1975). Machines have

(a) operational parts, which perform the primary output function of the machine, namely the manufacture of a product, e.g. the chuck and drill bit of a vertical drill; and
(b) non-operational or functional parts, which convey power or motion to the operational parts, e.g. drives to motors.

The functional parts comprise the prime mover and transmission machinery, which are defined in the Factories Act 1961, sec 176(1), as follows:

Prime Mover – means any engine, motor or other appliance which provides mechanical energy derived from steam, water, wind, electricity, the combustion of fuel or other source.

Transmission Machinery – means every shaft, wheel, pulley, drum, system of fast and loose pulleys, coupling, clutch, driving belt or other device by which the motion of a prime mover is transmitted to or received by any machine or appliance.

A motor car is a typical machine. The engine is the prime mover; it provides the power to drive the transmission machinery, in this case the transmission shaft(s), which results in the wheels turning. All machines operate on this principle.

The principal legal requirements relating to machinery are dealt with in the Factories Act 1961, Part II, Safety (General Provisions), in particular sections 12–16, as follows:

Section 12 – Prime movers
Section 13 – Transmission machinery
Section 14 – Other machinery
Section 15 – Provisions as to unfenced machinery
Section 16 – Construction and maintenance of fencing

Machinery hazards

A person may be injured at machinery through

(a) coming into contact with it, or being trapped between the machinery and any material in or at the machinery or any fixed structure;
(b) being struck by, or becoming entangled in or by, any material in motion in the machinery;
(c) being struck by parts of the machinery ejected from it;
(d) being struck by material ejected from the machinery [BS 5304:1975, cl. 6].

(For the effect of claims litigation on statutory fencing requirements, etc., *see* the end of this chapter.)

Assessment of danger from machinery

The objective of machine safety strategy is the prevention of injury to operators and other persons. Assessment of new and existing machinery should, therefore, consider design features, the circumstances involving operators and other persons in the use of the machine, and specific circumstances or events which can lead to injury.

Design features

Many machines, including new machines, incorporate hazards in their basic design. BS 5304:1975 'Safeguarding of Machinery' classifies these hazards as follows:

Traps

There are three principal forms of trap:

(a) Reciprocating trap – featured in the vertical or horizontal motion of machinery such as presses. At the point where the injury occurs, the limb is stationary (Fig. 31.1).
(b) Shearing trap – this is the guillotine effect produced by a moving part traversing a fixed part or by two moving parts traversing each other, similar to the operation of garden shears (Fig. 31.2).

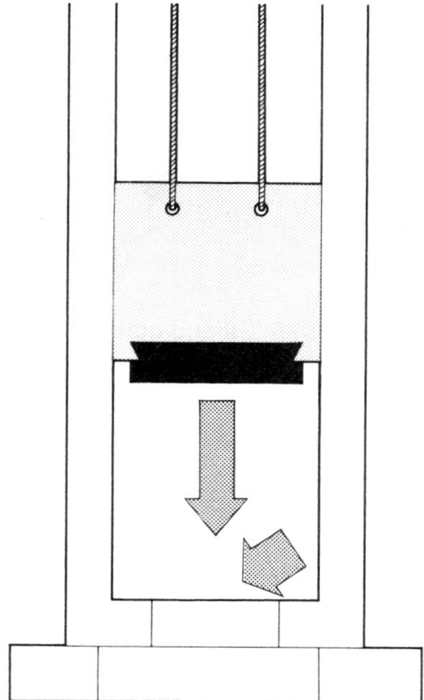

Fig. 31.1 Vertical reciprocating motion of a power press
Source: BS 5304: 1975 'Safeguarding of Machinery'

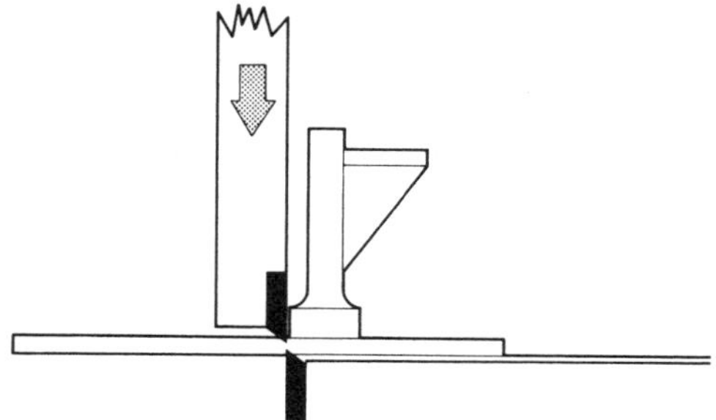

Fig. 31.2 Guillotine

(c) In-running nips – these are traps created where a moving belt or chain meets a roller or toothed wheel, or at the point where two revolving drums, rollers or toothed wheels (gears) meet (Fig. 31.3).

Entanglement

Wherever there are unguarded revolving shafts, drills or chucks to drills, there will always be a risk of entanglement of limbs, hair or clothing (Fig. 31.4).

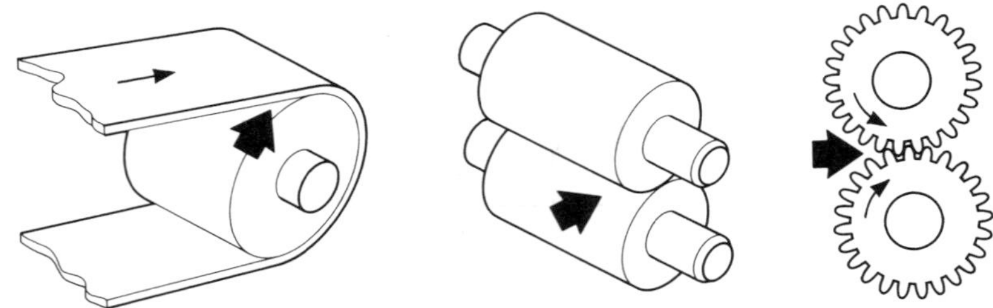

Fig. 31.3 In-running nips
Source: BS 5304: 1975 'Safeguarding of Machinery'

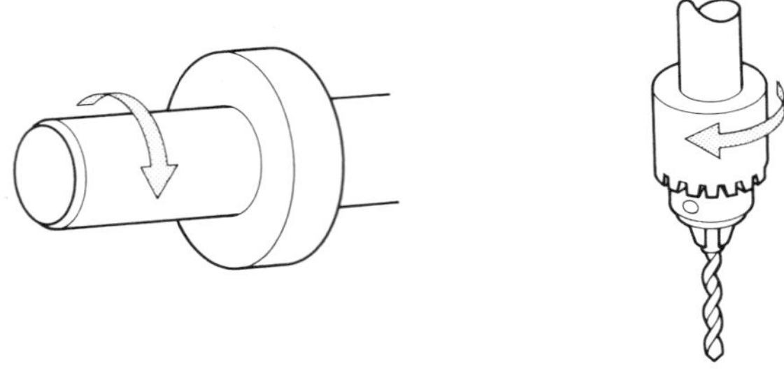

Fig. 31.4 Examples of risk of entanglement
Source: BS 5304: 1975 'Safeguarding of Machinery'

Ejection

Many machines can eject particles of metal or actual parts of the machine. Grinding machines can emit particles of the metal being ground or chips and parts of the grinding wheel.

Contact

Contact with the machine may cause injury, for instance burns from hot exposed surfaces or lacerations from the metal fastenings of a belt to a belt conveyor (Fig. 31.5).

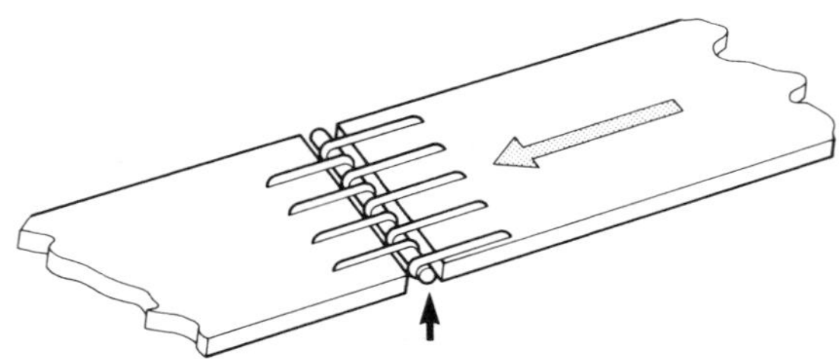

Fig. 31.5 Metal fastenings
Source: BS 5304: 1975 'Safeguarding of Machinery'

Circumstances involving operators and other persons

Specific activities associated with machinery can result in injuries to operators and others in the immediate vicinity. These include job loading and removal, tool changing, the removal of waste and scrap items, actual operation of the machine, particularly if located in a congested area or one frequented by other personnel, routine maintenance and adjustment, gauging, breakdown situations, trying out after adjustment or setting, and unauthorised presence, e.g. persons taking short cuts through the machining area. (The fact that a person's presence is unauthorised does not prevent his obtaining damages for injury, though damages are likely to be reduced owing to his contributory negligence. The case of *Uddin* v. *Associated Portland Cement Manufacturers Ltd* [1965] 2 AER 213 concerned a worker who trespassed in order to retrieve a pigeon from machinery and was injured, but still obtained partial damages.)

Specific circumstances or events which can lead to injury

A number of circumstances or events need particular consideration, e.g. the likelihood of unexpected start-up or movement, uncovenanted stroke of the machine, mechanical failure, and operators reaching into the feeding device or danger area of the machine. Access to and egress from the machine area must also be considered, in particular the provision of sound floor surfaces, freedom from slippery substances and machinery waste products which could cause falls onto machinery, and sufficient free workspace around the machine.

The seventeen dangerous parts of machinery

Certain parts, or combinations of parts, of machinery are classified by the HSE as dangerous should workers operate unsafely or should an unsafe action develop in respect of their motion. Such parts must be securely fenced. The seventeen dangerous parts are listed below, with examples.

(a) Revolving shafts, spindles, mandrels and bars, e.g. line and counter shafts, machine shafts; drill spindles; chucks and drills, etc.; boring bars; stock bars; traverse shafts.
(b) In-running nips between pairs of rotating parts, e.g. gear wheels; friction wheels; calendar bowls; mangle rolls; metal manufacturing rolls; rubber washing, breaking and mixing rolls; dough brakes; printing machines; paper-making machines.
(c) In-running nips of the belt and pulley type, e.g. belts and pulleys, plain, flanged (i.e. V-belts) or grooved; chain and sprocket gears; conveyor belts and pulleys; metal coiling and the like.

(d) Projections on revolving parts, e.g. key heads; set screws; cotter pins; coupling bolts.
(e) Discontinuous rotating parts, e.g. open arm pulleys; fan blades; spoked gear wheels and spoked flywheels.
(f) Revolving beaters, spiked cylinders and revolving drums, e.g. scutchers; rag flock teasers; cotton openers; carding engines; laundry washing machines.
(g) Revolving mixer arms in casings, e.g. dough mixers; rubber solution mixers.
(h) Revolving worms and spirals in casings, e.g. meat mincers; rubber extruders; spiral conveyors.
(i) Revolving high-speed cages in casings, e.g. hydro-extractors; centrifuges.
(j) Abrasive wheels, e.g. manufactured wheels; natural sandstone.
(k) Revolving cutting tools, e.g. circular saws; milling cutters; circular shears; wood slicers; routers; chaff cutters; woodworking machines such as spindle moulders, planing machines and tenoning machines.
(l) Reciprocating tools and dies, e.g. power presses, drop stamps; relief stamps; hydraulic and pneumatic presses; bending presses; hand presses; revolution presses.
(m) Reciprocating knives and saws, e.g. guillotines for metal, rubber and paper; trimmers; corner cutters; perforators.
(n) Closing nips between platen motions, e.g. letter press platen printing machines; paper and cardboard platen machine cutters; some power presses; foundry moulding machines.
(o) Projecting belt fasteners and fast-running belts, e.g. bolt and nut fasteners; wire pin fasteners and the like; woodworking machinery belts; centrifuge belts; textile machinery side belting.
(p) Nips between connecting rods or links, and rotating wheels, cranks or discs, e.g. side motion of certain flat-bed printing machines; jacquard motions on looms.
(q) Traps arising from the traversing carriages of self-acting machines, e.g. metal-planing machines.

Safeguarding machinery

Legal requirements relating to the safeguarding of machinery are outlined in the Factories Act 1961, secs 12–16, and in specific Regulations made under the Act, e.g. the Abrasive Wheels Regulations 1970, Power Presses Regulations 1965 and amendment Regulations 1972, Woodworking Machines Regulations 1974. The authoritative guide to machinery guarding is BS 5304:1975 'Safeguarding of Machinery'. Here a *safeguard* is defined as 'a guard or device to protect persons from danger'. The British Standard defines *danger* as follows: 'When applied to machinery in motion, it is a situation in which there is a reasonably foreseeable risk of injury from the mechanical hazards referred to in clause 6.' (These mechanical hazards are itemised under 'Machinery Hazards' earlier in this chapter.) To ensure maximum safety with machinery, therefore, the appropriate guard or safety device – or, in some cases, both – must be used. The forms of guards and safety devices are outlined below, using the definitions contained in BS 5304:1975. It should be noted that the law defines machinery as *dangerous* when 'it is a possible cause of injury to anybody acting in a way in which a human being may be reasonably expected to act in circumstances which may reasonably be expected to occur' (*Walker* v. *Bletchley Flettons Ltd* [1937] 1 AER 170).

Machinery guards

Fixed guard

This is 'a guard which has no moving parts associated with it, or dependent upon the mechanism of any machinery, and which, when in position, prevents access to a danger point or area' (BS 5304:1975). (Case law supports the view that a fixed guard should not be readily removable, i.e. its removal should require recourse to a hand tool. The use of wing nuts for securing fixed guards, for instance, is not accept-

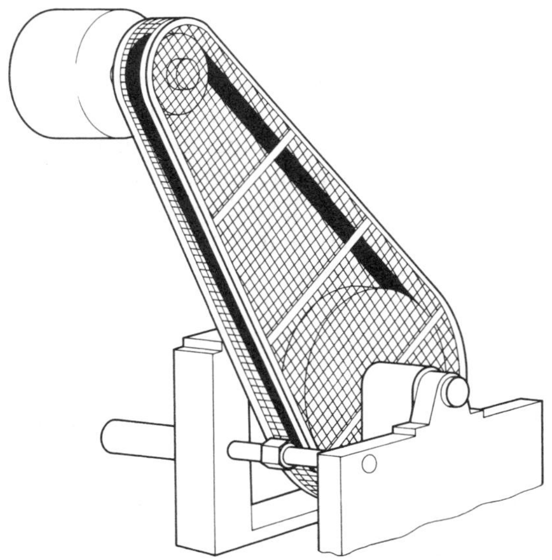

Fig. 31.6 Fixed guard to transmission machinery

able.) An example of a fixed guard constructed of wire mesh and angle section to prevent access to transmission machinery is shown in Fig. 31.6.

Adjustable guard

This is 'a guard incorporating an adjustable element which, once adjusted, remains in that position during a particular operation' (BS 5304:1975). An adjustable guard for use on a band-saw is shown in Fig. 31.7. The height at which the guard is set can be adjusted according to the thickness of the material being cut.

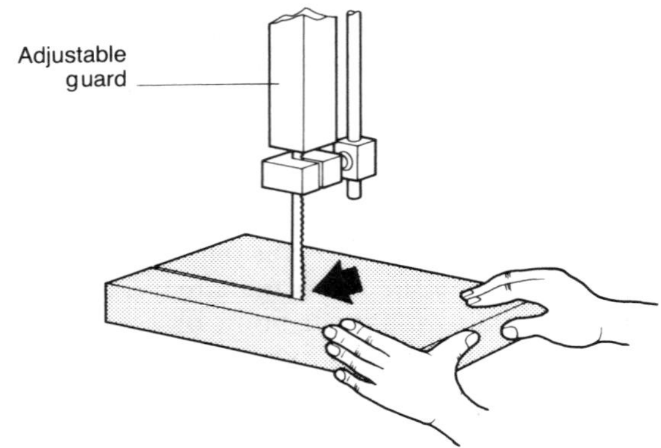

Fig. 31.7 Adjustable guard to a band-saw blade

Distance guard

This is 'a guard which does not completely enclose a danger point or area but which places it out of normal reach' (BS 5304:1975). A typical example of a distance guard is a tunnel guard. Figure 31.8 shows a tunnel guard appropriate for use on a metal-cutting machine. The strip metal is fed through the tunnel guard to the cutters. In this case an interlocking device is fitted so that if the guard is lifted the power supply to the machine is cut off.

Interlocking guard

This

> is a guard which has a movable part so connected with the machinery controls that:
>
> (a) the part(s) of the machinery causing danger cannot be set in motion until the guard is closed;
> (b) the power is switched off and the motion braked before the guard can be opened sufficiently to allow access to the dangerous parts; and

(c) access to the danger point or area is denied while the danger exists [BS 5304:1975].

In order to achieve the same level of safety as that attained with fixed guards, reliability and maintenance of interlocking guards are important.

Interlocking systems may take a number of forms – mechanical, electrical, hydraulic, pneumatic or a combination of these. Whatever the form, the system should fail to safety (fail-safe).

NOTE. The term 'failure to safety (fail-safe)' is commonly used in machinery guarding. It implies that 'any failure in, or interruption of, power supply will result in the prompt stopping or, where appropriate, stopping and reversal of the movement of the dangerous parts before injury can occur, or the safeguard remaining in position to prevent access to the danger point or area' (BS 5304:1975).

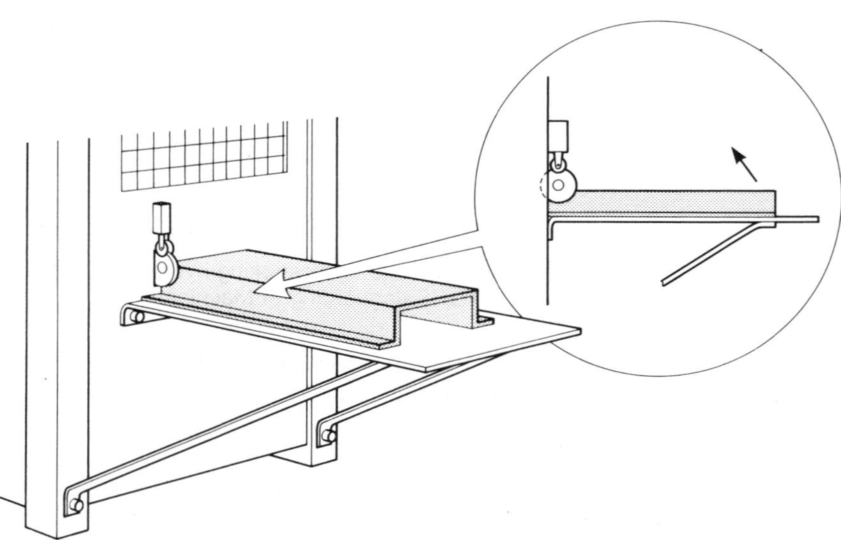

Fig. 31.8 Tunnel guard for a metal-cutting machine

Mechanical interlocking: Mechanical interlocking incorporates two specific elements: first, the operation or actuation of a device, which may be a hydraulic or pneumatic valve, and second, as a result of the operation of the device, the movement of a particular component, generally a guard. In the example shown in Fig. 31.9 the guard slides horizontally to close. When the guard is open the control level is held down, i.e. 'safe'. Only after the guard has been closed can the control lever be raised so as to initiate the machine sequence. The lever then holds the guard in the closed position.

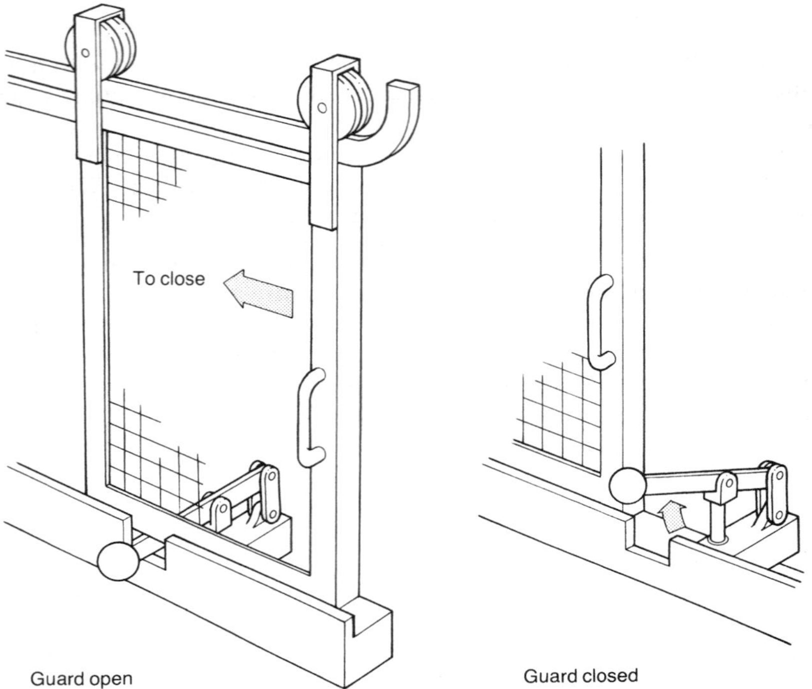

Fig. 31.9 Horizontal sliding guard fitted to an upstroking hydraulic press
Source BS 5304 = 1975 'Safeguarding of Machinery'

Electrical interlocking: BS 5304:1975 identifies four methods of electrical interlocking of guards, as follows:

(a) Control interlocking

This incorporates an actuating switch operated by the guard, interposed electromechanical relays and/or solid state switching devices, if any, the electromagnetic contactor (or solid state equivalent e.g. thyristor), and/or a pneumatic or hydraulic solenoid valve controlling power to the drive. Failures of any of these elements or of the wiring interconnecting them can all be failures to danger. All elements of the system should therefore be designed to give the maximum degree of reliability.

The range of switching methods used for associating guard movement with an on/off electrical control signal includes:

(i) cam or track operated limit switches,
(ii) captive key switches,
(iii) trapped key control of electrical switches,
(iv) magnetic switches, and
(v) diode links [cl. 44].

Specific aspects of these switching methods are shown in clause 44 of BS 5304:1975.

(b) Power interlocking

Power interlocking is achieved by direct mechanical control of a switch in series with the main power supply to the drive of the machinery. The direct mechanical control may be by links etc., by captive key or by trapped key.

Power interlocking is inherently superior to control interlocking, and thus acceptable for high-risk situations, because the mechanical link between the guard and the switch ensures that the guard cannot be opened if, for any reason, the switch contacts stick in the 'on' position. However, because direct power interlocking involves the stopping of the drive motor(s) it should only be applied to machinery where the requirement to open the guard is infrequent, or the motor is of low power [*see* further BS 5304:1975, cl. 45].

(c) Control interlocking with back-up

In high-risk situations where frequent access to the danger area is required control interlocking is acceptable if combined with a back-up power drive interlock incorporated in the cyclic control element, for example direct pneumatic or hydraulic actuation of the ram etc. or air-operated or electromagnetic clutch. The basic requirement of back-up power drive interlocking is that the air or hydraulic pressure to the drive cylinder or clutch has to be exhausted or dumped automatically in the event of control interlock failure [*see* further BS 5304:1975, cl. 46].

(d) Dual circuit interlocking

Where direct mechanical linkage between the guard gate and the back-up exhaust or dump valve is not practicable electrical actuation of the back-up is acceptable. It is essential that the normal control interlock and back-up circuits are kept wholly separate from each other, except for connection to the supply, to minimise the possibility of common faults. The control and back-up limit switches should be arranged in opposite modes, the control being negative and the back-up positive [*see* further BS 5304:1975, cl. 47].

Automatic guard

This is a 'guard which is associated with, and dependent upon, the mechanism of the machinery and operates so as to remove physically from the danger area any part of a person exposed to the danger' (BS 5304:1975). Automatic guards are frequently used on power presses and paper-cutting guillotines. In the first case, the guard is connected to the moving part of the press. The guard closes automatically when the machine cycle commences. Trip devices are generally fitted on power press guards where trapping points occur as the two parts of the guard meet.

Self-adjusting automatic guard: 'This is a guard which prevents accidental access of a person to a danger point or area but allows the access of a workpiece which itself acts as part of the guard, the guard automatically returning to its closed position when the operation is completed.' This form of guarding is particularly appropriate to portable electric circular saws, as shown in Fig. 31.10.

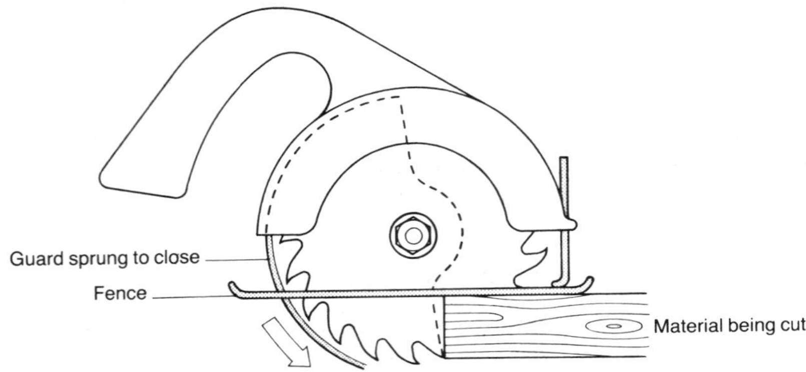

Fig. 31.10 Self-adjusting guard to a portable circular saw

Safety devices

A safety device is a 'protective appliance, other than a guard, which eliminates or reduces danger before access to a danger point or area can be achieved'. There are several types of safety device.

Trip device

This is a means whereby any approach by a person beyond the safe limit of working machinery causes the device to actuate and stop the machinery or reverse its motion, thus preventing or minimising injury at the danger point' (BS 5304:1975). Trip devices take several forms.

Mechanical trip device: This device incorporates a barrier which is contacted by part of the body as it approaches the danger area. Contact with the barrier operates the device which brings the machine to rest. Fig. 31.11 shows a safety trip bar for horizontal two-roll mills used in the rubber industry.

Movement of the trip bar A towards the front roll switches off the drive to the rolls by means of limit switch B and applies a brake. The position of the trip bar is important. Its height above the floor and its horizontal distance from the in-running nip should be such that the operator cannot reach beyond the safety limit C which is dependent upon the efficiency of the brake, making allowance for brake wear. After the trip bar A has been tripped the brake should arrest the motion of the rolls before a hand can be drawn into the nip.

Fig. 31.11 Safety trip bar on a horizontal two-roll mill
Source: BS 5304: 1975 'Safeguarding of Machinery'

Photo-electric trip device:

A photo-electric trip device provides a curtain of light which can be arranged in either a horizontal (A) or vertical (B) configuration [as shown in Fig. 31.12]. Interruption of the curtain while the dangerous parts of the machine are moving results in a signal being given for the machine to stop. The speed of stopping should be such as to ensure that the dangerous parts have come to rest before they can be reached by the operator. Access to the danger area from any direction not protected by the device should be prevented by effective fixed or interlocking guards.

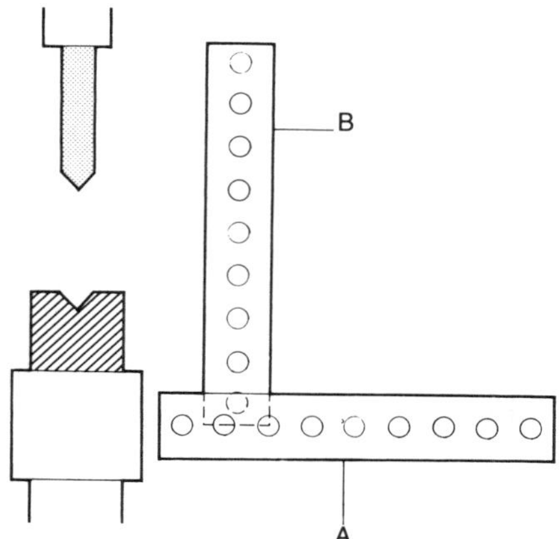

Fig. 31.12 Photo-electric trip device
Source: BS 5304: 1975 'Safeguarding of Machinery'

Photo-electric trip devices are particularly suitable for guarding power presses, hydraulic presses and guillotines and trimmers.

Pressure sensitive mat:

This device operates by means of a number of suitably spaced electrical or fluid switches/valves contained within a mat connected to a control unit and covering the approaches to the danger area. Pressure on the mat operates one or more of these switches. Electrical pressure-sensitive mats are connected into machine control circuits and their use should therefore be restricted to normal risk situations. A pressure sensitive mat may be appropriate in circumstances where the use of a fixed guard is impracticable, and is particularly suitable for use as an emergency stopping device, as a means of protecting a person who may be inside machinery, or as a secondary safety device to augment a conventional guard.

Ultrasonic devices: With these devices, inaudible high-frequency sound senses the presence of an object or person in the danger area. Ultrasonics are not affected by strong light or dirt, but sound attenuates over a distance so the width of protection is limited. This variation in sensitivity with distance can create difficulties in ensuring the effectiveness of the device, however, and BS 5304:1975 recommends that such devices should be restricted to the guarding of machinery at which normal interlocking is appropriate.

Two-hand control device

This is a device which requires both hands to operate the machinery controls, thus affording a measure of protection from danger only to the machinery operator and not other persons. The provision of two-hand controls at the clicking press shown in Fig. 31.13, used in the manufacture of footwear, ensures that the operator has both hands in a safe position while the press head descends. To protect against accidental operation, the buttons should be shrouded (*see* inset).

A two-hand control device should be designed in accordance with the following requirements outlined in BS 5304:1975:

(a) The hand controls should be so placed, separated and protected as to prevent spanning with one hand only, being operated with one hand and another part of the body, or being bridged by a tool.
(b) It should not be possible to start the machinery unless the controls are operated within approximately one second of each other. This prevents the operator from locking one control in the start position so allowing him to operate the machinery by means of the other control leaving one hand free.
(c) Movement of the dangerous parts should be arrested immediately or, where appropriate, arrested and reversed if one or both

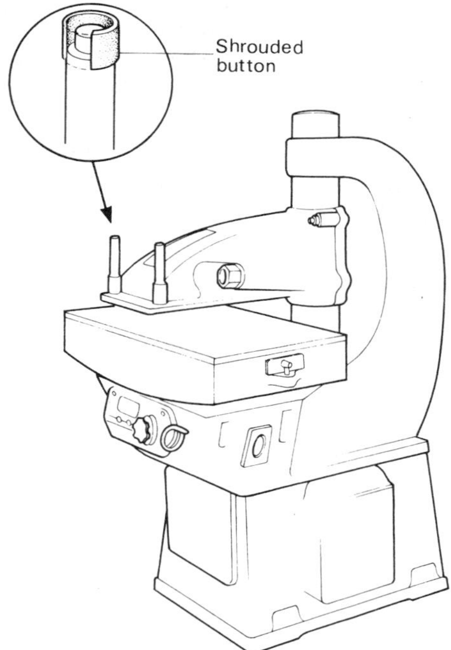

Fig. 31.13 Two-hand control on a clicking press
Source: BS 5304: 1975 'Safeguarding of Machinery'

controls are released while there is yet danger from the movement of these parts. This should ensure that both hands of the operator are clear of the danger area during the whole of the dangerous movement.

(d) It should not be possible to initiate a subsequent cycle until both controls have first been returned to their original position. This prevents the possibility of one control being locked in the start position.

Overrun device

'This is a device which, used in conjunction with a guard, is designed to prevent access to machinery parts which are moving by their own inertia after the power supply has been interrupted, so as to prevent danger' (BS 5304:1975). Where a machine is liable to overrun after the power supply has been switched off it is necessary to ensure that the guard cannot be opened until the motion has ceased. This can be achieved by one of three means:

(a) A 'rotation sensing device – which ensures that after the power has been cut off the guard remains locked closed until the device has sensed that rotation of the dangerous parts has ceased'. These are used with high-speed mixers and centrifuges.

(b) A 'timing device – which ensures that after the power has been cut off the guard remains locked closed until the dangerous parts have come to rest'.

(c) A 'brake – which is interlocked with the guard and the machine controls so that the act of cutting off the power to the dangerous parts or opening the guard applies the brake'. A brake is virtually instantaneous in action.

Mechanical restraint device

'This is a device which applies mechanical restraint to a dangerous part of machinery which has been set in motion owing to failure of the machinery controls or other parts of the machinery, so as to prevent danger' (BS 5304:1975). Mechanical restraint devices are commonly found on pressure die-casting machines and plastics injection-moulding machines. With these hydraulically or pneumatically powered machines a trap is created between a fixed and a moving platen to which access is required usually once in every cycle. With horizontally moving platens, a simple method of applying mechanical restraint is to provide a scotch in the form of a strut which falls into place between the platens as soon as they are fully open. A device of this kind gives adequate protection provided the guard remains locked closed until the platens are fully open.

The use of microprocessors in machine guarding

A recent development in the safeguarding of machinery has been the introduction of microprocessors and microcomputers. One microchip can now replace a whole series of electromechanical switches, relays and circuits, which implies less wear, less noise and reduced maintenance costs. Microprocessors operate according to specific programmes (or 'software') which are conveyed to the microprocessor unit through a manually operated keyboard or keypad, prerecording on magnetic tape or floppy disc or by 'hard wiring' or 'burning on' one or more of the microchips in the microprocessor unit. Whilst this is a new departure in machinery safety, the integrity and reliability of software systems are critical if accidents are to be prevented. HSE (1981) Occasional Paper *Microprocessors in Industry: Implications in the Use of Programmable Electronic Systems* provides further information on this subject.

Robots in industry

Industrial robots did not appear until the 1960s, being referred to by R. H. Warring as 'metal collar workers'. The 1982 estimate of first generation industrial robots installed in factories throughout the world was approximately 17,000. Robots fall into three categories, namely fixed sequence robots, variable sequence robots and playback robots.

Fixed sequence robots

These are capable of performing successive steps of a given operation in a predetermined sequence, condition and position. The present information is normally programmed into the robot and cannot easily be changed.

Variable sequence robots

Essentially these are similar to fixed sequence robots except that set information can be more readily changed. The original design of the mechanical system is more complex than that of a fixed sequence robot. It must be capable of fulfilling a variety of movements to accommodate different sets of instructions or programmes. The advent of the microprocessor, with its reduction in size and corresponding increase in capacity ratios, has greatly influenced the performance of this type of robot.

Playback robots

This robot has a memory, but has to be taught the sequence, positions and operations required by a human operator. When required, this information is recalled and the operations are repetitively carried out automatically from memory.

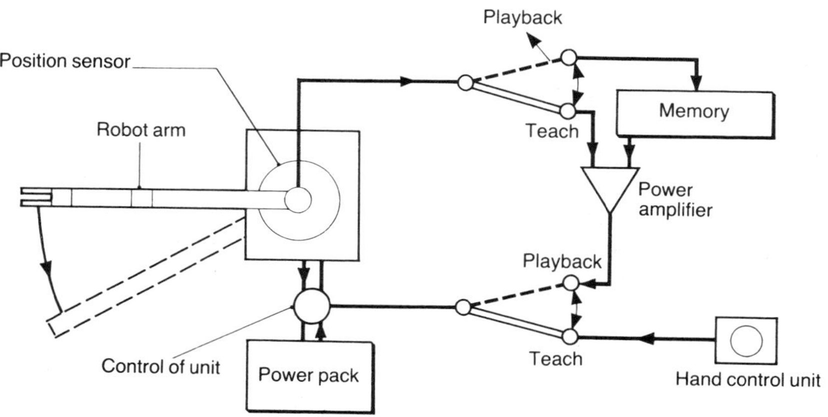

Fig. 31.14 Block diagram of point-to-point playback robot system

Two systems operate with playback robots, point-to-point and continuous path.

In the first system (*see* Fig. 31.14) the human operator has a control unit to operate the robot. The robot is thus moved to its 'start' position which is then stored in the robot memory. The movements, position, actions are then carried out in sequence, each step being recorded as an instruction in the memory until the final 'stop' position is reached. From then on the human operator should no longer be needed and the robot will repeat its taught working programme continuously, e.g. spot welding on a vehicle assembly line.

The continuous path system requires a more sophisticated and skilful 'teacher', so that the robot can continuously record all the movements initiated by the human operator. Equally, it will record and repeat all the faults made by the operator. This technique produces a smooth movement following a continuous path, e.g. paint spraying.

The main industrial robot applications are in handling, assembly work, hot forging, spot welding and finishing. Handling or pick-and-place robots are used for handling heavier loads, i.e. above 15 kilograms. The handling of billets in hot forging and the unloading of die-casting machines are typical examples which can demonstrate significant increases in production whilst releasing the worker from hazardous or tedious tasks. The robot can do much to reduce danger to workers by replacing them in potentially hazardous situations. However, the robot itself can introduce dangers into the work situation through impact injuries from the moving parts of the robot, trapping the worker against a fixed part, ejection of the material or object being handled against the worker, and traps within the body of the robot when its 'metal clothes' are removed for maintenance. The robot is, of course, a machine and the hazards it presents when operating may be viewed as similar to those presented by the dangerous moving parts of any other machine. It is during maintenance, adjustment, programming and fault-finding operations that the robot can be at its most dangerous. Sections 12–16 of the Factories Act 1961 apply to robots as do the recommendations in BS 5304:1975. Thus where the machine is in operation these legal requirements must be applied. In many cases the provision of fixed perimeter guards with interlocked access gates to the robot enclosure must be considered. The access gates to the enclosure should be interlocked in such a way that when they are opened power is cut off from all the machinery until they are closed again. An emergency stop to the mains supply of all the machinery should be situated on the robot control box outside the fencing.

In situations where workers require access for maintenance, lubrication, fault finding or programming (the last two cases requiring the robot to be 'live'), then a specific procedure or safe system of work is vital. In this case, the safe system of work to be used for reprogramming a robot should ensure that

(a) the programmer is highly trained and skilled;
(b) he enters the work area on his own, ensuring that any equipment used by the robot is correctly located and the door closed so that no one else can enter;
(c) he carries with him a mobile emergency stop device that is connected to a relay box from the mains supply, within the perimeter of the fencing, after ensuring that the emergency stop device is functional; and
(d) the robot is designed and set to run at 'creep' speed only during this operation.

Criteria for assessment – machinery guards and safety devices

Design considerations

(a) Wherever practicable, dangerous parts should be eliminated or effectively enclosed in the initial design of the machinery. If they cannot be eliminated, then suitable safeguards should be incorporated as part of the design. If this is impossible, provision should be made for safeguards to be easily incorporated at a later stage.
(b) Provision should be made to facilitate the fitting of alternative types of safeguards on machinery where it is known that this will be necessary because the work to be done on it will vary.
(c) Where a movable guard, cover, etc., is used as a safeguard, it should be interlocked with the drive, of whatever kind, to the parts being safeguarded; maintenance operations may require complete isolation of the machinery from the power supply.
(d) The guard must be securely attached to the machine in such a way that it can only be removed by a tool.
(e) Lubrication and routine maintenance facilities should be incorporated remote from the danger area.
(f) Suitable supplementary lighting should be provided at operating points; a light fitting which is portable or which relies on manual action for directional adjustment should preferably be supplied at extra-low voltage, i.e. normally not exceeding 50 V between conductors and not exceeding 30 V a.c. or 50 V d.c. between any conductor and earth.
(g) Every mechanism and control forming part of a safeguard should, so far as is practicable, be of fail-safe design.

Construction of safeguards

(a) All safeguards should be of sound design and adequate strength.

(b) Guards may be made of metal, timber, laminated or toughened glass, suitable plastics or a combination of these, as may be appropriate to the conditions; the use of shatter-resistant materials may be an advantage.

(c) The size of openings between the interstices of wire mesh guards should be properly considered in relation to finger and hand access.

(d) Whatever safeguard is selected, it should not itself present a hazard such as trapping or shear points, splinters, rough or sharp edges, or other sources likely to cause injury. In the case of food processing machinery, the safeguard should not constitute a source of contamination of the product.

(e) Where an opening in a fixed guard is necessary for the purpose of feeding material by hand, it should not allow the operator access to the dangerous parts. Where it is necessary to provide such an opening, it should be at a sufficient distance from a danger point. Fig. 31.15 provides a guide to show the relationship between the guard opening and the distance of the guard from the danger point which, if followed in the design, should prevent unsafe access.

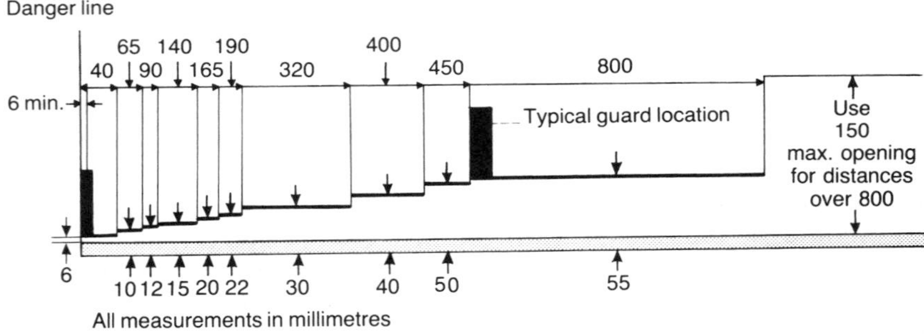

Fig. 31.15 Prevention of unsafe access to danger point
Source: BS 5304: 1975 'Safeguarding of Machinery'

(f) The guard must be securely attached to the machine and must require use of a tool to remove it.

The more common machinery hazards

Drilling machines

Contact with revolving spindles, chucks and drills

Spindles and chucks should be guarded by means of telescopic or spring-loaded guards which completely enclose the danger point. Alternatively, the 'Quickstop' or 'Deadstop' type of trip device (*see* Fig. 31.16) can be fitted. This consists of a telescopic vertical trip bar suspended from the drilling head approximately 75 mm from the spindle. At the top of the trip bar is an electrical switch, and when the bar is pivoted a few degrees from the vertical in any direction the switch is operated and a brake is applied.

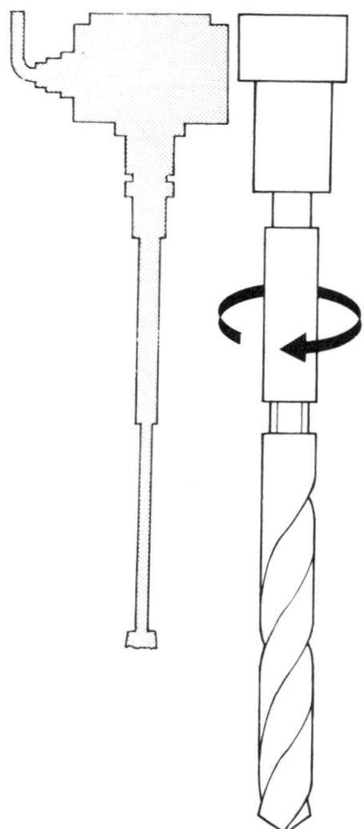

Fig. 31.16 Telescopic trip device for a drilling machine
Source: BS 5304: 1975 'Safeguarding of Machinery'

Injury from broken or splintered drills

Only properly sharpened drills should be used and these should be checked to ensure that they are running true. The drill should be run at the correct speed and never forced.

Injury from the workpiece

The work should always be clamped securely to the table. No attempt should be made to hold the work while drilling. All burrs in drilled holes should be filed.

Pedestal and bench-mounted grinding machines

Shattering of artificially bonded wheels

Before mounting all wheels should be closely inspected and 'rung' to ensure they have not been mishandled in transit or storage. A sound wheel will have a clear ring when tapped gently with a small hammer, whereas a cracked wheel will not ring. 'Ringing' should be undertaken by a trained operator, whose appointment is recorded in the Factories Act register, otherwise tapping can weaken the wheel and cause it to burst when mounted. The wheel should be mounted only by this statutorily trained and appointed operator, at the correct tension and in full compliance with the detailed arrangements of the Abrasive Wheels Regulations 1970, who should ensure that the safe working speed marked on the wheel is correct for the speed of the driving motor or shaft. An unmarked wheel should never be used. The face of the wheel should be flat and ungrooved, and dresssing of the wheel (if necessary) should be carried out with the proper tool. (This may consist of star wheels separated by washers on a spindle attached to a handle, or a diamond in a proper holder.) The tool rest should be adjusted as close as possible to the face of the wheel, the clearance not exceeding 3 mm. Too much clearance may allow the workpiece to jam and burst the wheel.

Contact with the wheel; trapping between the wheel and the machine casing

Correct setting of the tool rest is vital. Operators should not set the tool rest while the machine is in motion. The work should be held firmly to prevent slipping. When grinding small jobs, a clamp or holding device should be used. The wheel should never be left running when not in use, nor left unattended during the run-down period after switching off. Guarding for a bench-mounted grinder is illustrated in Fig. 31.17.

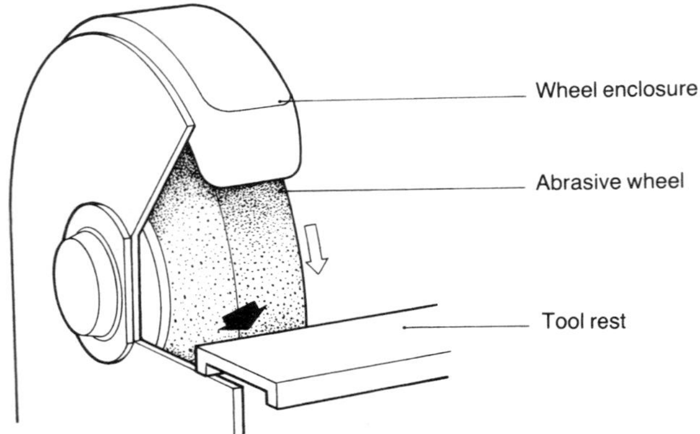

Fig. 31.17 Guarding for a bench-mounted grinder

Eye injuries

Eye protection should always be used, either the fixed transparent guard on the machine (*see* Fig. 31.18) or goggles or safety spectacles. These precautions are dictated by both current good practice and the requirements of the Protection of Eyes Regulations 1974.

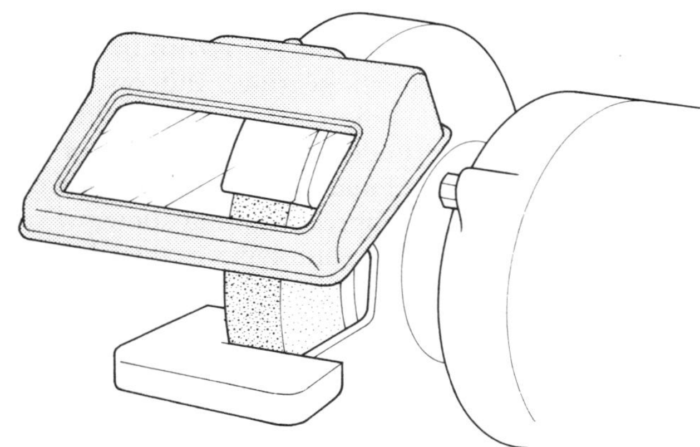

Fig. 31.18 Fixed transparent guard to a grinder

Power presses

Specific requirements relating to power presses are contained in the Power Presses Regulations 1965 and amendment Regulations 1972. These Regulations provide for the regular and thorough examination, inspection and testing of presses and associated safety devices, and for the appointment of tool setters, the examination and testing of the press and guards by a competent person, and the recording of defects and certification procedures. The principal hazards associated with power presses are outlined below.

Trap between the tool and the die

Secure fencing must be provided, and there must be no access to the danger point or area from any direction. Guards should always be in position when the press is under power, whether for production or for test after setting up. Young persons must not operate presses unless they have been thoroughly instructed and are either fully trained or under supervision.

Traps between the ram and parts of the guard

Guards should be so constructed and set that no trap exists between the ram or any projection on it and the guard itself. If this occurs the guard must be readjusted.

Uncovenanted strokes

An uncovenanted stroke occurs when a press makes a second stroke while the guard is open. On positive clutch presses, uncovenanted strokes can occur through the extractor failing to return to the fully disengaging position when the control is released, breakage of the clutch key, failure of the extractor mounting and excessive wear on the rubbing faces of the extractor and/or key tail. On positive clutch or friction clutch presses, there may also be seizure or collapse of the flywheel bearing, or other clutch bearing, and on friction clutch machines, clutch drag, and the unintended entry, or the retention, of air in the clutch operating cylinder due to electrical or mechanical faults. Good design and planned maintenance should prevent most of these occurrences. It should be appreciated that some presses may be inherently unsuited for use with certain types of guard. The fitting of single stroke devices can eliminate this problem. Such a device is provided for the purpose of disengaging the clutch withdrawal device, e.g. extractor, from the influence of the operating control so that it will disengage the clutch before a second stroke can occur. An arrestor brake is also used to arrest the crankshaft, flywheel and ram of a press within specified limits in the event of an uncovenanted stroke.

Overrun

Overrun occurs when the crankshaft does not come to rest, after disengagement of the clutch, in the correct position at the end of a cycle or, in some cases, at part stroke. On some types of press the crankshaft can 'run away' from the flywheel. The fitting of a press brake, correctly adjusted and regularly maintained, including the replacement of brake linings as necessary, correct lubrication and correct braking by the operator should considerably reduce this problem.

Horizontal milling machines

Contact with the cutter; splintering of the tool and injury through flying particles

Operators should ensure that the cutter is sharp and in good condition. The guard should also be maintained in good condition and correctly adjusted. When setting up, the traverse table should be taken to the maximum out-run and not in close proximity to the cutter. The arbour nuts should not be adjusted when the machine is running.

Eye injuries

Eye protection should always be worn when machining, and chips of metal and swarf removed by brush, never by hand.

These precautions are dictated by current good practice and the requirements of the Horizontal Milling Machines Regulations 1928 and 1934 and the Protection of Eyes Regulations 1974.

Guillotines

Trapping between the blades or under the hold-down pads

The blades of a guillotine should always be enclosed by fixed guards, front and rear, which should effectively prevent all access of fingers to the danger zone (*see* Figs 31.19 and 31.20). Guards should be in sound condition and properly adjusted.

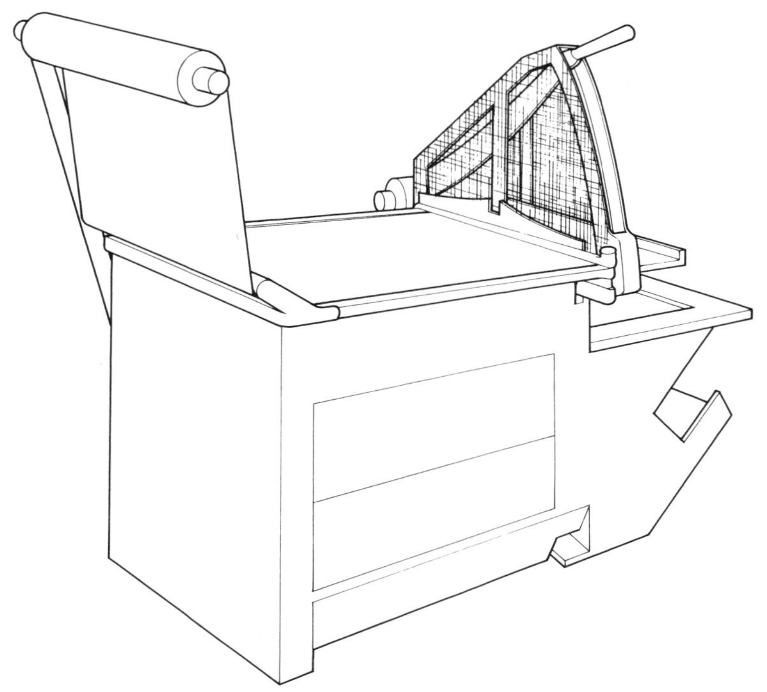

Fig. 31.19 Guard fitted to a hand-operated paper guillotine

Lathes

Contact with revolving parts; contact with work; trapping between work and tool; contact with transmission machinery

The chuck or face plate should be removed or replaced only when the machine is stationary. The work, tool-holder and tail-stock should be securely clamped before the machine is switched on, and no adjustment to the tool or measurements of the work should be undertaken

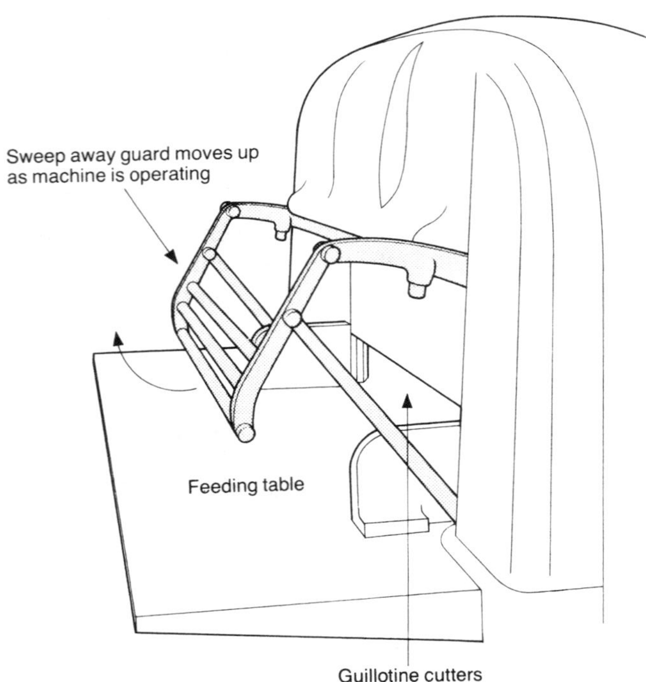

Fig. 31.20 Guarding to a power-operated guillotine

whilst the machine is operating. Belts should be shifted and gears changed only when the machinery is stationary. (These items must be fully guarded when the machine is in motion.) A proper polishing stick should always be used.

Sudden ejection of work or tool from the machine

Any wrench or other tool should always be removed from the chuck before switching on the machine. Only light cuts on long thin work should be taken due to the risk of the job flying from the machine.

Lacerations from swarf

A rake or similar tool should always be used for the removal of swarf. Operators should wear heavy-duty gloves.

Contact with stock bar

All stock bars must be adequately guarded for the whole of their length, including the section nearest the machine.

Vertical spindle bowl mixers

Trapping and entanglement through contact with the rotating spindle
The bowl and rotary arm should be completely enclosed using two semi-circular guards, hinged at the rear and interlocked at the front, with a top mesh cover incorporated each side. A funnel inlet in the top or side can be incorporated for the addition of ingredients and liquids during mixing.

Circular saws

Contact with the moving saw blade; disintegration of the saw blade
The fencing requirements for a wide range of woodworking machinery are outlined in the Woodworking Machines Regulations 1974, e.g. circular saws, band-saws.

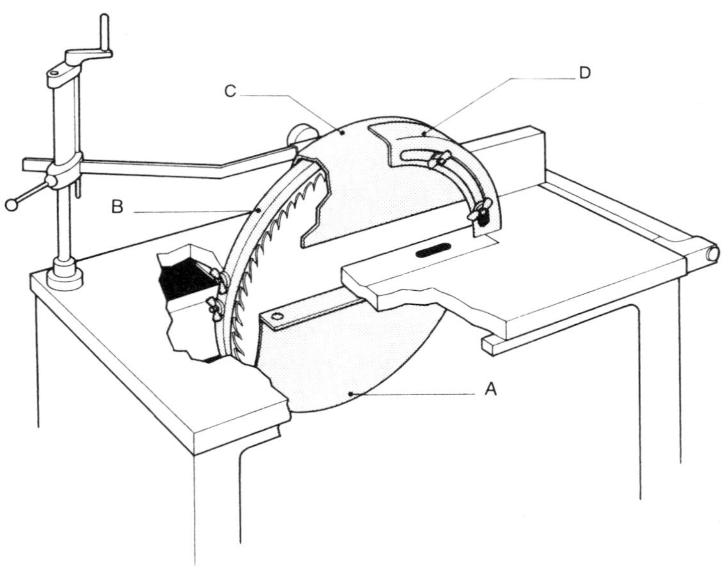

Fig. 31.21 Guards for a floor-mounted circular saw

The guarding arrangements for a floor-mounted circular saw are shown in Fig. 31.21. Such a saw should be provided with guards for three portions of the blade, i.e. the part below the bench table, the up-running part above the bench at the rear of the blade, and the crown and front cutting part of the blade. Guarding for the part below the bench table incorporates two plates of metal or other suitable material (A), one on each side of the saw set not more than 153 mm apart and extending outward from the axis of the saw to a distance not less than 51 mm beyond the teeth of the saw. The metal plates must normally be of a thickness at least equal to 14 gauge, but if the edges are beaded they must be of a thickness not less than 20 gauge. The up-running part is guarded by a riving knife (B) set directly behind the saw and extending upwards from the table to within 25 mm of the top of the saw. The riving knife must be capable of horizontal adjustment so that its front edge at table level can be kept within 12 mm of the teeth of any size of saw which may be used in the bench. The crown and front cutting part of the blade incorporates a U-section or L-section cover (C) for the top of the saw supplemented by an L-section extension piece (D). The vertical flanges on (C) and (D) should be of sufficient width to extend below the roots of the teeth on the side of the saw remote from the fence. The guard should be strong and capable of easy adjustment, to allow for variations in the thickness of wood being cut.

Push sticks must be provided and used with a circular saw. Where wood which has been cut is removed from the saw table by a second operator during operation of the saw, he must stand at the delivery end of the machine and the machine table must extend at least 1,200 mm from the up-running part of the saw blade.

Circular saws frequently overrun or continue in motion after the power has been switched off. The installation of a braking system is, therefore, recommended. Provision for lowering the saw below the bench top when not in use is also an effective safeguard.

Band-saws

Contact with the moving blade; breaking of the blade

These saws should be provided with a guard or guards (A), as shown in Fig. 31.22, which totally enclose the pulleys around which the saw band runs and all parts of the band except the part between the bench table and the top pulley. The part of the band between the friction disc or rollers and the top pulley should be provided with a U-section guard (B) with the sides of the guard extending behind the saw band.

Small printing machines

Traps between gear wheels and chain and sprocket drives

These parts should normally be completely enclosed by a guard. However, on small hand-turned machines an interlocked guard should be provided.

In-running nips between the plate and blanket cylinders, between inking rollers, or between the cylinder and inking roller

When two cylinders or rollers revolve, a finger trap is created at the

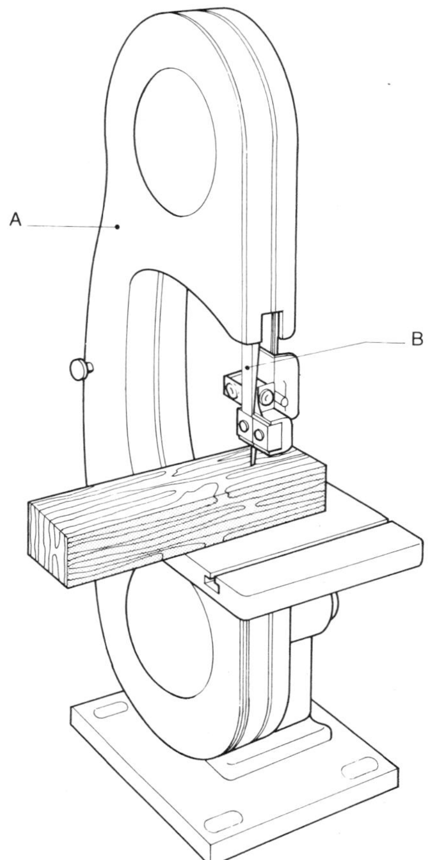

Fig. 31.22 Guards to a band-saw

in-running nip. A common method of guarding is to fit a nip bar which prevents access to the nip (*see* Fig. 31.23). On small machines, where this is impracticable, a hinged interlocked guard should be fitted so as to enclose completely the rollers or cylinders.

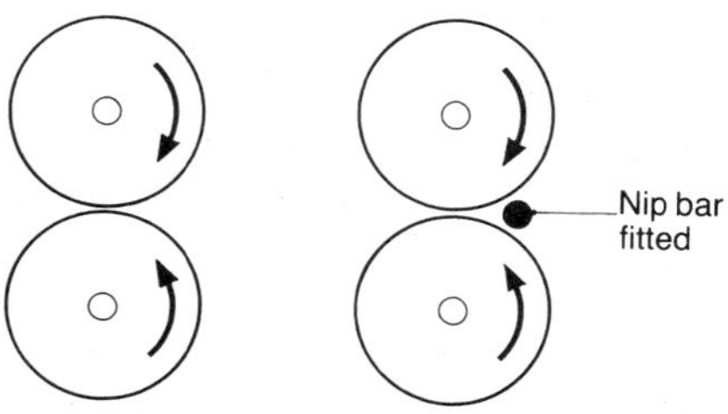

Fig. 31.23 Nip bar fitted to revolving rollers on a small printing machine

Traps between the gap in the plate cylinder and fixed parts

Offset printing machines often incorporate a gap in one of the two revolving cylinders. As the gap passes the nip bar a trap is created between the rear edge of the gap and the bar. Traps will also occur between the rear edge of the gap and any fixed member of the machine in the vicinity of its travel. There are two methods of guarding, either

(a) to fit a gap plate (*see* Fig. 31.24) which is normally only practicable on large machines; or
(b) to fit a hinged interlocked guard without a nip bar, which can usually only be adopted for smaller machines.

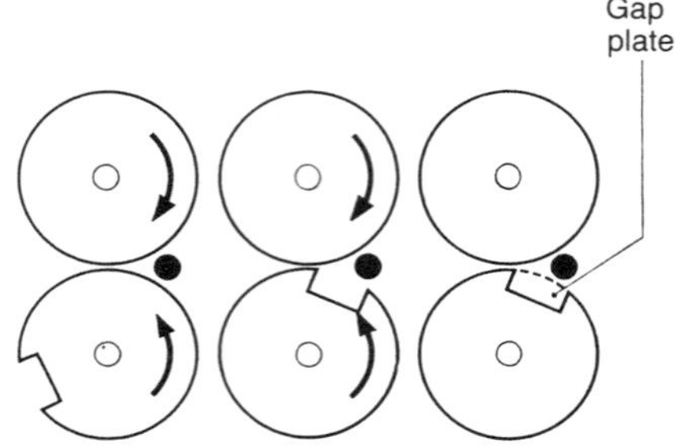

Fig. 31.24 Positioning of a gap plate

Summary

Figure 31.25 presents in diagrammatic form a checklist for ensuring the safety of machinery.

Main developments in the law relating to machinery safety

The following factors have had a major impact on the law relating to machinery safety.

(a) The legislative premise that machinery cannot be made design-safe; hence the statutory (and judicial) preoccupation with the need to guard or fence factory machinery. This approach pervades sections 12–14 of the Factories Act 1961. The consequence is to stifle the emergence of a 'product liability' approach, where safety features can be established and designed into the product from drawing-board stage.
(b) Machinery and machine parts should be so guarded as to prevent machine operators being injured by coming into contact with machines rather than by the ejection of workpieces from machines.

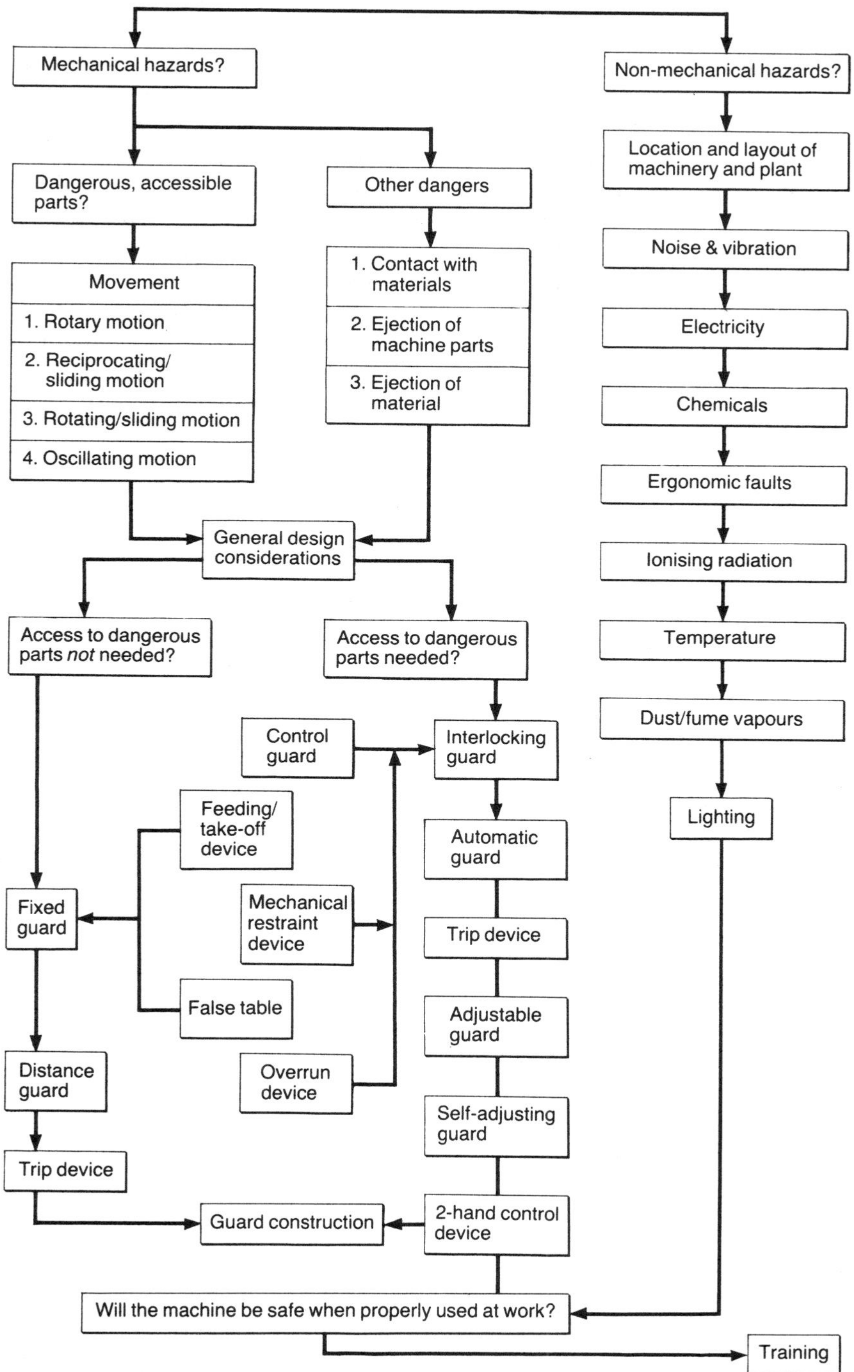

Fig. 31.25 Is the machine safe for use at work?

(c) Causation. This is tantamount to an infusion of common law negligence criteria into statutory requirement. Here the courts say that breach of statutory duty must have been a predominant cause of injury and/or disease at work, otherwise there is no civil liability on the part of the employer and so no damages will be payable. A case encapsulating this approach is *Bonnington Castings* v. *Wardlaw* [1956] 1 AER 615, which concerned a worker who contracted pneumoconiosis. This may seem illogical, indicating, as it does, that breach of statutory duty is not in itself negligence. This is unlike the situation in the USA, where breach of governmental standards often does amount to negligence (without the need to prove causation) for the purpose of product liability. (*See also* Chapter 2, section on 'Negligence'.)

32

Fire

P. Waterhouse, PhD, BSc, CChem, MRSC, MIOSH

Occurrence through combustion

Fire is a spectacular example of a fast chemical reaction between a combustible substance and oxygen accompanied by the evolution of heat. An explosion is an even more spectacular example of the same reaction. The three requirements for fire are

(a) oxygen, except in very special circumstances;
(b) a fuel or combustible substance; and
(c) a source of energy.

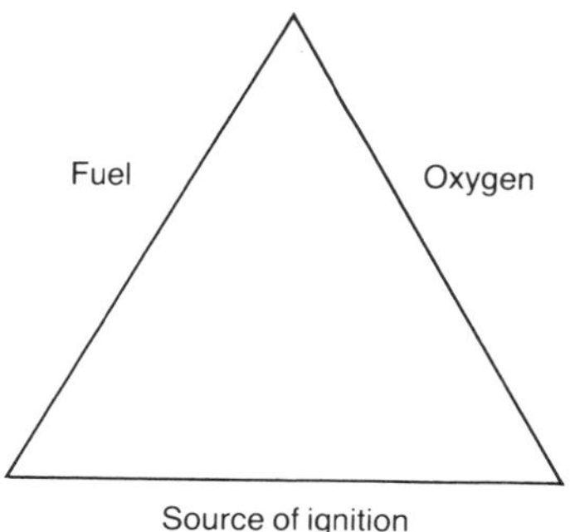

Fig. 32.1 The fire triangle

These three requirements are easily remembered in the form of the fire triangle (Fig. 32.1). The triangle, however, says nothing about the relative importance of each of the requirements or their states of matter. These come from a full knowledge of the chemistry of combustion.

Elements of fire

Oxygen

A fire always requires oxygen for it to occur or, having started, to continue. The chief source of oxygen is air, which is a mixture of gases comprising nitrogen (78 per cent) and oxygen (21 per cent). The remaining 1 per cent is made up of water vapour, carbon dioxide, argon and other gases. A number of substances can be a source of oxygen in a fire, e.g. oxidising agents. These are substances which contain oxygen that is readily available under fire conditions and include sodium chlorate (Na_2ClO_3), hydrogen peroxide (H_2O_2), nitric acid (HNO_3) and organic peroxides ($R—O—O—R^1$). A third source of oxygen is the combustible substance itself, e.g. ammonium nitrate (NH_4NO_3).

Combustible substance

This is the second requirement for fire and includes a large group of organic substances, i.e. those with carbon in the molecule, e.g. natural gas (methane) (CH_4), butane (C_4H_{10}), petrol, plastics, natural and artificial fibres, wood, paper, coal and living matter. Inorganic substances, i.e. those not containing carbon in the molecule, are also combustible, e.g. hydrogen (H_2), sulphur (S), sodium (Na), phosphorus (P), magnesium (Mg) and ammonium nitrate (NH_4NO_3).

Ignition source

This is the energy that has to be applied to the oxygen/fuel mixture to start the fire. Usually this energy is in the form of heat, but not necessarily. The heat can be simply that contained in the combustible substance. This is often the source of ignition energy when hot fuel leaks from a pipe and fires, but it can be heat generated by friction such as rubbing a match against sandpaper or a hot bearing in a machine. Electrical energy in the lightning of a thunderstorm or when an electrical contact, such as a switch, is made or broken, would also qualify.

Chemistry of combustion

Combustion chemistry is an example of a larger group of chemical reactions known as oxidation reactions. Other examples are the rusting of iron and the process of breathing. Chemically the process can be written as:

Fuel plus oxygen gives products of combustion and heat

If the fuel is natural gas (i.e. methane), the reaction is written as:

$$\underset{\text{methane}}{CH_4} + \underset{\text{oxygen}}{2O_2} \rightarrow \underset{\text{carbon dioxide}}{CO_2} + \underset{\text{water}}{2H_2O} + \text{Heat}$$

If the fuel were hydrogen, the equation would be:

$$\underset{\text{hydrogen}}{2H_2} + \underset{\text{oxygen}}{O_2} \rightarrow \underset{\text{water}}{2H_2O} + \text{Heat}$$

Or if it were sulphur, it would be:

$$\underset{\text{sulphur}}{S} + \underset{\text{oxygen}}{O_2} \rightarrow \underset{\text{sulphur dioxide}}{SO_2} + \text{Heat}$$

However, for ammonium nitrate, which has its own source of oxygen, the equation is:

$$\underset{\text{ammonium nitrate}}{NH_4NO_3} \rightarrow \underset{\text{nitrous oxide}}{N_2O} + \underset{\text{water}}{2H_2O} + \text{Heat}$$

Generally, the carbon in the fuel is oxidised to carbon dioxide and hydrogen to water. The other elements will be oxidised to a variety of substances.

Initiation energy – explanation of ignition

When the chemical reaction

$$H_2 + 2O_2 \rightarrow H_2O + \text{heat}$$

is taking place, it can be thought of as molecules hitting one another and sometimes bouncing off like balls or otherwise mutually breaking up into different molecules. In the latter case a chemical reaction has occurred. Characteristic of the 'ball' theory (more properly known as the Kinetic Theory of Gases) is that kinetic energy possessed by the balls, i.e. their speed, is a function of the temperature of the gas. In particular, the higher the temperature the higher the kinetic energy of the molecules. The reaction may be described as one where the energy of the collision has to be greater than some value for the molecules to hit and break up into different molecules. If the collision energy is below this value the molecules will just bounce off one another and no reaction will take place. Collision energy is the physical representation of the initiation energy required for a fire to start. It is usually heat, i.e. increasing the temperature of the combustion mixture, but it can be electrical energy from a spark.

The final feature of all combustion reactions is that they emit energy. These reactions are known as exothermic reactions.

Table 23 shows the heat of combustion in kilogram calories per molecular weight of the substance when combustion takes place at atmospheric pressure and 20 °C. Table 24 gives the minimum ignition energy of substances in millijoules.

Table 23: Standardised values of heat output

Fuel	*kcal*
Acetone $(CH_3)_2CO$	126.8
Benzene C_6H_6	782.3
Carbon disulphide CS_2	246.6
Cyclohexane C_6H_{12}	937.8
Dimethyl ether $(CH_3)_2O$	347.6
Ethane C_2H_6	368.8
Ethyl alcohol C_2H_5OH	327.6
n-Hexane C_6H_{14}	989.8
Hydrogen H_2	58.3
Methane CH_4	210.8
Methyl alochol CH_3OH	170.9
Propane C_3H_8	526.3

Table 24: Standardised values of ignition energy

Minimum ignition energy	*mJ*
Benzene	0.22
Carbon disulphide	0.01–0.02
Ethane	0.24
n-Hexane	0.25
Hydrogen	0.019
Methane	0.39
Propane	0.25

The fire process – a summary

A fire may be described as a mixture in gaseous form of a combustible substance and oxygen, with sufficient energy being put into the mixture to start the fire. Once started, the energy output from the fire provides a continuous source of energy for it to be sustained and excess is given off as sensible heat (*see* Fig. 32.2). For all practical purposes, fire takes place in the gaseous state and division of fires into those of solids (e.g. wood), liquid (e.g. petrol) and gas (e.g. a gas flame) is convenient but not accurate. This can be seen with burning wood and liquid where close observation reveals that the flame burns at a small distance from the wood or liquid.

Ignition energy – liquids and gases

Ignition energy of liquids and gases can be measured, and is expressed in different ways. The three measures are

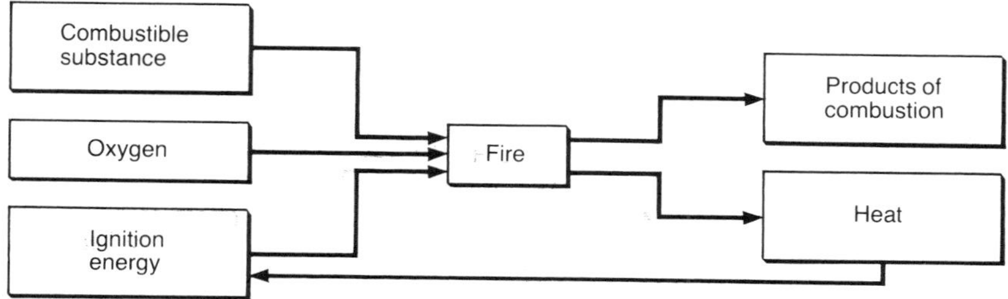

Fig. 32.2 The fire process

(a) Flash point. The flash point is the minimum liquid temperature at which sufficient vapour is given off to form a mixture with air capable under prescribed test conditions. There are two sets of prescribed conditions, the Abel and the Pensky-Martin. The former usually yields slightly lower results. It is necessary to cite the method used when quoting flash point values.
(b) Fire point. This is the lowest temperature at which the heat from combustion of a burning vapour is capable of producing sufficient vapour to sustain combustion.
(c) Spontaneous ignition temperature, or ignition temperature. This is the lowest temperature at which the substance will ignite spontaneously.

Usually, for a given combustible substance the flash point is less than the fire point, which is less than the ignition temperature. Since energy is measured by temperature and two effects are being studied, i.e. the evaporation of the liquid and combustion of evaporated vapour, the ignition temperature must be the highest value because the whole of the required energy comes from the heat, i.e. temperature, of the liquid. The flash point must be the lowest because the source of ignition is external to the evaporation of the liquid.

Hitherto it has been assumed that a mixture will only react if sufficient energy is put into it. This is not always the case. Consider an oxygen/methane mixture. If there are very few methane molecules in the mixture these will react very quickly and the fire stops. As the concentration of methane increases, a point will be reached when the heat output from the fire will eventually be sufficient to provide the source of ignition for the rest of the methane and the fire is sustained. Similar conditions apply if the oxygen/methane mixture is rich in methane and weak in oxygen. Here it is the oxygen, however, that is instantaneously used up until only sufficient oxygen is present for the heat output to sustain combustion. These two concentration values which exist for all gaseous combustible substances and oxygen are known as the lower and upper flammability limits.

Lower flammable limit

The lower flammable limit (lower explosive limit) is the smallest concentration of flammable gas or vapour which, when mixed with air, is capable of ignition and subsequent flame propagation under prescribed test conditions.

Upper flammable limit

The upper flammable limit (upper explosive limit) is the highest concentration of flammable gas or vapour which, when mixed with air, is capable of ignition and subsequent flame propagation under prescribed test conditions. Table 25 gives values of flammable limits for some common substances.

Table 25: Properties of some flammable substances

Substance	*Flash point (°C)*	*Ignition temperature (°C)*	*Flammable range (% v/v in air)*
Acetic acid	40	485	4–17
Acetone	−18	535	2.1–13
Acetylene	−18	305	1.5–80
Ammonia	Gas	630	1.5–27
Benzene	−17	560	1.2–8
n-Butane	−60	365	1.5–8.5
Carbon disulphide	−30	100	1–60
Carbon monoxide	Gas	605	12.5–74.2
Cyclohexane	−20	259	1.2–8.3
Ether	−45	170	1.9–48
Ethanol	12	425	3.3–19
Ethylene	Gas	425	2.7–34
Hydrogen	Gas	560	4.1–74
Methane	Gas	538	5–15
Toluene	4	508	1.2–7
Vinyl chloride	−78	472	3.6–33

Spontaneous combustion

The final combustion characteristic is spontaneous combustion. Sometimes material bursts into flames without apparent means of ignition. Examples are haystacks, rags soaked in linseed oil and oil-soaked lagging. This is called spontaneous ignition. It is clear from the mechanism of fire that there must be a source of ignition but the source itself is not obvious. Some organic substances, when exposed to oxygen, undergo slow oxidation, a process similar to fire, releasing little sensible heat. Slow oxidation does not result in carbon dioxide and water but other substances chemically smaller and more easily combustible than the original substance. In effect, the original substance is being made more combustible by oxidation and, in consequence, little heat is generated. When reduction in combustibility and heat output match, a fire occurs. The source of ignition is the heat of oxidation.

Extinction

Extinction means putting out a fire. It can be achieved by one or more of the following:

(a) starvation – a reduction in concentration of the fuel;
(b) smothering – a reduction in concentration of oxygen; and
(c) cooling – a reduction in the rate of energy input to the fire.

It is a reduction that is required and not necessarily the removal of any one of them, since a fire occurs when the fuel/oxygen mixture is within two concentrations and it receives a minimum amount of energy.

Starvation

There are three ways that this can be achieved:

(a) take the fuel away from the fire,
(b) take the fire away from the fuel, and
(c) reduce the quantity or bulk of the fuel.

The first is achieved every day on the gas stove when the tap is turned off. For large chemical plants this means isolating the feed at the remote isolation valve. Examples of taking the fire away from the fuel include breaking down stacks and dragging away the burning debris. Breaking down a fire into smaller units is an example of reducing the quantity or bulk of the fuel.

Smothering

There are two ways of achieving this:

(a) allow the fire to consume the oxygen while preventing the inward flow of more oxygen, and
(b) add an inert gas to the burning mixture.

Wrapping a burning person in a blanket is an example of smothering. Other examples include pouring foam on top of a burning pool of oil or putting sand on a small fire. A danger inherent in extinguishing fires by smothering occurs when the fire is out but everything is still hot. Any inrush of oxygen, caused by disturbing the foam layer or opening the door to a room, could result in reignition as there may still be sufficient energy in the form of sensible heat present.

If an inert gas is to be used as an extinguisher, carbon dioxide or halogenated hydrocarbons such as BCF are suitable. Alternatively, nitrogen can be used, and is in fact more common for petrochemical plant fires. If a flammable gas pipeline leaks and the escaping gas fires, nitrogen blanketing can be achieved by injecting nitrogen into the gas stream downstream of the release. Smothering is only effective when the source of oxygen is air. It is totally ineffective when the burning substance contains oxygen, such as ammonium nitrate.

Cooling

This is the most common means of fighting a fire, water being the cheapest and most effective medium. For a fire to be sustained, some of the heat output from the combustion is returned to the fuel, providing a continuous source of ignition energy. When water is added to a fire, the heat output serves to heat and vaporise the water, i.e. the water provides an alternative heat sink. Ultimately, insufficient heat is added to the fuel and continuous ignition ceases. In order to assist rapid absorption of heat, water is applied to the fire as a spray rather than a jet, the spray droplets being more efficient in absorbing heat than the stream of water in a jet. Another example of heat absorption is provided by dry chemical extinguishers. These are very fine powders which readily absorb heat and in one case, MONEX, break up into small even particles. Dry powders can also be used for the smothering method.

Classification of fires

Fires are commonly classified into four categories according to the fuel type and means of extinction.

Class A

Fires involving solid materials, normally of an organic nature, in which the combustion occurs with the formation of glowing embers, e.g. wood, paper, coal and natural fibres. Water applied as a jet or spray is the most effective way of achieving extinction.

Class B

Fires involving (i) liquids or (ii) liquefiable solids. Liquids fall into two groups:

(i) miscible with water – methanol, acetone, acetic acid; and
(ii) immiscible with water – petrol, benzene, fats and waxes.

Foam, light water, vaporising liquids, carbon dioxide and dry powder can be used on both B(i) and B(ii) type fires. Water spray can be used on type B(i) but not on type B(ii). There may also be some restriction on the type of foam which can be used because some foams break down on contact with alcohols. In all cases extinction is mainly achieved by smothering. However, water on a B(i) fire also acts by cooling, and by removal of the fuel in that the fuel dissolves in the water.

Class C

Fires involving gases or liquefied gases, e.g. methane, propane and butane. Both foam and dry chemicals can be used on small liquefied gas spillage fires, particularly when backed up by water to cool the leaking container or spillage collector. A fire from a gas leak can be extinguished either by isolating the fuel remotely or by injecting an inert gas into the gas stream. Direct flame extinguishment is difficult and may be counterproductive in that if the leak continues there may be reignition, often in the form of an explosion. Extinguishers used on liquid gas spillage fires work by smothering.

Class D

Fires involving metals, e.g. magnesium or aluminium. They can only be extinguished by use of dry powders which include talc, soda ash, limestone and dry sand. All the extinguishers work by smothering.

'Electrical' fires

This is now an obsolete classification. Fires which involve electrical equipment must always be tackled first by isolating the electricity and then by use of carbon dioxide, vaporising liquid or dry powder. The use of these agents minimises damage to equipment.

Portable fire extinguishers

These are appliances designed to be carried and operated by hand. They contain an extinguishing medium which can be expelled by action of internal pressure and directed onto a fire. The pressure may be stored, or obtained by chemical reaction or by release of gas from a cartridge. The maximum mass of a portable extinguisher in working order is 23 kg. Portable extinguishers are grouped and coded as shown in Table 26.

Water-containing extinguishers

There are three kinds, i.e. soda acid, gas cartridge and stored pressure.

Soda acid

This is the original form of water-containing extinguisher, and is gradually being replaced by the gas cartridge and stored pressure types.

Table 26: Grouping and coding of portable fire extinguishers

Extinguishers	*Colour code*
Water	Red
Foam	Cream
Carbon dioxide	Black
Dry chemical powder	Blue
Vaporising liquid	Green

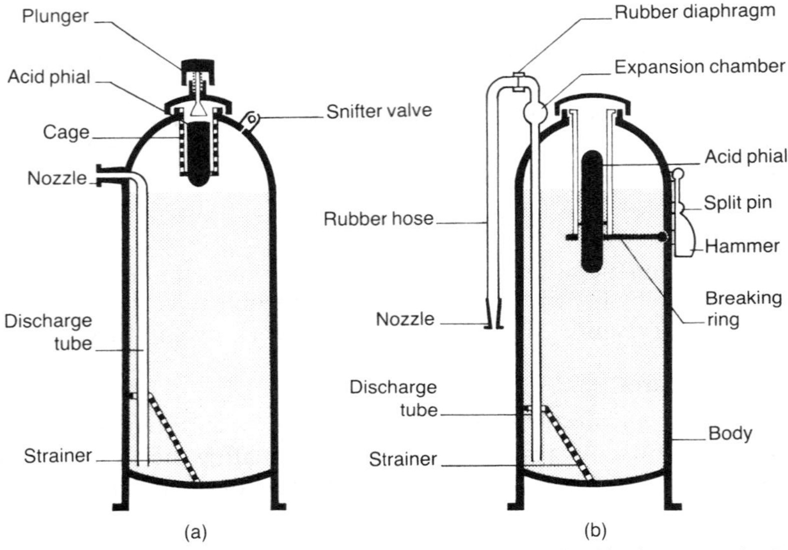

Fig. 32.3 Sections through a soda acid extinguisher (a) with plunger at the top; (b) with hammer at side
Source: Home Office, *Manual of Firemanship*

Two common types are shown in Fig. 32.3. Gas is generated in the cylinder when the acid phial is broken, and this expels all the water through the discharge tube.

Gas cartridge

With this type, carbon dioxide is held in a small pressure cylinder, the seal being broken by a plunger. The gas so released expels the water out of the nozzle (*see* Fig. 32.4).

Stored pressure

This appliance contains carbon dioxide under pressure. Water is expelled when the trigger is pulled. Closing the trigger stops the water flow (*see* Fig. 32.5).

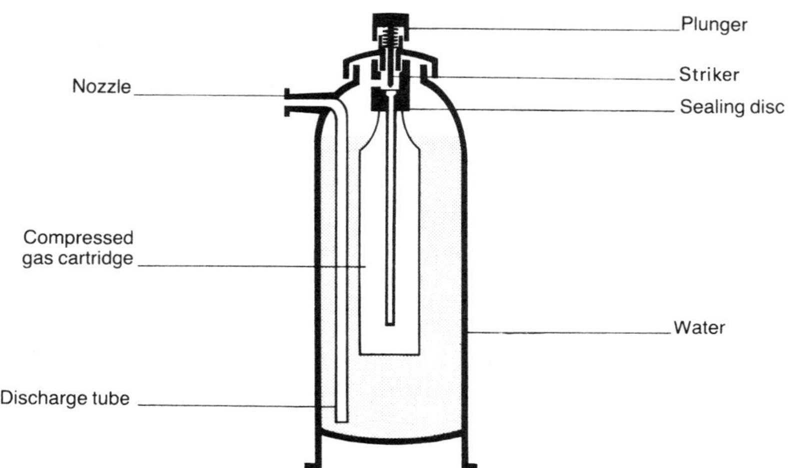

Fig. 32.4 Section through a water (gas cartridge) type extinguisher
Source: Home Office, *Manual of Firemanship*

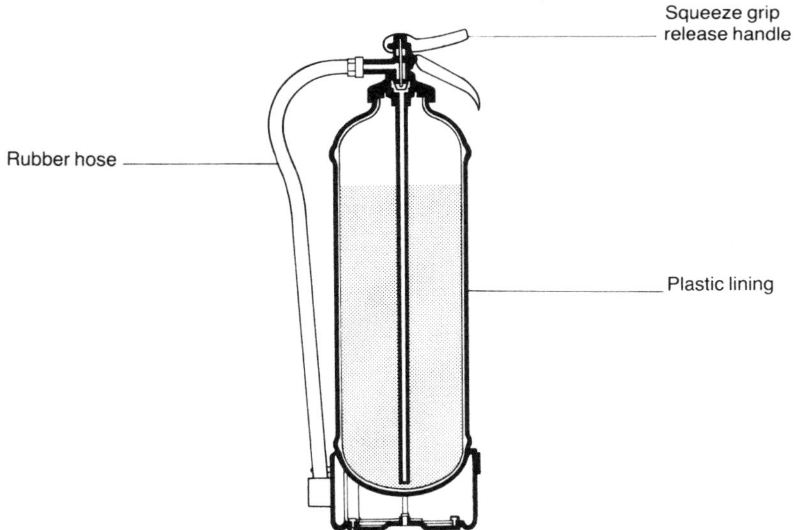

Fig. 32.5 Section through a stored pressure type of water extinguisher
Source: Home Office, *Manual of Firemanship*

Precautions relating to water extinguishers

All water extinguishers are pressure vessels, so they must be regularly maintained in accordance with the maker's instructions (*see* Chapter 34). The interior of the vessel must be protected against corrosion and the water in it may need anti-freeze treatment. It must be operated in the upright position in order to discharge water and not gas.

Water extinguishers are ideal for small Class A fires and are effective for Class B(i). They must not be used, however, on Classes B(ii), C or D, and certainly not on live electric wiring.

Foam extinguishers

Of the four types of foam extinguisher (illustrated below), three contain foam solution which is expelled by carbon dioxide. With the fourth (gas cartridge type), foam is generated at the exit by carbon dioxide.

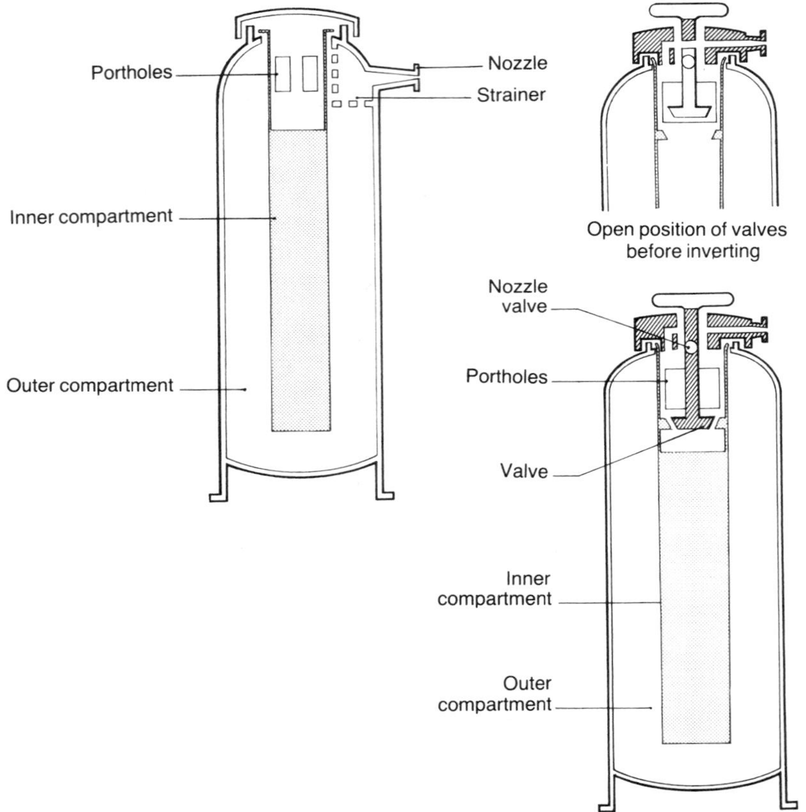

Fig. 32.6 Sections through foam extinguishers
(a) Turn-over type without seal
(b) Bayonet seal turn-over type
Source: Home Office, *Manual of Firemanship*

Chemical foam

The cylinder contains two solutions which are mixed on inversion, viz. aluminium sulphate and sodium bicarbonate. The cylinder itself is filled with sodium bicarbonate solution containing about 3 per cent of a stabiliser, such as saponin, liquorice or turkey red oil. The inner compartment contains 13 per cent of aluminium sulphate. The foaming mixture is expelled in the inverted position by carbon dioxide generated in the chemical reaction. In some chemical foam extinguishers, the inner cylinder is sealed and has to be broken with a plunger before inversion (Fig. 32.6).

Stored pressure

The alternative to the chemical foam extinguisher is the self-aspirating type. Here the cylinder contains foam concentrate which is expelled either by stored pressure or by gas cartridge. There are four types of foam concentrate – protein, fluor-protein, fluor-chemical and synthetic. In a stored pressure foam extinguisher the cylinder is filled with foam concentrate and pressurised to 10 bar with air or nitrogen. Operation of the trigger valve allows the pressure to expel the foam concentrate through the exit pipe where foam is generated at the end of the hose (Fig. 32.7).

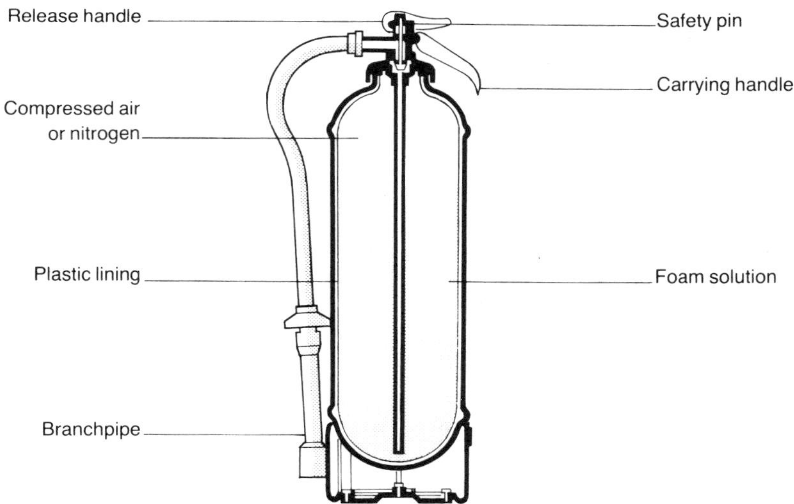

Fig. 32.7 Foam extinguisher (stored pressure) type
Source: Home Office, *Manual of Firemanship*

In the gas cartridge extinguisher the foam concentrate is expelled by breaking a seal on a carbon dioxide cartridge (Fig. 32.8). Alternatively, the cylinder can be filled with water, the foam concentrate being contained in a plastic bag which surrounds the gas cartridge (Fig. 32.9). Breaking the seal on the cartridge releases the carbon dioxide which then bursts the plastic bag. Pressure expels the foam concentrate through the exit hose, releasing foam at the exit.

Fig. 32.8 Gas cartridge foam solution type of foam extinguisher
Source: Home Office, *Manual of Firemanship*

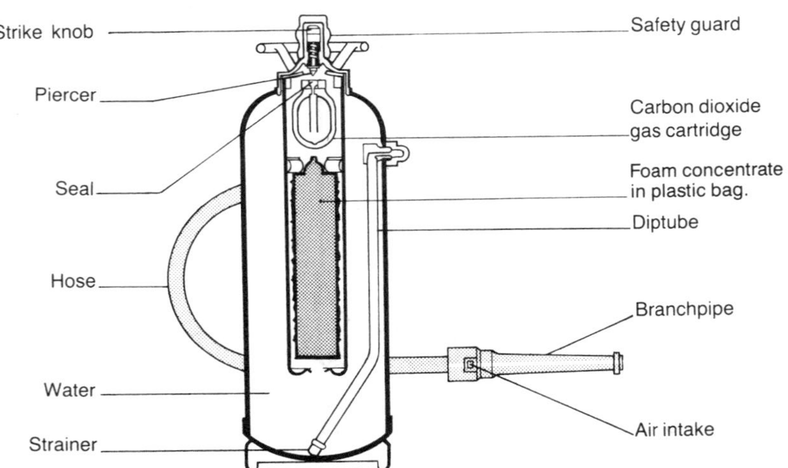

Fig. 32.9 Foam extinguisher (gas cartridge) type
Source: Home Office, *Manual of Firemanship*

Precautions relating to foam extinguishers

The cylinders of foam extinguishers are pressure vessels and so must be maintained in accordance with the maker's instructions and protected against internal corrosion (*see* Chapter 34). Because chemical foam extinguishers operate by inversion, they must always be completely discharged. The self-aspirating types can be stopped simply by releasing the trigger.

Foam extinguishers are best used on Class B(ii) fires, but can also be used on Classes A and B(i). In the latter case, however, foam must be compatible with the burning liquid. In use on a contained liquid fire, the foam should be directed to the back or side of the containers and allowed to spread over the fire. On a liquid spillage, foam should be directed to the front and spread over the fire with a side-to-side movement until the fire is covered.

Carbon dioxide

This extinguisher consists of a pressure cylinder filled with liquid carbon dioxide. A trigger allows the liquid to be discharged through a horn under its own pressure. On discharge the liquid is converted into carbon dioxide snow in the nozzle which is converted to gas in the fire. It is noisy on discharge and the horn can become very cold (Fig. 32.10).

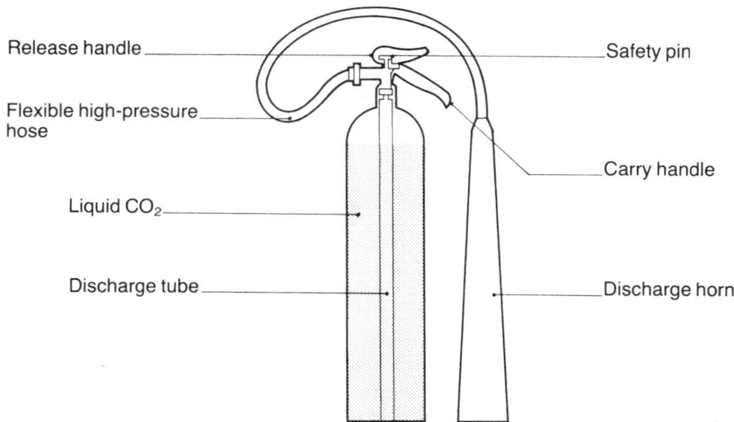

Fig. 32.10 A carbon dioxide extinguisher showing the piercing mechanism, control valve and discharge horn
Source: Home Office, *Manual of Firemanship*

Carbon dioxide can be used on both Classes A and B fires and on fires involving electrical equipment. On Class A fires it is less efficient than water because of limited cooling, and on Class B it is less efficient than vaporising liquid. A second extinguisher should be available because of the limited cooling effect. Carbon dioxide is an asphyxiant and is heavier than air. It can collect in pits and hollows where it may be a risk to people entering the premises.

Dry chemical powder

These are of two types – stored pressure and gas cartridge. In both cases the cylinder is fed with dry powder, but in the stored pressure type the cylinder is pressurised to 10 bar with dry air or nitrogen. Operating the trigger allows the pressure to expel the dry powder through the hose. With the gas cartridge type the seal on the cartridge is broken by a plunger and the flow of powder is controlled by a trigger valve on the hose (Fig. 32.11).

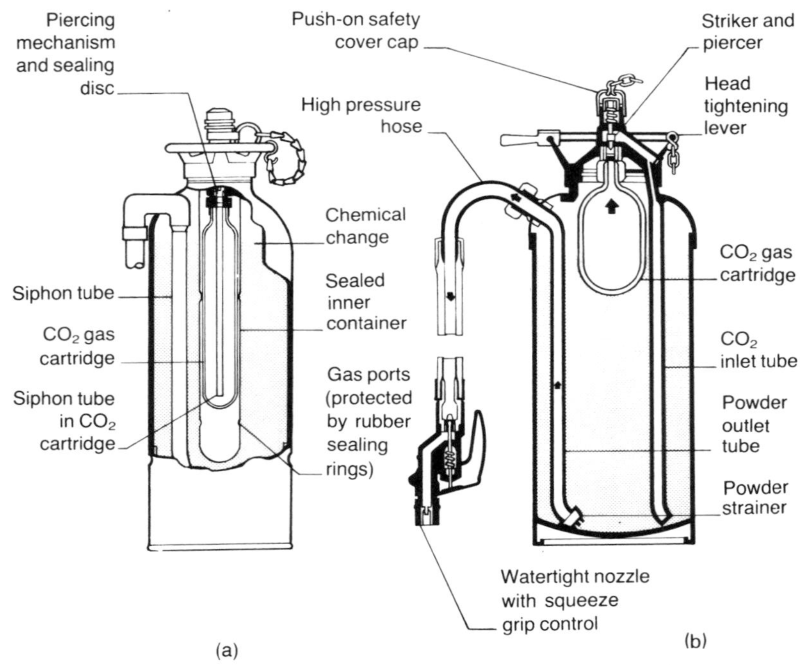

Fig. 32.11 (a) One type of dry powder (gas cartridge) extinguisher. (b) Another type with a squeeze grip control
Source: Home Office, *Manual of Firemanship*

Precautions relating to dry chemical powder extinguishers

The cylinder is a pressure vessel so it needs to be maintained in accordance with the maker's instructions (*see* Chapter 34). Dry powder has a tendency to cake during prolonged storage in the cylinder. Moreover, after discharge, the trigger end of the hose can become blocked, necessitating thorough cleaning.

These extinguishers can be used on Class A and Class B fires provided that they contain general purpose powder.

Vaporising liquid

All vaporising liquid extinguishers consist of a cylinder containing the liquid which is pressurised to 10 bar with dry carbon dioxide or nitrogen. Striking a knob allows the pressure to expel the liquid (Fig. 32.12).

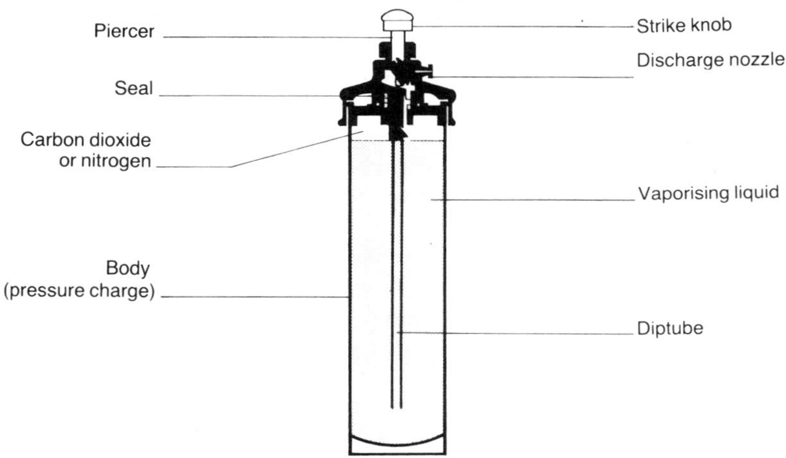

Fig. 32.12 Section through vaporising liquid (stored pressure) extinguisher
Source: Home Office, *Manual of Firemanship*

These extinguishers are useful for Class A and Class B fires and small or incipient fires involving burning liquids. They are less efficient than foam on large liquid fires because the heat dissipates the vaporising liquid, and less efficient than water on Class A fires as they have a lower cooling effect. On fires involving electrical equipment they are particularly effective because they are non-conducting and do not cause damage to the equipment. Vaporising liquids should not be used in a confined space as the liquids and their combustion products are toxic. Discharge should be started at one edge of the fire, then swept across the surface of the burning material to concentrate on the heart of the fire.

Fire-fighting equipment

Portable fire extinguishers

Portable extinguishers provide first aid fire fighting for Class A and Class B fires, but not in general for Class C and Class D fires. They are only useful, however, if sufficient are provided of the right type, in the right place, if they are properly maintained and if people are available who have been trained in their use. They should be located in conspicuous positions – identified with an approved sign – usually on exit routes by doors in corridors or landings. In multi-storey buildings they should be stored in the same position on each floor, to be available for use at all times. They must be easily accessible at all times and free from obstruction. The travel distance from a possible fire to the nearest appropriate extinguisher should not be more than 30 metres. For a special fire risk, appropriate fire extinguishers should be provided (*see* Table 27). (No one should have to make a choice regarding the specific extinguisher necessary for a particular fire.) Where a fire can occur in a confined space, extinguishers should be kept outside and be suitable for use in a confined space. All extinguishers should be protected against excessive heat or cold; storage in easily opened containers will provide some protection against external corrosion.

A monthly inspection routine should be undertaken for all extinguishers and the maker's instructions followed for all routine and non-routine maintenance. Maintenance and internal replacements should be carried out by trained personnel and accurate records kept of all inspections and maintenance of extinguishers.

Table 27: Classification of fires which can be controlled by portable extinguishers

Class of fire	*Description*	*Appropriate extinguisher*
A	Solid materials, usually organic, with glowing embers	Water, foam, dry powder, vaporising liquid, CO_2
B	Liquids and liquefiable solids:	
(i)	miscible with water, e.g. methanol, acetone	Water, foam (but must be stable on miscible solvents), CO_2, dry powder
(ii)	immiscible with water, e.g. petrol benzene, fats, waxes	Foam, dry powder, vaporising liquid, CO_2

Hose reels

Hose reels are a form of fixed fire-fighting installation and consist of a coil of 25 mm ID flexible hose directly connected to a rising main. They should be located in a recess so as not to obtrude into an access way, each container being clearly marked with the standard notice. The complete fixed installation, with the hose reel as the terminal point, consists of either a wet or a dry rising main and a landing valve or fire hydrant. The main consists of a heavy quality wrought steel pipe of not less than 100 mm ID. A wet rising main should be full of water and connected directly into the fire main with the water at fire main pressure, whereas with a dry rising main the pipe has to be charged with water prior to use. This can be done either by opening out the main to the fire main or by charging the main via a water pump. Wet rising mains are subject to frost damage if not suitably protected. The inlet to a dry rising main must be in a convenient position for the fire brigade to gain access to it, and it must be provided with hard standing for pumps. The inlet must be suitably identified and kept free for access at all times. In addition to hose reels, rising mains are fitted with landing valves which allow the connection of a standard fire hose. Both landing valves and hose reels must be kept free from obstruction at all times and should be sited not more than 30 metres from a possible fire location.

Sprinkler systems

Sprinkler systems provide an automatic means of detecting and extinguishing or controlling a fire in its early stages. The system consists of an overhead pipe installation on which sprinkler heads are fitted at suitable intervals. The installation is supplied with water from a head tank and/or water main. Each sprinkler head acts as a valve which is preset to open at a given temperature and release water onto the fire. For the system to be effective, the water supply must be automatic, reliable and not subject to freezing or drought. As each head is temperature-operated only, those heads nearest the fire open and are not subject to smoke or fume. Being overhead, they do not block or restrict access routes and can be arranged to operate an alarm on releasing water (Fig. 32.13).

Fire detection

Fire can be detected in one of three main ways:

(a) by sensing heat – actual temperature or the rate of rise of temperature,
(b) by detecting the presence of smoke, or
(c) by detecting flame.

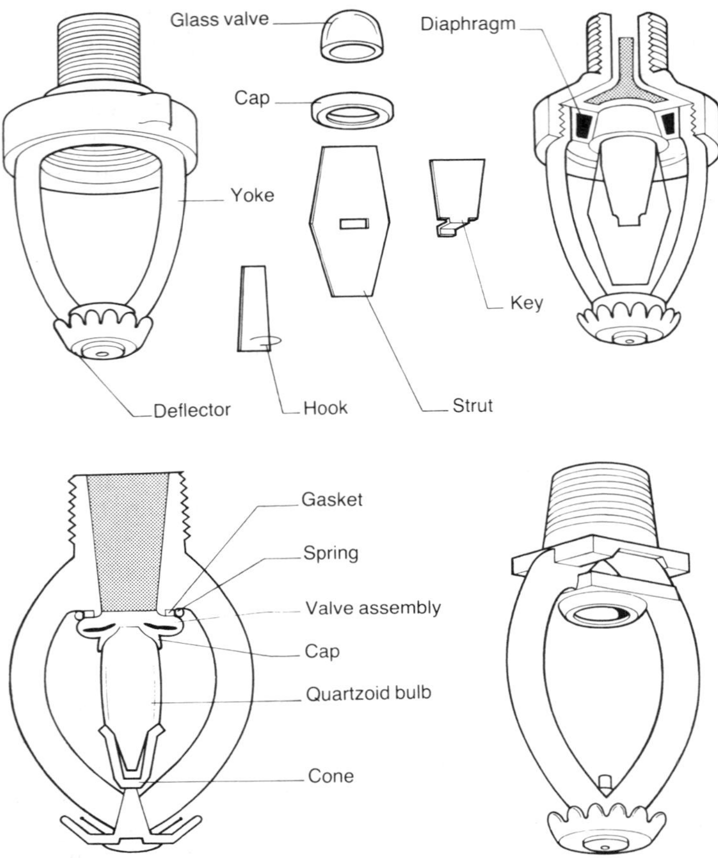

Fig. 32.13 Typical sprinkler heads
A fusible solder type sprinkler head
Bulb type sprinkler head
Source: Home Office, *Manual of Firemanship*

Heat detectors

Heat detectors are of two kinds: fusion and expansion.

Fusion heat detectors

Here a metal melts, completing an electrical circuit and releasing water. Alternatively, the expansion of a solid, liquid or gas activates some other device. The simplest form of fusion detector consists of an electrical circuit containing a switch held in either the open or the closed position by a piece of low melting alloy. In the heat of the fire, this alloy melts, the switch is released and the circuit conditions change (Fig. 32.14).

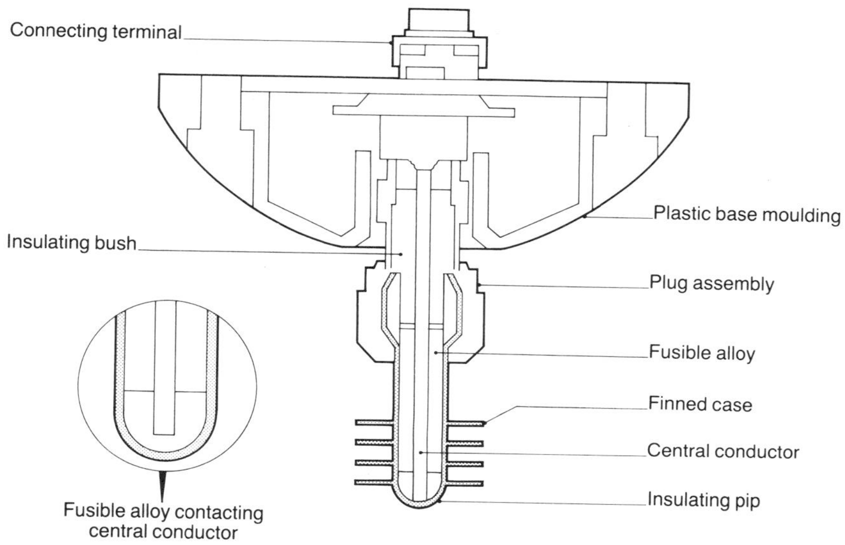

Fig. 32.14 Chubb fixed temperature detector
Source: Home Office, *Manual of Firemanship*

Expansion heat detector

The simplest form of a thermal expansion heat detector consists of a bimetallic strip which expands in a circular mode under the influence of heat, closing off an electrical circuit. Gases and liquids have greater coefficients of heat expansion than metals and as such are potentially more sensitive than metals as heat detectors. The most common use of liquid expansion occurs in the quartzite bulb used in sprinkler systems. The final 'valve' consists of a quartzite bulb filled with liquid and on contact with fire the liquid expands. At a predetermined temperature the bulb bursts and water is released.

The flame of a fire emits not only visible light but ultraviolet and infrared radiation. Each one of these can be used to detect fire. Although visible radiation is obscured by smoke, ultraviolet and infrared radiation remain unaffected. Flame detectors operate on the principle of detecting either or both of these. The disadvantages of these detectors is that they react to any source of ultraviolet or infrared radiation, such as the sun or the moon. Hence they can be subject to spurious alarms as well as circuit failure.

Smoke detectors

Smoke detectors are of different types operating on the basis of ionising radiation, light scatter or obscuration.

Ionising detectors

This form of detector utilises a small radioactive source which maintains a level of ionisation in two chambers, one of which is open to the atmosphere. When smoke enters this chamber, the smoke particles absorb some of the ionisation, causing an electrical imbalance detected by the instrument.

Light scatter detectors

The light scatter detector works on the easily observed fact that smoke scatters light. A photo-electric cell is fitted in a chamber at right angles to a source of light. In a fire-free condition the cell would receive no light, but when smoke enters the chamber, light is scattered and detected by the cell.

Light obscuration detectors

With this detector the photo-electric cell is mounted opposite a light source in a chamber so when smoke enters some of the light is obscured. The cell detects decreases in light intensity.

Flammable gas detectors

Technically, a flammable gas detector is not a fire detector because it works on the pre-fire condition, measuring the concentration of flammable gas in the atmosphere and raising the alarm when the concentration reaches a predetermined fraction of the lower explosive limit. The gas mixture is drawn over a catalytic surface on which the flammable gas is oxidised. In turn, the heat of oxidation raises the temperature of the catalyst surface and the device responds to the rise in temperature dependent on the concentration of the air/flammable gas mixture passing over it. These detectors have to be calibrated to take into account the different gases to which they will be exposed; for instance, different calibrations are required for propane and petrol.

Fire alarms

The most effective fire alarm system is the human voice, but this can be very expensive when 24-hour coverage is needed. Routine patrols of premises, carried out diligently and in a disciplined way, will detect most fires before they become a serious risk. Alarm should be raised by telephoning a local centre or the local fire brigade.

A fire can also be detected by any of the detectors outlined above. Each device can be made to operate an alarm system which alerts employees or an in-house fire brigade. Some detection devices will automatically start to fight the fire – e.g. sprinkler systems, where the flow of water sets off the alarm.

The major disadvantage of all automatic alarms is the frequency of false alarms. All systems suffer from this problem and should be tuned to deal with the local situation.

Fire prevention

It is impossible to prevent the occurrence of a fuel/oxygen mixture in many situations. Most fire prevention activities, therefore, consist of controlling sources of ignition. The most common are lighting, heating, ventilation equipment and machinery, tools and people. Moreover, electric sparks can cause fires (not, however, electricity itself – a popular myth).

Lighting

Here it is not the light which is the source of ignition but the heat generated by the light. Incandescent lights present a greater risk than discharge lights because they give off more heat. The heat from a light will transfer to any object by a combination of conduction, convection and radiation. For conduction, the object must be in contact with the light: obviously, any flammable object in actual contact with a light will heat up. With convection the heat transfer medium is air which travels upwards when heated. Any object, therefore, which is above a light will heat up by convection, and the nearer the object is to the top of the light source the hotter it will get. Radiation decreases rapidly with distance, the rate of decrease being dependent on the temperature of the radiating object.

Lights should be so placed that the heat rising from them will not be transferred by convection to objects which are placed above them. A good practice is to mount each lamp in a cage so that objects cannot be inadvertently placed in direct contact with the lamp. An unusual form of lighting is burning gas or oil. Both the hot wick and the mantle are sources of ignition, and so is the heat from the flame.

Heating

Heating is a source of ignition, emanating from stoves, boilers, open fires, electric strip and bar heaters, as well as lagged and unlagged steam heating and hot water pipes. Heat transfer occurs through conduction and convection. In order to prevent conduction, objects should never be placed in direct contact with sources of heat. Convection takes place in an upward direction, being more effective the nearer the object is to the source of heat. If heat transfer by convection is to be avoided, therefore, objects should not be placed above a source of heat.

Stoves and portable heating appliances should always stand on a non-combustible surface and, if possible, be surrounded by a low kerb and guard rail. The area itself should be kept free from all rubbish and debris. Any portable stoves should be secured to prevent overturning. When they are in use the handling of flammable fluids should be forbidden. Moreover, permanent heating systems require installation, maintenance, operation and repair in accordance with the manufacturer's recommendations. Strict control of access to boiler rooms is necessary and they should be kept clean and tidy.

Ventilation equipment, machinery, etc.

Dangers arising from ventilation equipment and machinery result from electrical connections, overheated bearings and hot surfaces. With machinery these are often detected by the operators. Ventilation equipment is often installed in inaccessible places and dangers remain undetected for long periods. Such equipment is designed to operate in a good air draught, thereby assisting the spread of fire.

Tools can be a source of ignition. Burning gear, blow lamps and soldering irons present obvious dangers as well as uncooled cutting edges, electrically powered tools and steel scrapers. Control methods include a high standard of housekeeping, particularly in the case of burning and welding gear, when the surrounding area must be free from all combustible material. Ideally, soldering irons should never be put down except onto an insulated rest. These and other 'hot' tools should never be used close to flammable materials.

Construction and layout

All buildings contain an extensive variety of materials without taking into account working materials and people. When a fire starts each of these materials will react in a different way and it is virtually impossible to predict what will happen. Fire normally spreads upwards as the hot gaseous products of combustion rise. It can also spread horizontally due to conduction and radiation, but it very rarely spreads downwards.

The layout of a room or factory floor affects fire spread. Where possible, all high fire risk processes should be grouped together to permit appropriate fire prevention and protection. Stores containing flammable materials must be separate from other stores. In general storage areas, combustible goods should be segregated from non-combustible ones. If it is not possible to segregate work processes or stores according to flammability, then the highest risk must be assumed to apply to the whole area.

Waste paper, scrap products and by-products, wrapping materials and redundant items form the fuel for fires, the spread of which can be rapid. The most effective fire prevention activity is good housekeeping. Refuse should be removed at least daily and stored in a fireproof location, such as a metal skip kept in a non-smoking area. Spillages, particularly of oil and other flammable substances, should be removed. Flammable liquids must always be handled in special containers. Housekeeping inspections should be frequently undertaken, not only static situations being examined but the housekeeping standards of operators too (*see* Chapter 14).

Means of escape in case of fire

A *means of escape* in case of fire is a continuous route by way of a space, room, corridor, staircase, doorway or other means of passage, along or through which persons can travel from wherever they are in a building to the safety of the open air at ground level by their own unaided efforts. An *alternative means of escape* is a second route, usually in the opposite direction, but which may join the first means of escape. The alternative means is not the second best route, but rather another main means, and should be planned and maintained as such.

Considerations to be taken into account in planning and maintaining a means of escape are travel distance, doors, signs, lighting and protection of the route.

Travel

There are three travel stages:

(a) travel within rooms,
(b) travel from rooms to a stairway or final exit, and
(c) travel within stairways and to a final exit.

The following general rules apply to means of escape:

(a) The total travel distance between any point in a building and the nearest final exit or protected stairway should not be more than
  (i) 18 m if there is only one exit, or
  (ii) 45 m if more than one exit.
(b) Two or more exits are necessary
  (i) from a room in which more than 60 people work, or
  (ii) if any point in the room is more than 12 m from the nearest exit.
(c) Minimum width of exit should be 750 mm.
(d) (i) Corridors should not be less than 1 m in width; and
  (ii) in the case of offices, where corridors are longer than 45 m, they should be subdivided by fire-resisting doors.
(e) Stairways should be at least 800 mm in width, and fire resistant, along with doors connecting them.
(f) A single stairway is sufficient in a building of up to four storeys only.

(g) The following are not acceptable as means of escape:
   (i) spiral staircases,
   (ii) escalators,
   (iii) lifts,
   (iv) lowering lines, and
   (v) portable or throw-out ladders.

(h) Fire doors must open outwards only.

(i) Doors providing means of escape should never be locked. (If they have to be kept locked for security purposes, panic bolts should be fitted or keys maintained in designated key boxes close to the exit.) A notice should indicate that the doors can be opened in the case of fire.

(j) A fire exit notice should be fitted to or above fire exit doors.

(k) Appropriate notices should be affixed along fire escape routes, which should be provided with emergency lighting.

(l) Corridors and stairways forming a means of escape should have half-hour fire resistance, i.e. no fire should be able to break through within 30 minutes. This means that a corridor or stairway should be built from non-combustible materials, i.e. brick or concrete. The surface finish should also be non-combustible.

(m) Fire alarm warnings must be audible throughout the building. In larger buildings this will require the provision of electrically operated alarms, whereas in smaller buildings a manually operated gong or bell may suffice.

(n) Normally no person should have to travel more than 30 m to the nearest alarm point.

Fire instructions

A fire instruction is a notice informing people of the action they should take on either

(a) hearing the alarm, or
(b) discovering a fire.

A typical notice is shown in Fig. 32.15.

However, fire instructions do not end at issuing a notice to the employees and displaying a copy in a prominent position. People need training as well, i.e. regular fire drills and/or simulated fire exercises. These can disrupt working, but are the only way employees can learn what they must do in a real situation. The alarm should be sounded weekly at the same time so that employees become familiar with its sound. An evacuation exercise should be held annually. In all workplaces, trained employees should be designated as fire wardens, i.e. to carry out a head count on evacuation. They may also act as 'last man out' in large buildings and as helpers to the public. Training of selected employees in the correct use of fire extinguishers may well be necessary, so that they can act as first aid firemen.

WHEN THE FIRE ALARM SOUNDS

1. Close the windows, switch off electrical equipment and leave the room, closing the door behind you.
2. Walk quickly along the escape route to the open air.
3. Report to the fire warden at your assembly point.
4. Do not attempt to re-enter the building.

WHEN YOU FIND A FIRE

1. Raise the alarm by ... (If the telephone is to be used, the notice must include a reference to name and location.)
2. Leave the room, closing the door behind you.
3. Leave the building by the escape route.
4. Report to the fire warden at the assembly point.
5. Do not attempt to re-enter the building.

Fig. 32.15 Fire instruction

Liaison with the fire authority

Apart from visits made by officers of the fire authority in connection with fire certificates, the authority is a valuable source of practical information on fire protection, fire precautions and training. Before any change of use is made in premises, consultation should take place, so that the views of the fire authority can be accommodated in the design, thereby saving expense later. In many cases, the fire authority will give assistance in training. In large establishments, it is advantageous for a fire officer to visit regularly to familiarise himself with the layout, the people and any special fire-fighting needs. These visits can save valuable minutes in the event of fire.

Fire certificates

The Fire Precautions Act 1971 requires that a fire certificate shall be issued for factory and commercial premises

(a) in which more than 20 persons are employed to work at any one time; or

(b) in which more than 10 persons are employed to work at any one time elsewhere than on the ground floor; or
(c) which are in the same building as other factories, offices, etc., and the sum total of employees in all the premises exceeds 20 or exceeds 10 elsewhere than on the ground floor;

or for a factory,

(d) if explosive or highly flammable materials are stored or used in or under the premises, unless the fire authority determines that, because the type and quantity of such materials do not constitute a serious additional risk to persons in the premises in case of fire, there is no need for a fire certificate.

A fire certificate specifies

(a) the use or uses of the premises it covers;
(b) the means of escape in the case of fire indicated on a plan of the building;
(c) the means for ensuring the safety and effectiveness of the means of escape, such as fire and smoke stop doors, emergency lighting and direction signs;
(d) the means of fighting fire for the use of persons on the premises;
(e) the means of raising the alarm; and
(f) particulars of explosive or highly flammable liquids stored and used on the premises.

The fire certificate may also impose requirements relating to

(a) the maintenance of the means of escape and keeping it free from obstruction;
(b) the maintenance of other fire precautions;
(c) the training of people and the keeping of records;
(d) limitations on numbers of persons in the premises; and
(e) any other relevant fire precautions.

When a fire certificate has been issued the fire precautions specified must be kept in accordance with the specification and all other requirements must be observed. The fire certificate must be kept on the premises to which it refers. When changes to conditions or alterations to premises are being considered, the fire authority must be notified in advance of any proposal such as

(a) to make a material extension of, or material structural alteration to, the premises; or
(b) to make a material alteration in the internal arrangements of the premises or in the furniture or equipment with which the premises are provided.

By 'material' is meant any alteration which would render the means of escape and related fire precautions inadequate in relation to the normal conditions of use of the premises. If changes are proposed they may be considered as though a new application has been made for a certificate.

33

Lifting machinery and equipment

Definitions

Lifting machinery

The statutory definition of *lifting machinery* is 'a crane, crab, winch, teagle, pulley block, gin wheel, transporter or runway' (Factories Act 1961, sec 27(9)). Also included are hoists, cranes, elevators and lifts, whether used for carrying people, goods or both.

Lifting tackle

The statutory definition of *lifting tackle* or *lifting equipment* is 'chain slings, rope slings, rings, hooks, shackles and swivels' (Factories Act 1961, sec 26(3)). Hence the general meaning of lifting tackle is taken to include various types of ropes, chains, hooks, eyebolts, 'D' rings and other items.

NOTE. The Construction (Lifting Operations) Regulations 1961 lay down detailed requirements in respect of lifting appliances and lifting equipment used in building operations and works of engineering construction. The Offices, Shops and Railway Premises (Hoists and Lifts) Regulations 1968 (as amended in 1974) provide detailed requirements relating to hoists and lifts in offices and shops.

Lifting machinery – legal aspects

Lifting machinery may be classified thus:

(a) hoists,
(b) cranes, and
(c) lifts.

Outline of statutory requirements relating to lifting machinery

Statute law relating to lifting machinery is covered in the Factories Act 1961, secs 22–5 and 27. The following is an outline of the requirements relating to lifting machinery used in factories.

Hoists and lifts – general requirements

(a) Every hoist or lift shall be
  (i) of good mechanical construction, sound materials, adequate strength and properly maintained (sec 22(1)); and
  (ii) examined by a competent person once every 6 months at least and a report in the prescribed form produced; the details of the examination must be attached to or entered in the general register within 28 days; where defects indicate that future operation of the equipment may be unsafe the HSE must be notified by a competent person within 28 days (sec 22(2)).

(b) Every hoistway or liftway shall be efficiently protected by a substantial enclosure fitted with gates of such design and layout as to prevent, when the gates are shut, any person falling down the way or coming into contact with any moving parts of the equipment. Any such gate must be fitted with an efficient interlocking device (sec 22(4)).

(c) Every hoist or lift and every enclosure shall be so constructed as to prevent any part of any person or any goods carried from being trapped between any part of the hoist or lift and any fixed structure or between the counterbalance weight or any other moving part (sec 22(7)).

(d) The safe working load of the hoist or lift must be conspicuously marked and must not be exceeded (sec 22(8)).

Hoists and lifts for carrying persons

The following requirements, in addition to those listed above, apply:

(a) provision of efficient automatic devices to prevent the cage or platform overrunning (sec 23(1)(*a*));

(b) provision of a gate on every side where access to a landing is afforded; efficient devices must be provided to prevent the cage being set in motion when the gate is open and to ensure that the cage will come to rest when the gate is opened (sec 23(1)(*b*)); and

(c) where the platform or cage is suspended by a rope or chain, there must be at least two ropes or chains separately connected to the cage or platform, each rope or chain and its attachments being capable of carrying the whole weight of the platform or cage and its maximum working load; efficient devices must be provided and maintained which will support the platform or cage with its maximum working load in the event of a breakage of the ropes or chains or any of their attachments (sec 23(3)).

Teagle openings

A *teagle opening* is an opening in the fabric of a building above ground level through which goods can be hoisted into the building. Such openings are common in flour and agricultural mills in particular. They also feature in older types of factories and in warehouses. The Factories Act 1961, sec 24, requires that every teagle opening or similar doorway used for hoisting or lowering goods or materials, whether by mechanical power or otherwise, must be securely fenced and provided with a secure handhold each side. The fencing must be properly maintained and kept in position, except when hoisting or lowering goods or materials.

Work at teagle openings and platform edges

What constitutes 'secure fencing' within the requirements of section 24 is a matter for legal interpretation, but it is quite common to see openings fenced solely by a metal bar or wooden beam set horizontally approximately 1 metre from the floor. This arrangement relies heavily on operators replacing the bar after loading or unloading operations, and there is always the risk of operators falling over or under the bar. Furthermore, the sole provision of handholds at each side of the opening is of limited value in preventing falls from teagle openings and platform edges.

In recent years a number of safety barriers for high-level openings have been developed, the Ajax safety barrier being the most common (*see* Fig. 33.1). It is designed to give continuous protection to anyone working at a high-level loading point or teagle opening. The barrier operates on the basis that when a load has to be placed on a platform or through a teagle opening, the barrier is pivotted laterally through 180 degrees and comes to rest in a similar position some distance back from the edge of the platform or opening. Once the materials have been placed on the platform, the barrier is pivotted upwards and over the load until it rests in its original position at the platform edge so that the load can be removed. The moving part of the barrier is spring-loaded for ease of operation and a simple automatic catch locks the barrier in the closed position.

While the standard application is at loading points on platforms or mezzanine floors, the barrier can also be made to suit difficult installations where it is not practicable to make structural alterations, such as teagle openings, where doors may be involved or the pallet load is too large for the standard type of barrier.

Fig. 33.1 The Ajax safety barrier
Reproduced by courtesy of Weller Engineering Ltd

Cranes and other lifting machines

(a) All parts and working gear shall be of good construction, sound materials, adequate strength and free from patent defect, and be properly maintained (sec 27(1)).

(b) All parts and working gear shall be examined by a competent person at least once every 14 months; a report containing the prescribed particulars of every such examination must be kept in a register; where defects indicate that operation of the equipment may be unsafe in future, a copy of the report must be sent to the HSE within 28 days (sec 27(2)).

(c) All rails on which a travelling crane moves and every track on which the carriage of a transporter or runway moves shall be of proper size and adequate strength and have an even running surface; any rails or track must be properly laid, adequately supported or suspended and properly maintained (sec 27(3)).

(d) The safe working load or loads must be plainly marked on every lifting machine. In the case of a jib crane, so constructed that the safe working load may be varied by raising or lowering the jib, there must be attached to it either a safe working load indicator or a table indicating the safe working loads at corresponding inclinations of the jib or corresponding radii of the load (sec 27(4)).

(e) Except for the purposes of a test (proof testing), no lifting machine must be loaded beyond the safe working load (sec 27(5)).

(f) No lifting machine may be taken into use in a factory for the first time unless it has been tested and all parts thoroughly examined by a competent person; a certificate of the test and examination, specifying the safe working loads of the machine, must be issued and signed by the person making the test and examination, and the certificate must be kept available for inspection (sec 27(6)).

(g) If any person is employed or working on or near the wheel-track of an overhead travelling crane in any place where he would be liable to be struck by the crane, effective measures must be taken, e.g. by warning the driver of the crane, to ensure that the crane does not approach within about 6 metres of that place. Where any person is working at a place above floor level, where he would be liable to be struck by an overhead travelling crane or its load, effective measures must be taken to warn him of the approach of the crane, unless his work is so connected with or dependent on the movements of the crane as to make a warning unnecessary (secs 27(7) and 27(8)).

Safety aspects of lifting machinery

Cranes

Cranes have numerous applications in industrial activities, construction, docks and shipbuilding, and on railways. The principal hazard associated with any crane operation is the risk of collapse or overturning of the crane which can be caused by a variety of factors such as overloading, incorrect slewing or even incorrect construction of the crane. One of the principal causes of crane overturning is associated with the crane operator exceeding the 'maximum permitted moment', which is the product of the load and the radius of operation of the crane. (The radius of operation is the horizontal distance between the crane's centre of rotation and a vertical line drawn through the crane hook.) If the maximum permitted moment is exceeded, the crane is in danger of overturning or collapse.

There are many types of crane in use. Several of the more common forms of crane are discussed below.

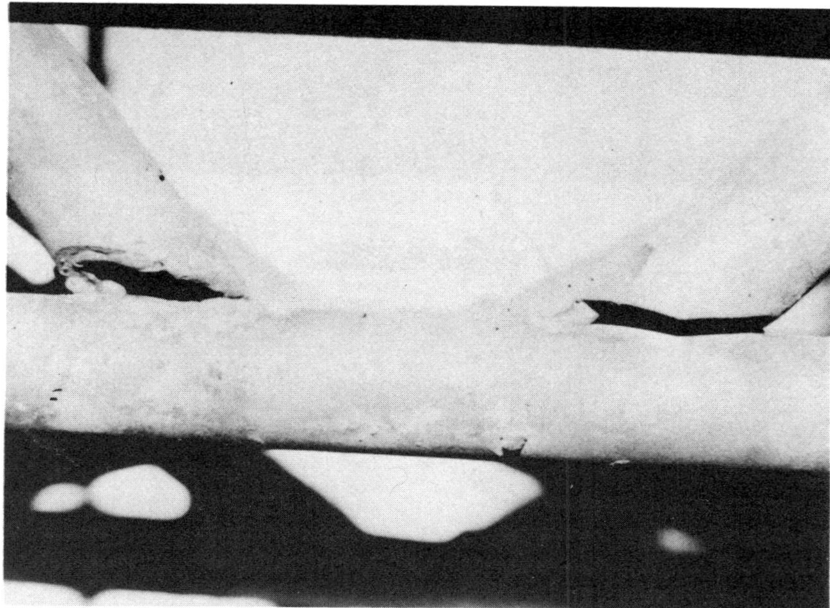

Fig. 33.2 Defects in cranes
Unsatisfactory welds between braces to the jib of a mobile crane. This could seriously reduce the strength of the crane and lead to failure
Reproduced by courtesy of National Vulcan Engineering Insurance Group Ltd

Some defects in cranes which could result in accidents are illustrated in Figs. 33.2–33.5.

Fixed cranes

This type of crane is permanently fixed in one location, such as a wharf, loading bay, dock or rail siding. It may incorporate a fixed angle or adjustable angle jib, and may rotate through 360 degrees. Accidents involving fixed cranes with resultant crane collapse, fall of the load and/or injury to operatives can occur in many ways. One principal cause of accidents is the failure to lift vertically. This may arise through the physical impossibility of getting the load directly below the lifting point, or the use of a fixed crane in a deliberate attempt to drag a load sideways, a very dangerous practice. Loads treated in this way can overstress the crane and cause collapse, or the load may swing violently, crushing people and damaging property. Alternatively, loads being raised or lowered may catch in a fixed structure causing damage. The 'snatching' of loads, instead of operating a slow and steady lifting action, can cause crane failure. Moreover, attempting to pull an object from under other material can impose loads of up to one hundred times

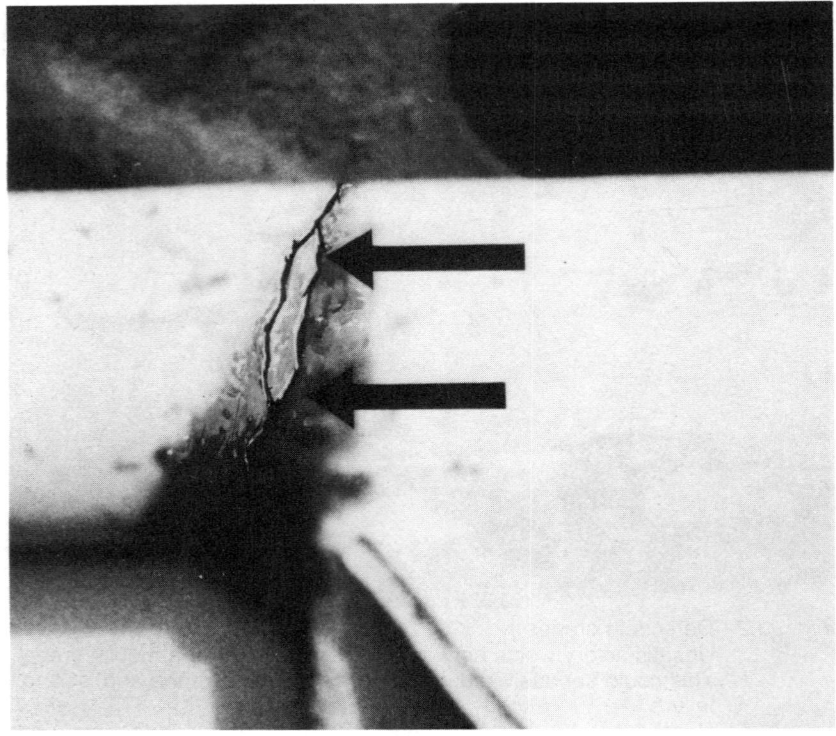

Fig. 33.3 A close-up of cracking originating from a weld in a 57 mm diameter tubular section of a part of a crane jib head fabrication. Further development of this defect, aided by internal corrosion of the member, could lead to jib failure
Reproduced by courtesy of National Vulcan Engineering Insurance Group Ltd

that anticipated, often with disastrous results. Cranes with adjustable angle jibs have collapsed through the operator's failure to observe the reduction in the safe working load as the jib moves towards the horizontal.

Similar observations apply in the case of rotational cranes. Accidents are caused by incorrect lifting and slewing, failure of the rotating gear when slewing and, more commonly, slewing too fast. Variations in wind speed, particularly while slewing, have a direct effect on the strength and stability of this type of crane.

Tower cranes

These cranes are often covered by the Construction (Lifting Operations) Regulations 1961, and are highly complex items of plant. Accidents are caused through incorrect assembly of the crane, and insufficient access to the jib, mast and driver's cab. The need for the

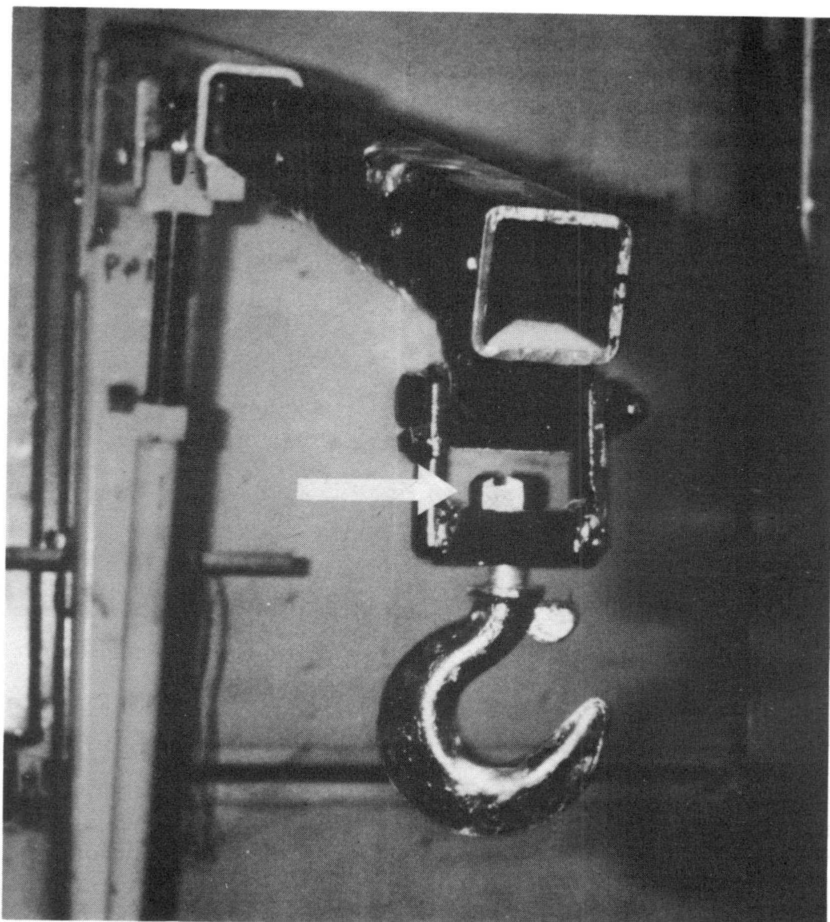

Fig. 33.4 A dangerous situation with a manual hydraulic portable jib crane. The hook-retaining nut is only engaging one or two threads. Provision was made for locking the nut with a split pin which is missing
Reproduced by courtesy of National Vulcan Engineering Insurance Group Ltd

driver to reach the cab safely is well recognised, but safe access to other parts of the crane is necessary during inspection, maintenance and repair, and in the course of erection or dismantling. Modifications to tower cranes may affect their strength and stability, and the manufacturer's advice should be sought prior to any modification. Rail-mounting arrangements and the system for maintenance of such cranes must be considered in any assessment of safe working operations.

Mobile cranes

Mobile cranes are used increasingly for lifting heavy items into specific

Fig. 33.5 Cracks in the spokes to a jib head sheave of a large crane. Such cracking would eventually result in failure of the crane
Reproduced by courtesy of National Vulcan Engineering Insurance Group Ltd

locations. Some incorporate a telescopic or articulated boom and rotate through 360 degrees on the chassis of a purpose-built road vehicle. In addition to the precautions outlined previously for fixed cranes, it is imperative that any lift takes place on solid level ground, using the vehicle's outriggers fully extended to spread the load through the vehicle to the ground. The principal cause of accidents is their use on uneven sloping ground, where the centre of gravity of the load combined with the crane has fallen outside the wheel base of the vehicle, resulting in overturning.

Overhead travelling cranes

The most common application of this crane is in heavy fabrication shops and foundries where the crane runs along a fixed traverse. The crane may be fixed to operate in one position or to rotate through 360 degrees. The main hazards are derailment due to overloading, obstructions on the traverse or rail track, and the absence of adequate stops at each end of the traverse or rails. With rail-mounted cranes, either the crane must be fitted with effective brakes for the travelling motion, or sprags, scotches or chocks must be provided and used.

Many accidents are attributed to overhead travelling cranes crushing or striking operators working in the vicinity of the track. Previous reference has been made to the requirements of the Factories Act 1961, sec 27(7), whereby effective measures must be taken to prevent a crane approaching within about 6 metres of any place where a person may be working on or near the wheel track of such a crane. The only reliable 'effective measures' are the complete isolation and locking off of the electrical supply to the crane, coupled with the issue of a permit to work indicating that the isolation procedure has been carried out and that it is safe for work to proceed in the vicinity of the crane track (*see also* Chapter 13). The mere switching off of the electrical supply at a control box, even with the display of a cautionary notice on the switchbox itself, is not considered sufficient. The starter switch should be physically locked in the OFF position, or where this is not possible, the fuses removed from the operating circuit.

Hand signals to be used when directing the driver of an overhead travelling crane are shown in Fig. 33.6.

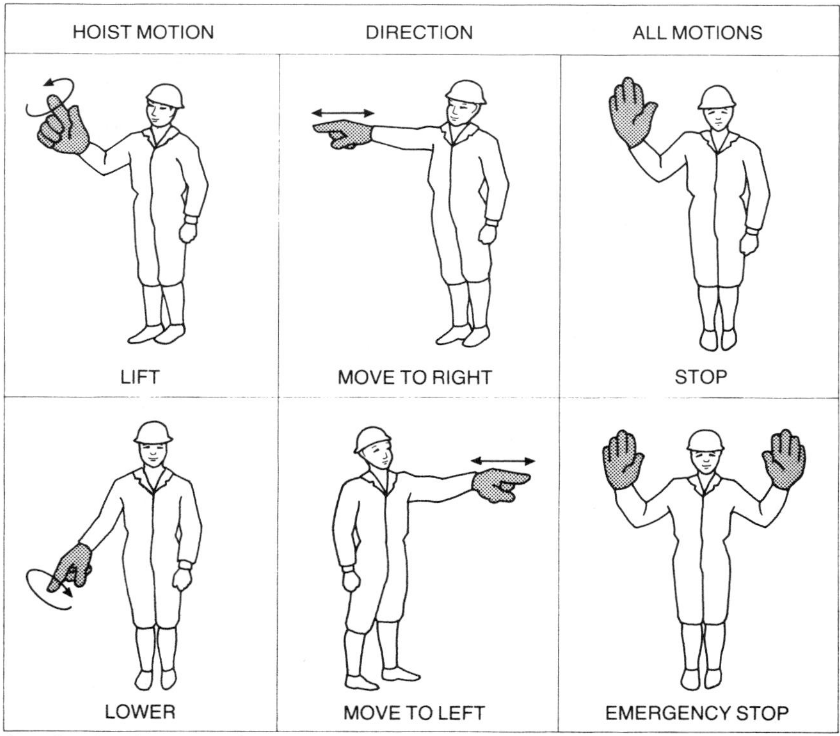

Signaller should stand in a secure position where he CAN SEE the LOAD and CAN BE SEEN CLEARLY by the driver. Face the driver if possible. Each signal should be distinct and clear.

Fig. 33.6 Hand signals for overhead travelling crane operation

Hoists and lifts

The Factories Act 1961, sec 25, broadly defines a hoist or lift as a 'platform or cage whose movement is restricted by a guide or guides'. A similar definition is incorporated in the Construction (Lifting Operations) Regulations 1961, and the Hoists Exemption Order 1962 exempts certain classes or types of hoist or lift from some or all of the requirements under the Factories Act. Sections 22, 23 and 25 prescribe comprehensive requirements for the design and mechanical construction of hoists and lifts. The requirements differ for hoists operated by power and by hand. In general, all hoistways and liftways must be protected by a substantial enclosure fitted with gates so as to prevent a person from falling down the way or coming into contact with any moving part of the hoist. Automatic devices are required on hoists and lifts used for carrying people to prevent the cage or platform of a hoist from overrunning. All cage gates must be interlocked so that a cage cannot be moved until the gates have been shut and will come to rest as soon as a gate is opened. The interlocking system must ensure that the hoistway gate cannot be opened unless the cage or platform is at that level.

Hoistways and liftways inside buildings must be completely enclosed with fire-resisting materials, and all means of access to the hoist or lift fitted with doors of fire-resisting material. The top of a hoistway, however, must be enclosed only by material easily broken by fire, or be provided with a vent at the top.

The provisions of the Factories Act 1961, secs 22 and 23, and the Offices, Shops and Railway Premises (Hoists and Lifts) Regulations 1968 (as subsequently amended) require that every power-driven lift be properly maintained and thoroughly examined by a competent person once every 6 months, and a report of the result of every such examination detailed on prescribed form F54 and signed by the person carrying out the examination. Legal responsibility for ensuring that lifts are, at all times, properly maintained, and that statutory examinations are carried out, rests generally with the occupier of the premises. This accords with the general position under the Factories Act and Offices, Shops and Railway Premises Act where both criminal and civil liability tend to attach to occupation or control (or management) of premises, rather than ownership. Neither Act defines 'occupation', but it is invariably regarded as synonymous with control or management.

New lifts

There is no statutory requirement for new lifts to be tested before being taken into service. It is recommended, however, that all new lifts be tested and examined in accordance with Part 7 of BS 2655:1970 'Lifts, Escalators, Passenger Conveyors and Paternosters' and a test certificate obtained.

Examination of personnel lifts

The purpose of periodic examination is to determine whether the condition of the lift installation is such that it can continue to be operated safely. The design and construction of many lifts are such that occasionally component parts will need to be dismantled. There is a need to consider at periodic examinations those parts which are not normally accessible. Recommendations should be made for the testing of safety equipment. The following items should be subject to examination within the periods stated:

(a) landing and car door interlocks – not exceeding 12 months;
(b) worm and other gearing – not exceeding 10 years;
(c) shafts, bearing and pulleys – not exceeding 10 years;
(d) stepped diameter shafts – regularly;
(e) governors – not exceeding 4 years.

If safety gear has been fully tested and certified before hand-over as specified in BS 2655, Part 7, then a full speed test should be required only after a major overhaul involving a change of rated load or rated speed, or the disturbance of the car sling and/or safety gear assembly. The checking of linkages and the moving parts of safety gear for free and effective operation should be carried out at every periodic examination. In the case of suspension ropes, examination should take into account the number of broken wires, their position, surface wear, the presence of excessive stretching, inequality in rope tension and diameter, internal conditions and corrosion (as opposed to surface rust). Where overload protection devices are fitted, a full load calibration test should be carried out at intervals not exceeding 12 months.

Maintenance work on both personnel and goods lifts should incorporate the complete isolation and locking off of the electrical supply to the lift, together with the operation of a permit to work system. Apart from the risk of injury to maintenance engineers, there is the risk of members of the public or other employees falling down a lift shaft during routine servicing. A high degree of supervision and control is needed, therefore, possibly to the exent of employing personnel to direct people away from the lift entrance area and/or the provision of fencing and notices, particularly where the gates will be left open for long periods.

Goods lifts

There must be an efficient gate, and a device to ensure that the cage or platform cannot be raised or lowered unless the gate is closed and will come to rest when the gate is opened, or, where it is not reasonably practicable to fit such a device, the gate should be kept closed and fastened when the cage or platform is at rest at the gate, i.e. not being loaded or unloaded. Personnel must not travel on specifically designated goods lifts. The hoistway of a goods lift should be properly enclosed and maintenance requirements apply similar to those for personnel lifts.

Man hoists

This is a continuous belt hoist within the meaning of the Factories Act 1961, sec 25(2). Man hoists are commonly installed in flour mills and other premises where there is a continuous need for operators to move between floors. Provisions relating to belt diameters and strengths, clearance at the top of the man hoist, monthly inspections in addition to statutory annual examination, the provision of guards above and below the floor, the provision of hand-holds, emergency ladders, arrangement of ladders, openings in floors, the warning notices necessary and maximum permitted speeds are outlined in the revised recommendations on man hoist produced by the National Joint Industrial Council for the Flour Milling Industry (1956), in their *Health and Safety Handbook*.

Paternoster lifts

This type of lift is defined as 'a continuous running appliance for transporting passengers in a substantially vertical direction, in which a number of cars are suspended by two endless chains attached to the cars diagonally, so that the car floors are substantially horizontal when changing direction at the extremities of travel'. Fundamentally, a paternoster lift is another form of continuous hoist within the meaning of the Factories Act 1961, sec 25(2). The lift does not incorporate a front gate, and comprises a series of compartments or cars capable of holding four to six persons, moving at a speed of 18–20 metres per minute. Platforms are hinged at the front to prevent trapping of feet between the landing opening and the moving floor of the compartment. This type of lift can be dangerous if the level of supervision is poor. Its safety relies heavily on the visual perception of the user in deciding at what point to step onto the slowly moving platform. Such lifts are not suitable for use by the aged, the infirm, the disabled or children. The same provisions relating to testing and examination of lifts apply to paternosters.

Powered working platforms

These platforms are now commonly used where quick and safe access to overhead machinery and plant, electrical installations, lighting equipment and stored goods is needed, and for lifting people and equipment into position where high-level maintenance of buildings, ships, aircraft and public service vehicles is undertaken. Where height, reach and mobility are required, these aerial working platforms have substantial advantages over other systems such as fixed or rolling scaffolding, access towers, bosun's chairs and working platforms fitted to fork lift trucks. They are completely mobile, operating from either a self-propelled electric trolley or a light trailer. Their operations take three specific forms:

(a) self-propelled hydraulic boom operation,
(b) semi-mechanised articulated boom operation, and
(c) self-propelled scissor lift operation.

Safety procedures for powered working platforms

Whilst such platforms do not come within the general definition of lifting machines or appliances under the Factories Act 1961, a number of aspects relating to their safe use should be considered. Above all, the user and operator must be aware, from a study of the manufacturer's specification, of the scope and capabilities of the machine, and the machine must not be used beyond its recommended design capabilities. The following points must be considered in their operation and use.

Siting

Platforms should be sited on firm level working surfaces, and attention paid to the risk of aerial collision with nearby platforms and cranes, and possible contact with electrical conductors and power lines. Ample room must be allowed for passing vehicles; traffic cones and barriers, to warn approaching vehicles, should always be used when these platforms are in use.

Transportation

Care must be taken when loading and unloading platforms from road transport trailers, and ramps should always be used. Platforms should be driven by trained personnel only. When towing platforms on sites, it must be appreciated that the majority of self-propelled platforms do not have automatically applied brakes when under tow. Platforms should be lowered and correctly stowed before transporting and wheels chocked. Care should be taken in lifting any powered platform by crane or fork lift truck. The manufacturer should always be consulted prior to any lifting operation of this type.

Overturning

Hazards from overturning may be created by overloading of the platform, wind loading, impact or shock loading, and improper use. The maximum lifting capacity must be marked on the platform and shown in the manufacturer's specification. In no circumstances should this be exceeded. If any tools or equipment are carried, their extra weight must be considered. When assessing the weight of person to be carried in terms of overall safe working load, it is good practice to work on the basis of the first person weighing 100 kg and each subsequent person 75 kg.

For normal applications, it is considered impracticable to operate a working platform in wind speeds above Force 4 (Beaufort Scale), i.e. fair breeze, which is equal to 16 mph or 7.3 m/sec or 14 knots. Care must be exercised when using a platform on high-rise structures, e.g. bridges, elevated roadways.

Shock loading through dropping heavy materials or articles onto the platform should be avoided, and particular care exercised when using a platform or folding extension for overreach purposes. Platforms should never be used for jacking or as lifting appliances unless specifically designed for this purpose, and only when written approval, together with a test certificate, has been granted by the manufacturer. Moreover, the platform should not be moved in an elevated condition on uneven surfaces. Outriggers must only be operated with a platform in the lowered position. They must always be used where recommended by the manufacturer and for greater stability. The maximum gradient for safe use must not be exceeded, and on soft ground or unsurfaced areas supporting plates or timber mats should be used. (All platforms are rated for use on firm level ground, even when supplied with rough-terrain wheels.) Care must be taken when using the machine close to excavation or trenches, or on embankments. (Maximum gradient = 1:40.)

Falls and trapping

Personnel working on a platform should wear safety harness with lanyards attached to the platform and not to an adjacent structure. Loose tools and articles should be properly stowed on the platform. No attempts to extend the working height of the platform with boxes, steps, planks, trestles, etc., should be permitted. Operators should not use excessive force against the hand rails.

Trapping can occur between the chassis and a wall or by the working platform against roof trusses, overhead cranes, pipelines and bridges. Guards fitted around a scissor mechanism and baseframe must be adequately maintained and kept in position.

Electric cables and bare conductors present a major hazard. No platform must come within 6 metres, with the platform at maximum elevation, of a power cable. Inside this limit, a permit to work system should be used, in conjunction with the power supply authority. (*See also* HSE Guidance Note GS6, *Avoidance of Danger from Overhead Electric Lines.*)

Maintenance

Regular maintenance is crucial to platform safety. The manufacturer's instructions should be followed and fitters trained in specific maintenance procedures. When undertaking maintenance on, or inspecting, the working platform mechanism, a 'scotch' or mechanical locking bar should be used to sustain the platform in a raised position should the hydraulics, etc., fail. (Numerous fatal and severe accidents are on record where this vital advice has not been followed.)

Operators

No one should be allowed to drive a power-operated platform unless he has been selected, trained and authorised. Operators should be reasonably fit and intelligent. Persons suffering from disorders such as epilepsy, poor hearing and/or poor eye-sight should be health screened before a decision as to their fitness to operate is made. Operator training should be taken in three stages by the company operating the platform, i.e. basic operating skills and knowledge of the platform operation; specific job training for the particular needs of the site employer; and familiarisation training at the work area, e.g. emergency procedures.

Lifting tackle and equipment – legal aspects

The main law relating to chains, ropes and lifting tackle is embodied in the Factories Act 1961, sec 26, and the Construction (Lifting Operations) Regulations 1961 together with the Chains, Ropes and Lifting Tackle (Register) Order, 1938 (SR&O 1938, No. 599). This chapter confines itself to mention of the provisions of the Factories Act 1961.

Section 26(1) lays down specific provisions in respect of every chain, rope or lifting tackle used for the purpose of raising or lowering persons, goods or materials.

(a) No chain, rope or lifting tackle shall be used unless it is of good construction, sound material, adequate strength and free from patent defect (sec 26(1)(*a*)).
(b) Subject to section 26(2) (i.e. safe working load plainly marked), a table showing the safe working loads (SWLs) of every kind and size of chain, rope or lifting tackle in use and, in the case of a multiple sling, the SWLs at different angles of the legs, shall be posted in the store in which the chains, ropes or lifting tackle are kept, and in prominent positions on the premises, and no such items not shown in the table shall be used (sec 26(1)(*b*)).
(c) No chain, rope or lifting tackle shall be used for any load exceeding its SWL (as shown by the table mentioned in section 26(1)(*b*) or marked as mentioned in section 26(2)) (sec 26(1)(*c*)).

(d) All chains, ropes and lifting tackle in use shall be thoroughly examined by a competent person at least once every 6 months or at such greater intervals as the minister may prescribe (sec 26(1)(*d*)).

(e) No chains, rope or lifting tackle, except a fibre rope or fibre rope sling, shall be taken into use in any factory for the first time unless it has been tested and thoroughly examined by a competent person and a certificate of test and examination, specifying the SWL, and signed by the person making the test and examination, has been obtained and is kept available for inspection (sec 26(1)(*e*)).

(f) Every chain and lifting tackle, except a rope sling, shall (unless of a class or description exempted by certificate of the chief inspector upon the ground that it is made of such material or so constructed that it cannot be subjected to heat treatment without risk or damage, or that it has been subjected to some form of heat treatment (other than annealing) approved by him, be annealed at least once every 14 months or, in the case of slings or chains of 12.7 mm (half inch) bar or smaller, or chains used in connection with molten metal or slag, every 6 months; but chains and lifting tackle not in regular use need be annealed only when necessary (sec 26(1)(*f*)).

(g) A register (Form 88) containing the prescribed particulars shall be kept in respect of all such chains, ropes or lifting tackle, except fibre rope slings (sec 26(1)(*g*)).

Exception to SWL requirements

Section 26(1)(*b*) does not apply in relation to any lifting tackle if its SWL or, in the case of a multiplying sling, the SWL at different angles of the legs, is plainly marked upon it.

Safety aspects of chains, ropes and lifting tackle

Ropes

Natural fibre ropes

This is a rope made from material of vegetable origin, generally comprising manila hemp, sisal, coir and cotton. Manufacturers do not normally provide a certificate stating the SWL. However, the purchaser should obtain the guaranteed breaking strength from the manufacturer in order to assess the SWL. For new ropes used on a direct lift, the factor of safety (i.e. ratio of ultimate stress to the maximum design stress) should not be less than 6 under favourable conditions. For ropes used for slings, the factor of safety should be increased to at least 8. Fibre ropes are not legally required to have a test certificate before being taken into service. They do, however, require examination every 6 months (and hence be capable of identification), and when deterioration takes place to such an extent that the SWL cannot be guaranteed, the rope must be withdrawn and destroyed. Great care must be taken with fibre ropes. When they have become damp or wet, they should be dried naturally, as direct heat will cause brittleness. They should be kept in a well-ventilated store, hung on wooden or galvanised steel pegs, within a temperature range of 13–19 °C.

When lifting loads with sharp edges, the rope should be protected with packing. When reeved through blocks, the sheaves must be of adequate diameter, with the grooves of the sheaves of adequate diameter and in sound condition to allow the rope to seat correctly. Fibre ropes should be inspected before use by opening the strands slightly and checking for serviceability. If discoloured, weak or rot (mildew) has occurred, the rope should be destroyed. A reduction in circumference will generally indicate that the rope has been overloaded. The rope should also be examined for chemical action, particularly by acids. (Nylon or Terylene ropes are recommended where there is any possibility of acid attack.)

Figs. 33.7 and 33.8 illustrate ropes which are dangerously worn.

Wire ropes

There are many types of wire rope specified for cranes, lifts, hoists, elevators, construction site equipment, such as excavators, and those for use in general engineering. Wire rope is designated by diameter, except when used in shipping, and the tensile strength of the wire used ranges within 1,550–700 N/mm^2 (100–10 tons/in^2) and 1,700–850 N/mm^2 (110–20 tons/in^2). The diameter is normally measured by rope calipers and the average of three measurements, taken at intervals of about 127 mm, is construed as the rope diameter. A wire rope is made up of strands and the number of wires per strand is termed the 'construction' of the rope. Thus a rope of 6 × 19 construction has 6 strands each having 19 individual wires. Ropes of ordinary or regular 'lay' have the direction of the lay of the strands opposite to the direction of helix of the individual wires which balance the rope against twist. Where flexibility is needed, then a rope with a greater number of wires should be selected. Thus a 6 × 24 rope is more flexible than a 6 × 19 rope, and a 6 × 37 rope even more flexible than a 6 × 24 rope for the same approximate strength. If, however, hard wear is significant, a 6 × 19 rope would be more suitable because of the larger size of wires.

In a wire rope, broken wires must be regarded as a warning sign, but the actual position of the breaks is significant. If the breaks occur over a short distance, or occur in one or two strands, then the rope should be

Fig. 33.7 Dangerous ropes
This is the condition of a closing rope found during examination of a 1.13 cubic metre grab. The frequent examination of ropes is crucial in these situations
Reproduced by courtesy of National Vulcan Engineering Insurance Group Ltd

removed from service and the cause investigated. If breaks occur as a result of normal service over a reasonable period, this may well indicate that the rope is reaching the end of its life and should be replaced. In the interests of safety, however, there must be a limit to the number of broken strands. Reg 20 of the Docks Regulations 1934 requires that 'no rope shall be used in hoisting or lowering if in any length of eight diameters the total number of visible broken wires exceeds 10% of the total number of wires . . .'. Reg 43 of the Shipbuilding and Ship-repairing Regulations 1960 imposes a far stricter standard of 5 per cent in ten diameters, and this standard should be used as a general guide. When broken wires appear, more frequent examination of the rope is needed.

Fig. 33.8 A badly worn rope on a trolley crane
Failure of the rope would result in the trolley travelling towards the mast with possible impact and consequent risk to people below and to the main structure of the crane itself
Reproduced by courtesy of National Vulcan Engineering Group Ltd

The ends of the wires should be manipulated until they break off inside the rope and should never be trimmed with pliers.

During manufacture, wire ropes are thoroughly impregnated with a lubricant to reduce wear, exclude moisture and delay corrosion.

Frequent relubrication is necessary depending upon the nature of service and the degree of use. A number of proprietary lubricants are available.

Wire ropes should never be knotted as a means of joining ropes. They may be joined by the use of sockets, swaged ferrules, bulldog clips or by splicing. Proof testing may be required in any event as a splice is never as strong as the parent rope and strength may vary from 85 to 95 per cent according to rope size. Where a mechanical splice is used, proof loading to twice the safe working load is required before placing the wire rope into service.

Wire ropes should be stored in a clean dry place. Wire rope slings should be cleaned after use, inspected and hung on pegs to prevent corrosion and kinking.

Man-made fibre ropes

Ropes of this type, generally manufactured in nylon or Terylene, have the following advantages over natural fibre ropes:

(a) higher tensile strength;
(b) greater capacity for absorbing shock loading;
(c) freedom from rotting, mildew formation, etc.;
(d) they can be stored away whilst still wet;
(e) their performance is the same whether wet or dry;
(f) some degree of immunity from degradation due to contact with oil, petrol and many solvents; and
(g) resistance to acids and other corroding agents.

Procedures for the care of man-made fibre ropes are similar to those for other types of rope, viz. clean dry storage, frequent inspection for cuts, abrasions, signs of overloading and evidence of chemical attack and exposure to extreme heat. Exposure to strong sunlight may weaken the fibres and unnecessary exposure should be avoided.

Chains

Despite the increased use of wire rope, chain is still one of the principal components of lifting gear. For the same safe working load, it is five to six times heavier than rope but it has a longer life, stands up to rough usage, is almost 100 per cent flexible and can be stored externally for long periods without deterioration. Chains do not kink or curl; they grip the load better and possess superior shock-absorbing properties. Moreover, chain is available in several grades – mild steel, high-tensile steel and alloy steel – and it is common practice to designate these grades by their minimum ultimate strength in terms of the diameter of the bar from which the links are made – i.e. breaking strength = $30d^2$ – measured in tons or tonnes.

Classification of chain strengths

Wrought iron: Each link is hand-welded by a scarf weld at the end or crown of the link. The weld is distinctive and serves to identify the chain. The safe working load of the chain under normal working conditions is $6d^2$ and minimum breaking strength is $27d^2$. The skin of wrought iron chain is liable to embrittlement due to impact in service causing fine hairline cracks. These act as stress leading to failure without stretching. Under the Factories Act 1961, sec 26, wrought iron chains must be annealed every 14 months or more frequently when used in connection with molten metal, and this process recorded in the Factories Act register. Annealing involves the chain being heated uniformly until the whole of the metal has attained a temperature of between 600 and 650 °C, after which it is withdrawn from the furnace and allowed to cool in still air. Wrought iron chain has largely been superseded by alloy steel chain.

Mild steel: Mild steel chain incorporates a machine-made butt or flash resistance welded joint in the middle length of the link. The safe working load is assessed at $6d^2$ and the minimum breaking strain is $30d^2$, identified by the figure '3' on the links. Mild steel is liable to embrittlement and should be subject to 'normalising', a form of heat treatment, at frequent intervals. The use of mild steel chain is rapidly declining.

High-tensile steel grade 40: This grade of steel has mechanical properties which are superior to those of mild steel, the safe working load being 30 per cent higher. The safe working load is assessed at $8d^2$ and the minimum breaking strain is $40d^2$, identified by the figures '4' or '04' on the links.

Alloy steel grade 60: This type is 50 per cent stronger than high-tensile steel grade 40 chain and twice as strong as mild steel chain. It is suitable for most lifting purposes. The safe working load is assessed at $12d^2$ and the minimum breaking strain is $60d^2$. Such chain is subjected to hardening and tempering during manufacture and is marked '06' on each twentieth link.

Alloy steel grade 80: Grade 80 chain is designed for specific purposes, for instance as load chain for pulley blocks and similar applications which require an accurately calibrated chain of great strength and wear resistance. Its proof load is only one and a half times the safe working load due to the fact that the standard proof load of twice the safe working load for other chains listed above can disturb the pitch of the links. The safe working load is rated at $24d^2$, and the minimum breaking strain is $80d^2$. This type of chain is not suitable for slings. It requires considerable technical and manufacturing resources, as does the actual servicing of it. The length of the chain is regarded as a complete unit; individual links are not marked but the chain is identified by a disc attached.

Table 28: Comparison of chain strengths (12.7 mm ($\frac{1}{2}$") diameter)

Type	*SWL (tonnes)*	*Proof load (tonnes)*	*Minimum breaking (tonnes)*	*Marking*
Wrought iron	1.5	3.0	6.75	–
Mild steel grade 30	1.5	3.0	7.15	3
HT steel grade 40	2.0	4.0	10.00	4 or 04
Alloy steel grade 60	3.0	6.0	15.00	06
Alloy steel grade 80	3.5	8.0	20.00	08

Chain breakages

Generally, chains break for one of three reasons:

(a) from a defect in one of the links;
(b) through the application of a static load in excess of its breaking load; or
(c) through the sudden application of a load which, but for the shock, the chain would have been capable of withstanding.

In no circumstances should nuts and bolts be used to replace broken chain links, nor must chains ever be knotted.

A comparison of the strengths of the various types of chain is shown in Table 28.

Lifting tackle

The same safety principles as those for ropes and chains apply to items of lifting tackle such as slings, hooks, grips and eyebolts. In the majority of cases, the complete set of tackle in a lifting situation must be viewed as one specific unit. For instance, it is unwise to use a particular sling for a particular lifting job if the rope or chain being used for the lift is of inadequate strength.

Slings

All slings should be made of chains, wire ropes or fibre ropes (whether man-made or natural) of adequate strength. Rings, hooks, swivels and end links of hoisting chains should be fabricated in the same metal as the chain. Tables showing the maximum safe working loads for slings at various angles should be conspicuously displayed (*see* Fig. 33.9 and Table 29), and workers using slings should be trained in the use of these tables, particularly the fact that sling leg tension increases rapidly with

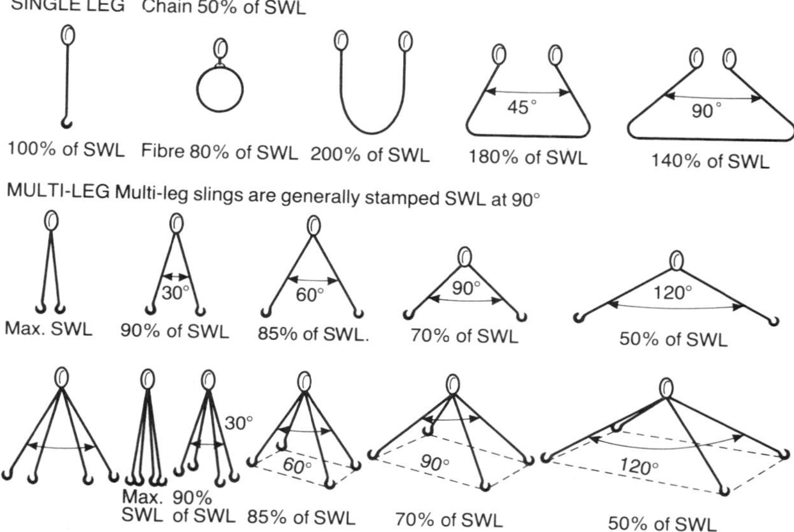

Select the correct size of a sling for the load taking into account the included angle and the possibility of unequal loading in the case of Multi-leg slings

Fig. 33.9 Maximum safe working loads for slings at various angles
Reproduced by courtesy of G. W. Sparrow & Sons Plc

Table 29: Estimation of sling leg angles

Sling angle	*Distance apart of legs*
30°	$\frac{1}{2}$ leg length
60°	1 leg length
90°	$1\frac{1}{3}$ leg length
120°	$1\frac{2}{3}$ leg length

increase in leg angle. For instance, for a 1-tonne load, the tension in the leg increases as shown in Table 30. Reference to this table indicates how important it is for anyone dealing with multi-leg slings to appreciate fully how changes in the angles of the legs affect the safe working load, particularly for angles in excess of 120°.

Slings that show evidence of cuts, excessive wear, distortion (*see* Fig. 33.10 and 33.11) or other dangerous defects should be withdrawn. Wire rope slings should be well lubricated. To prevent sharp bends in slings, corners of loads should be packed. When multiple slings are

Table 30: Relationship between sling leg angle and tension in leg

Sling leg angle	*Tension in leg (tonnes)*
90°	0.7
120°	1.0
151°	2.0
171°	6.0

Fig. 33.10 Defects in lifting tackle
A comparison between a new hook (left) and one found at examination. This hook has been opened out by about 15 per cent and the safety latch is missing. A hook in this state will increase the possibility of a sling slipping off, and the distortion will get progressively worse
Reproduced by courtesy of National Vulcan Engineering Insurance Group Ltd

used, the load should be distributed evenly among the ropes, and where double or multiple slings are used for hoisting loads, the upper ends of the sling should be connected by means of a ring or shackle and not put separately into a lifting hook. When bulky objects are being raised, the correct number of slings should be selected to ensure stability and support the weight of the load. (*See* Fig. 33.12.)

Fig. 33.11 Badly distorted chain links in a sling which could lead to failure of the sling
Reproduced by courtesy of National Vulcan Engineering Insurance Group Ltd

Hooks

Hooks for lifting appliances should be manufactured from forged steel or an equivalent material, and fitted with a safety catch shaped so as to prevent the load from slipping off (*see* Fig. 33.13). In certain situations a hook must be provided with an efficient device to prevent displacement of a sling, or be of such a shape as to reduce, as far as possible, the risk of displacement (Reg 36 of the Construction (Lifting Operations) Regulations 1961 is a typical example).

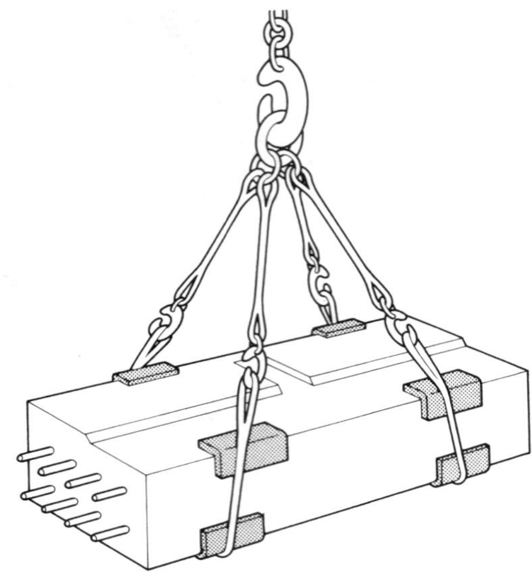

Fig. 33.12 When lifting a bulky object, use a lifting ring and pack the edges of the object

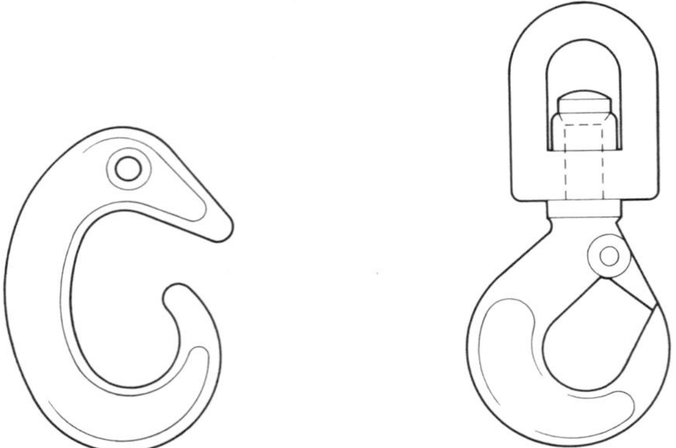

Fig. 33.13 Hooks for lifting appliances
Hook specially shaped to prevent the load from slipping off
Hook incorporating a safety catch

In potentially dangerous lifting operations, hooks should be provided with a hand rope (tag line) long enough to enable workers engaged in loading to keep clear. Parts of hooks likely to come into contact with ropes and chains should have no sharp edges.

Pulley blocks

Pulley blocks should be manufactured from shock-resistant metal, e.g.

mild steel. Axles of pulleys should be made of metal of suitable quality and of adequate dimensions. The diameter of the pulley should be at least twenty times the diameter of the rope to be used. The axle in the blocks should be capable of lubrication and a suitable lubricating device provided. (Regular and adequate lubrication of pulley blocks is essential.) The sheaves and housing of blocks should be so constructed that the rope cannot become caught between the sheave and the side of the block, and the grooves in the sheaves should be such that the rope cannot be damaged in the sheave. (Badly worn blocks should be taken out of use.) Blocks designed for use with fibre rope should not be used with wire rope. A pulley within reach of workers should be provided with a guard that effectively prevents a hand being drawn in.

Shackles

Shackles used for joining lines should have a breaking strength of at least 1.5 times that of the lines joined. In the case of shackles used for hanging blocks, the breaking strength should be at least twice that of the pulling lines, and the pins should be secured by locked nuts or other suitable means. Shackle pins should be secured by keys or wire, unless bolts are employed.

Eyebolts

Eyebolts are used for lifting loads which may be heavy and concentrated. (Three common types of eyebolts are shown in Fig. 33.14.) The use of the wrong type of eyebolt is a common contributory cause of accidents. A typical example of this is when a dynamo eyebolt is used for other than a vertical lift.

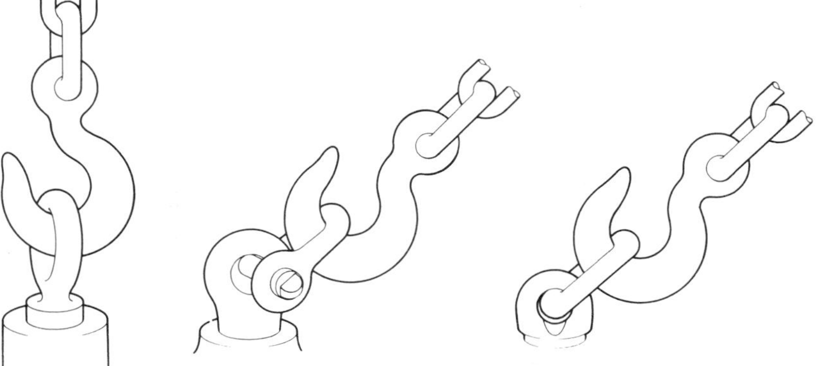

Fig. 33.14 Eyebolts
Dynamo eyebolt
Collar eyebolt
Eyebolt with link

Dynamo eyebolts are large enough to receive a hook of a comparable safe working load, but should only be used for a vertical lift because the eye is so large that it is likely to bend, should an inclined load be placed upon it. Furthermore, a load which is only slightly out of the vertical plane places an undue stress on the screw threads of the eyebolt shank. Where dynamo eyebolts are fitted in pairs, a spreader bar should form an integral part of the lifting gear used to move the load. The dynamo eyebolt is designed to receive the hook directly, and in all cases the hook should be able to operate freely. It is extremely dangerous to use a hook which jams in an eyebolt because, under load, serious weakening of both hook and eyebolt could occur leading to failure at some later date. If the hook available for the eyebolt is too large, a shackle of adequate size should be fitted to the eyebolt to accommodate the hook.

Where inclined loads are encountered, e.g. when a multi-leg sling is in use, collar eyebolts or eyebolts with links must be used. The collar eyebolt, or service eyebolt, has a squat eye that is too small to accommodate a hook, so a shackle is always necessary. Collar eyebolts are intended for permanent attachment to heavy pieces of equipment and are usually fitted in pairs for use with shackles or two-leg slings. When two pairs of eyebolts are fitted to a single load, then two-leg slings and a spreader bar (lifting beam) should be used in lifting (*see* Fig. 33.15).

Fig. 33.15 Typical lifting beam (spreader bar)

The third type of eyebolt, that incorporating a link, is intended for general lifting. Although its rated load decreases as the angle of the load to the axis of the screw thread increases, by virtue of its special construction these rated loadings are greater than those of a collar eyebolt of equivalent vertical safe working load.

Lifting beams (spreader bars)

A lifting beam is a special purpose device which enables a particular load to be lifted in a particular way, often to prevent horizontal stressing of eyebolts. Lifting beams are commonly used in foundries for transporting vats of molten metal prior to casting or for the transport of engines in vehicle assembly. This is far safer than the use of multiple slings.

Lifting beams incorporate three basic parts:

(a) the beam, which is made from rolled steel section or plate;
(b) the means of attaching the beam to the lifting machine, such as a ring, shackle, eyebolt or hole in the main structure of the beam; and
(c) the means of fixing the beam to the actual load to be lifted, such as chain or wire rope slings which are fixed to the beam with fittings at the ends for securing the load, such as shackles or locking pins.

Lifting beams are designed using standard steel rolled section or plate, angles, tees, universal beams or hollow sections. To ensure rigidity and resistance to accidental damage, the thickness of metal should not be less than 6 mm. This thickness can be reduced to 4.5 mm with hollow sections provided that they are adequately sealed against ingress of water or other damaging material. Many beams will be left outside and exposed to all weather conditions, so care must be taken in their design to avoid places where water might lodge; where this is not practicable, suitable drainage holes should be provided. If corrosion is the agent most likely to affect the beam, an allowance of up to 2 mm should be added to the minimum dimensions determined from all other strength calculations.

34

Pressure vessels

A *pressure vessel* is a closed vessel which operates at a pressure greater than atmospheric. Within this definition of pressure vessel are included steam boilers, steam receivers and containers, and air receivers.

Classification of pressure vessels

Steam boiler

A *steam boiler* is defined as 'any closed vessel in which for any purpose steam is generated under pressure greater than atmospheric and includes any economiser used to heat water being fed to any such vessel, and any superheater used for heating steam' (Factories Act 1961, sec 38).

Steam receiver

A *steam receiver* is 'any vessel or apparatus, other than a steam boiler, steam container, steam pipe or coil, or part of a prime mover, used for containing steam under pressure greater than atmospheric pressure' (FA, sec 35(8)).

Steam container

A *steam container* is 'any vessel, other than a steam pipe or coil, constructed with a permanent outlet to atmosphere or into a space where pressure does not exceed atmospheric pressure, and through which steam is passed at atmospheric pressure, or at approximately that pressure, for the purpose of heating, boiling, drying, evaporating or other similar purpose' (FA, sec 35(8)).

Air receiver

An *air receiver* is

(a) any vessel (other than a pipe or coil, or an accessory, fitting or part of a compressor) for containing compressed air and connected with an air-compressing plant; or

(b) any fixed vessel for containing compressed air or compressed exhaust gases and used for the purpose of starting an internal combustion engine; or
(c) any fixed or portable vessel (not being part of a spraying pistol) used for the purpose of spraying by means of compressed air any paint, varnish, lacquer or similar material; or
(d) any vessel in which oil is stored and from which it is forced by compressed air (FA, sec 36(6)).

Steam boilers

The purpose of a steam boiler or, more specifically, a steam generator, is to produce steam under pressure from the raw materials, fuel, air and water. The potential heat of the fuel is made available through combustion, and this is transmitted to and stored by water vapour in the form of sensible and latent heat. There are two principal types of steam boiler: the vertical boiler and the horizontal boiler.

The vertical boiler

In its simplest form the vertical boiler would be a metal cylinder containing water, with a firebox at the bottom and a flue passing up the centre to carry hot gases away. However, such a boiler would be inefficient, as there would be little opportunity for hot gases to give up their heat through the sides of the flue to the water. In order to ensure that more heat is transferred, a greater part of the metal surface must be exposed to hot gases. One way of achieving this is by means of water tubes located across the central flue, as in the vertical cross-tube boiler shown in Fig. 34.1(a). In addition, extra exposed surface can be provided by the use of smoke tubes or fire tubes to carry the flue gases through water space, as in the fire-tube boiler shown in Fig. 34.1(b). This latter is more efficient mainly because the firebox is shaped to expose a larger area to heat from fire. Vertical fire-tube boilers are used mainly in small factories where steam requirements are not excessive. They are moderately cheap and do not occupy a great deal of room.

The horizontal boiler

This comprises a horizontal cylinder three-quarters full of water, with one or more furnace tubes passing through the water space. The fire is located at the front of the furnace tubes and hot gases travel through these tubes, heating the surrounding water prior to reaching the flue. The most common form of horizontal boiler is the Economic boiler, shown in Fig. 34.2. This boiler consists of a cylindrical shell with two flat end plates. One or more flue tubes are disposed between the end plates below the centre of the boiler, the grate or other fuel burning

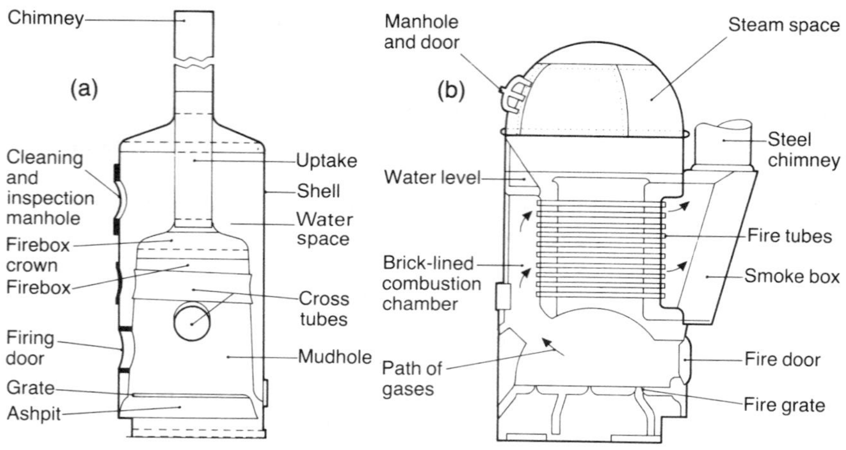

Fig. 34.1 Vertical boilers
(a) Vertical cross-tube boiler
(b) Vertical fire-tube boiler with horizontal tubes

equipment, e.g. pressure jet oil burners, being arranged at the front end of these flues. The hot gases traverse the flue tubes to the back of the boiler where they enter a brick-lined combustion chamber in the case of a 'dry back' boiler or a water-cooled combustion chamber in the case of a 'wet back' boiler. Here the gas path is reversed and the gases travel to the front of the boiler through a bank of smoke tubes located above the flues. These tubes are normally about 8 cm in diameter and, by their use, the gas stream is broken up into a number of small elements, materially increasing the rate and efficiency and heat transfer. After passing through the smoke tubes, the gases are collected in a smoke box, whence they are led to atmosphere. This is the normal arrangement of a 'double pass' Economic boiler. A 'treble pass' Economic boiler has a second bank of tubes superimposed through which gases traverse the boiler from front to back, being finally collected in a smoke box, whence they are led to atmosphere.

Statutory precautions in respect of pressure vessels

The following statutory precautions are laid down by the Factories Act 1961 in respect of

(a) steam boilers,
(b) steam receivers and steam containers, and
(c) air receivers.

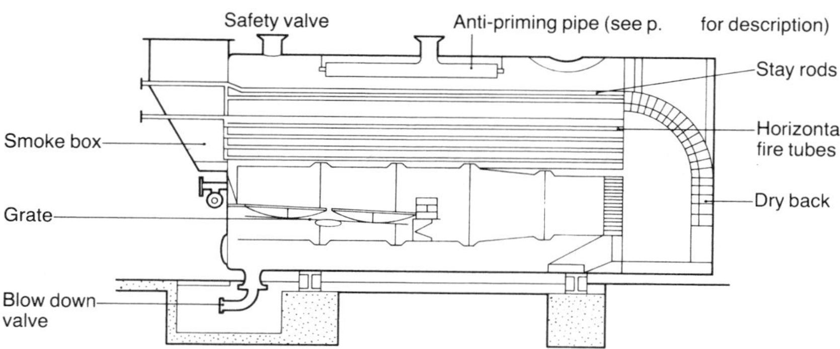

Fig. 34.2 Economic boiler (solid fuel fired)

Steam boilers

Attachments and construction

Every steam boiler, whether separate or one of a range,

(a) must be provided with means for attaching a pressure gauge;
(b) unless externally fired, must be provided with a fusible plug or an efficient low-water alarm device (FA, sec 32(1)).

Moreover,

(c) it must have attached to it the following devices:
  (i) a suitable safety valve, separate from any stop valve, which must be so adjusted as to prevent the boiler from being worked at a pressure greater than maximum permissible working pressure and be fixed directly to, or as close as practicable to, the boiler;
  (ii) a suitable stop valve connecting the boiler to the steam pipe;
  (iii) a correct steam pressure gauge connected to the steam space and easily visible by the boiler attendant, which must indicate the pressure of the steam in the boiler and have marked on it in a distinctive colour the maximum permissible working pressure;
  (iv) at least one water gauge of transparent material or other type approved by the Chief Inspector of Factories to show the water level in the boiler and, if the gauge is of the glass tubular type and the working pressure of the boiler normally exceeds 2.75 bars, an efficient guard provided so as not to obstruct the reading of the gauge; and
  (v) where the boiler is one of two or more boilers, a plate bearing a distinctive number which must be easily visible (sec 32(2)).

Every part of every steam boiler must be of good construction, sound material and adequate strength, and free from patent defect (sec 32(5)).

Maximum permissible working pressure: For most purposes, the maximum permissible working pressure is the pressure specified in the report of the last examination under sec 33(4) (*see below*) (FA, sec 38).

Maintenance, examination and use

Every steam boiler and all its fittings must be properly maintained (FA, sec 33(1)). There must be a procedure for:

(a) testing new boilers (sec 33(2));
(b) testing existing boilers after repair or modification (sec. 33(3));
(c) reporting boiler examinations and the results of tests (sec 33(4));

NOTE. Procedures for the examination of steam boilers are laid down in the Examination of Steam Boilers Regulations 1964 (SI 1964 No. 781) and the Examination of Steam Boilers Reports (No. 1) Order 1964 (SI 1964 No. 1070).

(d) the provision of a certificate, stating the maximum permissible working pressure, by the manufacturer in the case of new boilers (sec. 33(5));
(e) certification following the testing of boilers. The report of any examination must go to the Factories Inspector for the district within 28 days (secs 33(4) and 33(7)).

Moreover, the Chief Inspector is empowered to nominate his own examiner in the event of unsatisfactory, false or deficient report by a boiler examiner (sec 33(9)).

Restrictions on entry

No person must enter or be present in any steam boiler which is one of a range of two or more steam boilers unless

(a) all inlets for steam and hot water are disconnected, or
(b) all valves or taps controlling the entry of steam or hot water are closed and securely locked (sec 34).

Steam receivers and steam containers

Attachments and construction

If a steam receiver is not so constructed and maintained as to withstand with safety the maximum permissible working pressure (*see above*) of the boiler, or the maximum pressure which can be obtained in the pipe connecting the receiver with any other source of supply, it must be fitted with

(a) a suitable reducing valve, or other suitable automatic appliance to prevent the safe working pressure being exceeded;
(b) a suitable safety valve so adjusted as to permit the steam to escape as soon as the safe working pressure is exceeded, or a suitable appliance for cutting off automatically the supply of steam as soon as the safe working pressure is exceeded;
(c) a correct steam pressure gauge, which must indicate the pressure of steam in the receiver;
(d) a suitable stop valve; and
(e) a plate bearing a distinctive number which must be easily visible, unless only one steam receiver is in use (FA, sec 35(1)).

The safety valve and pressure gauge must be fitted either on the steam receiver or on the supply pipe between the receiver and the reducing valve or other appliance in order to prevent the safe working pressure being exceeded (sec 35(2)).

Every steam receiver must be of good construction, sound material, adequate strength and free from patent defect (sec 35(4)).

Maintenance, examination and use

Every steam receiver and its fittings must be properly maintained and thoroughly examined by a competent person at least once every 26 months, so far as the construction of the receiver permits (FA, sec 35(5)).

A report of the result of every examination containing the necessary particulars (including particulars of the safe working pressure) should be entered in or attached to the general register (sec 35(6)).

Safe working pressure: *Safe working pressure* in the case of a steam receiver is that specified by the maker, and in the case of a steam receiver which has undergone examination, that specified in the report of the last examination (sec 35(8).

Air receivers

Attachments and construction

Every air receiver must

(a) have marked on it, so as to be plainly visible, the safe working pressure;
(b) if it is connected with any air-compressing plant, either be constructed so as to withstand with safety the maximum pressure that can be obtained in the compressor, or be fitted with a suitable

reducing valve or other suitable appliance to prevent the safe working pressure of the receiver being exceeded;

(c) be fitted with a suitable safety valve so adjusted as to permit the air to escape as soon as the safe working pressure is exceeded;

(d) be fitted with a correct pressure gauge indicating the pressure in the receiver;

(e) be fitted with a suitable appliance for draining the receiver;

(f) be provided with a suitable manhole, handhole or other means which will allow the interior to be thoroughly cleaned; and

(g) in a case where more than one receiver is in use in the factory, bear a distinguishing mark which shall be easily visible (FA, sec 36(1)).

Every air receiver and its fittings must be of sound construction and properly maintained (sec 36(3)).

Cleaning and examination

Every air receiver must be thoroughly cleaned and examined at least once in every period of 26 months. However, an exception occurs in the case of air receivers of solid drawn construction, where

(a) the person making any examination may specify in writing a period of more than 26 months but not more than 4 years within which the next examination should be made; and

(b) if it is so constructed that the internal surface cannot be thoroughly examined, a suitable hydraulic test of the receiver must be carried out in lieu of internal examination (FA, sec 36(4)).

Every examination and test must be carried out by a competent person and a report of particulars (including particulars relating to the safe working pressure) entered in or attached to the general register (sec 36(5)).

NOTE. As stated elsewhere in this book, it is unfortunate that the legislation does not define a 'competent person'.

Factors affecting the design of pressure vessels

The most important stage in the design of any pressure vessel is that of determining the conditions to which the vessel will be subjected. Any assessment should, therefore, take into account system faults and test conditions as well as normal working. The main conditions likely to be encountered in normal working are

(a) working pressure;

(b) working temperature;

(c) cyclic conditions of temperature and pressure which may cause fatigue failures;

(d) the effects of the contents of the vessel;
(e) the effect of induced loads from pipework and auxiliary equipment;
(f) the effects of mechanical vibration; and
(g) the effects of weather – snow, wind, rain, excessive variations in temperature.

The testing of pressure vessels

A pressure vessel consists mainly of a series of sheets of metal suitably shaped and welded together. Most pressure vessel failures are associated with the blowing of a welded joint and, in order to ensure that a welded joint has properties comparable to those of the original materials and is metallurgically satisfactory, it is necessary for the actual physical properties of the weld to be investigated by destructive as well as non-destructive tests. Of course, the former cannot be carried out on the actual seams and it is undertaken using test plates. The normal system is to approve the manufacturer's procedures for the type of welding and the materials used in the vessel manufacture, as well as individual welders for certain classes of work, by the mechanical testing of separate test plates prepared by them before the actual production welding is commenced. Depending upon the requirements of the pressure vessel code used, the thickness of the materials, the difficulty in welding the materials selected, the future use of the vessel and the safety criteria used in the design code, non-destructive testing will be called for on the materials of construction and on the welding undertaken.

Although radiography has been used for non-destructive testing of pressure vessels for many years and produces a permanent record (radiograph), its effectiveness for identifying defects is dependent on the techniques used. Therefore, the radiograph should never be regarded as evidence of quality unless full details of the procedures are also known. Ultrasonic techniques are now also widely used, and in the construction of nuclear reactor vessels they are, on balance, more effective than radiography. There is, however, only limited scope for a permanent record of the results of the inspection.

As for inspection of boilers and other pressure vessels by non-destructive methods, it is essential to decide what defects require identification and to choose the particular method to suit. As the most serious defect likely to be encountered in a pressure vessel is a crack, it is important to recognise that radiography only discloses a fine crack if it is parallel to the direction of the radiation, i.e. approximately perpendicular to the X-ray film. Ultrasonic methods do not identify a crack in the direction of the ultrasonic beam, and dye penetrants only show a crack which breaks the surface. These limitations should be appreciated prior to testing.

Installations and fittings – safety requirements

To ensure maximum safety of operation, the following installations and fittings are recommended for all pressure vessels, in particular steam boilers:

(a) two water gauges,
(b) two safety valves,
(c) a pressure gauge,
(d) a fusible plug or high and low water alarm,
(e) a blow down valve,
(f) a stop valve (steam),
(g) a feed check valve, and
(h) an anti-priming pipe.

The functions of these installations and fittings are outlined below.

Water gauges

All boilers with an evaporative capacity exceeding 136 kg of steam per hour should be fitted with two water gauges. For boiler pressures up to 4,400 kg/cm^2 it is usual to fit tubular gauges which must be protected, protection usually consisting of a shield of specially toughened glass. Water gauges should be so situated that the water level can be easily seen by the operator and so arranged that the lowest visible section of the glass is higher than the minimum working level. It is good practice to test water gauges and cocks (a form of hand-operated tap or valve) once per shift by opening and closing the cocks in the prescribed manner.

Safety valves

Every boiler should have at least two safety valves, each capable of discharging the total peak evaporation of the boiler. The valves can be arranged on a single chest. This recommendation for two valves on each boiler is made on the assumption that if one valve fails to act, the other will function. However, this is not by itself a sufficient safeguard, and the safety valves should receive frequent attention and maintenance.

There are three types of safety valve – deadweight, lever arm or steelyard, and spring-loaded (*see* Fig. 34.3 for the latter two).

A safety valve is fitted to open at a set pressure, higher than the normal working pressure but below the maximum working pressure established by the insurance company. Steam will be discharged until

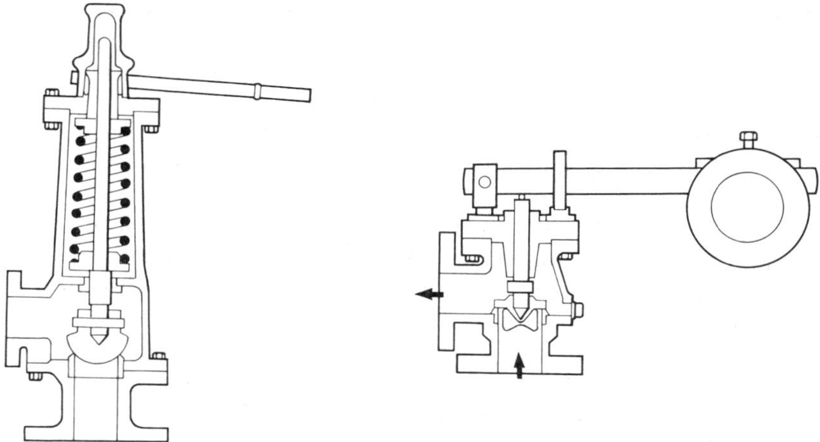

Fig. 34.3 Safety valves
Spring-loaded safety valve
Lever arm safety valve

the pressure drops sufficiently for the valve to close again. Each type is manufactured in a variety of patterns (the more modern having means for locking and adjustment). Each valve is so arranged that no unauthorised person can tamper with its setting. Valves should be tested periodically to ensure their reliable operation, in accordance with boiler insurance requirements. Failure to comply with insurance requirements, although not in itself a breach of law, may wholly or partially invalidate cover, as it is an implied term of insurance contracts that the insured will take steps to mitigate loss, e.g. will take practical safety measures.

Pressure gauge

This must be connected to the steam space and indicate the pressure of steam in the boiler. The maximum permissible working pressure should be clearly marked on the gauge or the gauge glass.

Fusible plug, and high and low water alarm

A steam boiler must be equipped with either a fusible plug (if of the shell type) or a high and low water alarm, which makes a sound that can easily be recognised by the operator. A fusible plug is a plug of metal with a low melting point and is set into the boiler shell at low level. If the water level falls, and the boiler overheats, the plug melts, allowing the boiler water to escape and dowse the fire.

There are two types of high and low water alarm, internal and external. The internal type of alarm consists of two floats, one at each end of a long arm suspended from the crown of the boiler shell. The arm is attached in such a manner as to pivot about an axis so that one float acts at a dangerously high level, the other at a dangerously low level. At correct levels of the water in the boiler the low-water float lies on the surface of the water, the high-water float being suspended clear of the surface, the system being maintained in equilibrium. When the water level falls, the low-level float drops and actuates a lever which operates a steam whistle. When the water level rises to the level of the top float, the upward movement of the bottom float being restricted, buoyancy occurs and causes the arm to tilt in the same direction as before so that the whistle again sounds.

The internal type of alarm is now being superseded by the external types: float and thermostatic. The first system, i.e. float, consists of chambers mounted at the normal working level of the water in the boiler and they are connected to the steam and water spaces. The floats respond to changes in the level of the water in the boiler and, at predetermined high and low positions, actuate a steam whistle, or two whistles of different notes, one for high-water conditions and the other for low. The thermostatic type, on the other hand, consists of rods that expand and contract according to whether they are in steam or water. When the water is at normal working level the upper rod is immersed in steam and the lower one in water. If, through a rise in the water level, the upper rod becomes immersed in water, it contracts, and if the lower rod becomes immersed in steam, it expands. Either movement actuates an electric circuit which causes a bell to ring.

Blow down valve

A blow down valve has three important functions:

(a) deconcentration of the boiler water to prevent the solids content rising above prescribed limits;
(b) ejection of sludge and solids precipitated from the boiler water which settle at the bottom of the boiler; and
(c) for emptying the boiler prior to inspection or for other purposes.

Blow downs may be continuously or intermittently operated. The former method is more effective in deconcentrating the boiler to prevent priming or foaming. In many cases the blow down is located near the surface of the water in the boiler shell. The intermittent blow down valve is used for the systematic ejection of unwanted solid matter deposited from the boiler water, as well as for emptying the boiler. It is an essential fitting and must be of first-class structure. It is necessarily situated at the lowest part of the boiler. Consequently it may be in a position where it is not continuously under the eye of the attendant. Discharge from the valve should be piped to a place where it can easily be inspected, as undetected leakage can cause serious wastage of fuel, together with corrosion.

When two or more boilers discharge their blow downs into the same pipe, each valve should be operable by only one key that remains locked in position when the valve is open and is removable only when it is completely closed. In this way only one blow down in a bank of boilers can be operated at any one time.

Stop valve (steam)

This valve is located between the boiler and the steam pipe or outlet, and is used to control the flow of steam from the boiler.

Feed check valve

This valve is situated on the boiler shell or steam drum, usually just below the low water level. It is essentially a non-return valve to prevent water escaping from the boiler should the pressure in the feed line be less than that of the boiler. A stop valve must be inserted between this non-return valve and the boiler. This may be incorporated in the feed check valve but the arrangement should be such that when the stop valve is closed it will be possible to remove the non-return valve for inspection, adjustment or minor repair while the boiler continues in operation. When more than one boiler is being fed by a single pump, the stop valve can be manipulated to control the rate of feed to the boilers.

Anti-priming pipe

Priming is the phenomenon whereby water is carried over from one part of the boiler into another part, such as a superheater. The action is mainly siphonic in nature. To prevent the loss of water which would result, an anti-priming pipe is fitted to break this siphonic action.

Hazards associated with boiler operation

The two principal hazards are overheating caused by low water level, which is the most frequent cause of boiler explosions and other damage, and the long-term effects of corrosion, which often result in explosion but, more frequently, boiler failure.

Overheating in boilers

The main causes of overheating incidents are

(a) lack of testing and maintenance of controls and alarms, leading to malfunction;

(b) occasional inadequate standards of control; and
(c) (less frequently nowadays) isolation of control chambers.

Causes (a) and (b) above are associated with poor standards of boiler operation. Isolation of the control chambers (caused by the attendant closing and leaving closed either the water or the steam isolating valve, or both, after closing the drain valve) has in the past resulted in cases of explosion and damage from overheating of the boiler brought about by the resulting low water level. This hazard has largely been eliminated through improved boiler design.

Boiler corrosion

The long-term effects of corrosion in boilers can be both explosions and boiler failure. The principal sites and causes of corrosion are as follows.

Vertical boilers (*see* Fig. 34.1)

(a) external shell crown 'wastage' (loss of metal thickness, and therefore strength, due to corrosion) and internal and external uptake wastage, due to the effects of damp lagging and gases;
(b) internal wastage of the upper firebox due to heat intensity, the effects of gases and ingress of water;
(c) cross-tube wastage (gas side) due to the effects of gases and moisture;
(d) lower firebox wastage caused by the excessive accumulation of ash in the ashpit which can be further accelerated by moisture;
(e) wastage around the attachments of boiler mountings to the shell, in most cases due to leakage;
(f) wastage at leaking mudhole doors, in many cases due to faulty or unsuitable jointing material; the lagging retains moisture and the wastage occurs unseen;
(g) 'grooving', a form of mechanical corrosion, due to expansion and contraction, and accelerated by a build-up of solids, occurring at the junction of the firebox and shell;
(h) grooving at the junction of the firebox and uptake due to pressure and temperature fluctuations and, possibly, continued forced firing of the boiler;
(i) wastage on the water side of the uptake between high and low water levels due to ebullience at the water surface and oxygen release on the uptake surfaces;
(j) wastage around the mudhole door and compensating ring caused by leakage or a badly fitting door or door joint;
(k) grooving at the vertical lap joint of boiler shell plates due to steam pressure tending to improve the circular shell form; this is largely mechanical action which is localised at seam edges;

(l) general wastage of the internal surfaces of the ashpit plating and wastage of rivet heads, largely caused by sulphur in ash deposits and moisture.

Horizontal boilers (*see* Fig. 34.2)

(a) distorted chamber tube plates, a situation where the tubes have been allowed to develop excessive scale and push the plate inwards;
(b) 'necked' stays – wastage of the stays or stay tubes at plate entry due to leakage at the thread; this is accelerated through the tensile forces acting;
(c) shell wastage at the mountings due to leakage at the joints, especially under the lagging;
(d) combustion chamber crown distortion resulting from overheating;
(e) girder stay wastage caused by leakage at the entry of the stay into the plate;
(f) stay tube leakage as a result of incorrect welding giving inadequate support;
(g) fractured stays caused by forcing the boiler;
(h) radial grooving around the stays, a mechanical action caused by varying expansion of the heating surfaces; this weakens and breaks down the material structure;
(i) cracks from rivet holes to the plate edge due to overheating and subsequent corrosion;
(j) front end plate grooving caused by cyclic variations in pressure; this accelerates with the age of the boiler;
(k) front tube plate wastage due to leakage past defective tube ends; and
(l) sulphur attack from the slaking of ashes; this attacks most metal surfaces and will waste rivets away.

Automatic controls on steam and hot water boilers

The majority of steam boilers are now automatically controlled, and the most common water level and firing controls are float-operated controls situated outside the boiler. The floats are housed in chambers which are connected to the steam and water spaces in the boiler so that the water level in the chambers will be approximately the same as that in the boiler. Water level controls, low-water alarms and firing controls may be incorporated in the same chamber, but an additional chamber, with an independent electrical control circuit and independently connected to the boiler, is required for overriding low-water alarm and fuel cut-off in the case of fully automatically controlled steam boilers.

Standards for automatic controls

Automatic water level controls are of two basic standards:

(a) controls to assist the boiler attendant who constantly supervises the boiler, and
(b) controls intended to replace continuous supervision with occasional supervision.

The minimum recommended requirements for automatic controls for boilers not continuously supervised are as follows.

Automatic water level controls

These should be so arranged that they positively control the boiler or the feed pumps, or regulate the water supply to the boiler and effectively maintain the level of water in the boiler between certain predetermined limits.

Automatic firing controls

These should be so arranged that they effectively control the supply of fuel to the burners of oil- or gas-fired boilers, and shut off the supply in the event of any one or more of the following circumstances:

(a) flame/pilot flame failure on oil- or gas-fired boilers; the control should be of the lock-out type requiring manual resetting;
(b) failure to ignite the fuel on oil- or gas-fired boilers within a predetermined time; the control should be of the lock-out type requiring manual resetting;
(c) when a predetermined high pressure at or below the safety valve set pressure is reached;
(d) when the water level falls to a predetermined point below the normal operating level; this control should also cause an audible alarm to sound; and
(e) failure of forced or induced draught fans, or any automatic flue damper, when these are provided.

Independent overriding control

This control should cut off the fuel supply to oil- or gas-fired boilers or air to the mechanical stokers of solid fuel fired boilers and cause an alarm to sound when the water level in the boiler falls to a predetermined low water level. The control or its electrical circuit should be so arranged that it has to be reset manually before the boiler can be brought back into operation.

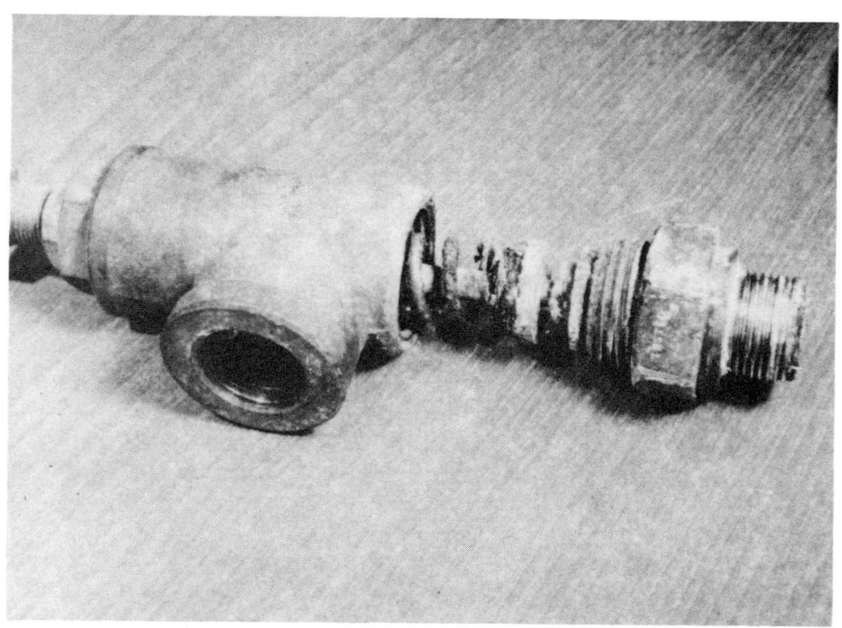

Fig. 34.4(a)

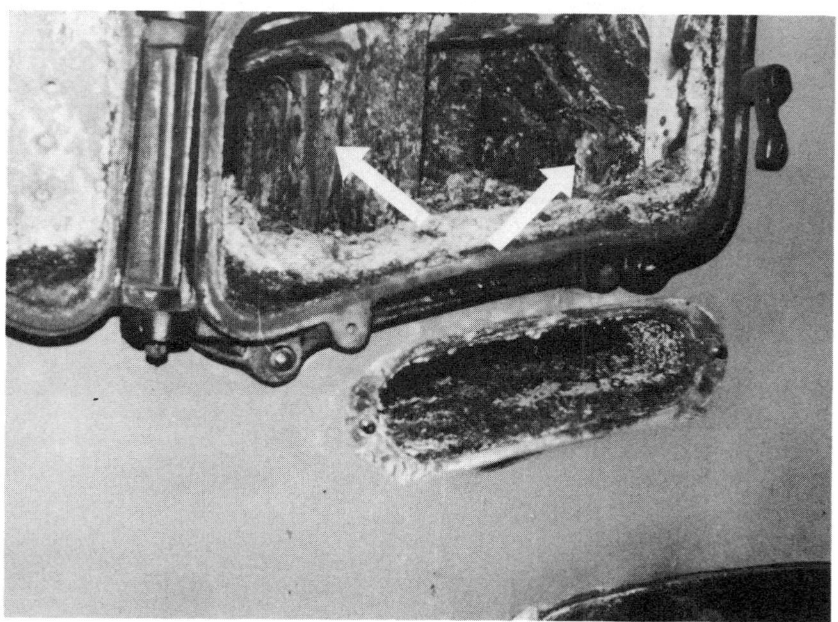

Fig. 34.4(b)

Fig. 34.4(c)

Fig. 34.4(d)

Fig. 34.4 Corrosion in pressure vessels

(a) Corrosion of a safety valve to a calorifier making it totally inoperable. The seat is completely corroded and the spring actually corroded away. In addition, this valve was not fitted with a test lever so that, without dismantling it at examination, no evaluation of the operational performance of the valve could be made

(b) The flues of a cast iron water-heating boiler showing evidence of extensive corrosion

(c) General corrosion in a cast iron water-heating boiler can occur extremely rapidly. In this case the surveyor's hammer has gone through the shell where the cast iron had been corroded to paper thinness

(d) Primary to secondary leakage in heat exchangers results in loss of efficiency or in overpressure failure of the lower pressure side. The photograph shows the effect of a hydraulic test on the tube nest of a calorifier which indicated failure of one tube and prevented a more serious failure later

Reproduced by courtesy of National Vulcan Engineering Insurance Group Ltd

Electrical failure to safety

All electrical equipment for water level and firing controls should be so designed that faults in the circuits cause the fuel and air supply to the boiler to be automatically shut off. Positive means, requiring manual resetting, should be provided to cut off the fuel and air supplies to the boiler, should there be a failure of electrical supply to water level and firing control equipment. All electrical conductors and equipment in connection with water levels and firing controls should be of adequate size, properly insulated and protected to prevent danger and including, where necessary, adequate protection against the ingress of moisture or the effects of high temperature.

35

Electrical safety

Edwin G. Hooper, MPhil, CEng, FIEE, FIOSH

Electricity is perfectly safe if treated with respect. If misused, like many other things, it can have harmful effects on people and plant.

The purpose of this chapter is to explain certain facts about electricity and how to use it safely. We all use electricity in our daily lives – at work, in the home and in a host of other pursuits. Most of the time, we take it for granted. Occasionally, things go wrong, usually for simple reasons; however, if the advice given in this chapter is heeded, death, injuries and damage will be prevented.

Causes of electric shock and effects on the body

Electric shock is a possible outcome of electric current flowing through the human body, which causes disturbance in the normal functions of the body's organs and nervous system. Death occurs if the rhythm of the heart is upset for long enough to stop the flow of blood to the brain. It is crucial to act quickly in such emergencies, i.e. with first aid and resuscitation treatment, particularly simple oral resuscitation treatment. (*See* the standard St John's Ambulance Association (1972) *First Aid Manual* or RoSPA's factory Electric Shock placard; also Chapter 29.) Fortunately, death and serious injury from electric shock are relatively rare. Most electrical injuries, in fact, arise from burns received at the point of contact with the body. However, some of these burns can be deep-seated and immediate careful treatment is required.

To understand the electric shock phenomenon, the relationship between voltage (the 'driving force' of electrical energy), the current (the actual 'flow' of electricity) and the resistance (the characteristic of the circuit or path through which electricity flows and which offers resistance to the current) must be understood. In alternating current circuits, because resistive components are added vectorially, the term used is 'impedance'.

Ohm's Law

Ohm's Law is a simple mathematical relationship and it may be expressed as

$$\text{Current} = \frac{\text{Voltage}}{\text{Resistance}}$$

or, using the actual measurement terms for these values, as

$$\text{Amps} = \frac{\text{Volts}}{\text{Ohms}}$$

from which, by simple transposition of the formula, may be derived the following:

$$\text{Volts} = \text{Amps} \times \text{Ohms} \quad \text{and} \quad \text{Ohms} = \frac{\text{Volts}}{\text{Amps}}$$

It is usual to derive the simple power equation from Ohm's Law. Hence power (measured in watts) may be found from the following formula, although in strict alternating current theory it is somewhat more complicated mathematically.

$$\begin{aligned}\text{Watts} &= \text{Volts} \times \text{Amps}\\ &= \text{Amps}^2 \times \text{Ohms}\\ &= \frac{\text{Volts}^2}{\text{Ohms}}\end{aligned}$$

Effect of current

If a person is in contact with a live conductor (a conductor being a material that readily conducts electricity) and another part of his body is touching a conducting path, such as an earthed metal pipe, then the voltage to earth of that conductor will cause current to flow, through the body's resistance, to earth. The amount of current flowing will depend upon the voltage (which is usually the standard 240 volts supply) and upon the resistance of the body and other parts of the conducting path for the current to earth.

For a given current flow through a body, the severity of electric shock depends upon the length of time that the current flows, but it must be realised that only a small current flowing for a moment in time can be dangerous. Thus a current of 0.05 amp (50 milliamps) flowing for up to 4 or 5 seconds will probably not cause harm, but a current ten times the value but still only 0.5 amp (500 milliamps), flowing for 0.05 seconds (50 milliseconds), could be fatal.

The effect of electric shock varies with age, sex, medical and physical condition and the body's resistance to current flow, but a normal mains voltage of 240 volts, with an average body resistance of 1,000 ohms, would result in a current flow of 0.24 amps (240 milliamps) (*see* Ohm's Law above). This is a dangerously high value.

Fortunately, the shock current path contains more than the human body. Additional resistance to current flow may be found in the circuit, the contact with earth, any footwear worn, or the surface (a wooden floor, for example) on which the person may be standing. *It follows that contact with live electrical parts must be avoided. This is the first step to the prevention of electric shock.*

Legal requirements

Statutory regulations

The main legal provisions for electrical safety in factories are contained in the Factories (Electrical Energy) Regulations 1908 and the Electricity (Factories Act) Special Regulations 1944. HSE Inspectors use the requirements of these Regulations as a standard when enforcing the Health and Safety at Work Act in places of work where the Regulations may not actually apply.

In any mention of electrical safety, reference must be made to Reg 1 of the 1908 Regulations, for it really says it all, although it was written over 75 years ago. It states: 'All apparatus and conductors shall be sufficient in size and power for the work they are called upon to do, and so constructed, installed, protected, worked and maintained as to prevent danger so far as it is reasonably practicable.'

Regulation 28 of the Factories (Electrical Energy) Regulations 1908 requires that, in order to avoid danger, no person except an authorised person (or a competent person acting under his supervision) must carry out work requiring technical knowledge or experience. Moreover, where work requiring technical knowledge or experience is involved, the person carrying out such work must be accompanied. It has been established that

(a) the purpose of Reg 28 is to save trained and experienced employees from their own acts of carelessness;
(b) in consequence, Reg 28 is binding on employers irrespective of how careless a trained and experienced employee has been, and whether or not he is in breach of company rules and good electrical maintenance practice;
(c) Reg 28 applies to both live and dead equipment; and
(d) there is no requirement that the person accompanying the employee working on the equipment should be qualified or experienced in first aid, or even competent (*Vosper Thornicroft (UK) Ltd* v. *HSE*, Crown Court, Portsmouth 1978 (unreported)).

IEE regulations

The Institution of Electrical Engineers (1981) publishes a code of practice entitled *Regulations for Electrical Installations* but commonly known as the IEE Wiring Regulations. Fixed electrical installations, installed in accordance with these Regulations, should be safe for general purposes.

Principles of electrical safety

The prime objective of electrical safety is to protect people from electrical shock, and also from fire and burns, arising from contact with electricity. There are two basic preventive measures against electric shock, namely:

(a) protection against direct contact, e.g. by providing proper insulation for parts of equipment liable to be charged with electricity; and
(b) protection against indirect contact, e.g. by providing effective earthing for metallic enclosures which are liable to be charged with electricity if the basic insulation fails for any reason.

When it is not possible to provide adequate insulation as protection against direct contact, a range of measures is available, including protection by barriers or enclosures, and protection by position, i.e. placing live parts out of reach.

Earthing

The provision of effective earthing, to give protection against indirect contact, can be achieved in a number of ways, including connecting the extraneous conductive parts of premises (water pipe, taps, radiators) to the main earthing terminal of the electrical installation. This would create an 'equipotential' zone and eliminate the risk of shock that could occur if a person touched two different parts of the metalwork liable to be charged, under earth fault conditions, at different voltages. It is crucial to ensure that in the event of earth fault, such as when a live part touches an enclosed conductive part (usually metalwork), that the electricity supply is automatically disconnected. Such disconnection is achieved by the use of overcurrent devices (correctly rated fuses or circuit breakers) or by correctly placed and rated residual current devices. (More details of these and other circuit components will be given later.) Maintenance of earth continuity is also vital.

Reduced voltage

Another protective measure against electric shock is the use of reduced voltage systems, the most commonly used being the 110 volt centre point earthed system, i.e. the secondary winding of the transformer providing the 110 volt supply is centre tapped to earth, thus ensuring that at no part of the 110 volt circuit can the voltage to earth exceed 55 volts. (*See* BS 4363:1968 and BS Code of Practice CP 1017.) Safe extra-low voltage systems are also available. These operate at 50 volts and obviously have limited though safer application.

Public electricity supply systems

Generation, transmission and distribution

Electrical energy in the UK is generated at power stations located at strategic places to ensure an economic and safe supply of energy to industrial, commercial and domestic consumers.

Turbo-alternator sets convert pressurised steam into electrical energy which is then transmitted, via an extensive overhead line and underground cable system, to consumers. The standard transmission voltages are 400,000 volts (400 kV) and 132,000 volts (132 kV), whereas the standard distribution voltage is largely at 11,000 volts (11 kV), and large industrial consumers receive energy at this voltage for local transformation within their own systems.

For domestic and other small consumers, however, the standard 415/240 volts three phase/single phase distribution system is received direct from the public supply 'mains'. Transformation of systems of supply from one voltage to another is necessary for economic transmission and distribution purposes. Substations are used for this purpose, where energy at one voltage is received and given out at another voltage via transformers and related switchgear. Public supply systems are almost exclusively alternating current (a.c.); any direct current (d.c.) systems required for special industrial purposes are usually converted by special apparatus, called 'rectifiers', from a.c. systems.

Electricity boards

The public electricity supply industry comprises the following organisations:

(a) The Central Electricity Generating Board (CEGB) which is responsible for the power stations and transmission systems.
(b) The twelve Area Boards in England and Wales, which have responsibility for the distribution systems and for the sale of electricity and appliances to consumers.
(c) The North of Scotland Hydro-Electric Board and the South of Scotland Electricity Board are two 'all-purpose' boards which are responsible for generation, transmission and distribution in Scotland. For further information on the public electricity supply

system, with free descriptive leaflets, contact your local Electricity Board or write to the Electricity Council, 30 Millbank, London SW1P 4RD.

Electric generators

Simple generation

A simple basic generator comprises two main parts, the rotor, which is the rotating part, and the stator, the fixed part. The rotor contains insulated conductors wound around a metal cylinder and, as it rotates under the action of an external mechanical power source, these conductors cut across a magnetic field from the electro magnet housed in the stator. The laws of electromagnetism, which apply to the interrelationship between electricity and magnetism, are such that this action causes voltage to be induced in the rotor conductors. By suitably connecting these conductors to an external circuit, the electric current thus produced can be tapped and used.

Alternatively, the conductors and electromagnets can be housed in the stator and rotor respectively, without affecting the generation of electricity in the conductors. It is the motion of the conductors in relation to the magnetic field that matters. The value of the current, voltage, etc., depends upon the characteristics of the generator. In modern power stations, for example, the generators (usually called 'alternators') may each have output in excess of 500 MW which is 500 million watts!

Small portable and mobile generators

These are used for a variety of purposes. On construction sites, for example, they are used to provide an emergency and temporary supply of electricity or to serve particular items of plant, such as electric arc welding sets. Most generators on construction sites are capable of supplying at 240 volts and 120 volts, which enables them to supply a 55 volt system via special transformers available for this purpose. The generator's frame, metallic parts of the transformer and centre point of the secondary winding of the transformer should be bonded electrically and suitably earthed.

It is important that the manufacturer's instructions on the installation and use of generators are known and understood by operators and other staff involved. (For further information see BS Code of Practice CP 1017.)

Alternating and direct currents

The natural current generated is alternating in kind (a.c.) which, in a normal single cycle of 1/50 second, alternates in value from zero to maximum in one direction, back to zero and to maximum in the opposite direction, and back to zero again, thus producing the standard 50 cycles per second (50 hertz) system used in the UK.

To change an a.c. generator to one that produces direct current (d.c.) it is necessary to rectify the positive and negative surges of the a.c. current so that it flows only in one direction at a constant value. One way of doing this is to use a commutator.

So far as safety is concerned, a.c., because of its effects on the heart, is rather more dangerous than d.c., but it is best to assume that the same preventive measures apply to both and to act accordingly.

Single and three phase systems

A single phase a.c. system, normally at 240 volts, is one in which the circuit comprises two conductors (called 'live' and 'neutral') usually with an additional conductor for 'earth'. A three phase a.c. system, normally at 415/240 volts, has four conductors. Three of them are live and the fourth is neutral. The three phase supply is for larger equipment and the maximum voltage of the system (415 volts) is utilised. But 240 volts may be obtained between one of the live phase conductors and neutral.

Electrical installation

An electrical installation comprises such items as cables, conduit or other mechanical protection, main and local switches, distribution boards, fuses, socket outlets, etc.

Circuits

For electric current to flow and provide a source of energy, it must be contained within a circuit comprising conductors. These conductors contain a suitable inner metal core (e.g. tinned copper or aluminium) which conducts the electricity, together with an outer sheath of insulating material (e.g. rubber or similar man-made substance) which normally safely 'contains' the electricity within the circuit.

Fuses and circuit breakers

In the event of a fault on overload, it is necessary for a circuit to be disconnected or excessive current could flow and the resulting overheating could cause fire. Automatic disconnection is provided by the fuse or circuit breaker.

A fuse is a protected strip of thin metal which melts at a value well below an excessive value of current and cuts off supply. It will be readily appreciated that a fuse should be of the type and rating appropriate to the circuit and appliance it protects. Clearly, it would be folly to provide a 30 amp fuse, or a makeshift one of the same value, when only a 13 amp fuse is required. It should also be remembered that fuses will protect against overheated circuits and fires, but *not* against receipt of a potentially lethal or dangerous electric shock. (The fault current required to blow a fuse will invariably be far higher than the minimal current which would present danger to human beings.) Fuses protect the equipment but not necessarily the user.

A circuit breaker is a device that looks like an enclosed switch. It has a mechanism that trips the switch from 'on' to 'off' position if an excess current flows in the circuit. As with the fuse, the circuit breaker should be of the type and rating for the circuit and appliance it protects.

It must be stressed that whereas fuses and circuit breakers, of themselves, provide protection from excess current flow, they may not, unaided, provide complete protection against electric shock. A special type of circuit breaker, known as a 'residual current circuit breaker', helps here in that it provides a good standard of protection (i.e. at very low fault currents) against earth leakage faults, particularly at locations where effective earthing cannot otherwise be achieved.

Socket outlets and plugs

Socket outlets are the means of 'tapping' into the circuit to allow electricity to be used to supply an appliance. A plug, attached to a flexible cable supplying the apparatus, is used to 'plug in' to the socket outlet and thus form another circuit.

Fixed apparatus, such as large electric motors which drive equipment, do not require socket outlets and are supplied from their own circuit, controlled by a separate motor control which not only incorporates 'stop' and 'start' facilities, but also protection against overload.

Nature and purpose of electrical use

Equipment

Electricity is an efficient and convenient form of energy used for lighting, heating and power applications in occupational life. Consider for example, just one group of uses, electric heating processes, which are finding ever-increasing applications in industry. Typical applications are electric furnaces and ovens, resistance and induction heating, electric arc melting, microwave heating, lasers and electron beams, and infrared and ultraviolet processes. Such equipment operates at frequencies from the standard 50 Hz for resistance heating to THz (THz =

10^{12} Hz) for lasers. Power ranges of typical heating processes are from 1 kW to 100 MW.

Use

The flexibility and ease of use of equipment brings its own dangers, and the design, installation, operation, control, use and safety requirements of the type of equipment just described are highly specialised. However, certain basic requirements apply for all electrical equipment.

(a) The equipment should be of adequate design, construction and performance for the intended use. Reference to appropriate British Standards and codes should ensure a satisfactory product.
(b) The equipment should be properly installed with a comparable standard for circuitry and control equipment to ensure that location and environmental conditions do not invalidate the specification.
(c) Adequate information should be supplied to the user so that when the equipment is properly used it will be safe and without risk to health.
(d) The equipment should be properly used for the purpose for which it is intended. Any unreasonable departure from the maximum loading, rating, temperature and other characteristics, or any misuse, is liable to lead to breakdown, plant damage or even shock, burns or fire.
(e) Operators should receive proper training, instruction and supervision so that skills match operational requirements.
(f) There should be regular on-site inspection of equipment and associated circuitry to detect any obvious deterioration or other defect.
(g) There should be an adequate maintenance system undertaken at the required periods by competent staff. Records of all maintenance, testing and repairs should be kept.
(h) Where work on high-voltage electrical apparatus is to be undertaken, a permit to work system should be operated (*see* Chapter 13). The permit to work should indicate that, prior to work commencing, the apparatus to be worked on is dead, is properly isolated from all live conductors, has been discharged of electricity and is efficiently connected to earth. The operation should be supervised and controlled by an authorised person, namely a person appointed in writing by management to issue and cancel permits to work, and who is competent, through training and experience, to undertake specific operations and/or work on high-voltage systems and apparatus.

(i) Where work of a general nature needs to be undertaken in high-voltage switchrooms by maintenance staff, general building workers or electrical engineers who may be competent persons, but not authorised persons, they must always be accompanied by, and under the supervision of, an authorised person or senior authorised person.

Portable tools

Portable electrical apparatus is a common cause of electric shock and burns. Whereas some of these accidents occur as a result of defects in the apparatus itself, such as missing covers or lack of adequate earthing for exposed metallic parts, others result from defects in the flexible cable supplying the apparatus. Defects in cables arise through damage from vehicles and other objects passing over them as they lie strewn over the floor, or from excessive wear and tear from arduous construction site use. Plugs are sometimes wrongly connected or repairs are attempted with the equipment still switched on.

As with other apparatus, portable apparatus requires protection against overload and short circuit. Earth fault protection must be provided and the integrity of the earth core of flexible cables is crucial to such protection.

Various proprietary additional protective systems are available for portable apparatus, including reduced voltage systems (110 volts), circulating current earth monitoring, and residual current devices. The risk of electric shock can also be reduced by using all-insulated or double-insulated tools. (*See* BS 2754:1976 'Construction of Electrical Equipment for Protection Against Electric Shock'.)

Flameproofing

The use of electrical equipment in flammable atmospheres is a highly specialised topic, detailed treatment of which is beyond the scope of this book.

Clearly, electrical equipment which can give rise to heat or sparking will provide a source of ignition for a flammable atmosphere of the right mixture, and it is therefore necessary to take adequate precautions. In industry, potentially flammable hazardous areas are classified according to a graded probability of an explosive gas or vapour concentration occurring. Three classifications, or zones, are usually referred to as follows:

(a) Zone 0 – which is a zone in which a flammable atmosphere is known to be continuously present, or present for long periods;

(b) Zone 1 – which is a zone in which a flammable atmosphere is likely to occur, at least during normal working; and
(c) Zone 2 – which is a zone in which a flammable atmosphere is unlikely to occur save under abnormal conditions, such occurrence being of only short duration.

The particular zone is predetermined at the design stage and it is in everyone's interests to 'design out' the more hazardous zones so far as possible.

Types of protection

The type of protection required for electrical equipment which is to be placed at a particular location depends upon the zone. First, the possibility of excluding electrical equipment from the zone should be considered. If this is not a practicable proposition, consideration should be given to segregation of the electrical equipment within the zone, say by suitable barriers. However, the installation of electrical equipment in hazardous areas may be unavoidable, in which case special types of protection are available and designated as in the following examples.

Type N equipment

This equipment is designed for use in zone 2 conditions and is so constructed that, properly used, it will not ignite flammable atmospheres under normal conditions.

Type E equipment

This includes equipment such as transformers and squirrel cage motors. They do not normally produce sparks and are suitable for zone 2 conditions.

Pressurising or purging methods

These are methods of using pressurised or inert gases to prevent ingress of flammable gases, and are suitable for all zone conditions.

Intrinsically safe equipment

This is used for instrumentation and low-energy equipment. Intrinsically safe equipment is categorised 'ia' or 'ib' if it can be used in zones 1 and 2. Exceptionally, category ia may be used in zone 0 if sparking contacts are not part of the equipment.

Flameproof equipment

This is probably the most familiar term and is a well-tried British approach to the problem. The principle of 'flameproofing' is that the apparatus so described is constructed to withstand any explosion, within the apparatus, arising from ignition of flammable gas that may enter through the casing or other enclosure. All flanges and other joints of the casing or enclosure of the apparatus are well designed and constructed so as to prevent any internal ignition of gas from moving out of the enclosure and igniting a surrounding flammable atmosphere. By its nature, flameproof equipment is substantial, heavy and rather costly. It is intended for application in zones 1 or 2 but is not suitable for use in zone 0.

Marking

Each item of electrical equipment for use in hazardous atmospheres should be marked with the appropriate group number for the range of gases it was designed for, and also with a temperature classification indicating the maximum allowable surface temperature of the equipment used.

Circuitry

Electrical apparatus for use in hazardous atmospheres has to be supplied with electricity via a cable circuit and control gear. As much as possible of this should be located outside the hazardous zone. Within the zone, however, the suitability of the metallic cable sheathing, armouring or conduit must be ensured, with provision of special cable sealing glands and fittings. Earthing requires particular attention.

Principles of welding – dangers and precautions

Electric arc welding may be either by alternating current (a.c.) or by direct current (d.c.). Given similar conditions, d.c. is safer but is probably less convenient.

An a.c. supply for welding sets is obtained from a transformer, but for d.c. a transformer must be supplemented by a rectifier. Alternatively, a d.c. generator could be employed.

Output voltages for welding sets are up to 100 volts for a.c. and 80 volts for d.c.

Particular care is required when electric arc welding, if electric shock or burns from contact with parts of the electrode holder or the live electrode are to be avoided. 'All insulated' electrode holders are recommended.

Principal components

The principal components of a welding circuit are

(a) the welding lead, which carries the current from the welding set to the electrode and to the workpiece;

(b) the welding return lead, which returns the current from the workpiece to the welding set; and
(c) the welding earth, which must be connected to the workpiece.

The welding return lead is essential to prevent current taking random paths, say, via structural steelwork, metal pipes, railway lines, etc. A particular danger is that if a random path includes a loosely bolted connection, a high resistance is set up which will cause heat to generate as the current flows through it, possibly resulting in fire. The welding return lead should be firmly clamped to the workpiece.

The welding earth is necessary to maintain the workpiece at earth potential and thus prevent shock by safeguarding against the possibility of the workpiece becoming energised at mains voltage, or energised because of lack of continuity in the welding return.

A.c. welding sets can be provided with a special device that prevents the voltage of the electrode holder from rising above 50 volts during the periods when no arc is being struck. This is a recommended precaution.

Personal protection

Apart from electric shock and fire, there is also a danger to the eyes and skin from the effects of ultraviolet light from the arc. This can cause painful maladies. One is known as 'arc eye', a form of conjunctivitis, and the other is a nasty 'sunburn' effect on the exposed skin.

As an essential precaution, the welder's eyes (and those of his mate) must be protected by a suitable electric arc welding filter lens in the welding helmet or in a hand-held face shield. Additional protection must be provided for the skin in the form of suitable welder's gloves and sensible footwear and clothing.

For regular welding jobs in a workshop, a properly constructed welding booth is necessary to protect the eyes of people working or passing in the vicinity. When working at heights, screens and fire blankets are necessary to prevent, so far as possible, arc eye and/or sparks from the process falling on to people or on to flammable materials below.

Training of electrical personnel

The need for training

A key to safe working on electrical installations and apparatus is that all those engaged on such work shall have been adequately trained. The training, backed up by relevant experience in a working environment, should be aimed to ensure that the trainee acquires the skills, related knowledge and attitudes necessary for safe and efficient working. Both off-the-job and on-the-job training must be properly supervised, and at each stage the trainee must be made aware of the extent and limitations of the job in hand, the hazards that may be present, and the precautions that have to be taken to ensure safe working.

Precautions

Before any trainee commences work, the electrical circuit or apparatus to be worked on must be properly isolated and locked off from all sources of electricity supply, and proved dead by means of a suitable instrument. Where necessary, appropriate measures should be taken to ensure that the isolated parts cannot be re-energised during the course of the work. At an early stage of training it is necessary that trainees should be familiar with emergency procedures and with the treatment for electric shock.

Suitable guidance regarding both off-the-job and on-the-job training in electrical skills is contained in two booklets, under these titles, issued by the Manpower Services Commission (n.d.).

Training programme

The training programme itself will normally follow the recommendations of the particular training board, company scheme or apprenticeship applicable, and will be incorporated in the academic syllabus of any associated training establishment, possibly leading to the attainment of a qualification. Particular topics that should be covered, at a fundamental level, to ensure a sound knowledge of electrical safety include

(a) rudiments of electrical circuits, including the terms used, the function of earthing, and circuit protection;
(b) the physiological effects of electricity, electric shock and burns, including measures both to avoid shock and to treat its consequences;
(c) basic principles of generation, accumulation and dissipation of static electricity;
(d) safety measures for both dead and live work, and the application, limitation and use of voltage indicators and test instruments;
(e) use of insulated tools, rubber mats and rubber gloves;
(f) use of temporary screens, shrouds and covers to prevent inadvertent contact with live conductors and earthed metalwork;
(g) special hazards of particular locations such as hazardous atmospheres and work on switchboards, in confined or restricted spaces, or in the vicinity of crane trolley wires and the like;
(h) special hazards of particular plant or equipment, including portable tools;

(i) scope and application of company safety rules, including standardised safety procedures, permits to work and safety documentation; and
(j) the law on electrical safety, relevant HSE Guidance Notes and BSI standards and codes of practice.

Updating training

Training in electrical safety is not a once and for all activity, but must be updated from time to time so as to take account of such matters as changes in the law or in methods of work, or following the introduction of new equipment, changed workshop procedures and new techniques. Persons so trained will also require adequate instructions for the job in hand. It must never be presumed that the trained person will always be familiar with likely hazards in a particular job and the means of overcoming them. This is where proper planning and control of the job comes in and reinforces the need for adequate information and instruction.

Principles and practice of electrical testing

The need for testing

Electrical testing is necessary to ensure that the design, construction and performance specifications of the items being tested are maintained at an adequate standard for the anticipated continued use. Electrical testing also enables faults to be detected so that remedial measures can be taken before the fault develops and damage or personal injury arises.

Types of testing

Routine testing of production lines

Equipment such as electric motors and various types of industrial, commercial and domestic apparatus require individual or batch testing. Procedures include resistance and insulation tests for correct polarity, connection and operation. It is important that those undertaking the testing have adequate skills and proper equipment. The layout of the work area should be such as not to expose anyone to live and other dangerous parts. 'Anyone' means not only the tester but other persons present.

Testing of electrical installations

A prerequisite to such testing is visual inspection to ensure that all circuits and equipment comply with an accepted standard and are properly installed, and that circuit protection and earthing arrangements appear in order.

The method adopted for testing should not, of course, be liable to endanger people or plant. Thus the testing operation must be under proper control and the testing equipment suitable for the required use.

Ordinary test lamps, and leads with excessively exposed test prods or even bare ends, have caused numerous flashovers, and the dangerous practice of using metal lampholders is, unfortunately, still encountered. Properly designed, protected and approved test equipment, employing current limiting resistors, well-shrouded test prods, and properly insulated handles are available, and should always be used.

Apart from tests to determine correct polarity, the measurement of earth fault loop impedance is required to check that the earthing arrangements will ensure a safe and automatic disconnection of electricity supply in case of a fault.

It is a requirement of the IEE Wiring Regulations that on final circuits the circuit protective device (e.g. fuse or miniature circuit breaker) will, in the event of a fault to earth, operate within 0.4 seconds for socket outlets in bathrooms and outdoor circuits and within 0.5 seconds for circuits supplying fixed equipment. The time taken for protective devices to operate and clear a fault depends upon the device's time/current characteristics and the earth fault impedance, the maximum values of which should not be exceeded. Maximum values to meet a range of conditions are laid down in the IEE Wiring Regulations. For example, with a 0.4 second disconnection and a 50 amp rated fuse, the value should not exceed 0.6 ohms.

Testing of electronic telecommunications and similar equipment

The dangers of working on and testing components inside television sets, without first having disconnected the set from the power supply, are obvious. Repair and testing bays in workshops should be in earth-free areas, set apart, with special arrangements such as the provision of a single isolating transformer and proper test benches and equipment.

The testing of electronic equipment with earthed metal casings requires special precautions to remove the risk of electric shock through the casing. This may be achieved by provision of current-limiting devices for the testing circuit. Testing is a specialised operation and for further information and advice the fifteenth edition of the Institution of Electrical Engineers' (1981) wiring regulations and HSE's (1980) booklet should be consulted.

Conclusion

Electricity is a technical subject, a comprehensive study of which requires complex theory and a treatment far beyond the scope of this chapter. Even an attempt at a basic approach has its limitations, particularly if explanation has necessarily to be oversimplified. It is hoped that readers will, nevertheless, understand the problem of safety and will be encouraged to take their studies of electrical matters much further. Some excellent textbooks and courses are available for this purpose.

The safe use of electricity requires competence, concern, skill, related knowledge and care not only on the part of those who may be exposed to danger or who supervise and manage. Such 'care and competence' qualities are also required by those who design, install and maintain electrical equipment and – dare we say it – by those who practice safety and health in areas where electricity is generated, distributed and used.

36

Construction safety

Construction safety is a very broad area, comprising plant construction, roof work, scaffolding, trenching, use of machinery and plant, demolition, tunnelling, use of explosives and fire protection procedures on site. It is an industry which employs much casual labour, skilled and unskilled, who transfer from site to site according to the availability of work. In the past its safety record was poor, a fact which led to the need for specific regulations. These regulations, namely:

(a) Construction (General Provisions) Regulations, 1961 (hereafter cited as C(GP)R)
(b) Construction (Lifting Operations) Regulations, 1961 (C(LO)R)
(c) Construction (Working Places) Regulations, 1966 (C(WP)R), and
(d) Construction (Health and Welfare) Regulations, 1966 (C(HW)R)

are known collectively as the 'Construction Regulations', and were passed under the Factories Act 1961, a key feature being that a building operation or work of engineering construction is regarded as a 'notional factory' (Factories Act 1961, sec 127(4)).

As a result of these Regulations safety standards have improved quite significantly and there has been some reduction in the number of fatal and seriously incapacitating accidents in the construction industry.

Accidents in the construction industry

The most common fatal type of accident in construction remains falling from a height, and the most common non-fatal type of accident is that of manual handling. A more complete categorisation of accidents is as follows.

Ladder accidents

This may be due to the ladder slipping outwards at the base, to the use of defective or rotten wooden ladders, or as a result of overreaching when working at the top of a ladder, causing the ladder to fall sideways. Even if a ladder is of sound construction and in good condition, it is still dangerous if improperly used. Placing it too close to, or too far away from, a wall can have tragic consequences and anyone using a ladder should be aware of the '1 out, 4 up' rule. This rule is that the vertical height from ground to point of rest of the ladder should, wherever practicable, be four times the distance between the base of the vertical dimension and the foot of the ladder. Failure to adopt this rule can result in the ladder becoming unstable (*see* Fig. 36.1).

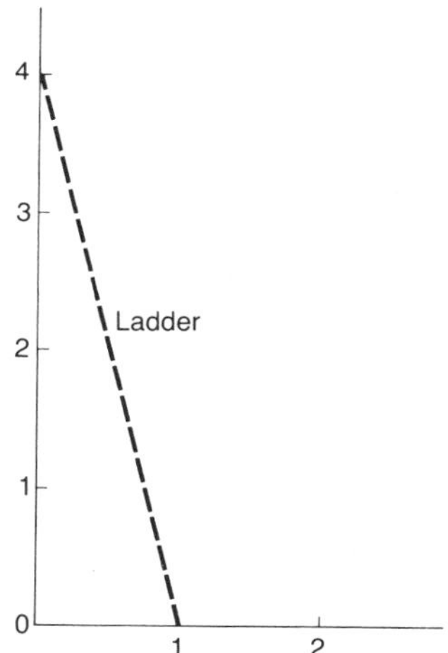

Fig. 36.1 The '1 out, 4 up' rule for ladders

A standing ladder must be securely fixed near to its upper resting place (or its upper end if vertical). Where such fixing is impracticable, the ladder must be fixed at or near its lower end. If this is also impracticable, a person must be stationed at the foot of the ladder to prevent it from slipping. Except where there is an adequate handhold, ladders must rise to a height of at least 1,070 mm above the landing place or above the highest rung reached by the feet of persons using the ladder. (When this is impracticable, the ladder must rise to the greatest practicable height (C(WP)R 32(2), (3) and (5)).)

Falls from working platforms

Working platforms include fixed scaffolds and lightweight, readily assembled mobile access equipment commonly used in factories and commercial premises for maintenance work, painting, cleaning and installation work. Causes of accidents include the use of unfenced and inadequately fenced platforms, insufficient or inadequate boarding, or even boarding which is rotten and defective. The need for structural stability of lightweight mobile platforms is important, particularly where they may be subject to wind loading. Mobile platforms should be stationed on a firm level base and, where practicable, tied to the structure to prevent sideways movement. They should incorporate a wheel-locking device. For routine work the following height: base ratios should be taken into account: work indoors – 3.5:1; work outdoors – 3:1.

Falls of materials

Small objects such as hammers, roof tiles, bricks and even 6″ nails, dropped from a height, can have serious consequences if they hit someone below. The main causes of falls of materials are poor housekeeping by people working above, absence of toe boards and edge barriers on working platforms, incorrect assembly of gin wheels for raising materials, incorrect hooking and slinging prior to raising and, in many cases, failure to install catchment platforms or 'fans' which are designed to catch small objects which may fall during construction. The provision of fans is particularly appropriate where construction work may take place above or adjacent to a public thoroughfare.

Falls from pitched roofs or through fragile roofs

Workers sliding down a slippery pitched roof, particularly if it is wet after rain or covered in moss growth, and falling to the ground below is a common construction accident. There is often a need, therefore, for eaves and roof edge protection, coupled with the use of crawl boards or firmly fixed ladders. The practice of stacking building materials on roofs should be prohibited, as should working on roofs without crawl boards.

Falls through openings in flat roofs and floors

The principal cause of this type of accident is failure to cover openings or to replace covers after use. In other cases, covers have not been properly marked 'Hole Below', with the result that workers have walked on them, causing the cover to collapse. Edge protection, in the form of rails and toe boards, is preferable to covers as the worker is given a clear indication of the hazard involved. (Numerous accidents are on record where two employees have been involved in removing a cover to a floor hole, such as a large sheet of plywood, without actually realising that the hole existed under the cover. The employee at the leading edge of the horizontally held sheet has walked off in a certain direction unharmed, but his colleague at the trailing edge has followed him and fallen through the hole which he could not see.)

Collapse of excavations

Absence of timbering to trenches, or insufficient timbering in relation to depth and width of the trench and nature of the surrounding ground, are the main causes of excavation collapse, resulting in workers being buried alive. Careful examination of the subsoil, particularly where water and/or shifting sand may be present, is essential prior to excavation. A further cause of trench collapse is the stacking of excavated ground and building materials such as pipes, blocks and bricks too close to the edge of the excavation, causing excessive loading on supporting timbers.

Site transport

Many accidents result from site transport. They include men falling off machines not designed to carry passengers, such as dumper trucks, being run down or crushed by reversing lorries, or crushed when vehicles overturn. Great care is needed in the maintenance of all site vehicles, particularly their braking and reversing systems. Furthermore, only competent and trained personnel should drive site vehicles. Site road maintenance is very important, as poor standards of maintenance and housekeeping can cause skidding and overturning. Site transport can be subject to misuse. Where, for instance, an employee gives another employee, whether from the same workforce or not, a lift on site in a dumper truck, as a result of which the latter is injured or killed, the former employee's employer is almost certainly liable at civil law for the injury, even though the driver was acting contrary to orders. An act committed during the course of, and within the scope of, employment will attract the principle of vicarious liability. (*See* the case of *Rose* v. *Plenty* [1976] 1 AER 97.)

Machinery and powered hand tools

All moving parts of machinery and plant with which operatives may come into contact should be securely guarded (C(GP)R 42 and Woodworking Machines Regulations 1974). This includes power take-offs, engines, cooling fans and belt drives, together with various items of woodworking machinery such as circular saws and planing machines.

Electric hand tools should comply with BS2769:1964 and, unless 'all insulated' or 'double insulated', must be effectively earthed. Reduced voltage distribution for portable tools and temporary lighting, using 110 volt mains isolation transformers with the secondary winding centre tapped to earth, is always recommended.

Housekeeping

Poor standards of housekeeping are frequently a contributory cause of accidents resulting in trips and falls over debris and building materials, and puncture wounds to the feet from nails projecting from pieces of timber left lying around; the careless use and storage of chemical-based compounds and other materials is another hazard. Inadequate facilities for the storage of flammable refuse is frequently a contributory cause of fires on sites.

Work on scaffolds

The basic requirements for safe working on scaffolds are:

(a) correct erection of the scaffold;
(b) a suitable system for inspection and maintenance of the scaffold, taking into account the frequent likelihood of alterations to the scaffold as the work progresses.

Erection of scaffolds

(a) A competent person must inspect scaffolding materials before each occasion on which they are to be used (C(WP)R 8).
(b) Any erection, substantial alterations or additions to, or dismantling of a scaffold must be undertaken under the immediate supervision of a competent person (C(WP)R 8).
(c) Only competent and experienced workers should be employed, so far as possible, for any erection work, substantial alterations to and additions to scaffolds or for dismantling work (C(WP)R 8).
(d) Every part of a scaffold should be so fixed, secured or placed as to prevent accidental displacement, as far as is practicable (C(WP)R 11).
(e) Scaffolds should be constructed of suitable and sound materials of adequate strength (C(WP)R 9(1) and (2) and 10(1)).
(f) A scaffold should be rigidly connected to the building or other structure unless designed and constructed as an independent scaffold (C(WP)R 15(1)).
(g) Parts of buildings or other structures must not be used to support scaffolds unless they are of sound material and sufficiently strong and stable (C(WP)R 15(2)).
(h) Gutters must not be used for supports unless they are suitable for the purpose and of adequate strength. In particular, overhanging gutters must not be used unless designed specifically as walkways (C(WP)R 18).
(i) Bricks and small blocks should not be used as supports except for certain low platforms (C(WP)R 15(4)).

Inspection and maintenance of scaffolds

(a) All scaffolds in use must have been inspected by a competent person within the preceding 7 days. They must also be inspected after exposure to weather conditions likely to affect their strength or stability, or which could have displaced any part of the scaffold. The results of such inspections must be entered in or attached to the prescribed register, except for:
  (i) ladder scaffolds,
  (ii) trestle scaffolds, and
  (iii) those scaffolds from which persons cannot fall more than 2 metres (C(WP)R 22 and 39).

(b) Each employer whose men use a scaffold must satisfy himself that the scaffold complies with the Regulations, whether or not his own men have erected it, and prior to his men first using the scaffold (C(WP)R 23). Behind this key Regulation lies the assumption that plant and scaffolding is invariably available for use by employees of other contractors on site in addition to the direct workforce of the scaffolding contractor. This duty is strict. (In *Vineer* v. *Doidge & Sons Ltd* [1972] 2 AER 794 it was held that where an employee of a subcontractor, sent to measure windows in a building for glass installation, was injured by scaffolding erected by the main contractor, his employers, the glass installation subcontractors, were liable for breach of Regulation 23, even though the employee was competent.)

(c) All scaffolds must be properly maintained (C(WP)R 11).

Prohibitions on the use of platforms and scaffolds

(a) Platforms, gangways, runs and stairs must be kept clear of unnecessary obstruction and material and free from rubbish and any projecting nails. Slippery platforms, gangways, runs and stairs must be sanded, cleaned or otherwise treated as soon as practicable (C(WP)R 30(1)).

(b) Scaffolds must never be overloaded, and materials must be stored on scaffolds unless needed within a reasonable time. Where materials are loaded onto scaffolds, this must be done without causing violent shock to the system. When loads are stored on scaffolds, they must be evenly distributed as far as is practicable (C(WP)R 37(1)).

(c) Partly erected or dismantled scaffolds must either comply with the Regulations, even in their incomplete state, or else have prominent warning notices displayed indicating that they must not be used. Access to such scaffolds must also be blocked as far as is reasonably practicable (C(WP)R 12).

(d) Before the site is vacated for the day,
   (i) all overhead scaffolds must be left in a safe condition, and
   (ii) all loose tools should be removed to a safe place or secured against falling.

Further detailed guidance on scaffolds is available in BS5973:1981, in the RoSPA (1982) *Construction Regulations Handbook* and the RoSPA (n.d.) *Supervisors' Guide to the Construction Regulations.*

Roof work and work at high level

Accidents associated with people falling from or through roofs, or from high-level working positions, are common in the construction industry and maintenance activities. Many of these accidents could be avoided by the operation of a safe system of work. Such systems include careful planning prior to the operation, use of trained and experienced operators, effective supervision and control, and use of permit to work systems where there is a high degree of foreseeable risk coupled with complex precautions. (*See* HSE Guidance Note GS10, *Roofwork: Prevention of Falls.*)

Two specific aspects merit closer attention, namely,

(a) the means of access to the roof or high-level working position, and
(b) the system of work adopted once the working position has been reached.

Access by ladder

The most common means of access is by portable ladder. There are many types; they can be manufactured from aluminium, fibreglass or timber. Most accidents, however, arise in connection with timber ladders. The following points are relevant to the safe use of ladders.

(a) The ladder should be strong enough for the work to be undertaken.
(b) Only sound ladders should be used. Ladders with split uprights, broken feet or loose rungs, or which have become distorted, should not be used but rather destroyed. Ladders should not be painted, since this can hide any defect which may have developed. However, this prohibition does not extend to ladders being varnished or treated with wood preservative.
(c) A ladder should be long enough for the work to be undertaken. Except when there is adequate handhold, a ladder should extend to a height of at least 1,070 mm above the landing place, or above the highest rung on which the user has to stand.
(d) The ladder should be placed at the correct angle. (*See* earlier in this chapter, 'Ladder Accidents'.)

(e) Support for the ladder should be strong enough to withstand the thrust imposed by the ladder.
(f) 'Home-made' ladders, the rungs of which depend for support solely on nails, must not be used.
(g) Subject to size, the ladder should be securely fixed near to its upper resting place or, if impracticable, at its lower end, to prevent it slipping sideways. Someone should foot the ladder until secured.
(h) All ladders should have clearly marked identification numbers for company records and inspection purposes. It is recommended that they be inspected at regular intervals of not more than 6 months and details of this inspection entered on a record card.
(i) Ladders should not be stored on wet ground or left exposed to weather. They should be stored at normal ambient temperature under cover to prevent warping, and never be hung from brackets, as this tends to separate the rungs from the stiles.

The above points are important in preventing typical ladder accidents. Consider now working on a roof. Much will depend upon the pitch of the roof, its construction and the form of roof covering.

Working on roofs

Flat roofs and roofs up to 10° pitch

The main hazard is falling from the edge of the roof, especially where work is being carried out, or through openings in the roof. Guard rails and toe boards should be provided in these circumstances. One method of guarding the edge of a flat roof is with freestanding frames (*see* Fig. 36.2). A series of triangulated tubular steel frames are anchored to the roof by means of precast concrete counterweights attached to the inner ends of the frames. The frames are placed at approximately 2.4 m centres. Guard rails and toe boards are attached to the frames, the toe boards being held in position by purpose-made brackets. The frames can be moved to allow roofing felt to be laid. The frames can form part of a roofer's equipment which can be carried from site to site. As the concrete counterweights each weigh about 30 kg, care must be exercised when lifting or moving them manually.

Sloping roofs over 10° pitch

Three hazardous situations exist, namely working close to the edge, at the edge, or at some part where a person is likely to slide down the roof and fall from the edge. In the latter case, the degree of danger depends upon the pitch of the roof, the possibility of the surface being made slippery by ice, rain, moss or moisture, and the type of footwear worn by the individual. It can also be hazardous working on roofs in extreme

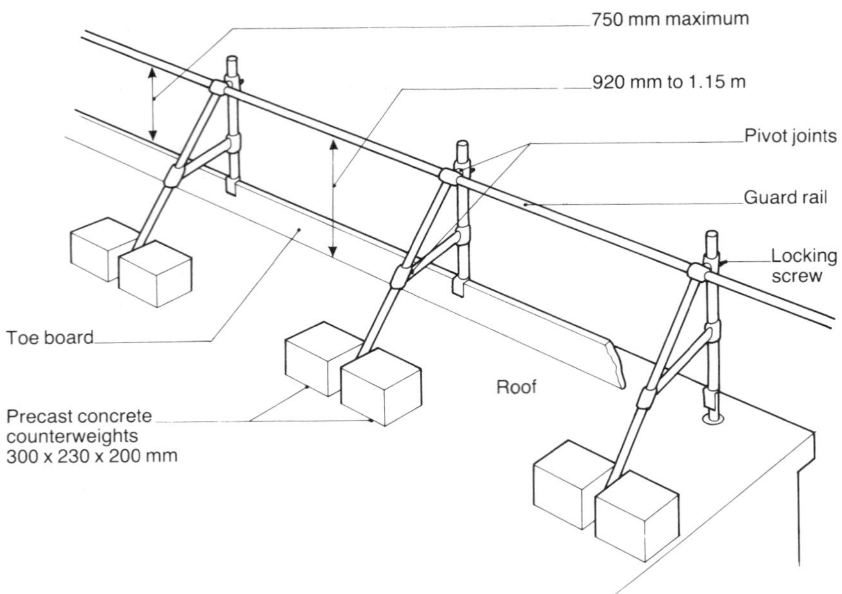

Fig. 36.2 Use of freestanding frames

weather conditions such as high winds. In such cases, interlocking crawl boards or roof ladders should be provided and used (C(WP)R 35). (*Provided* means 'made available in a reasonably accessible place' by the employer; *Ginty* v. *Belmont Building Supplies Ltd* [1959] 1 AER 414.) This rule may well have been superseded by HSWA, sec 2(2)(*c*), which requires employers to inform, train, instruct and supervise their employees in the use of safety equipment, as well as merely 'providing' the requisite equipment.

Fragile roofs

Many accidents are associated with workers falling through fragile roofs. In many cases these are fatal accidents caused by a false sense of security created through long experience of working on such roofs. Asbestos cement roof covering, for instance, may be capable of carrying some distributed load and give the impression of a surface which is solid enough to bear a man's weight. It will not, however, carry a concentrated load such as that applied by the heel of a man walking, or the shock load imposed by a man stumbling and falling. Many types of single thickness asbestos cement sheeting simply shatter without warning, and experience shows that walking along the lines of the sheeting bolts, i.e. on the purlins, does not always offer sufficient security. Asbestos cement becomes brittle with age.

Before any work is undertaken on a roof, or where a roof may be used for access, it is essential to identify the parts covered by fragile materials and to decide on precautions to be taken. For instance, on roofs covered with fragile material, at least two crawl boards or roof ladders should be used so that the worker will always have one ladder at his side to stand on when moving the other ladder to a new working position. Where a valley or parapet gutter is used as a means of access and the adjacent roof is of fragile material, suitable precautions, such as the provision of covers, should be taken to prevent a person falling through the fragile material. Valley gutters which are overhung by roof sheets, to such an extent that there is inadequate clearance for a man's feet, should not be used for access along the roof. Prominent warning notices (e.g. 'CAUTION – FRAGILE ROOF – USE CRAWL BOARDS') should be fixed at the approaches to each fragile roof. With large buildings, such notices should be displayed at 50 metre intervals along all faces of the building and at all normal access points, e.g. valleys and junctions with vertical structural members (C(WP)R 36).

Practical precautions when working at high levels

Work at high levels covers a wide range of activities from the simple replacement of roof tiles to the complete stripping and recovering of existing roofs. With each job, the requisite practical precautions must be considered before anyone is permitted to start work.

Consideration of weather conditions

Hazards resulting from adverse weather conditions must be anticipated. In windy weather, work involving the fixing of roof sheets, in particular, should not be carried out, as a man can easily be blown off balance whilst carrying a sheet up to or on the roof. The presence of moisture, ice or snow can turn an apparently safe foothold into a hazard.

Safety harnesses and belts

Where harnesses and belts are to be used because safe means of access cannot be arranged, suitable anchorage points must be provided which are capable of sustaining an anticipated shock load. Excessive shock loads on the anchorage, the equipment and the wearer should be avoided. 'Free fall' distance should not be more than 2 metres in the case of a safety harness or 0.6 metres where a safety belt is used. Use of inertia-controlled reels or slides designed to allow greater freedom of movement without excessive slackness in the rope, and to act as an arrestor if a sudden pull is exerted as the result of a fall, should be considered. (Guidance on standards for the design and construction of safety harnesses and belts is given in BS1397:1968 'Industrial Safety

Belts, Harnesses and Safety Lanyards'.) The use of safety harnesses and safety anchorage points is particularly relevant to cleaning outer surfaces of windows of high-rise office and industrial properties. (For a more detailed examination of this subject, *see* later in this chapter, 'Window Cleaning'.)

Safety nets

Where safety nets are installed to catch men and materials falling from working positions, the nets should be rested as close to the working level as possible (C(WP)R 38).

Personal protective equipment

Like all construction workers, workers engaged in high-level work should be provided with safety helmets and other personal protective equipment appropriate to the task, e.g. gloves, one-piece overalls and non-slip safety shoes or boots. Safety helmets should be fitted with chin straps. Failure to wear such personal protective clothing can result in

(a) prosecution (*see* Chapter 4);
(b) job dismissal, including summary dismissal (*see* Chapter 5); and
(c) loss, either partial or total, of compensation for injury (*see* Chapter 2).

Work below ground level

This covers activities such as tunnelling, excavating and the digging of shafts, all of which have been responsible for many deaths. Often it involves working in confined spaces, which may require the operation of permit to work systems (*see* Chapter 13). The following precautions are necessary in any type of work below ground, irrespective of the depth of the excavation.

(a) Except where an excavation is less than 1.21 metres deep, or where the slopes of the sides make it impossible for slides to occur, supports – e.g. poling boards, walings, struts, sheet piling – whether constructed in timber or other materials, must be available and in position as from the start of work. Supports must be of sound construction and inspected daily by a competent person (C(GP)R 9).
(b) Construction of the support system and any work involving alterations to, additions to or dismantling of the system, must be carried out under the supervision of a competent person (C(GP)R 10).
(c) In the event of flooding, there must be adequate means of egress from the excavation to a position of safety (C(GP)R 11).

(d) Excavation work must not affect the security or stability of a structure (C(GP)R 12).
(e) Excavations more than 2 metres deep must be adequately fenced by barriers to prevent people falling into them (C(GP)R 13). (Common sense also suggests that barriers should be provided for lesser depths.)
(f) Excavations and approaches to them should be well lighted (C(GP)R 47).
(g) No materials (or excavated ground), plant or equipment should be located near the edge of an excavation owing to the risk of the sides collapsing (C(GP)R 14).
(h) Cables and underground services should be located before any form of excavation is undertaken. Careful consultation with the supply authorities, use of cable detection equipment and hand digging of trial holes may well be necessary.
(i) The possiblity of ingress of toxic or asphyxiant gas must be considered. Many fatalities have occurred, for example, as a result of carbon dioxide accumulation in pits, chambers, ducts, etc. This gas arises from chalk or limestone in the ground reacting with acidic rain. Where gas ingress is suspected, the air purity must be tested by a competent person before entry of workers is permitted (C(GP)R 21), and a permit to work system should be operated.

Demolition

Demolition is one of the most dangerous activities undertaken in the construction industry. Yet there will always be a need for it as buildings deteroriate with age to the point of instability and where existing buildings must be replaced in the cause of redevelopment. For maximum safety, the following features of demolition work need consideration.

Predemolition survey

Prior to demolition taking place, a safe system of work must be established. The system will be determined by a predemolition survey – including perusal of the original building plans, if they are still in existence – undertaken by a competent person. The use of a demolition hazard check list is recommended (*see* Fig. 36.3). This survey should identify

(a) the nature and method of construction of the building;
(b) the arrangement of buildings adjacent to that for demolition and the condition of this adjoining property;

SERVICES	Gas	Electricity	Water
	Telephone	Sewers	Others
GLASS	Doors/windows	Partitions	Sky lights
ROOF	Fragile	Weak	
BASEMENT	Sumps/wells	Extensions under pavements/ other buildings	
STRUCTURAL TIMBER	Decayed	Damaged	
ADJACENT BUILDINGS	Bracing or shoring required	Weather-proofing required	
OVERHEAD HAZARDS	Materials	Cables	
INDUSTRIAL PLANT	Carboniferous dust deposits	Gas tests required	
AFTER-EFFECTS OF FIRE, FLOODING, BLASTING	Bracing or shoring required		

Fig. 36.3 Demolition hazard check list

(c) the location of underground services, e.g. water mains, electricity cables, gas pipes, drains, sewers, telephone cables, etc.;
(d) the previous use of premises, e.g. for the storage of flammable substances;
(e) the presence of dangerous substances, e.g. asbestos lagging;
(f) the method of bonding of the main load-bearing walls;
(g) the system of shoring or other supports necessary during demolition;
(h) the presence of cantilevered structures, their form of construction and the nature of the danger;

(i) the presence of basements, cellars, vaults or other spaces affecting the structure of adjoining properties;
(j) the potentially dangerous effects of removing superstructure stabilising loads from an old basement or vault retaining walls;
(k) the presence of storage tanks below and above ground, and the nature of their contents; and
(l) the actual sequence of operations, which should generally take place in the reverse order of building erection.

Demolition work should be undertaken in accordance with the BS Code of Practice for Demolition (CP 94:1971) by registered demolition contractors listed in the *Demolition and Dismantling Industry Register*.

Action prior to demolition

Prior to actual demolition, a number of actions must be taken. Form 10 (Notice of Commencement of Building Operations or Works of Engineering Construction) must be submitted to the local offices of the HSE. Local authorities, statutory undertakings (Gas Board, Water Authority, etc.) and the owners of adjoining property must be notified and consulted. Services, such as water, gas and electricity, must be isolated. A competent supervisor, with experience of this type of work, must be appointed to take charge of the operation, and all persons employed on the site adequately briefed. All dangerous areas, particularly those affecting members of the public, should be fenced off or barricaded and appropriate warning notices displayed.

NOTE. The effect of such notices, in so far as they might attempt to 'contract out' of liability in the event of death and/or personal injury, either to employees or to an indirect labour force on site, or even to members of the public, is severely inhibited by the Unfair Contract Terms Act 1977, sec 2(1). This Act makes it illegal to contract out of negligence, whether by means of a notice or otherwise.

'Fans' or catching platforms should be installed not more than 6 metres below the working level, when there is a risk to the public. Personal protection equipment, including safety helmets with chin straps, goggles, heavy duty gloves and safety boots with steel insoles, must be provided and worn during the total period when demolition is in progress. Respiratory protection, together with the use of safety belts or harnesses, may also be necessary.

Action during demolition

Where possible, demolition should be carried out in the reverse order of building erection. No isolated freestanding wall should be left unless judged to be secure by the competent person in charge. Scaffold working platforms should be used, all refuse and debris being removed from these temporary structures on a regular basis to avoid overloading. Debris which has accumulated behind walls should also be removed. Independently supported working platforms over any reinforced concrete slabs should be demolished. Support for members of framed structures must be provided before gutting, along with temporary props, bracing or guys to restrain remaining parts of the building. On no account must operators work from the floor being demolished, and site control must ensure that all personnel are kept at a safe distance from the scene of operations when pulling arrangements, demolition balls, pusher arms and/or explosives are being used.

Above all, an on-going system of inspection must be maintained during demolition to detect further hazards which may result from the demolition process, e.g. loosened materials, overloaded floors.

Regulating the work of the contractor

From the viewpoint of legal liability and practical safety, the relationships between the occupier of the premises and the main contractor, subcontractors, etc., are of key importance. In the case of legal liability, building owner(s), main contractor(s) and subcontractors, nominated or domestic, may often be said to be in joint occupation or control. (The main contractor has the greater liability under the Construction Regulations as he has the greatest control.) This has practical consequences in relation to the Health and Safety at Work etc., Act 1974, sec 4, as far as criminal liability is concerned. In the case of civil liability, all three parties can be construed as being in occupation for the purposes of the Occupiers' Liability Act 1957, and can be proceeded against accordingly including, if necessary, any architect, civil engineer or geotechnical consultant who has been negligent.

The legal position notwithstanding, organisations should endeavour to operate some form of practical regulation of contractors on their premises. Contracting operations can cover a wide range of situations, from activities such as window cleaning or maintenance of plant and equipment, to large-scale construction works, such as extensions to premises or the building of new premises on a 'green field' site. Consultation with the contractors prior to the commencement of the work and/or the contract being signed, and during the course of the work, is of the utmost significance if a safe site is to be maintained. The various facets of this relationship between the contractor and the occupier of the premises are as follows.

Consultation prior to commencement of contract work

Before any contract work is commenced, a responsible person representing the main contractor must discuss with the occupier the safety precautions necessary as far as his own workforce is concerned and any other parties on site. This requirement is graphically underlined by the decision in *R* v. *Swan Hunter Shipbuilders Ltd* (reported in *The Times*, July 1981) where the main contractor and the subcontractor, Telemeter Installations Ltd, were fined £3,000 and £1,000 respectively for failing to inform incoming subcontract labour of the dangers produced by oxygen-enriched atmospheres in confined spaces. As a result eight workmen were burnt to death whilst working below decks on HMS *Glasgow*. Hence, except on clearly defined 'green field' sites, where the main contractor has full contractual responsibility for safety, both occupier and contractor should ensure that

(a) the site of operations is clearly defined, if necessary on a factory plan, including those areas which contractors' staff are not permitted to enter (for the purposes of the Factories Act 1961, sec 175(6), there will be two separate factories here);
(b) agreement is reached as to whether any amenties are to be made available by the occupier for the contractors' employees, e.g. catering, washing, sanitation, first aid and clothing storage;
(c) where applicable, the contractor has full information concerning the occupier's processes or activities which may affect or involve contract work, e.g. parking limitations, specific hazards, hygiene requirements; and
(d) the contractor has, or will shortly obtain, adequate insurance cover to indemnify the occupier in respect of any negligence resulting in personal injury and/or death, or damage to property and plant, arising out of or in connection with contract work.

Use of owner's equipment

Contractors should generally be expected to provide all their own tools, plant, equipment and materials necessary for the satisfactory performance of work. On no account should use be made of the owner's electricity, gas or air mains without appropriate authority. Where such permission is granted, the method of connection should be approved by the appropriate manager.

Reporting, recording and investigation of accidents and dangerous occurrences

The contractor should be aware of the requirements of the Reporting of Injuries, Diseases and Dangerous Occurrences Regulations 1985, and of details of any internal system for the reporting, recording and investigation of accidents. Except on 'green field' sites, all accidents, including traffic accidents, and all dangerous occurrences involving contractors should be reported to the occupier.

Permit to work systems and other procedures

The contractor should be informed by the occupier of the need to follow the latter's safe systems of work, including permit to work and other systems, particularly where contract work may involve the occupier's staff and/or other subcontractors, or where failure to do so might endanger the plant, etc., involved.

Plant and machinery

Only in specifically controlled circumstances should a contractor remove the guard, fencing or other safety equipment from machinery and plant, and any guards or safety devices should be reinstated and operational before the machinery or plant is handed back for use. Plant and machinery belonging to the contractor should be adequately guarded before being operated on the premises. Electrically operated hand tools should be of the low-voltage type and connected to a 110 volt mains-isolated circuit where applicable. Alternatively, contractors should provide their own step-down transformer (250/110 volts, 50 cycles) with the mid-point of the secondary winding efficiently earthed. In all cases, the metalwork on portable equipment and any flexible metallic covering of conductors should be efficiently earthed and in all other respects constructed and maintained in compliance with the Factories (Electrical Energy) Regulations 1908 and the Electricity (Factories Act) Special Regulations 1944. Cables supplying portable apparatus should be of the correct size and properly connected to standard plugs and sockets. Makeshift and/or unsafe connections are dangerous and must not be permitted. In the case of a.c. welding equipment, contractors should limit d.c. to 40 volts, and ensure the correct use of earth leads at all times, including the earthing down wherever possible of the article being welded.

Noise

Where noisy equipment is used in close proximity to a working area on site, operatives should be provided with a recognised form of hearing protection (e.g. ear muffs), use of which must be encouraged. Moreover, noise from equipment should be minimised in working areas, e.g. by the use of bag mufflers on pneumatic drills. Contractors should also take all reasonable steps to prevent the inhabitants of the neighbourhood being troubled by noise.

Fire protection

Every year fires of varying degrees of severity cause loss of life and devastation on building sites. The Fire Triangle in Chapter 32 shows the three requisites for fire to take place, i.e. an ignition source, fuel and oxygen. Ignition sources are many and varied – welding and cutting activities, people smoking whilst working on site or in site offices, cooking on open flames in site huts, the use of blow lamps and gas or liquid fuel fired heating applicances. The fuel, again, can take numerous forms – timber, bitumen impregnated paper, plastics, flammable substances such as paraffin, and combustible refuse produced during the erection of buildings and other site work. Oxygen, which is naturally present in air, will, on a windy day, cause fire to spread at a rapid rate. The need, therefore, for effective fire protection procedures on construction sites cannot be overemphasised.

Fire protection procedures will vary to some extent according to the type of site. For example, they will be different on a 'green field' site, where no construction work has previously taken place, from those on an existing site, where modification or extension to existing buildings may be taking place.

'Green field' sites

Planning of fire protection procedures should take place well before site work commences. Here consideration should be given to the following:

(a) provision of access for fire brigade appliances;
(b) location of buildings and the separation of high-risk buildings from low-risk buildings;
(c) the provision of adequate space between buildings;
(d) the construction of buildings, e.g. site huts, canteens, offices, flammable stores, equipment stores, etc.;
(e) the establishment of areas where smoking and the use of naked lights are forbidden;
(f) the system for the storage and disposal of combustible and flammable refuse;
(g) the provision of a separate flammable materials store;
(h) the availability of a water supply for fire brigade appliances and on-site fire fighting;
(i) the provision of adequate fire-fighting appliances, located according to the fire risk involved, and an effective fire alarm system;
(j) evacuation procedures in the event of fire, including the training of site operators in such procedures;
(k) the appointment of fire wardens and the use of fire patrols, particularly at night and weekends; and

(l) the system for liaison with the local fire authority, including frequent inspections by the fire protection officer, not only to ensure compliance with the terms of the fire certificate but to see that any new risks which may have arisen are quickly and effectively controlled.

Existing sites

All the contractor's employees should understand the fire warning systems currently in operation throughout the premises. Instructions on action to be taken in the event of fire should be made available to the contractor and workforce by being clearly displayed on site. Fire-fighting equipment installed by the occupier should also be made known to contractors; alternatively, fire-fighting equipment should be provided by the contractors at the consultation stage. Where any work involves interference with or removal of fire-fighting appliances, alarms or systems, prior notification should be given to the contractor. Moreover, use of petroleum, petroleum mixtures, liquefied petroleum gas, celluloses and other highly flammable and/or explosive substances should comply with the requirements of the Petroleum Consolidation Acts and the Highly Flammable Liquids and Liquefied Petroleum Gases Regulations, 1972. Where any form of protection material or covering is used, whether against dust or climatic conditions, it should be fire resistant or treated with fire-resistant solution.

Further guidance on fire precautions and procedures is given in Chapter 32.

Welding operations on site

Operations involving the use of oxy-acetylene welding and cutting equipment, electric arc welding, blow lamps or other flame-producing equipment should not be commenced until authority to do so (written or verbal) has been received from the occupier. In certain cases this may require issue of a permit to work (hot work permit). Gas cylinders, particularly acetylene, should be stored in a manner required by the Highly Flammable Liquids and Liquefied Petroleum Gases Regulations 1972. The contractor should provide and ensure use of welding screens to give protection to all persons in respect of any arc flash caused by his workforce. Combustible material, such as paper, timber, rags, should be placed in suitable refuse containers. Non-combustible blankets, i.e. fibreglass, should be used to afford protection against 'welding batter'. Burning refuse on site should be prohibited.

Dangerous substances and wastes

Two aspects must be considered here:

(a) the legal requirements to protect the contractor's workforce and workers employed by any subcontractors on site from exposure to dangerous substances (HSWA, secs 2 and 3, and the Construction Regulations 1961–6); and

(b) requirements of environmental health legislation, covering air, water and ground pollution, and waste disposal procedures.

Dangerous substances on site

A wide range of toxic and other dangerous substances can be encountered on construction sites. These include asbestos, lead and flammable substances. Site management must be aware of the hazards associated with such substances, ensuring correct storage, use and disposal (*see* Chapter 38).

Prevention of pollution from construction sites

The relevant legislation is as follows:

Air: HSWA, sec 5
Alkali, etc., Works Regulation Act 1906
Public Health Acts 1936 and 1961
Public Health (Recurring Nuisances) Act 1969
Control of Pollution Act 1974

Water: Rivers (Prevention of Pollution) Acts 1951–61
Public Health (Drainage of Trade Premises) Act 1937
Public Health Acts 1936 and 1961
Water Resources Act 1974

Waste disposal: Public Health Act 1936
Control of Pollution Act 1974
Refuse Disposal (Amenity) Act 1978

These Acts, enforced by the HSE and/or local authority environmental health departments, can carry heavy penalties for breach. Moreover, after development, failure to 'secure' a site from contamination can give rise to actions in negligence and/or nuisance for up to 6 years after the injury and/or damage has been discovered by a property owner/occupier, and not from the time when the act of negligence or nuisance took place. This makes liability limitation periods long, e.g. 20 years or more. (Environmental health legislation is beyond the scope of this book. Nevertheless, its importance in relation to the reclamation of derelict land should not be overlooked.)

Reclamation of derelict land

Following the introduction of the Derelict Land Act 1982, coupled with the Local Government, Planning and Land Act 1980, much derelict land is being reclaimed. Former industrial sites, mines and gasworks are being converted into trading estates and housing estates. Land reclamation by developers can be hazardous, often involving land highly contaminated with toxic materials. Contractors engaged on this work should comply with the legislation listed above.

The following two examples illustrate the practical problems that can arise in the reclamation of derelict land.

Former gas works sites: These present a wide range of contaminants, including phenolic oils, heavy metals (lead and arsenic) and cyanides. There are dangers to workers in excavating trenches or removing contaminated soils. Risks include contact with corrosive and toxic liquids, resulting in skin absorption of, for example, phenol into the body, gassing hazards from pockets of cyanides or sulphides which may be unearthed, and dry dust hazards from many other deposits such as asbestos.

It is necessary to evaluate all these hazards by systematic and careful sampling and analysis, using toxicological and other data, to enable workers to receive adequate protection. Moreover, disposal of such wastes presents serious problems and there are strict requirements for transportation and tipping to landfill.

Domestic refuse landfill: These sites present construction problems in terms of foundation performance and, because of land subsidence, any structures should be carefully designed. They can also produce a flammable gas mixture containing about 65 per cent methane, which accumulates in voids and trenches, resulting in a significant fire hazard.

There is little chemical toxicity on a well-managed domestic refuse tip. The gases evolved, however, may well be offensive and create a statutory nuisance within the meaning of the Public Health Acts. Environmental health departments have power to issue abatement notices, and failure to comply with an abatement notice can result in prosecution.

Personal protective equipment

Personal protective equipment should be provided wherever hazards to the contractor's workforce exist. This includes safety helmets, eye protection, respirators and safety boots. Contractors should also be familiar with the National Working Rule, agreed by the National Joint Council of the Building Industry and Civil Engineering Construction Conciliation Board in 1981, which requires operatives to wear safety helmets at all times 'when in the vicinity of construction operations' except 'where the foreseeable risk of head injury is negligible'. (This 'requirement' underlines the force of the legal maxim 'volenti non fit injuria', i.e. to one who is willing no harm is done. *See* Chapter 2.)

Contractors' vehicles

The movement of vehicles within premises on which construction work is taking place should be consistent with safety and any speed limit specified on notices displayed there should not be exceeded. Drivers should comply with any traffic direction systems and signs in use on site. Vehicles used by contractors or their employees should be parked only in locations specified for that purpose. All vehicles on premises should be prohibited from moving during times when access roads are crowded with people arriving at or returning home from work, as the risk of accidents is greater at these times. This prohibition extends to cranes, mobile cranes, dumpers, concrete supply vehicles and vehicles. All mechanically propelled vehicles and trailers used on sites must be in efficient working order and in good repair, and must not be used in an improper manner (C(GP)R 34).

Site clearance

On completion of work, contractors should be required to remove all unused materials and leave the site clean and tidy. This may include reinstatement of the perimeter fencing, removal of mud and debris from roads, removal of waste building materials and site refuse, and the levelling of disturbed ground. On no account should items such as empty gas cylinders, oil drums or paint cans be buried. Excavations and trenches should be filled in and levelled.

Window cleaning and external painting

Cleaning the outer surfaces of high-rise office blocks and industrial premises, as well as the external painting of such buildings, has spotlighted many hazards.

Window cleaning

There is a general legal requirement to keep windows and skylights, used for the natural lighting of workrooms and offices, clean (FA, sec 5(4), and OSRPA, sec 8(3)). Much of this work is now undertaken by window-cleaning contractors.

Painting

Painting, or repainting, of the interior of factory premises is, subject to certain exempted parts, compulsory every 7 years (Factories (Cleanliness of Walls and Ceilings) Order, 1960, cl 4).

In order to ensure safe working when cleaning windows or painting, the following should be considered.

(a) The contractor should ensure that any ladder, safety harness or other appliance used, or intended for use, by his employee, be of sound construction, adequate strength, sufficient length and properly maintained.
(b) Where it is not practicable to clean windows or paint external surfaces from a ladder, and the contractor's employee has to work at a height of more than 1.98 metres, or otherwise in conditions where any specific danger or risk might be involved, the contractor, or his authorised representative – e.g. manager, supervisor – should inspect the place before work is commenced. The contractor should take all precautions to prevent an accident and instruct his employees in the precautions to be taken. (Failure to do so on the part of an employer/contractor can result in prosecution for breach of HSWA, sec 2(2)). Moreover, in the event of an employee being injured as a result of lack of instruction, a costly action for damages at common law may well follow. *See* Chapters 2 and 3.
(c) The contractor should satisfy himself that any structural handhold and/or foothold likely to be used by his employees is secure. Where the reliability of any handhold or foothold is in doubt, he should warn his employees and instruct them that it is not to be used. Failure to do so would result in breach of HSWA, sec 2 (*see* Chapter 3), and the common law duty to take reasonable care owed by all employers to their employees (*see* Chapter 2).

Further information is given in HSE Guidance Note GS10 'Roof Work – Prevention of Falls'.

37

Mechanical handling

A host of equipment is available to ease the task of handling goods and, whenever possible, mechanical handling systems should be used in preference to manual handling. This chapter examines four principal forms of mechanical handling, namely conveyorised systems, elevators, internal factory transport and the use of goods vehicles. The choice of mechanical handling system will depend on several criteria such as the weight, shape, size, form, distance and frequency of movement of loads, together with space restrictions, storage systems and the nature of the material to be handled.

Conveyors

The following are the most commonly used conveyors:

Belt conveyors

These may be flat or troughed and are commonly used for transporting materials over long distances. The flat type is largely used to convey bulky packages or boxed goods, whilst the trough type is employed to carry loose materials, such as coal and aggregates. These materials are prevented from falling over the sides of the belt because it forms a cross-sectional 'trough' which prevents side spillage unless the belt has been overloaded.

Roller conveyors

Roller conveyors, which can be of the gravity type or the powered type, are used for the movement of unit loads. The powered type is used where level or slightly rising runs are installed, where manual pushing of loads is impracticable, or where the incline necessary for gravity movement is not possible.

Chain conveyors

These are often of the 'scraper' type, used for pushing or pulling materials along a fixed trough. Overhead chain types employ 'hangers' attached to the chain from which are suspended the objects requiring transfer. 'Trolley' types comprise specially designed trolleys mounted on a guide system, and are used, for instance, for the transfer of vehicle bodies during vehicle assembly.

Screw conveyors

This type of conveyor is used mainly for the transfer of loose or free-flowing solid materials, generally over short distances, e.g. solid fuel from bunker to boiler furnace or grain from storage silo to processing plant.

Slat conveyors

These conveyors comprise a series of spaced wooden or metal slats moving on side chains. They are commonly used for the transfer of boxed or sacked goods, and can operate on inclined levels for the transfer of goods between floors.

Hazards associated with conveyors

Whilst the more general aspects of conveyor safety are dealt with in Chapter 31, the main hazards associated with conveyors of different types are:

(a) traps or 'nips' between moving parts of a conveyor, e.g. between a conveyor chain and chain wheels, or between a moving belt and rollers, particularly drive and 'end' rollers and also belt tensioning rollers;
(b) traps between moving and fixed parts of a conveyor, e.g. between the screw of a screw conveyor and the edge of the feed opening in the transfer tube;
(c) hazards associated with sharp edges, e.g. on worn conveyor chains and belts, which may be exposed;
(d) traps and nips created by the drive mechanism, e.g. V-belts and pulleys, chains and sprockets; and
(e) traps created at transfer points between two conveyors, e.g. between a belt conveyor and roller conveyor.

Specific aspects of conveyor guarding

Whilst all conveyors present similar trapping and contact hazards, the various forms of conveyor need guarding in different ways. The hazards and guarding requirements are outlined below.

Belt conveyors

Traps formed between belt and rollers: Traps formed between the belt and drive, driven and tension rollers (*see* Fig. 37.1) should be covered with fixed guards extending to 850 mm from the trapping point. Side guards should be provided along the whole length of the conveyor and extend to 25 mm below the return belt. Where there is pedestrian access, and the underside of the belt is carried by return roller, this section of the conveyor should be enclosed.

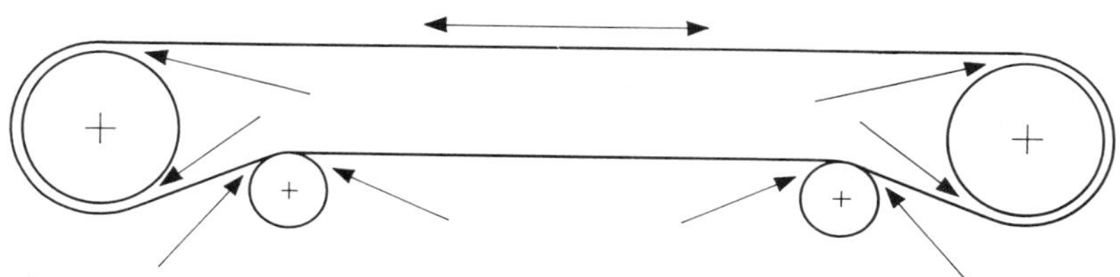

Fig. 37.1 A reversible conveyor showing trapping points

Traps between belts and end plates: In addition to providing guards as outlined above, a horizontal guard plate should be fitted (*see* Fig. 37.2). Clearance between plate and belt should not exceed 4 mm.

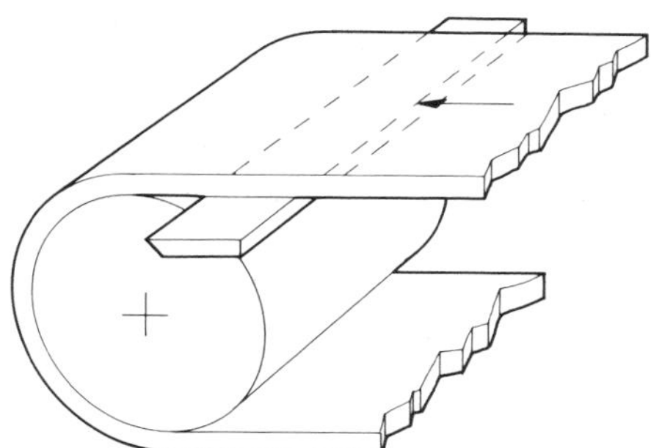

Fig. 37.2 Guarding of conveyor end using a horizontal guard plate

Traps at belt conveyor transfer points: Where static transfer plates (dead plates) are fitted at the junction of two belt conveyors, the gap between the top surface and the belt should not exceed 4 mm (*see* Fig. 37.3).

Traps between items conveyed and fixed structures: The risk associated with traps formed between a heavy item conveyed, e.g. a heavy crate, and fixed structures should be minimised by ensuring that there

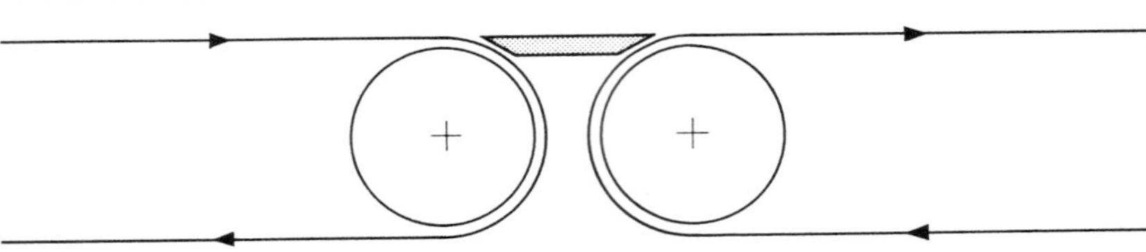

Fig. 37.3 Use of a dead plate where two conveyors meet

is a clearance of at least 50 mm between the item and any fixed structure. Support members should be free from sharp edges.

Hazards from worn and defective belts: Worn and defective belts and belt joints can create a hazard. Belts should be examined regularly and belt joints should be designed to be as smooth as possible. Worn belts or belts with loose fasteners should be replaced.

Roller conveyors

Traps between rollers and fixed structures across the conveyor: The gap between the rollers and fixed structures should be either 4 mm or less, or greater than 50 mm, to minimise trapping.

Hazards from rotating ends of exposed roller shafts: Rotating ends of roller shafts should be contained within the supporting frame for the rollers or flush with the bearing housing. They may, however, be exposed without guards outside the bearing housing up to a distance of 25 mm, providing they are smooth. If they extend more than 25 mm beyond the bearing housing, or if they have protrusions or irregularities, they should be fitted with fixed caps which completely enclose them.

Hazards from missing or jammed rollers: Missing, worn or jammed rollers may cause instability of the conveyed load and increased risk of trapping. These rollers should be replaced.

Hazards at transfer points: Where a roller conveyor is fed from another conveyor and the gap between the conveying surface is less than 50 mm, the first roller should not be power-driven, but so arranged that it would be displaced from its position should a hand be trapped between conveyors (*see* Fig. 37.4). Such a roller is termed a jump-out roller.

Chain conveyors

Traps between the conveyor chain and chain wheels: Fixed side and end guards (*see* Fig. 37.5) should be fitted at both the powered and free

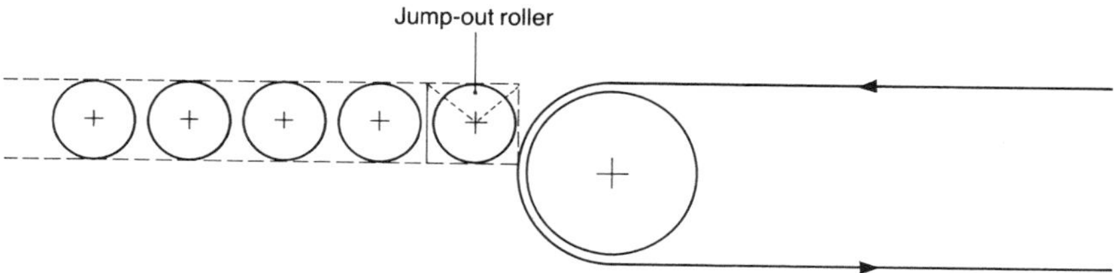

Fig. 37.4 Junction of a roller conveyor and belt conveyor showing position of jump-out roller

chain wheel ends of the conveyor, except where the conveyor is fitted in to the floor. Clearance between the lower edge of the guards and the floor, so as to facilitate cleaning, is allowable up to 180 mm, provided that the return chains are carried in guides and the guard extends to not less than 50 mm below the guide. On the top run of the conveyor, fixed in-fill plates should be fitted in the gaps between the chain guides and the side and end guards or the adjacent floor. All guards should be extended to 850 mm from the trapping points or otherwise prevent access. Clearance between guard and conveyor chain, where it runs over the chain wheel, should be 6 mm or less. Where a chain passes through a guard, clearance should not be less than 50 mm.

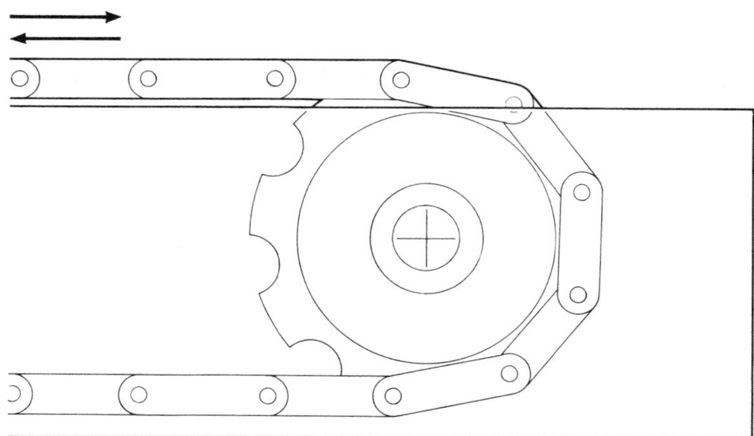

Fig. 37.5 Guarding at the end of a chain conveyor by enclosure of the sprocket wheels and nip points

Traps at overlapping sections between chains and chain wheels: At overlapping sections, side guards or in-fill plates should be fitted. Alternatively, only side guards need to be fitted, provided that the reach distance to the trapping points over the side of the guards corresponds with Table 2 of Appendix A of BS 5667:1980 Part 19 'Specification for Continuous Mechanical Handling Equipment – Safety Requirements: Belt Conveyors – Examples for Guarding of Nip Points'.

Traps between return chains and guide shoes, guide wheels and adjacent supporting structures: The return and carrying chain, where practicable, should be carried in continuous guides. Where this is not practicable and short guides, guide wheels or guide shoes are used, the chain should be free to lift 100 mm above the guide so as to reduce the risk of trapping. Guide wheels which have spoken or similar apertures should be fitted with discs to prevent hand and finger access.

Traps between carrying and return chains: Where carrying and return links of a chain run close together in guides, the return links should be positioned below guide level so as to reduce risk of trapping.

Hazards on bends caused by the chain slipping from its guide: The tendency for a chain to slip out of its guide on a bend can be reduced by

(a) inclining the guide away from the centre of the bend,
(b) use of wedge-shaped strips and plastic wearing strips so as to deflect the chain downwards in the guides, and
(c) fitting of specially coated metal blocks in place of guides.

On the return chain, a plate can be fitted on top of the guide to prevent the chain from slipping out.

Screw conveyors

Traps between the rotating auger (screw) and the fixed parts: A fixed or interlocked guard should be fitted to prevent access to the screw. Where mesh or bar guards are fitted to allow free passage of materials, there must be sufficient distance between the guard members and the screw flight to prevent contact with the screw.

Slat conveyors

Traps between the conveyor chain and chain wheels: Fixed side guards should be fitted below conveyor track level along the whole length of the conveyor. The clearance between the guard and the chain should be 4 mm or less, and the guards should extend below the return chain so that the distance between the chain and the bottom of the guard is not less than 25 mm. Guards to enclose the chain underneath are not generally necessary, except where there is pedestrian access beneath the conveyor.

Traps between conveyor chain wheels and fixed structure: Safeguarding should be provided as above.

Traps between conveyor chain and end plates, dead plates, rails and fixed structures: Safeguarding should be provided as above. In addition, fixed guards should be fitted at the driven end of the conveyor where the chain passes close to the end plate. The clearance between the guard or a dead plate and the conveyor chain should be 4 mm or less.

Traps between the slats of biplanar chain conveyors where the slats open and close on bends and are inadequately supported: Biplanar chains should, at bends where the slats open and close, be supported underneath by solid fixed plates extending to the edge of the slats, and guarded by protective hoods, as shown in Fig. 37.6, over the return point to a distance of not less than 850 mm.

Traps between rotating corner plates and fixed structures or conveyor chains: Fixed nip guards should be provided at circular corner plates where the plate is in-running with the conveyor chains or runs up to a fixed structure.

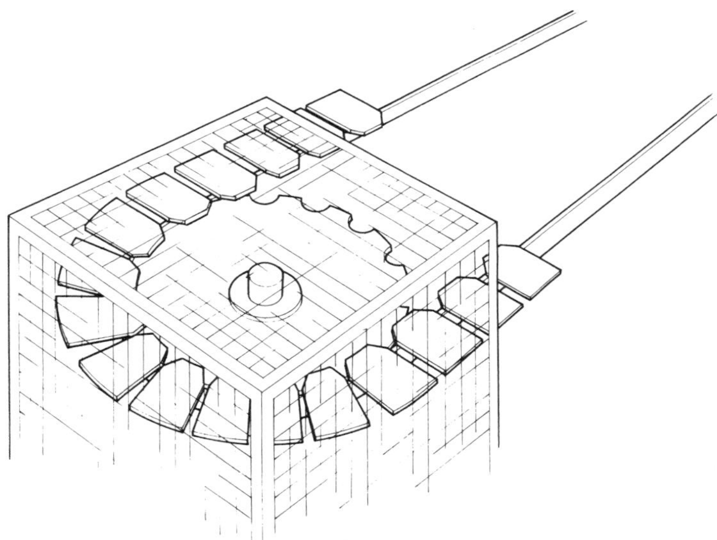

Fig. 37.6 Protective hood over the return point of a conveyor
Source: BS 5667 Pt 18 (1979)

Hazards from corner plates with exposed sharp edges: Before the edge of the corner plate becomes sufficiently sharp, it should be replaced or protected by a guard around the entire periphery.

Hazards from conveyor chain with exposed sharp edges: Before chain edges become sufficiently sharp, they should be replaced.

General aspects of conveyor guarding

Types of guard

Fixed guards: Fixed guards should be used wherever practicable and must be securely fixed in position when the conveyor is in motion or likely to be put in motion. It should not be possible to open or remove these guards without the aid of a specific tool. Moreover, the fastener should be captive to the guard. Fixed guards may be an integral part of the conveyor or freestanding from the floor and securely fixed to the floor of the conveyor structure. Guards should not allow space for a person to be trapped between the guard and the conveyor.

Interlocked guards: An interlocked guard should be so connected to the machine controls that

(a) until the guard is closed the machine cannot operate; and
(b) either the guard remains locked closed until the dangerous movement has ceased or, where overrun is insufficient to create danger, opening the guard disengages the drive. The interlocking system should be fail-safe.

Interlocked guards should be provided for dangerous parts of a machine where the operator needs frequent access. ('A part of machinery is dangerous if it is a possible cause of injury to anybody acting in a way in which a human being may be reasonably expected to act in circumstances which may reasonably be expected to occur' – per du Parcq J in *Walker* v. *Bletchley Flettons Ltd* [1937] 1 AER 170.)

Tunnel guards: A tunnel guard is a form of distance guard preventing access to a danger point by reason of the relationship of the guard opening dimensions to length of tunnel. Where tunnel guards are used, the guards should be so designed and fitted that the relationship between the opening and the distance from the opening to the danger point complies with BS 5304:1975 'Safeguarding of Machinery', cl. 10, Fig. 5, 'Openings in Fixed Guards'. (*See* Chapter 31.) Clearance between the sides of the opening to the tunnel guard and the items being conveyed should be not less than 50 mm.

Other safety aspects

(a) Where practicable, arrangements should be made for lubrication with the guards in position, e.g. through suitably located small openings which do not allow access to danger points.
(b) To minimise the risk of conveyed items jamming or falling from conveyors, the radius of all bends should be maximised at the design stage.
(c) All fixed support members, including guide rails, should be free from sharp edges.
(d) Where conveyors rise to more than 1 metre above floor or walkway level, suitable rails or side members should be provided to a sufficient height above the conveyor to contain the top item of the load being conveyed.

Emergency devices

(a) Where a conveyor is greater than 20 metres in length, an emergency stop (trip) wire should be provided. (The alternative is a series of emergency stop buttons.)
(b) Emergency stop buttons, which must be easily identifiable and designated as such, should be provided. An emergency stop button, however, is not a substitute for effective guarding. It is a device for cutting off the power in order to stop the conveyor. The position and number of stop buttons should be determined by the following criteria:
    (i) plant layout and product flow associated with the unit as a whole;
    (ii) the operator positions about the plant; no point on the conveyor should be more than 10 metres from an emergency stop button; and
    (iii) at any point on a conveyor where an emergency stop button is not visible, e.g. where a conveyor passes through a wall, a further stop button should be provided.

    Emergency stop buttons should be palm- or mushroom-shaped and coloured red. They should remain in the 'off' position until reset. Releasing the emergency stop button should not cause equipment to restart.

Elevators

Most elevators operate in a fixed position. In certain industries, however, mobile elevators, which can be moved from one point to another, are used for loading and unloading tasks.

Fixed elevators

Fixed elevators may be of the vertical or the adjustable angle type. Vertical elevators may take the form of

(a) bucket elevators for transferring loose materials, such as grain; or
(b) bar elevators, on which items are placed or hung, e.g. sacked or boxed goods.

The elevator may be enclosed in a fixed shaft or hoistway and is generally continuous in operation, often being linked with a horizontal conveyor prior to and/or after elevation. One of the greatest hazards with elevating loose materials is dust explosions, and in flour mills, for instance, all elevator heads must be fitted with explosion reliefs. To prevent the spread of fire between floors in mills using bucket elevators in particular, all hoistways and floor openings must be fire-proofed with fire-resistant materials giving a notional period of fire resistance of 30 minutes.

Adjustable angle elevators are commonly used for loading and unloading the holds of ships, particularly where loose materials such as grain, metal ores and coal are involved.

Both types of elevator normally run in either direction. A fixed guard should be installed at the base of the elevator to prevent direct access to the moving flights and in-running nips formed between the chain and sprocket.

Mobile elevators

Mobile elevators are used for loading and unloading commodities such as sacked goods, regular shaped containers, and luggage into and out of aircraft. They may be of the bucket or bar type. A trap is created at the in-running nip between the elevator chains and sprockets, and both ends of the elevator should incorporate fixed guards. A further hazard is that such elevators can be run at variable speeds. Hand, arm and shoulder injuries have been sustained by operators because they have been unable to keep up with the speed of the elevator. Adequate supervision and control over the operation of these elevators is, therefore, crucial to the prevention of accidents.

Mobile handling equipment

A wide range of equipment is used in storage and handling operations. Although such equipment is necessary for speedy movement of goods, its use has frequently led to accidents. The basic requirements for the safe operation of mobile handling equipment, such as fork lift trucks, are careful selection and use of the right equipment in the right place by the right people. With any mechanical handling task, the selection of the appropriate equipment for the material to be handled is important. The type and layout of the storage system, type, weight and shape of the materials to be handled, construction and layout of buildings and operational areas, as well as the potential for accidents, must be considered. Before acquiring mechanical handling equipment, manufacturers and/or suppliers should be consulted to ensure that the equipment selected matches the performance requirements. Where new storage systems are being developed, the manufacturer and/or supplier should again be consulted.

Classification of mobile mechanical handling equipment

Pedestrian-operated stacking trucks

These are of two types, manually operated and power-operated stackers (*see* Fig. 37.7). A manually operated stacker is normally restricted in operation to moving post pallets or heavy machinery. It has a manual shift with hydraulically operated lift, and cannot pick up directly from the floor. It has a capacity of 0.25 to 0.5 tonne, with a maximum lift of approximately 1.5 metres.

Power-operated stackers can be pedestrian or rider controlled, with power operation vertically and horizontally. They can pick up pallets from the floor. This type of stacker has a capacity of 0.5 to 1 tonne and a maximum lift of approximately 3 metres.

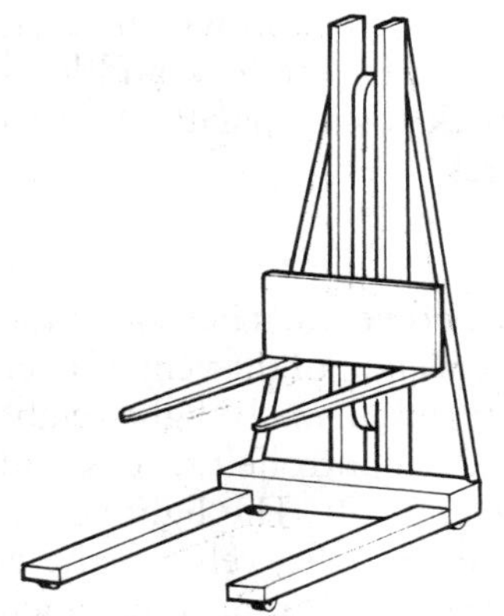

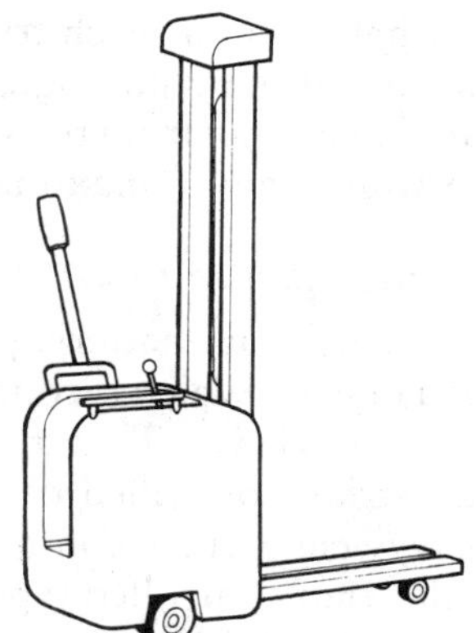

Fig. 37.7 Pedestrian-operated stacking trucks
Manually operated stacker
Power-operated stacker

Reach trucks

A reach truck is a fork lift truck that enables the load to be retracted within the wheel base, minimising overall working length and allowing reduced aisle widths. There are two separate forms, the moving mast reach truck and the pantograph reach truck (*see* Fig. 37.8). The former is rider-operated. Forward-mounted load wheels enable the fork carriage to move within the wheel base, so that forks can reach to pick up or deposit the load. The mast, forks and load move together. This truck has a capacity of 0.5 to 3 tonnes, with a maximum lift of 10 metres.

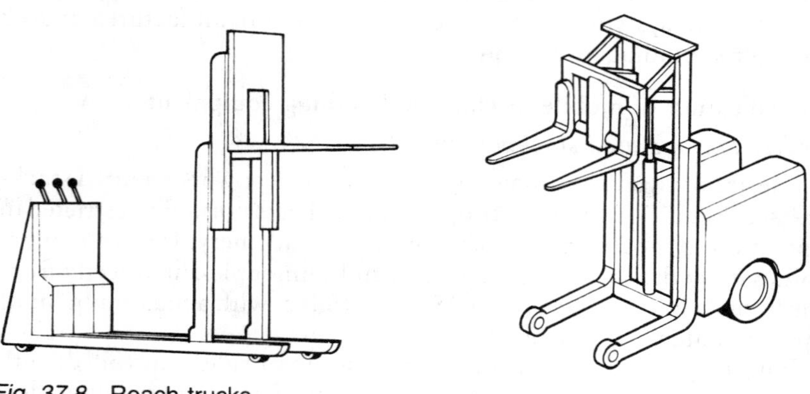

Fig. 37.8 Reach trucks
Moving mast reach truck
Pantograph reach truck

A pantograph reach truck is a rider-operated truck in which reach movement is by pantograph mechanism, whereby the fork and load can move away from the static mast. This truck has a capacity of 0.5 to 2.5 tonnes and a maximum lift of 10 metres.

Counterbalance fork trucks

Such trucks are battery, petrol, diesel or gas powered. They carry the load in front which is counterbalanced to the weight of the vehicle over the rear wheels. They take three specific forms, namely lightweight pedestrian controlled trucks, lightweight rider controlled trucks and heavyweight rider controlled trucks (*see* Fig. 37.9). The lightweight pedestrian controlled type is normally a three-wheeled vehicle, and is used mainly where stacking rather than transfer is important. Such trucks provide a greater load-carrying capacity than the pedestrian stacker. They have a capacity of 0.5 to 1 tonne and maximum lift of approximately 3 metres.

The lightweight rider controlled truck is similar to the pedestrian controlled truck, except that the operator sits inside the truck. The handling rate is higher. Such trucks have a capacity of 0.5 to 1.25 tonnes and a maximum lift of 6 metres.

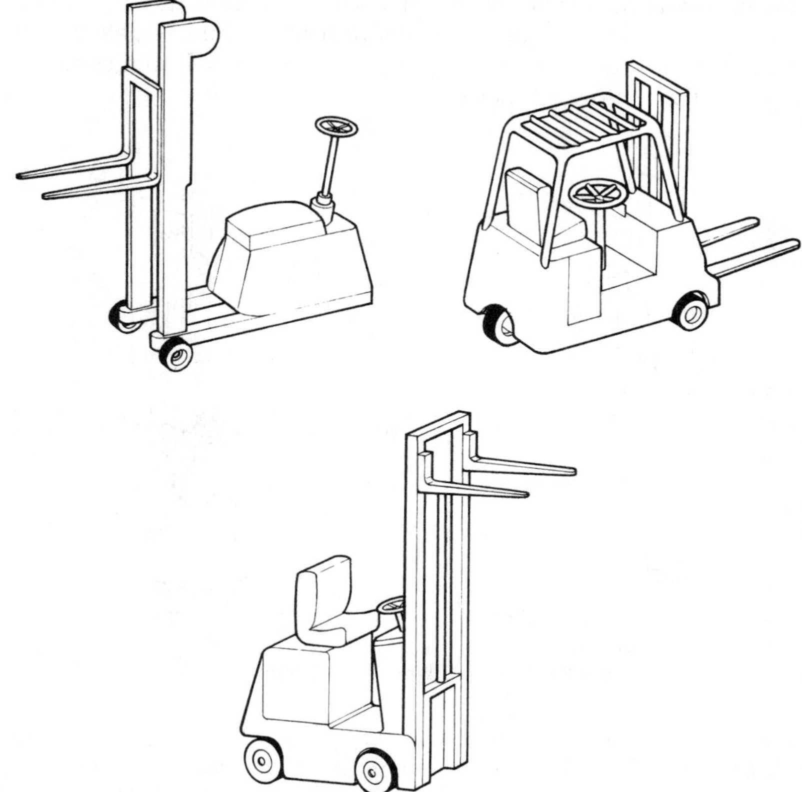

Fig. 37.9 Counterbalance fork trucks
Lightweight pedestrian controlled
Lightweight rider controlled
Heavyweight rider controlled

The heavyweight version is a four-wheeled truck, the high counterbalance weight over the rear wheels giving it a high load capacity. Many attachments, such as cradles, are available to suit different loads. They have a capacity from 1 to 9 tonnes and maximum lift from 6 to 12 metres.

Narrow aisle trucks

This type of truck differs from a reach truck in that the base of the truck does not turn within the working aisle to deposit or retrieve its load. This enables the aisle width to be kept to a minimum. This type of truck takes two forms, namely side loaders and counterbalance rotating load turret trucks (*see* Fig. 37.10). Side loaders are ideal for long runs down narrow aisles. They are, however, only capable of stacking down one side of the aisle at a time and a large turning circle is needed at each end of the aisle in order to serve both faces of a racking system. Reach trucks have a capacity of up to 1.5 tonnes and a maximum lift of 9 to 12 metres.

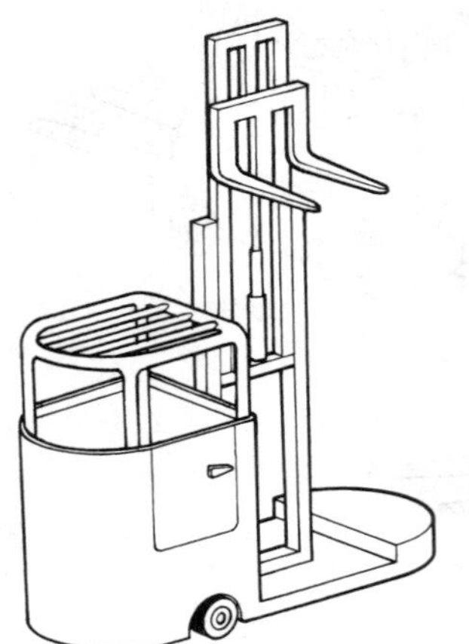

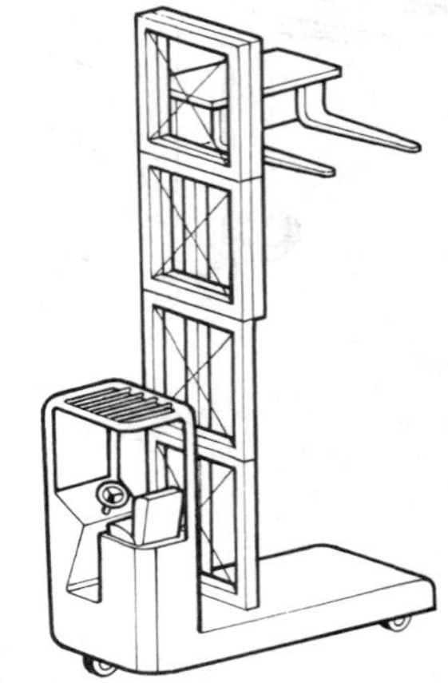

Fig. 37.10 Narrow aisle trucks
Side loader
Counterbalance rotating load turret truck

The counterbalance rotating load turret truck has a rigid mast with telescopic sections. It incorporates a head which rotates through 180°, enabling it to slide sideways to deposit or retrieve a load. This type of truck can serve both faces of a racking system, and is guided by tracks or rails at floor level. They have a capacity of 1 to 1.5 tonnes and a maximum lift of 12 metres.

Both types of narrow aisle truck are rider-operated.

Order pickers

This device is derived from the fork lift truck, incorporating a protected working platform permanently fixed to the lift forks. Thus the operator can pick goods from racking above floor level or place them in a racking system. The truck is operated from the picking platform and incorporates side shift, rotating mast and other purpose-added features. Order pickers allow maximum utilisation of racked storage areas owing to the narrowness of the aisles within which they can operate. Order pickers operate on a conventional basis or can be purpose designed for a specific task (*see* Fig. 37.11). Conventional order pickers operate on the same basis as a fork lift truck with a cage fitted for the operator. The cage incorporates a small platform for the placement of goods picked from the racking. They have a capacity of 0.5 to 1 tonne with a maximum lift of 6 to 9 metres.

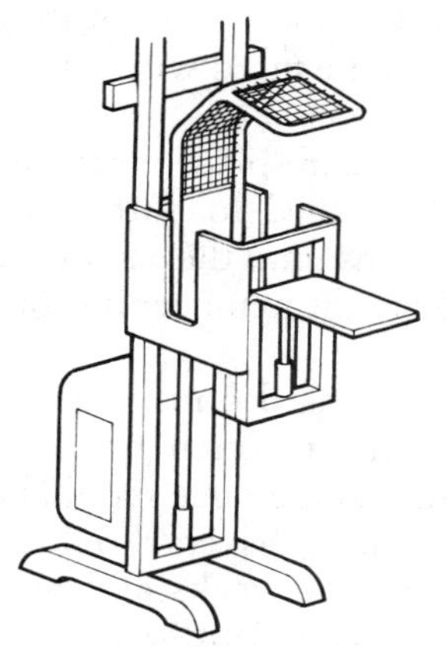

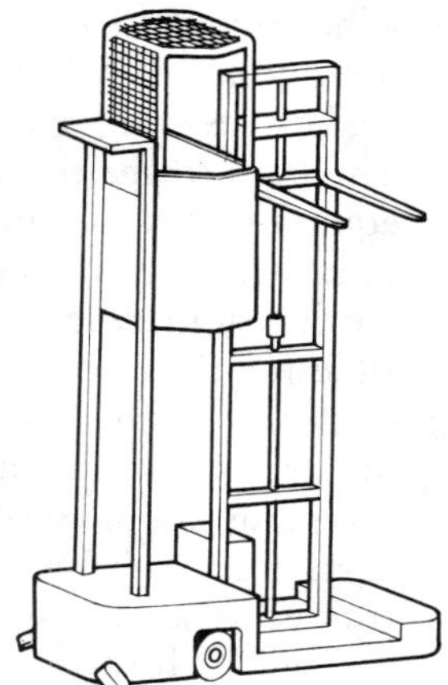

Fig. 37.11 Order pickers
Conventional
Purpose designed

Order pickers can be designed for a multitude of storage tasks. The heavy-duty type can incorporate traversing load masts or dual mast with independent load/operator control, and generally operates along rails or tracks within narrow aisles. With purpose designed order pickers, capacity and maximum lift would be specified at the ordering stage.

Safe operation of mechanical handling equipment

Equipment

The operation of mechanical handling equipment results in many industrial accidents. The following rules should be applied to such operations.

(a) Untrained and/or unauthorised personnel should not drive or operate powered mechanical handling equipment.
(b) Rider trucks left unattended should have the forks lowered and be immobilised by
   (i) leaving the controls in the neutral position,
   (ii) shutting off the power,
   (iii) applying the brakes, and
   (iv) removing the key or connector plug.
(c) The maximum rated load capacity of the equipment, as stated on the manufacturer's identification plate, should never be exceeded.

(d) On no account should passengers be carried, unless in a properly constructed cage or platform. (*See* 'Use of Fork Lift Trucks as Working Platforms' later in this chapter.)

(e) When powered industrial trucks are used on public highways, they must comply with the Road Traffic Acts and be fitted with lights, brakes, steering, etc.

(f) The keys to the truck should be kept in a secure place when the equipment is not in use. Keys should be issued to authorised operators only and be retained by such persons until the end of the work period, when they should be returned to the manager responsible for the operation.

(g) A clearly defined maintenance programme, based on the manufacturer's recommendations for inspection, maintenance and servicing, should be operated. Repairs and maintenance should be carried out only by trained and experienced staff. Drivers should be trained to undertake simple periodic maintenance checks, and there should be a formal procedure for reporting defects identified in such checks and during normal operation. A typical daily check by the operator would include an examination and/or test of lights, including warning beacon, horn, tyres, brakes, steering, tilting, lifting and manipulation systems, operator controls, fluid levels, security of the overhead cage/guard and load backrest, as well as the integrity of hydraulic pipes, pipe joints and connections.

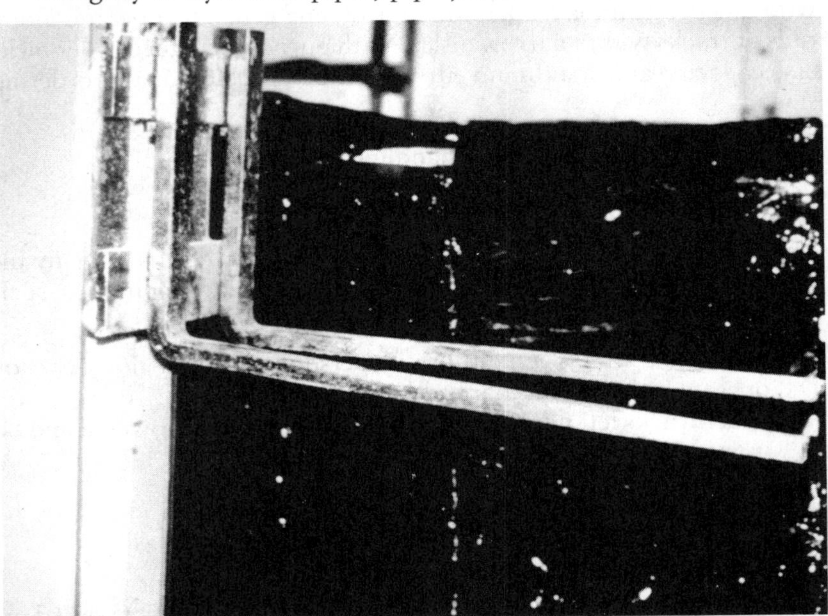

Fig. 37.12(a)

Fig. 37.12(b)

Fig. 37.12 Defects in fork lift trucks

(a) Serious distortion of the forks of a hand fork lift truck due to overloading

(b) The fractured bracket (arrowed) attached the steering base to the fork lift truck and affected the ability of the driver to steer the truck effectively

Reproduced by courtesy of National Vulcan Engineering Insurance Group Ltd

(h) Weekly maintenance on a truck should include all the operator checks mentioned above, together with an operational examination of steering gear, lifting gear, battery, mast, forks, attachments, and any chains or ropes used in the lifting mechanism.
(i) Mechanical handling and lifting equipment should also be subject to a 6-monthly and an annual examination. In the case of the 6-monthly examination (or 1,000 running hours) all parts of the truck should be examined by either a trained fitter or a representative of the manufacturer and a certificate issued by the examiner to the effect that the truck is safe to use. Lifting chains should be inspected on an annual basis and certificated in accordance with statutory requirements.

Operating area

Layout and maintenance of operating areas for mechanical handling equipment are important in ensuring safe operation. The following points are relevant:

(a) Floors and roadways should be of adequate load-bearing capacity as well as being smooth-surfaced and level. Moreover, a designer or consultant engineer of a factory or other workplace who fails to provide for this requirement can be sued for negligence (*Greaves & Company (Contractors) Ltd* v. *Baynham Meikle & Partners* [1975] 1 WLR 1095). Where 'sleeping sentries' ('sleeping policemen') are installed to slow down vehicular traffic, a bypass for mechanical handling equipment should be provided. Furthermore, the edges of loading bays should be protected when not in use and 'tiger striped' to warn the driver, particularly when operating at night. Sharp bends and overhead obstructions, such as electric cables and pipework, should be eliminated where possible.
(b) Ramps should be installed to prevent displacement of the load at gutters, changes in floor level, etc.
(c) Gradients should not exceed 10 per cent and there should be a smooth gradual change of gradient at the bottom and top of the slope.
(d) Bridge plates should incorporate an adequate safety margin to support loaded equipment. These should be clearly and permanently marked with the maximum permissible load, secured to prevent accidental movement, and surfaced with a high-friction finish.
(e) Aisles should be of adequate width and overhead clearance to facilitate turning and safe movement, and should be kept clear at all times.
(f) Lighting should be adequate with a minimum overall illuminance

level of 100 lux. If a permanent level of 100 lux is not available, auxiliary lighting should be installed on the equipment and so arranged to avoid glare which could affect other operators.

(g) Adequate general vehicle parking facilities should be provided away from the main operating areas and preferably in a secure compound.

(h) Actual layout of operating areas is crucial to the prevention of accidents. Doorways and overhead structures low enough to form an obstacle should have suitable warning notices displayed above them. Clear direction signs, marked barriers, electrically operated warning devices and convex mirrors should be used in order to prevent pedestrians coming into direct contact with trucks. Additionally, instructions to drivers to sound the horn and restrict speed should be posted at prominent positions. Separate routes, designated crossing places and barriers, clearly marked at frequent intervals, should be arranged so as to restrict access by pedestrians to operational areas. Where pedestrians and handling equipment use the same access between parts of a building, a separate pedestrian access door should be available; alternatively, tubular steel barriers should be installed 1 metre from the side of the opening to provide a pedestrian passageway at the side. Windows or ports should be installed in rubber doors through which trucks frequently pass. Columns, pipework, racking, exposed electrical conduits and items of plant should be protected by impact-absorbing barriers.

(i) In truck battery-charging bays ventilation should be sufficient to prevent accumulations of hydrogen gas. Although not a statutory requirement, smoking should be forbidden and other sources of ignition eliminated. Notices prohibiting smoking, the use of naked lights and other sources of ignition should be displayed. Moreover, before disconnecting the truck battery from the charger, the current should be switched off to reduce the risk of sparking.

(j) Refuelling areas for petrol-driven trucks should ideally be located outside the building and comply with the requirements of the Petroleum (Consolidation) Act 1928 and the Petroleum Spirit (Conveyance by Road) Regulations 1957.

The operators

To ensure the safe operation of mechanical handling equipment, it is essential that operators be responsible persons and physically fit for the job. They should be trained, and there should be an effective system for documentation of authorised operators, e.g. permits to drive. In particular:

(a) A high level of supervision and control should be exercised over all product- and goods-handling activities.
(b) Operators of mechanical handling equipment should be physically and mentally fit, intelligent, mature and reliable. Handicapped persons need not be excluded, but medical advice should be sought as to suitability for specific tasks.
(c) Training should be given to operators and supervisors, and to managers responsible for areas where mechanical handling is in operation, particularly to cover emergency situations.
(d) Operator training should be undertaken by trainers who are experienced in the specific tasks to be undertaken by trainees. Such training comprises three specific parts:
    (i) acquisition of the basic skills and knowledge required to operate the equipment safely and to undertake the required daily equipment checks,
    (ii) specific job training in a 'safe' working area to develop operational skills, and
    (iii) familiarisation training under close supervision in the workplace.

    Training should be provided for all operators, even if they have been trained by a former employer. Supplementary or refresher training should be undertaken
    (i) when there has been a significant change in operational layout;
    (ii) on transfer to a new operational area;
    (iii) when new or different equipment is introduced; or
    (iv) when there may have been a lapse in operator standards.
(e) Trainees should be tested. (*See* RoSPA's (1975) *Training Manual.*) On passing a truck driving test, the operator should receive a 'permit to drive' (a form of written authority) for the class of truck on which he has qualified. Management should not allow persons to operate any mechanical handling equipment without this written authority. Additionally, a record should be maintained of all authorised operators and the serial number of the permit to drive issued. The date of training, and that of the refresher training which will be required in the future, should also be recorded.
(f) Operators should be provided with safety footwear and a safety helmet and, where appropriate, hearing protection, together with protective clothing to suit weather and/or temperature conditions. For example, for work in cold stores or on external loading, donkey jackets and gloves should be provided.
(g) Supervisors are responsible for ensuring that all operators are trained and working safely, that they carry out periodic checks and that there is a system for reporting deficiencies. (*See* Chapters 2 and 3 for the legal position relating to supervision/management.)

Use of fork lift trucks as working platforms

There is now widespread industrial use of fork lift trucks as a means of elevating workers and contractors to undertake tasks at high level, e.g. painting, cleaning, maintenance, repairs. Although, in principle, the use of a fork lift truck affords considerable advantages for this type of work, nevertheless its primary function is the carriage and manipulation of materials and not as a means of support for a working platform. Therefore, if trucks are to be used for such purposes, certain safeguards are essential. Where practicable, the truck should be specifically designed for this purpose. In most cases, however, this is not the case and consequently working platforms are usually fitted to the forks of trucks. A platform designed for use on one particular truck should never be employed on any other type of fork lift truck.

Where trucks are specially designed for or are regularly used with working platforms, movement of the platform should be controlled by the person on the platform. When trucks are only occasionally used with working platforms, either full platform controls or a platform-mounted emergency stop control should be provided.

Precautions with working platforms on fork lift trucks

(a) The manufacturer's opinion as to the suitability of a truck for use in connection with a specific working platform should always be obtained.

(b) The weight of the platform and total superimposed load thereon should be not more than half of the truck manufacturer's rated capacity at the rated load centre distance of the truck at maximum lift height. A plate should be affixed to the platform indicating the maximum superimposed load and minimum rating of the truck on which it may be used.

(c) The platform should be secured to the forks and either the edges fenced to a minimum height of 1 metre either by guard rails comprising top rails, intermediate rails and toe board, or a steel mesh enclosure of similar height should be constructed.

(d) A locking device should be fitted to ensure that the mast remains vertical.

(e) Where controls are located on the platform, they should be of the 'dead man's handle' type, whereby the actuating lever or switch must be held or pressed continuously to effect motion of the platform. Preferably, controls should be positioned midway across the platform and at the rear to keep the operator away from the edges of the platform whilst it is in motion. This recommendation does not preclude provision of emergency controls at floor level which may be desirable to lower the platform in the event of breakdown or emergency. When fitted, such controls should be located and designed so as to prevent accidental or unauthorised operation.

(f) A prominent notice should be affixed to the platform with the instruction 'ENSURE THAT PARKING BRAKE IS APPLIED BEFORE ELEVATING PLATFORM'.

(g) On all machines designed specifically for, or likely to be used for, access purposes there should be a minimum of two suspension ropes or chains.

(h) No person should remain in the elevated working position when the truck is moved from one point to another.

(i) The applicance should only be used on well-maintained and level floors. (*See* reference earlier to the case of *Greaves & Company (Contractors) Ltd* v. *Baynham Meikle & Partners*.)

(j) All trapping points should be screened or guarded to protect persons carried on the platform, e.g. where a chain passes over sprockets, or where there is a crushing or shearing action between parts of the mast or its actuating mechanism.

Goods vehicles

Rail vehicles

Rail movement in depots and industrial complexes is a major hazard, frequently owing to poor visibility. The danger is greatly increased where long rafts or wagons are being shunted, especially by one-man diesel locomotives. Here the number of crossing places should be kept to a minimum and they should be clearly defined by signs and barriers. 'STOP, LOOK AND LISTEN' signs should be displayed well ahead of level crossings located in rail depots. Each crossing should be well lit at night and during bad weather. Shunting locomotives should be fitted with flashing beacons which operate during movement. Further guidance on rail vehicle operations is provided in the Factories (Locomotives in Sidings) Regulations 1906.

Motor vehicles

Many of the requirements for industrial powered trucks apply to the operation of motor vehicles within the boundaries of a factory or industrial complex. The careful layout of loading bays, approaches, and other areas will minimise those hazards which can exist when vehicles need to manoeuvre in awkward or confined spaces.

Although goods vehicles visiting factory premises are not 'machinery' for the purposes of the Factories Act 1961, sec 14(1) (per Viscount Dilhorne in *British Railways Board* v. *Liptrot* [1967] 2 AER

1072), they come within the general requirements for a safe system of work, as laid down in HSWA, sec 2(2) and at common law. Consequently, drivers of such vehicles, whether company employees or those of another company delivering to the premises, must not reverse vehicles, unless guidance is given by an authorised person. In particular, where there is extensive vehicle manoeuvring in a loading area, marshalling stewards should be employed to ensure the safe reversing, loading and unloading of vehicles (*see* Chapter 13).

38 Dangerous substances

Many dangerous substances are used in industry, commerce, agriculture, research activities, hospitals and teaching establishments. The majority take the form of chemical compounds, but there are also naturally occurring substances, such as asbestos, heavy metals and siliceous dusts which can have adverse effects (*see* Chapter 19). The meaning of the term 'dangerous substance' used in the major part of this chapter is, therefore, wider than the corresponding term used in the Dangerous Substances (Conveyance by Road in Road Tankers and Tank Containers) Regulations 1981 and the Classification, Packaging and Labelling of Dangerous Substances Regulations 1984, which are concerned with 'dangerous chemicals'. (*See* 'Transport of Dangerous Chemicals by Road' and 'Classification, Packaging and Labelling of Dangerous Chemicals' later in this chapter.)

Generally, dangerous substances are of two types. They can directly affect the individual by entry into the body through the lungs, skin or mouth, or they can have a secondary effect through his coming into contact with them, e.g. when a highly flammable substance is ignited. Much depends upon the form – dust, liquid, aerosol, etc. – taken by the substance and its method of use.

Classification

The classification of dangerous substances is based largely on the characteristic properties of such substances and their effects on Man. Legislation on this subject also requires the provision of a specific pictorial symbol on any container or package (*see* Fig. 38.1). The following terms are used in the classification of dangerous substances in the Classification, Packaging and Labelling of Dangerous Substances Regulations 1984.

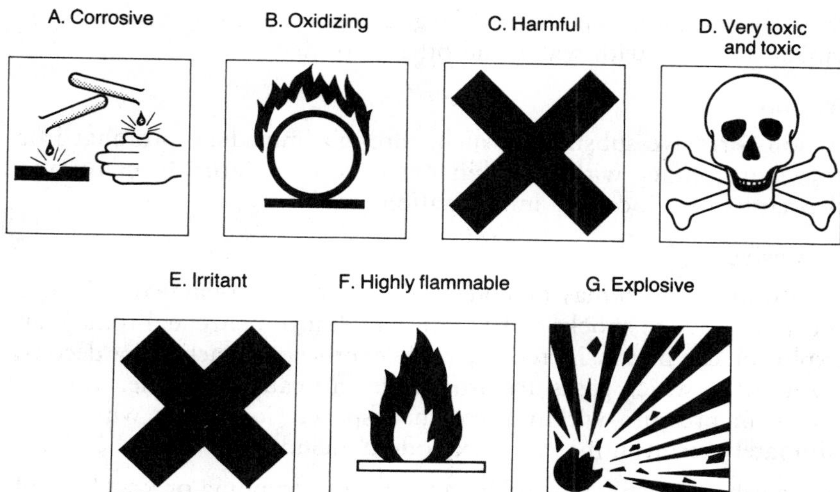

Fig. 38.1 Hazard warning symbols, as required by the Classification, Packaging and Labelling of Dangerous Substances Regulations 1984

Very toxic

A substance which, if inhaled or ingested, or if it penetrates the skin, may involve extremely serious, acute or chronic health risks and even death.

Toxic

A substance which, if inhaled or ingested, or if it penetrates the skin, may involve serious, acute or chronic health risks and even death.

Harmful

A substance which, if it is inhaled or ingested, or if it penetrates the skin, may involve limited health risks.

Corrosive

A substance which may, on contact with living tissues, destroy them. Corrosive substances are those which, by chemical action, can cause severe damage when in contact with living tissues or, in the case of leakage, will substantially damage or destroy other materials. Thus in relatively mild cases of contact with corrosives, dermatitis may occur, whereas in more severe cases the result may be chemical burns. Strong acids, including anhydrides and acid chlorides, strong bases, including hydroxides plus alkaline earth materials and their oxides halogens and oxidising agents are classic examples of corrosive materials. Some of these possess additional hazards, e.g. corrosion of their containers, or violent reaction with water and other substances.

Irritant

A non-corrosive substance which, through immediate prolonged or repeated contact with the skin or mucous membrane, can cause dermatitis or a localised inflammation.

Explosive

A substance which may explode under the effect of flame or which is more sensitive to shocks or friction than dinitro benzene. Broadly, an explosion can be considered as a rapid exothermic reaction (or decomposition) in which gases are produced. This causes a sudden vast increase in pressure within a confined space. Conditions which can ultimately result in materials exploding include

(a) mechanical shock – sudden movement, dropping or knocking of the containers;
(b) friction – stirring or transferring material;
(c) temperature – accumulation of heat can cause detonation;
(d) violent chemical reactions between reagents.

Substances capable of undergoing explosions include

(a) highly flammable materials if ignited in confined spaces, e.g. solvent vapours, gases;
(b) authorised explosives; and
(c) other thermodynamically unstable materials; classes of such materials include acetylides, acetylenic compounds, polynitro compounds, azides, diazo compounds, fulminates, certain nitrates, peroxy compounds, vinyl monomers, epoxides.

In addition, explosion hazards can result from the explosive oxidation of reducing agents by strong oxidising agents such as persulphuric acid, concentrated nitric acid and nitrates of sodium and silver.

Oxidising

A substance which gives rise to a highly exothermic reaction when in contact with other substances, particularly flammable substances. Strong oxidising agents include those substances which, though not spontaneously flammable themselves, are sources of oxygen. They present a fire hazard, in that they can

(a) support combustion in an otherwise oxygen deficient atmosphere; and
(b) react so vigorously with reducing agents – e.g. organic solvents, paper, cotton – as to bring about ignition.

Examples of this hazard category include concentrated perchloric acid, persulphuric acid and organic peroxy-compounds, many of which also represent an explosion hazard, together with concentrated nitric acid, potassium chromate, dichromate and permanganate.

Extremely flammable

Such substances are classified as liquids having a flash point of less than 0 °C and a boiling point of less than or equal to 35 °C, and when such a liquid forms more than 45 per cent by weight or more than 250 g of the contents of an aerosol dispenser, the contents of that dispenser.

Highly flammable

This is a substance which

(a) may become hot and finally catch fire on contact with air at ambient temperature without any application of energy;
(b) may readily catch fire after brief contact with a source of ignition and which continues to burn or to be consumed after removal of the source of ignition, e.g. methanol;
(c) is gaseous and flammable in air at normal pressure, e.g. butane;
(d) in contact with water or damp air evolves highly flammable gases in dangerous quantities, e.g. sodium produces hydrogen gas; or
(e) is a liquid having a flash point below 21 °C and when such a liquid forms more than 45 per cent or more than 250 g of the contents of an aerosol dispenser, the contents of that dispenser.

Flammable

A substance which

(a) is a liquid having a flash point equal to or greater than 21 °C and less than or equal to 55 °C, and which when tested in the manner specified in the Second Schedule to the Highly Flammable Liquids and Liquefied Petroleum Gases Regulations 1972 does not support combustion;
(b) forms the contents of an aerosol dispenser when they include more than 45 per cent by weight or 250 g of a liquid which has a flash point equal to or greater than 21 °C and less than or equal to 100 °C.

Radioactive

This means that the substance emits ionising radiations. Many such substances are isotopes of chemical elements such as cobalt-60 or strontium-90, and emissions may take the form of alpha particles, beta rays, gamma rays or neutrons. The precautions, therefore, will differ according to the type of emission (*see further* Chapter 23).

Narcotic

Some chemical substances, e.g. alcohol, affect the brain and central nervous system to cause a depressant effect on their functions.

Carcinogenic

A number of substances cause cancer. They may be in solid or liquid form and of a chemical or physical nature. For instance, β-naphthylamine is known to cause cancer of the bladder, and blue asbestos, and indeed other forms of asbestos, can cause lung cancer and mesothelioma. It should be appreciated that such cancers are only one aspect of the much wider problem of toxicity. Cancer is fundamentally a disease process which may affect tissues in the body and is a disorder of cell growth. The new growth may remain simple and localised, i.e. it is benign, or it may invade and destroy neighbouring tissues and distant body organs, i.e. it is malignant (*see* Chapter 19).

Cryogenic

Cryogenic substances are those which, because of their low temperature, present a special danger. They are generally liquefied gases at temperatures below 0 °C. Common examples are liquid nitrogen (b.p. − 196 °C), liquid oxygen (b.p. − 183 °C) and liquid helium (b.p. − 269 °C). The principal hazards associated with cryogenic substances are:

(a) chemical – violent reactions can occur when certain cryogenic substances react with other chemical substances, such as liquid oxygen with oil or charcoal, or liquid hydrogen with oxygen;
(b) physical – the normal properties of structural and other materials change at low temperatures and many are rendered brittle, e.g. rubber, plastic, metals;
(c) physiological – conditions such as frostbite and burns to the skin can result from contact with cryogenic materials. Furthermore, since such substances vaporise rapidly at room temperature, there is always the danger of anoxia (oxygen deficiency).

Mutagenic

A number of substances are capable of causing damage to the individual cell in such a way that subsequent cell division may become uncontrolled. In normal body cells, this may give rise to cancer.

Physical state of dangerous substances

The form taken by a dangerous substance – e.g., liquid, gas, dust, mist, vapour, etc. – is a contributory factor to its potential for harm.

Dangerous substances take many forms, the most common being as follows.

Dusts

These are solid airborne particles, often created by operations such as grinding, crushing, milling, sanding and demolition. Two of the principal harmful dusts encountered in industry are asbestos and silica (*see* Chapter 22).

Fumes

Fumes are solid particles which usually form an oxide in contact with air. They are created by industrial processes which involve the heating and melting of metals, such as welding, smelting and arc air gouging. A common fume danger is lead poisoning associated with the inhalation of lead fume.

Smoke

Smoke is the product of incomplete combustion, mainly of organic materials, and may include fine particles of carbon in the form of ash, soot and grit that are visibly suspended in air.

Mists

A mist is a finely dispersed liquid suspended in air. Mists are mainly created by spraying, foaming, pickling and electro-plating. Dangers arise most frequently from acid mists produced in industrial treatment processes.

Gases

These are formless fluids usually produced by chemical processes involving combustion or by the interaction of chemical substances. A gas will normally seek to fill the space completely into which it is liberated. One of the classic hazardous gases encountered in industry is carbon monoxide. Certain gases such as acetylene, hydrogen and methane are particularly flammable.

Vapours

A vapour is the gaseous form of a material normally encountered in a solid or liquid state at normal room temperature and pressure. Typical examples are solvents, such as trichlorethylene, which release vapours when the container is opened. Other liquids produce a vapour on heating, the amount of vapour being directly related to the boiling point of that particular liquid. A vapour contains very minute droplets of the liquid. However, in the case of a *fog*, the liquid droplets are much larger.

Solids

Certain substances in solid form can cause injury. Classic examples are cullet (broken glass), silica, asbestos and lead.

Liquids

Numerous dangerous substances are produced in liquid form including caustic and acid-based detergents, solvents and fuels.

Handling and storage

General precautions

Prior to handling and storing dangerous substances, it is imperative to consult sources of hazard data (*see* later in this chapter, 'Essential Data'). Basic safety rules apply, however, with all dangerous substances and these are outlined below. Some are statutory requirements (*see* Chapter 5), whereas with others current best practice is outlined.

(a) Meticulous standards of housekeeping are necessary for any activity involving the handling and storage of dangerous substances.
(b) Smoking and the consumption of food or drink should be prohibited in any area in which substances are used or stored, e.g. laboratory, bulk chemical store (*see* particularly the statutory prohibitions set out in Chapter 5).
(c) Staff must be reminded regularly of the need for good personal hygiene, in particular washing hands after handling any chemical-based substance.
(d) The minimum quantities should be stored in the work area. Extra bulk storage should be provided separately well away from the work area.
(e) Containers should be clearly and accurately labelled.
(f) Chemical substances should always be transported with care and carriers used for Winchesters and other large containers.
(g) Fume cupboards should have a minimum face velocity of approximately 0.4 m/sec when measured with the sash opening set at 300 mm maximum, and performance should be checked frequently.
(h) Staff should wear protective clothing and equipment whenever handling or using dangerous substances (*see* Chapter 24).
(i) Any injury should be treated promptly, particularly skin wounds.
(j) Responsibility should be identified at senior management level, and written procedures published and used in the training and supervision of staff.

Precautions with specific substances

Flammable liquids

(a) All containers should be of the self-closing type. Caps should be replaced after dispensing. Liquids should be dispensed in a drip tray.
(b) Containers should be stored in a well-ventilated fire-protected area.
(c) Fire appliances should be located in a readily accessible position and staff trained in their use.
(d) Flammable liquids should be transported in closed containers of metal construction. (Some plastics may, however, be acceptable for this purpose.)

Carcinogens, poisons, etc.

(a) Staff must wear the appropriate protective clothing and equipment.
(b) First aid treatment, including the appropriate antidote, must be known and readily available.
(c) Substances producing fumes must be handled in fume cupboards.
(d) Substances should be transported in sealed and labelled containers.

Radioactive materials

(a) Materials should be clearly identified by the appropriate warning sign.
(b) Materials should never be handled with bare hands.
(c) Materials should only be moved under the direct supervision of an authorised person, and transported in sealed or other appropriate containers.
(d) The level of radioactivity should be checked before any radioactive source is approached.
(e) Staff must be trained to know the hazards involved and the precautions necessary (*see* Chapter 23).

Solids

(a) In the case of dusts and particulate materials, e.g. powders,
   (i) respiratory protection should be worn unless control measures are adequate;
   (ii) atmospheric concentrations should be measured and related to the current hygiene standard in order to determine the degree of danger present; and

(iii) there should be a complete ban on smoking where the solid is flammable.

(b) In the case of all solids, the nature of the substance to be handled must be ascertained.

Bulk storage of dangerous chemical substances

In the design and use of bulk storage facilities, the following aspects need attention:

(a) the range and quantities of chemical substances to be stored;
(b) dependent on (a) above, the degree of segregation by distance of
  (i) the store from any other building; and
  (ii) certain chemical substances within the store from other chemical substances stored.

Segregation

The aim in segregating stored chemicals should be

(a) to facilitate emergency access and escape in the event of fire or other emergency;
(b) to separate incompatible chemicals to prevent their mixture, e.g. by spillage, or wetting during cleaning activities;
(c) to separate process areas, which normally contain relatively small quantities, from storage areas containing larger amounts;
(d) to prevent rapid fire spread, or the evolution of smoke and gases, which can be produced in a fire;
(e) to isolate oxidising agents which, when heated, will enhance a fire, perhaps to explosive condition;
(f) to isolate those substances which decompose explosively when heated;
(g) to minimise toxic hazards arising from loss of containment through spillage, seepage or package deterioration;
(h) to minimise risk of physical damage, e.g. by fork lift trucks, to containers; and
(i) to separate materials where the appropriate fire-fighting medium for one may be ineffective for, or cause an adverse reaction with, another.

Segregation distances: Reference should be made to Table 31 which specifies relative segregation distances for various forms of loose package. The hazard warning symbols for different forms of chemical substance classified in Table 31 are shown in Fig. 38.1. Table 32 details the categories of separation.

Table 31: The segregation of chemical substances

Hazard warning symbol	*Chemical substances*	*Alkali corrosives*	*Acid corrosives*	*Potential oxidising substances*	*Peroxides*	*Chlorine release agents*	*Flammable solids*	*Flammable liquids*	*Flammable gases*	*Non-flammable gases*	*Low-hazard products – human contact possible*	*Poisons*
A/E	Alkali corrosives		2	1	2	x	1	1	1	x	1	x
A/E	Acid corrosives	2		2	2	2	1	1	1	x	1	x
B/E	Potential oxidising substances	1	2		1	1	1	2	2	x	2	1
B/G	Peroxides	2	2	1		2	2	3	3	2	2	1
F/E	Chlorine release agents	x	2	1	2		2	2	2	x	1	2
F/C	Flammable solids	1	1	1	2	2		1	1	x	2	1
F	Flammable gases	1	1	2	3	2	1	2		x	2	1
C	Non-flammable gases	x	x	x	2	x	x	2	x		x	1
	Low-hazard products – human contact possible	1	1	2	2	1	2	2	2	x		2
D	Poisons	x	x	1	1	2	1	1	1	1	2	
	Food ingredients	3	3	3	3	3	3	3	3	1	1	3
	Miscellaneous dangerous substances			No general segregation requirements can be provided; consult individual data sheets								

Structural requirements

Chemical storage may take two forms, viz. an open area or a purpose-built store. Open storage is not recommended but, when it is unavoidable, it should comprise a secure area fenced to a height of 2 metres with a lockable access point.

Purpose-built stores should be of the detached single-storey brick-

Table 32: Categories of separation

Category of separation	*Requirement*
x	No specific separation required
1	Keep away from ...
2	Keep well separated from ...
3	Separate by fire-resistant partition or in a separate location

built type or constructed in other suitable materials, e.g. concrete panels, with a sloping roof of weather-proof construction, the structure to have a notional period of fire resistance of at least 1 hour. Other features include

(a) permanent ventilation by high- and low-level air bricks set in all elevations, except in those forming a boundary wall; low-level air bricks should be sited above door sill level;
(b) access doors constructed from material with at least 1 hour notional period of fire resistance; doorways should provide access for fork lift trucks, with ramps on each side of the door sill; separate pedestrian access, which also serves as a secondary means of escape, should be provided;
(c) an impervious chemical-resistant finish to walls, floors and other parts; and
(d) artificial lighting by sealed bulkhead or fluorescent fittings, to provide an overall illuminance level of 300 lux.

General requirements

In the cases of both open and closed storage, the following are required:

(a) provision of adequate space, with physical separation and containment for incompatible substances (*see* Table 31), each area to be marked with the permitted contents, the hazards and the necessary precautions, and incorporating an area for the storage of empty containers;
(b) fire separation of individual areas sufficient to prevent fire spreading; and
(c) provision of the following equipment in a protected area outside the store:
    (i) fire appliances – dry powder and/or foam extinguishers;
    (ii) fixed hose reel appliance;
    (iii) emergency shower and eyewash station with water-heating facility to prevent freezing;

(iv) personal protective equipment, i.e. safety helmet with visor, impervious gloves, disposable chemical-resistant overall, with storage facilities for same; and
(v) respirator and breathing apparatus in a marked enclosure;

(d) a total prohibition on the use of naked flames and smoking – appropriate warning signs should be displayed;
(e) prohibition on the use of the store for storage of other goods or for any other purpose; and
(f) provision of racking or pallets to enable goods to be stored clear of the floor.

Storage system

The system for storage must be simple to operate and compatible with existing legal requirements for classification and labelling.

Dangerous substances commonly encountered in industry

Within this category can be included materials such as cement, resins, coal tar pitch derivatives and fibreglass. Safety aspects of compressed gases are also considered.

Portland cement

Cement is used universally in the construction industry and other industries. Inhalation of cement dust may cause fibrosis, but the principal hazard is its propensity for causing dermatitis, through excessive contact or its specific sensitising effect. Cement, on contact with water, emits heat, resulting in burns to persons in contact with it.

Fibreglass

This material comes within the range of man-made mineral fibres. Continual contact with fibreglass causes dermatitis owing to the irritant effect of the fibres.

Coal tar pitch derivatives

This group includes pitch, creosote and tar produced in the distallation of crude hydrocarbon oils. Excessive contact may result in pitch warts, skin cancer and dermatitis. These substances are used widely in construction as constituents of roofing felt, bituminous paints, and asphalt for road surfacing, and in the form of creosote, are commonly used preservatives and water repellants for timber.

Resins

Epoxy and polyester resins are used in adhesives, paints and sealants.

Principal hazards are skin contact and inhalation of fumes. Other resins such as acrylic, phenolic and polyurethane resins have similar contact and inhalation risks. They should be used with considerable care and not in unventilated or badly ventilated areas.

Compressed gases

Compressed gases have numerous uses both commercially and domestically. In addition to their inherent flammable, toxic or corrosive properties, they are potentially dangerous as a consequence of their physical properties. Leakage from cylinders into an open room or workshop can give rise to dangerous concentrations resulting in fire, explosion, gassing incidents or oxygen depletion. The relative force with which the contents of a cylinder can be ejected can result in death, physical injury, damage to property and plant, and even the propulsion of the cylinder, like a rocket, across a working area.

Precautions with cylinders

Storage: One of the principal causes of accidents is incorrect storage of cylinders, resulting in incompatible reactions taking place between different gases leaking into the storage area. For this reason alone, the following precautions should be taken in the design of storage facilities:

(a) cylinders should be stored outside the main buildings in a purpose-built store;
(b) the store should be a detached structure and well segregated from buildings frequently occupied;
(c) storage should incorporate separate compartments for individual gases or groups of compatible gases;
(d) the structure should be of weather-proof lightweight construction – e.g. single skin brick or lightweight concrete block walls and partitions providing a notional period of fire resistance of at least 1 hour – and should have a sloping roof;
(e) high- and low-level ventilation by air bricks should be located in the end and back walls; and
(f) each compartment should be provided with a lockable welded mesh door of mesh size within the range XM21 to XM26 or XM41 to XM43 (*see* BS 405:1945).

Only compatible gases should be stored in individual storage compartments. A typical arrangement is:

Compartment A – propane, butane, hydrogen (one cylinder only);

Compartment B – oxygen, compressed air;

Compartment C – ammonia;

Compartment D – chlorine; this compartment should incorporate a lockable louvred door;

Compartment E – acetylene, arcton, freon, argon, nitrogen, helium, hydrogen (if not stored in Compartment A).

Other storage design features: These include

(a) concrete floor with slight fall to facilitate trolley loading; no drainage should be incorporated in the floor;
(b) total prohibition of the installation of electrical or heating equipment;
(c) marking of the store with approved signs indicating the contents and prohibiting smoking and the use of naked flames;
(d) racking, incorporating restraining chains, for cylinder storage; racking is not necessary where cylinders are of freestanding design;
(e) water supply through a 20 mm hose reel installation adjacent to the store, but well away from the chlorine cylinder storage compartment;
(f) artificial lighting to a minimum illuminance level of 150 lux, remote from the store but directed into the store and door openings; and
(g) fire appliances, e.g. dry powder, of adequate size, located at a specific point.

Storage buildings should be so spaced that the distance between any aperture in the wall and the nearest point of any other building, boundary or ignition source is

(a) not less than 3 m for storage up to 1,000 kg, and
(b) not less than 6 m for storage over 1,000 kg.

Where the above standard is not practicable, it may be possible to locate the store against an existing building wall. However, there should be

(a) no opening lights in the wall above the store, and any fixed lights should be glazed with georgian wired glass;
(b) no adjacent apertures – i.e. windows, doors – within 3 metres of the store; and
(c) no ventilation intake above or immediately adjacent to the store.

Empty cylinders should be treated in the same manner as full or partially full cylinders, and the valves maintained closed. 'Full' and 'empty' cylinder racks within each compartment should be conspicuously marked.

Handling of cylinders:

(a) Cylinders should not be dropped or allowed to come into contact with one another or with any hard object.
(b) Cylinders should be treated with extreme care; they are a potential source of energy.
(c) When transported, cylinders should be strapped in properly designed trolleys.
(d) Cylinders used for lecturing and training purposes should be handled in a fume cupboard and stood in a suitable rack.
(e) Improperly labelled cylinders should not be accepted. The colour code on the cylinder is only a secondary guide.

Use of cylinders:

(a) Cylinders should be stored and used in an upright position with the valve uppermost.
(b) A regulator should be used to maintain the outlet pressure at a correct and uniform value.
(c) Cylinders should *not* be used as rollers for moving heavy objects.
(d) Valves and fittings should not be lubricated.
(e) Cylinders and valves should be kept clean.
(f) Cylinders with damaged threads or valves should immediately be labelled 'defective' and returned to the supplier.
(g) When exchanging cylinders, the valves should be closed before the connections are transferred.
(h) After remaking a connection, the valve should be opened carefully in order to detect any leakage. In the event of leakage, the cylinder should be moved into the open air.
(i) Cylinder keys should not be extended to give greater leverage as valve spindles may be damaged.
(j) Leak detectors and alarms may be necessary when very dangerous gases are stored.
(k) Only the appropriate regulator should be used for each type of cylinder. Regulators should be examined at 6-monthly intervals and labelled for use with one specific gas.

Dangerous gases – special precautions

These gases, especially flammable gases, should be housed in a suitably ventilated compartment outside the building and the gas piped in to the working area. Cylinders must

(a) be fitted with automatic shut-off valves operable from inside the working area, e.g. laboratory;
(b) be fitted with flash-back arrestors in the line;

(c) have cylinder keys captive to the cylinder by non-ferrous chains; and
(d) have their lines examined for leaks on commencement of work and on change of cylinder.

When cylinders are not in use,

(a) cylinder and bench valves must be closed tightly, and
(b) protective caps screwed down over the valves.

Disposal

Procedures for the safe disposal of dangerous substances depend largely on the type and quantity of material involved. In all cases the local authority must be consulted since disposal facilities vary considerably in different areas of the country. The following must be considered prior to disposal of dangerous substances or their by-products.

(a) Only trained and authorised staff should be permitted to dispose of dangerous substances; where large quantities are concerned, disposal should be carried out in conjunction with the local authority.
(b) Where contractors provide a service, it is necessary to know
  (i) the location of the disposal site,
  (ii) the procedure for disposal,
  (iii) whether formal licensing is required for the disposal, and
  (iv) the mode of transport of the dangerous substances from the premises to the disposal site.

Transport of dangerous chemicals by road

Under the Health and Safety at Work Act etc., 1974, employers have a duty to protect members of the public from hazards arising from their activities. This duty applies particularly in the case of the transport of dangerous substances and is reinforced by the Dangerous Substances (Conveyance by Road in Road Tankers and Tank Containers) Regulations 1981 (SI 1981 No. 1059). The Regulations apply to the conveyance of dangerous chemicals by road in a tanker or tank container, including any loading and unloading activities at premises. The Regulations contain an 'Approved List' of dangerous substances (approved substance identified numbers, emergency action codes and classifications for dangerous substances conveyed in roads tankers and tank containers). A *dangerous substance* is defined with reference to the Approved List as any substance (including any preparation) which is either contained in Part I of the Approved List (unless it is in such a diluted form as not to create a risk) or any other substance which by reason of its characteristic properties creates a risk to the health and safety of any person in the course of conveyance by road, which is comparable with the risk created by substances which are specified in the Approved List.

These characteristic properties are listed in Schedule 1. An approved code of practice, 'Classification of Dangerous Substances for Conveyance in Road Tankers and Tank Containers', gives practical guidance on how substances not on the Approved List can be classified to see whether or not they come within the Regulations.

Vehicles or tanks must be properly designed, of adequate strength and of good construction from sound and suitable material before they can be used to convey dangerous substances by road. Operators must bear in mind the nature and circumstances of the journey and the characteristic properties and the quantity of substances being carried. Provision has been made for the testing and examination of tanks on road tankers and tank containers.

Under the Regulations, specific duties are placed on operators and drivers.

The 'operator' in relation to a road tanker or other vehicle is the person who holds, or should hold, an operator's licence for the use of the vehicle for the carriage of goods by road or, if no licence is required, the keeper of the vehicle. In the case of a tank container, the operator is:

(a) the owner of the tank container or his agent, if that person:
   (i) has a place of business in Great Britain; and
   (ii) is identified as the owner of or, as the case may be, as the agent of the owner of the tank container on the tank container itself, or on a document carried on that vehicle; or
(b) otherwise the operator of the vehicle on which the tank container is conveyed.

Considerable duties and responsibilities are placed on operators. They must ensure that they are aware of the risks by obtaining, from the consignor or others, relevant information on the dangerous substances. They must ensure that drivers are informed, in writing, of the identity of the substance and nature of the dangers to which the substance could give rise, together with the emergency action which should be taken (emergency action codes for each substance are shown in the Approved List). All operators must provide adequate instruction and training for their drivers, together with documentation of this training.

Specific duties on drivers include ensuring that vehicles, when not in use, are safely parked or supervised when they are carrying prescribed substances. They must also take the precautions necessary for the prevention of fire or explosion. This latter duty is imposed on every person who is engaged in the conveyance by road of a dangerous substance.

Tanker and tank container marking

All road tankers and tank containers must carry at least two hazard warning panels to the specification outlined in Schedule 4 of the Regulations. The panels must be weather-resistant, indelibly marked and rigidly fixed. Details relating to the form and specification of hazard warning panels and compartment labels are outlined below.

The form of the hazard warning panel is indicated in Figs 38.2(a) and 38.2(b). The allocation of the five spaces, as numbered in Fig. 38.2(a), is as follows:

(1) emergency action code;
(2) substance identification number and, if included, the name or, in the case of multi-loads, the word 'multi-load';
(3) hazard warning sign;
(4) telephone number or other approved text;
(5) optional manufacturer's or owner's name or house symbol or both.

The colour of the hazard warning panel must be *orange* and conform to the specification for that colour in Part 2 of Schedule 4 of the Regulations, except that the space for the hazard warning sign must be *white*, and the borders, internal dividing lines, letters and figures, *black*.

Specification for hazard warning panels for single loads is as shown in Fig. 38.2(b).

The specification for hazard warning panels for multi-loads is set out in Fig. 38.2(c).

Where the emergency action code or the multi-load emergency action code, ascertained from Schedule 1 or 2, is a *white* number and/or letter on a *black* background, it/they must be displayed on the panel as *orange* on a *black* background; the letters must appear in a *black* rectangle, having the height of 100 mm and a width of 10 mm greater than the width of the letter.

The form of the compartment label for multi-loads of substances of different hazards is set out in Fig. 38.2, and the spaces must be used for the following purposes:

(1) substance identification number and, if included, name; and
(2) hazard warning sign.

An example is shown in Fig. 38.2(e).

Where the multi-load consists of substances subject to the same hazards, the square labelled (2) in Fig. 38.2(d) can be omitted from the compartment label.

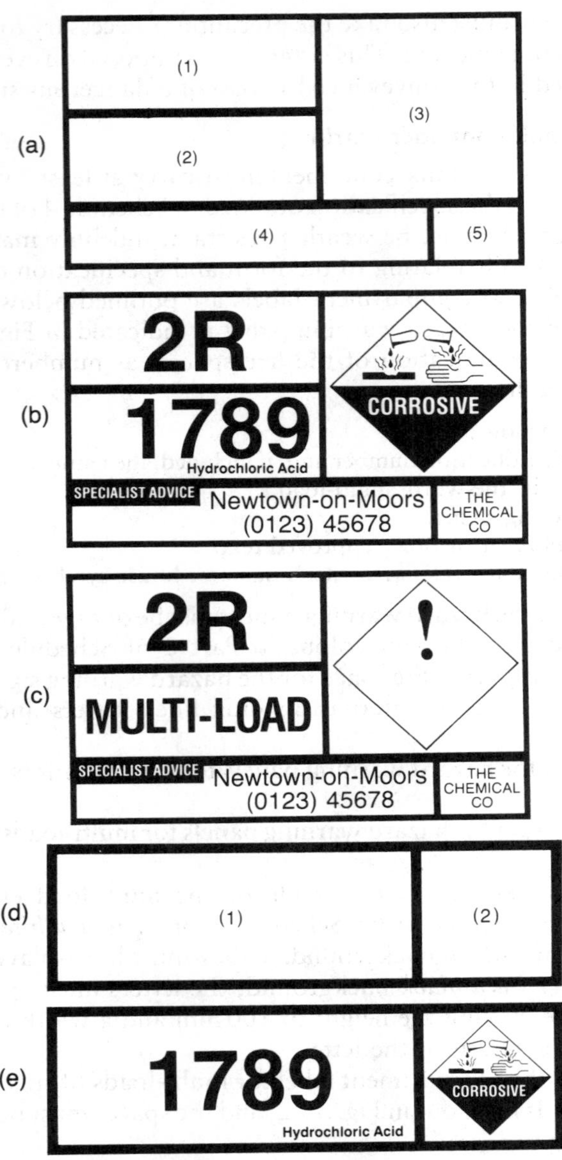

Fig. 38.2 Hazard warning panels and compartment labels, as required by the Dangerous Substances (Conveyance by Road in Road Tankers and Tank Containers) Regulations 1981
(a) Hazard warning panel: layout
(b) Hazard warning panel (single load)
(c) Hazard warning panel (multi-load)
(d) Compartment label (multi-load): layout
(e) Compartment label (multi-load): completed

The colour of the compartment label must be *orange* and conform to the specification for that colour in Part 2 of Schedule 4, except for the space for the hazard warning sign (where one is required), which must be *white* and the borders *black*.

The specification for compartment labels is set out in Fig. 38.2(e).

Definitions

Within the Dangerous Substances (Conveyance by Road in Road Tankers and Tank Containers) Regulations 1981, the following definitions are relevant:

The Approved List is the list of dangerous substances published by HSC on 25 July 1984 under the title 'Information Approved for the Classification, Packaging and Labelling of Dangerous Substances'. It lists approved substance identification numbers, emergency action codes and classifications. Part 2 of the list specifies a method for ascertaining the multi-load emergency action code. (The list may be revised from time to time.) Information contained in the list will enable operators to comply with the various duties imposed by these Regulations. The name of the substance (as given in this list) can include an alternative name in parentheses and/or the concentrations or conditions referred to in Regulations 9(c) in italics.

Classification: a substance is classified either by HSC and hence appears in the Approved List or, for a substance not on the list, by reference to Schedule 1 of the Regulations. The substances in the Approved List are normally single chemical substances. However, Schedule 1 should be used to classify any other substance, mixture or preparation which possesses one or more of the characteristic properties listed in Column 1 of this schedule; for such a substance the classification will be determined by whichever is the most hazardous property. Practical guidance on how to determine which property is, in a given case, the most hazardous will be found in the Approved Code of Practice 'Classification of Dangerous Substances for Conveyance in Road Tankers and Tank Containers'.

The *Emergency Action Code* informs the emergency services of the action to be taken in the event of an accident. The codes approved by HSC for dangerous substances are specified in the Approved List and have to appear on the hazard warning panel, fitted to vehicles, as required by these Regulations. Where a substance is not in the Approved List, the hazard warning panel must not show an emergency warning action code.

Multi-load is defined as a 'load consisting of two or more dangerous substances in separate compartments or tanks', but Regulation 16, relating to the labelling requirements for road tankers and tank containers conveying multi-loads, only applies to certain multi-loads, i.e. those carried in separate tanks or compartments in the tank when conveyed in a road tanker, or in a compartmented tank container.

The definition *road tanker* includes both rigid and articulated road tankers, and also draw-bar trailers which have a tank structurally attached to the frame of the trailer.

A *tank*, within the definition of the Regulations, is so constructed that it can be securely closed, except for the purpose of relieving excessive pressure, during the course of conveyance by road. This has the consequence that a tank which has any opening, other than for relieving excessive pressure, which cannot be securely closed by means of valves or covers, is not a tank for the purposes of these Regulations.

A *tank container* is any tank, with a capacity in excess of 3 cubic metres, which is not a tank or road tanker. This would normally be

(a) tank contained within an ISO framework (but would also include a large gas cylinder of the type used for compressed hydrogen or helium), or
(b) any other tank not within an ISO framework, if its capacity was in excess of 3 cubic metres.

Classification, packaging and labelling of dangerous substances

The Dangerous Substances (Conveyance by Road in Road Tankers and Tank Containers) Regulations 1981 lay down safety measures and precautions to be followed in connection with the conveyance by road in bulk of dangerous substances (as defined in the Approved List). A substance is classified as dangerous for the following purposes:

(a) conveyance by road in bulk, and
(b) commercial and industrial supply.

The Approved List contains

(a) a list of substances dangerous for supply purposes (Part 1A);
(b) a list of substances dangerous for conveyance by road purposes (Part 1A);
(c) a list of groups of substances dangerous for conveyance by road (not specified in Part 1A), for which HSC has approved the substance identification number (Part 1B);
(d) a list of articles relating to conveyance by road for which HSC has approved the substance identification number and classification number (Part 1C);
(e) for supply purposes only, a list of pesticides, as defined in Schedule 3;

(f) for supply purposes only, a list of solvents, as defined in Schedule 4;
(g) for supply purposes only, dangerous paints, varnishes, printing inks, adhesives, sealants, paint strippers, degreasing agents, preservatives and primers (other than pesticides), as defined in Schedule 6 (Regulations 5 and 6);
(h) for supply purposes, in the case of new substances, a list of those which have been notified in accordance with Regulation 4(1) of the Notification of New Substances Regulations 1982.

If a substance is classified as dangerous, the Classification, Packaging and Labelling of Dangerous Substances Regulations 1984 require specific safeguards in respect of

(a) packaging, and
(b) labelling.

For example, acetaldehyde is 'highly flammable and irritant', and the two appropriate pictorial symbols must appear on the supply package.

The Classification, Packaging and Labelling of Dangerous Substances Regulations 1984, which came into operation on 12 September 1984, replaced the earlier Packaging and Labelling of Dangerous Substances Regulations 1978 (as amended in 1981 and 1983).

The main reason for the appearance of the new Regulations is that, to date, only a small proportion of dangerous substances has been subject to statutory control as regards conveyance by road in bulk, and packaging and labelling requirements in the course of commercial and industrial supply.

Substances outside the scope of the 1984 Regulations

Substances conveyed by road (cited in Reg 3(1))

(a) radioactive substances,
(b) a substance in a tank container with a capacity of more than 3 cubic metres,
(c) food,
(d) animal feeding stuffs,
(e) cosmetics,
(f) medicines,
(g) controlled drugs,
(h) a disease-producing mirco-organism,
(i) a substance taken by way of sample by an enforcement authority, e.g. HSE.

Substances supplied in the course of commercial and industrial use (cited in Reg 3(2))

(a) munitions,

(b) a substance under the control of H M Customs,
(c) a gas, compressed, liquefied or dissolved (*but* an aerosol dispenser or a pesticide is included and within the Regulations),
(d) a pesticide approved for safety under the Pesticides Safety Precautions Scheme,
(e) a substance transferred from one part of a workplace or factory to another,
(f) a substance not yet fully tested and labelled in accordance with the requirements of the Notification of New Substances Regulations 1982,
(g) a fertiliser,
(h) all substances specified in 'Substances Conveyed by Road' above.

Packaging requirements

Dangerous substances must not be either conveyed by road or supplied unless they are in a package suitable for that purpose, and unless

(a) the receptacle containing the dangerous substance is designed, constructed, maintained and closed so as to prevent any of the contents of the receptacle from escaping when subjected to the stresses and strains of normal handling, though this does not exclude the fitting of a suitable safety device;
(b) the receptacle, in so far as it is likely to come into contact with the dangerous substance, is made of materials which are neither liable to be adversely affected by that substance nor liable in conjunction with that substance to form any other substance which is itself a health and/or safety risk;
(c) where the receptacle is fitted with a replaceable closure, that closure is designed so that the receptacle can be repeatedly reclosed without its contents escaping (Reg 7).

Labelling requirements of substances for supply

A substance dangerous for supply purposes must have certain particulars either

(a) on the receptacle containing the substance, or
(b) on any packaging containing the receptacle.

The required particulars are

(a) name and address of manufacturer, importer, wholesaler or other supplier;
(b) designation of the substance;
(c) indication of the general nature of the risk and symbols illustrative of the risk(s),

(d) risk phrases (these are listed in Part IV of the Approved List, and they indicate the particular nature of risk created by the substances so labelled);
(e) safety phrases (Reg 8).

Unhelpful and/or misleading descriptions, such as 'non-toxic' or 'non-harmful', should be avoided (Reg 8(3)).

Where it is not reasonably practicable to provide safety information on the main label, such information can be given on a separate label or on a sheet accompanying the package (Reg 8(7)).

Labelling requirements of substances dangerous for conveyance

Dangerous substances must not be conveyed by road unless the package in which the substance is conveyed shows the following particulars:

(a) name, and address or telephone number (or both), of the consignor;
(b) designation of the substance;
(c) substance identification number;
(d) hazard warning sign;
(e) where the quantity of the substance exceeds 25 litres, the nature of the dangers arising from the substance and the emergency action that should be taken – this can be provided on a separate sheet (Reg 9).

Labelling is not required where the volume of the receptacle or total volume of all receptacles in a package is

(a) in the case of toxic gas, 25 millilitres or less;
(b) in the case of flammable gas, 500 millilitres or less;
(c) in the case of non-flammable compressed gas, 5.5. litres or less;
(d) in any other case (total quantity of the dangerous substance), 1 litre or less.

Labelling requirements for particular preparations

In the case of

(a) paints and varnishes containing more than 0.5 per cent lead,
(b) cyanoacrylate-based adhesives,
(c) preparations containing isocyanates,
(d) preparations containing sensitisers, and
(e) sprays

the following risk and safety phraseology should appear on the labelling:

(a) Paints/varnishes:
   (i) 'Contains lead. Should not be used on surfaces liable to be chewed or sucked by children' (receptacles containing 125 millilitres or more of paint/varnish).
   (ii) 'Warning. Contains lead' (receptacles containing less than 125 milliltres).

(b) Cyanoacrylate-based adhesives: 'Cyanoacrylate. Danger. Bonds skin and eyes in seconds. Keep out of reach of children'.

(c) Receptacle containing preparation containing isocyanates must include on label: 'Contains isocyanates' and 'See information supplied by manufacturer'.

(d) Sensitisers: 'May cause sensitisation by inhalation' and/or 'May cause sensitisation by skin contact'.

(e) Sprays, e.g. paint, varnish, printing ink, adhesive: 'Do not breathe gas/fumes/vapour/spray' and 'In case of insufficient ventilation, wear suitable respiratory equipment' (Reg 12).

Aerosol dispensers

A preparation packed in an aerosol dispenser is classified as 'flammable' if that dispenser contains

(a) more than 45 per cent by weight of flammable substances,
(b) more than 250 grams of flammable substances.

A flammable substance means either highly flammable gases or flammable liquids having flash points equal to or less than 100 °C.

The dispenser must be labelled as 'flammable' (Reg 12(2)).

Essential data

In the assessment of danger from a particular substance the following are necessary:

(a) Identification – commercial name and synonyms, constituent parts, supplier and/or manufacturer.
(b) Physical properties – appearance, colour, toxicity, stability, flash point, pH value, solubility, specific gravity/density, explosive limits, auto-ignition temperature, critical pressure and temperature.
(c) Risk factors – hazards, precautions, personal protection requirements, disposal controls.
(d) Medical – acute effects, chronic effects, treatment.
(e) Welfare – pre-employment screen, periodic health examination.
(f) Process uses – solvents, lubrication, adhesive, heat treatment, paints, catalyst, plating.

(g) Legislation applying, e.g. Asbestos Regulations 1969; Carcinogenic Substances Regulations 1967; Ionising Radiations Regulations 1985.

Duty of manufacturer and supplier to provide information

The Health of Safety at Work Act, etc., 1974 places a duty on manufacturers, suppliers and importers of substances used at work to provide information 'about any conditions necessary to ensure that they will be safe and without risk to health when properly used'. However, the quality and quantity of information provided varies considerably. The use of a 'product data request' form with a view to, first, obtaining information about products and, second, standardising the approach to documentation of information is recommended. A typical product data request form is shown in Fig. 38.3. (The more reputable manufacturers and suppliers supply information in the form of 'product data sheets'.)

Monitoring

An important feature of preventing hazards to health associated with dangerous substances is the frequent assessment of systems and procedures relating to their identification, storage and handling, and of protection arrangements and the training requirements for operators. This monitoring exercise may take the form of a dangerous substances audit, and a typical example is shown in Fig. 38.4. The audit should be undertaken on either a weekly or a monthly basis dependent upon the range and quantities of dangerous substances being used and stored.

The 'Seveso' Directive

By virtue of the Control of Industrial Major Accidents Hazards Regulations 1984 (the so-called Seveso Directive), which came into effect mainly on 1 April 1985, certain plants and processes containing 'dangerous substances' (chemicals) are considered to be potentially too dangerous to be left to self-regulation on the part of employer and workforce. The substances are predominantly involved in chemical and petrochemical operations, and those in control of such operations must demonstrate to the Health and Safety Executive that they can control the hazards presented by such activities, whether they be hazards to the workforce or to the neighbouring area and the environment. Information on hazards must be updated if any changes take place. Those in control must prepare and update, as often as is necessary, an

Health and Safety at Work Act 1974.
Product Handling Information Request.
Please complete and return to:

PRODUCT NAME:		
MANUFACTURERS/ SUPPLIERS NAME ADDRESS	Tel No:	
RECOMMENDED USE		HAZARDOUS NATURE SYMBOL
PHYSICAL FORM		
PACKAGING		
METHOD OF USE		
APPROVALS (MAFF, HSE, etc)		HAZARDOUS NATURE SYMBOL
HAZARDOUS INGREDIENTS		
RISKS		
SAFETY PRECAUTIONS		
STORAGE	*Details of special precautions needed:*	
ACTION IN CASE OF SPILLAGE		
FLAMMABILITY		
TRANSPORT REGULATIONS	Dangerous Goods ☐ NO ☐ YES Details:	

SPECIAL DISPOSAL PRECAUTIONS		
EMERGENCY TELEPHONE		
HARMFUL EFFECTS	EYES	
	INHALATION	
	SKIN	
	INGESTION	
FIRST AID	EYES	
	INHALATION	
	SKIN	
	INGESTION	
ADDITIONAL INFORMATION		
OTHER OBSERVATIONS:		

APPROVED BY ____________________ DATE ____________________

HEALTH & SAFETY MANAGER

Fig. 38.3 Product data request form

ITEM	YES/NO	ACTION
1. INFORMATION AND IDENTIFICATION 1.1 Is an up-to-date list of all dangerous substances held on site readily available? 1.2 Are safety data sheets available for all dangerous substances on site? 1.3 Is this information adequate? 1.4 Are all packages and containers correctly labelled? 1.5 Are 'ready-use' containers suitable for that purpose and suitably marked?		
2. STORAGE 2.1 Are stores and external storage areas satisfactory in respect of construction, layout, security and control? 2.2 Are dangerous substances correctly segregated? 2.3 Are cleaning and house-keeping levels satisfactory? 2.4 Are all issues to staff controlled?		
3. PROTECTION 3.1 Are the necessary warning signs posted in appropriate areas? 3.2 Is suitable personal protective equipment – available serviceable used? 3.3 Are emergency eye wash facilities and showers – available suitably located serviceable? 3.4 Are the above facilities provided with frost protection? 3.5 Are adequate and suitable first aid materials – available suitably located?		

ITEM	YES/NO	ACTION
3.6 Are the appropriate fire appliances – available suitably located serviceable accessible? 3.7 Is a supply of neutralising compound readily available in the event of spillage?		
4. PROCEDURES 4.1 Are written safe-handling procedures prepared and available for all dangerous substances? 4.2 Is there a specific procedure for dealing with spillages? 4.3 Is there a routine inspection procedure for –personal protective equipment emergency showers and eye wash facilities first aid boxes fire appliances chemical dosing to plant neutralising compounds?		
5. TRAINING 5.1 Are staff trained in – safe-handling procedures use of fire appliances dealing with spillages use and care of personal protective equipment? 5.2 Are first aiders trained to deal with injuries associated with dangerous substances? 5.3 Are training records maintained?		

Signed .... Date ....

Fig. 38.4 Dangerous substances audit

on-site emergency plan, identifying the person(s) responsible for safety, as well as an off-site emergency plan, in conjunction with the relevant local authority. Moreover, persons living in the neighbouring area must be given information, through the local authority, of the potential hazards which the site presents.

39

Specific processes and activities

This chapter examines a number of typical processes and activities, many of which are ancillary to the principal activities of industry and commerce. These activities include catering, laboratory work, office work, workshop activities and welding operations.

Workshops

Many factors need to be considered to ensure safe working in engineering, vehicle maintenance and other types of workshop. A number of these factors are outlined below.

Structural features

Floors should be sound and kept clean, with adequate floor drainage where wet processes are undertaken. Vehicle inspection pits should be provided with safe access and egress, intrinsic flame-proof lighting, and a suitable cover, such as boards, when the pit is not in use. Moreover, elevated storage areas must be adequately lit, provided with safety rails and toe boards and a permanent safe means of access. In addition, there should be adequate external lighting.

Environmental features

The form of heating provided should be capable of maintaining a comfortable working temperature, e.g. 18 °C, and heating appliances should not emit fumes or gases. Both general and specific lighting at workbenches should be to Illuminating Engineering Society (IES) recommended levels and an emergency lighting system should be installed. Moreover, ventilation requirements should accommodate the possibility of fumes from welding, engine testing and vehicle painting. Noise-producing activities, such as panel beating, should ideally be separated from the main workshop.

Machinery and equipment

Various hazards associated with the operation of woodworking machinery, abrasive wheels, lathes, lifting tackle and equipment, drills and drilling machines, gas and electric welding, metal-cutting guillotines, vehicle lifts, air compressors, compressed air equipment, pressure grease guns, jacking equipment and tyre inflation equipment should be readily appreciated by all staff, who should be adequately trained and supervised in their use.

Hand tools

Many accidents are caused by the misuse of hand tools or the use of defective hand tools. Examples would be hammers with split shafts, cold chisels with mushroomed heads, files with defective handles, screwdrivers with worn blades. Hand tools should be examined on a regular basis and defective tools rejected.

Electricity

Hand tools should be of the low-voltage type with efficient switches, earthing and double insulation. Flexes and connections should be frequently examined for wear and damage. The practice of overloading sockets should be prohibited. Flexes, leads, connections and earth clamps to battery-charging equipment and portable welding sets, together with hand-held inspection lamps, need regular examination. In the latter case, hand lamp bulbs should be fitted with a cage and operate at low voltage.

Vehicles

Lorry tilt cabs should be fitted with self-locking stays to prevent the cab from falling back into position whilst fitters are working on the engine beneath the cab. Where stays are not fitted, cabs should be maintained in the forward position by use of chains, wedges and props.

Laboratories

The principal hazard in laboratories is fire. This may result from spontaneous combustion, incompatible reactions, evolution of flammable gases during experiments or the use of defective electrical equipment. Electrical faults, the main cause of fire, can result in equipment overheating. Thermostats should be supported by thermal cut-outs and all electrical equipment checked on a regular basis. Other hazards include the risk of explosion or implosion, skin contact with strong acids, alkalis and organic compounds, incorrect labelling of reagents and poor storage of flammable liquids, unstable solids and compressed and liquefied gases. Spillages of flammable, toxic and corrosive substances can result in the evolution of gases and an enhanced fire risk. Neutral absorbing materials should always be available.

Many injuries involving glassware are caused by breakage of glass vessels under pressure or through inserting glass tubing into corks. Vessels under pressure should be guarded with mesh or tape and corks properly bored. Where experiments are carried out at pressure greater than atmospheric, using glass vessels, solid metal or wire mesh screens should be used to surround the area of the experiment.

Where possible, autoclaves should be separated from the rest of the laboratory area. They should be fitted with pressure bursting discs and subject to annual examination.

Special precautions are needed in the case of compressed gases (*see* Chapter 38). Centrifuges should be fitted with an interlocking device and brake so that the lid cannot be opened until the moving parts have come to rest. Good waste disposal provision is also important. Special waste solvent drums should be provided along with metal bins with close-fitting lids for other substances. Waste containers should be clearly marked for specific types of chemical waste. Above all, the practice of mouth pipetting should be prohibited and replaced by the use of purpose-designed pipette fillers.

Principles of laboratory safety

Safe design

Ideally all laboratories should be of single-storey construction and separate from other buildings, built in non-combustible materials and with floors impervious to chemical substances. Where attached to other buildings, they should be separated by fire-resisting construction with a minimum of half an hour notional period of fire resistance, and stairways should be encased in fire-resisting walls. Heating should be automatic with a complete prohibition on all types of portable fire.

Housekeeping

Good housekeeping is a key factor in safe laboratory practice. Many hazards can be eliminated by meticulous attention to detail, including environmental hygiene, and tidiness of work sections, benches and storage areas.

General conduct

A high standard of discipline and operational conduct is essential. Young laboratory workers should be trained in safe procedures and subject to regular supervision.

Personal hygiene

Personnel should be trained in the elements of sound personal hygiene, particularly hand washing after handling chemical compounds. There should be a total prohibition on eating, drinking and smoking in laboratories.

Personal protective equipment

The need to use the equipment provided – e.g, eye protection, respirators, overalls, gloves and visors – should be stressed. Cleaning facilities should be provided for such equipment.

First aid

A high standard of first aid provision is necessary. Eye baths, drenches and an emergency shower are necessary where large quantities of chemical substances are used and stored.

Staff training

All new staff should receive induction training in the hazards present. Everyone should know the relevant flash points, ignition temperatures and other hazardous properties of materials, and appreciate the need to separate incompatible and mutually reactive materials. Above all, staff should be trained in fire protection procedures.

Offices

The principal hazard in offices is fire. Fire hazards are created as a result of defective wiring and sockets, overloading of electrical circuits and the use of freestanding heating appliances. Much office machinery is now electrically operated and many offices are simply not provided with sufficient power outlets to meet the demands of an increased electrical load. As a result, it is not uncommon to see the use of multipoint adaptors and extension leads and the wiring of more than one appliance into a 13 amp plug. All these various forms of electrical abuse and misuse increase the potential for fire. Moreover, materials used in offices are highly flammable, in particular spirit-based cleaning fluids, floor polishes and packing materials. Smoking by office staff greatly increases the fire risk through contact with waste paper and packing materials. Indeed, a high proportion of office fires have resulted from a cigarette end left smouldering on the edge of a desk at the termination of work.

Fire prevention measures in offices should incorporate the following elements:

(a) a total ban on the use of freestanding heating appliances, particularly radiant type electric fires, oil heaters and gas-fired appliances; the central heating system should cope with temperature variations from winter to summer;
(b) electrical circuits should be examined by a competent electrical engineer every 10 years, such examination to take account of current loading levels, the need for modifications to the system and electrical hazards which may exist;
(c) flammable substances should be stored in lockable metal cabinets;
(d) control over storage of waste paper and packing materials;
(e) a physical check of the premises prior to closing to ensure that all cigarettes and other ignition sources have been extinguished;
(f) a quarterly test of the fire alarm;
(g) an annual fire drill;
(h) annual servicing of fire appliances; and
(i) the training of personnel in the correct use of fire appliances.

Accidents in offices

Equipment and materials used in offices present a wide range of hazards. The introduction of equipment such as refuse balers, photocopiers and guillotines has increased risks to staff. Accidents caused by staff tripping over partly projecting drawers of a filing cabinet or trailing flex to an electric typewriter are common, and even the humble drawing pin can inflict injury if left carelessly on a desk or seat. Moreover, many accidents are caused by human error or lack of perception, for instance reading while walking along a corridor or up stairs, restricted vision whilst carrying bulky items or inattention to obstructions such as cleaners' equipment or tea trolleys.

The standard of housekeeping in many offices is poor. The practice of storing materials such as stationery on staircases and landings, in sanitation areas and basement boiler houses, is all too common, resulting in falls, contact accidents and an increased fire risk. Many offices are poorly lit, particularly in staircase and landing areas, with the attendant risk of falls and contact accidents.

Visual display units (VDUs)

Many office staff operate equipment incorporating VDUs. In the past, some units have suffered from poor ergonomic design leading to increased stress on the operator and accompanied by complaints of visual fatigue, postural fatigue, headaches, neck strain and nervous conditions. Therefore, the design of workstation, equipment and general environment, together with the occupational health aspects of VDU operation, need consideration.

The workstation

Chairs should have an adjustable back rest but no arm rests. Seat height should be adjustable at approximately 0.4 m above floor level, and chairs should be of the swivel type with a stable base, preferably mounted on castors. The keyboard top should be set at approximately 0.7 m above floor level, with the screen approximately at right-angles to the line of sight, but avoiding reflected light. The document holder should be of a simple type set at an angle of 45° with the actual table top or working surface readily accessible. In addition, a footrest should be provided with a minimum knee clearance of 0.2 m between seat and table. Any wires to the screen should be positioned behind the table.

Keyboard and screen characteristics

The luminance ratio between the screen and the rest of the work area should be not more than 1:10. (On a totally black screen the characters appear to float in space, making it difficult for the eye to accommodate properly.) The screen should be capable of both horizontal and vertical adjustment. Black keyboards should be avoided as they accentuate reflections from the immediate work area. Keyboards should preferably be detachable, since fixed keyboards result in an incorrect posture being adopted for typing (with the keyboard too high), or for viewing (with the screen too low to read).

The operator

Because of the potential for visual fatigue amongst operators, pre-employment health screening should include vision screening followed by regular screening on an annual basis. Wearers of spectacles designed for a narrow range of reading distances, and those with bifocal or other multifocal lenses may experience difficulties with tasks involving varying distances. They may find, for instance, that they need to adopt uncomfortable postures in order to view documents or display text satisfactorily. These individuals may need modifications to their prescription lenses to undertake work with VDUs, and should consult their optician before undertaking such work and thereafter whenever discomfort or eye strain is experienced.

The use of medication, such as minor tranquillisers and other psychoactive drugs, is now quite common. Occasionally side effects from these drugs may occur which may mimic some of the symptoms of visual fatigue, such as the slowing of eye movements. VDU operators who may have been prescribed such medication should be made aware of these side effects.

The problems of visual fatigue associated with the ageing process, loss of visual acuity and reduced visual performance must be appreciated by managers whenever considering complaints from VDU operators. However, much can be done to eliminate or reduce the stress associated with this operation. Whilst vision screening is an important means of assessing current and future visual performance, factors such as the location of equipment, regular maintenance, consultation with manufacturers on problems raised by operators, the use of correctly designed chairs, desks and ancillary equipment, and attention to environmental factors, such as background lighting, temperature and ventilation control, can go a long way in reducing operator stress and the related problems that this produces.

It should be noted that there is no scientific evidence linking VDU work and adverse reproductive consequences – e.g. miscarriages – or cataracts, epilepsy or facial dermatitis. Further guidance on VDUs in the workplace is given in the HSE (1983) booklet, *Visual Display Units*, available from HMSO.

Catering operations

The principal injuries associated with catering operations are

(a) scalds to hands, forearms, feet, legs and trunk through contact with boiling water, hot fats and hot liquids;
(b) cuts to hands from knives, bottles, slicing machinery and from the opening of cans;
(c) burns to hands and forearms from ovens, hotplates, ovenware, plates and hot liquids;
(d) bruising, abrasions and fractures from slips and falls caused by greasy floors and obstructions; and
(e) back injuries associated with incorrect lifting and carrying techniques.

Good standards of safety in catering originate from the design of the kitchen area. The kitchen should be large enough to allow for safe movement, floors should have a non-slip finish with adequate floor drainage, racking should be provided for storage of equipment and utensils, and a high level of cleaning and housekeeping maintained.

Machinery and plant, such as meat slicers, ovens, bains-marie, bowl mixers and dish-washing machines all present specific hazards. Such items should be frequently inspected and maintained in sound working order, with the appropriate guards and safety devices fitted. Hand tool accidents are common in kitchens, particularly through the use of knives, cleavers, saws and can openers. Staff should be trained in their correct use.

Lighting and ventilation levels should be of a high standard. The following illuminance levels are recommended:

Food preparation areas	500 lux
Storage and ancillary areas	300 lux
External storage areas	50 lux

This maintenance of good levels of illumination encourages safe working practices and sound standards of food hygiene. Ventilation levels should be within the range of 12 to 20 air changes per hour, with local exhaust ventilation over ovens and steam-producing appliances.

Kitchens also represent a considerable fire hazard, particularly where housekeeping standards may be poor. Fire appliances should be provided which are capable of dealing with electrical and fat fires, and staff should be trained in the correct use of such appliances. Fire exits should be clearly marked and kept unobstructed. In addition to regular fire drills being undertaken, there should be an effective fire alarm system.

Dry-cleaning processes

Dry cleaning involves the use of solvents, such as trichlorethylene and perchlorethylene, along with other solvent-based products which are both flammable and toxic. Under the Dry Cleaning Special Regulations 1949 flammable liquids with flash points below 32 °C must not be used, except as 'spotting agents' for the removal of stains and marks by hand. Here the liquid should be contained in a spotting bottle or container of not more than 570 ml capacity.

The various stages of the dry cleaning process can result in vapours entering the working area, particularly when garments are removed from dry cleaning plant. An effective exhaust ventilation system is, therefore, necessary to maintain concentrations in air well below dangerous levels. Before garments are handled or pressed, all residual solvent in them should have vaporised. Some dry cleaning plants use diatomaceous earth as a filtering medium for the solvent. This is later removed from the plant as a sludge. Care is necessary to ensure that the sludge is stored safely in lockable bins in a secure area outside the workroom prior to collection. Work at solvent recovery stills should be undertaken only by staff trained in the use of respirators.

Welding operations

The two main forms of welding are gas welding and electric arc welding. Whilst the hazards peculiar to each form of welding are considered later, the following hazards are common to both forms.

Fire and explosion

Arcs, flames, sparks and metal spatter are sources of ignition which will readily ignite waste and other flammable materials in close proximity to the welding operation. Welding on systems or vessels under pressure can result in explosion. Welders should, therefore, ensure that welding arcs and flames do not come into contact with flammable materials. Moreover, care should be taken to ensure that welding does not take place in areas where flammable gases and vapours may be present. This is particularly appropriate in painting and degreasing areas which should always be purged with an inert gas prior to welding commencing.

Burns

Welders should be provided with protective clothing to protect them from burns, i.e. face shields and helmets, gauntlets and aprons. Any newly welded work should be segregated from the workforce by barriers or screens, along with the display of warning notices.

Toxic fumes and gases

Inhalation of welding fumes and gases can lead to the condition known as 'welder's lung' or siderosis. Metallic fumes in the form of oxides can be evolved according to the nature of the base metals and electrodes in use. This is also true of fumes and dusts from flux coatings. The action of heat and ultraviolet leads to the evolution of ozone, carbon monoxide and oxides of nitrogen. Heavy particulate matters in the form of respirable dusts can be created as smoke and metal spatter. Many of the gases, vapours and dusts evolved during the welding process are invisible, colourless and odourless, and so considerable care should be taken during welding in confined spaces or unventilated areas. The operation of a permit to work system is, of course, necessary with such operations. (*See also* Chapter 22.)

Precautions during welding operations

(a) Welding workshops should be provided with effective mechanical ventilation capable of achieving 6 to 10 air changes per hour, together with local exhaust ventilation in a designated welding area.
(b) Portable extraction and filtration units should be used where welding is undertaken *in situ* on production machinery and plant.
(c) Environmental monitoring should be undertaken in welding workshops wherever there is evidence of dust and fume accumulation.
(d) Welding in confined spaces, particularly, can present a noise hazard. Hearing protection should be provided and worn. (*See* Chapter 21.)

Gas welding

Fuel gases commonly used are acetylene and propane, both of which are flammable and form mixtures with air or oxygen. Any leakage of fuel gas is potentially hazardous, as ignition may lead to rapid or explosive combustion, particularly in confined spaces or unventilated areas. Being heavier than air, propane can accumulate at floor level and will readily ignite. Acetylene, an unstable gas, can decompose explosively when subjected to heat or shock. This can occur in the absence of oxygen and under pressure.

A further hazard associated with gas welding is oxygen enrichment. Most welding and cutting operations use oxygen to support combustion of the fuel gas. Accidental leakage of oxygen has, therefore, considerable hazard potential. Oxygen enrichment will cause a change in ignition characteristics of all combustible materials, including those considered non-combustible. Any oxygen leakage in confined or unventilated areas is a matter for immediate concern. Oxygen should, therefore, never be used to purge or 'sweeten' the atmosphere of a confined space or vessel interior. Accidental leakage should be avoided by frequent inspections of hoses, valves and regulators.

Electric arc welding

Hazards can arise from poor standards of maintenance and/or repair of equipment, improper use, and use of unsuitable materials, e.g. insulation tape, to effect repairs to equipment and connections. Other dangers arise in the use of portable welding sets as a result of inadequate power supply, absence of isolating switches in the power supply circuit, the need to remake earth connections for each job, and strain or damage to terminals and connections of the welding set. A system for frequent examination, maintenance and repair of equipment is, therefore, essential. Such a system should ensure that

(a) the equipment rating is adequate for the job;
(b) the equipment is installed in accordance with the latest IEE (1981) *Regulations for Electrical Installations*, relevant British Standards and manufacturers' instructions;
(c) isolation switches are readily accessible;
(d) the set is frequently examined by a competent electrician;
(e) all mains and secondary cables, terminals and cable connectors are of adequate size and construction for the maximum welding current;
(f) terminal and live components are adequately protected;
(g) there is a separate earthing conductor in addition to the welding current return cable;
(h) earthing circuits are of adequate capacity;

(i) any damage to the insulation of cables, electrode holders, torches, etc., is repaired immediately or the item replaced;
(j) the amount of trailing cable is minimised to avoid impact damage and the danger from tripping;
(k) there are no exposed metal parts in clothing and protective equipment;
(l) accidental arcing is avoided;
(m) correct equipment is worn so that skin is protected, e.g. visor, gloves, apron, safety boots;
(n) extra care is taken when working in wet, hot or damp conditions, in confined spaces or areas where access is difficult, and when working at heights; and
(o) records of equipment examinations and subsequent repairs, replacements, etc., are kept in the general register.

Another hazard associated with arc welding is that from ultraviolet radiation. This can have an acute effect on the eye, causing burning of the conjunctivae with attendant irritation and a painful feeling of grittiness ('arc eye'). Chronic effects can include permanent vision damage or, in extreme cases, blindness following prolonged exposure. The effect of ultraviolet radiation on degreasing solvents can be phosgene evolution. Phosgene is a highly toxic gas.

Helmets and shields should be kept in good condition and fitted with the correct grade of filter. Non-reflecting welding screens, e.g. matt green canvas, should always be placed around welding areas, and reflected glare should be reduced where possible by the use of non-reflective surfaces for wall finishes in welding workshops. Notices should be displayed in welding areas giving warning of arc flash, and welders should be instructed to warn other people present prior to striking an arc. Moreover, degreasing solvents should be excluded from welding areas. (*See also* Chapter 35.)

40

Health and safety in agriculture, forestry, horticulture and associated activities

This chapter is principally concerned with health and safety aspects of agriculture. 'Agriculture' is a diverse industry, however. It encompasses horticulture, forestry, fisheries, the operation of cattle-breeding centres, zoos, safari parks and leisure parks, together with land clearance and fruit growing. The hazards in agriculture are also diverse. They can be associated with machinery, dangerous substances, livestock, vehicles and hand tools. These factors, coupled with frequent working in adverse weather conditions, create an environment fraught with danger to workers, children and members of the public.

Accident statistics show that there are two groups of people who are most vulnerable, namely elderly agricultural workers and young persons, including children. In the first case, many accidents are caused by overfamiliarity, whereas with young persons and children, inexperience and lack of training are prime causes of accidents, particularly when they become involved with machinery, tractors and farm implements.

Structural safety

The Agriculture (Safeguarding of Workplaces) Regulations 1959 require certain structural safety standards in agricultural workplaces. The duty to conform to these standards is laid on the occupier, i.e. a person or company in control of premises. In particular, every stairway and floor must be as safe as is reasonably practicable for the purposes for which it is used, and the provision of hand rails is included in this Regulation. Guarding of floor openings, grain pits, stokeholds and furnace pits, edges of floors and apertures in walls is particularly important, as are duties placed on farm workers, such as reporting defects in stairways and guard rails (Agriculture (Safeguarding of Workplaces) Regulations 1959, Parts II and III of Schedule).

Fatal accidents are common as a result of entry into confined spaces, such as silos, where there may be insufficient oxygen, or as a result of falls into slurry pits, many of which are over 6 metres deep, resulting in death through drowning. Wet surfaces, manure, mud and a general failure to maintain basic hygiene and housekeeping levels are contributory factors to accidents, along with uneven floors and yard surfaces, culminating in slips and falls.

All these factors point to the need for good standards of preventive maintenance on the farm, frequent inspections to ensure that structural items, such as hand rails, are secure and a system for ensuring that reported defects are remedied quickly.

Tractors

Overturning

Many accidents are associated with tractors overturning or going out of control due to their being driven too fast, insufficient braking or wheel grip, lack of awareness of the effect of ground conditions, especially on slopes, wheels going over unfenced edges, or incorrect hitching and loads. Experience has shown that as long as an operator stays within the confines of an approved safety cab (see later) he will not be crushed. However, in a high-speed or multiple roll this may not be easy to ensure and, in any incident, injuries may arise from his being thrown about inside the cab. Safe tractor operation depends upon a variety of factors including regular servicing and maintenance. Brakes should be connected and working efficiently. Steering should be adjusted so that there is no excessive free movement or play on the front wheel bearings. Tyres should be maintained at the correct pressure, have adequate tread and be in good condition.

Most overturning accidents on slopes take place on firm surfaces which give the driver the impression that they are free from danger. Comparatively few tractors overturn on slopes of cultivated soil. A tractor can usually travel along a side slope which is steeper than any slope it could safely climb or descend. However, when travelling along a side slope, the tractor wheels may tend to slide downhill. The maximum side slope on which it can travel will usually be determined by the extent to which the wheels can resist side slipping. On a steep side slope a tractor should not be accelerated or braked heavily since either action reduces a wheel's resistance to side slip. The tractor wheels should be set as wide as is practicable. Humps and hollows on a moderate slope may be sufficient to overturn a tractor before it actually slides. The danger of an accident on a side slope is increased if there is a heavy mounted implement at the rear of the tractor.

A two-wheel drive tractor can be driven up a slope which it cannot safely descend. During the climb the front of the tractor is raised by the slope, so there is a greater proportion of its weight on the rear drive wheels. This increases their grip on the ground and preserves traction. However, when coming downhill the weight is redistributed in the opposite direction. This lessens the grip of the drive wheels, making the tractor more liable to slide even when braking and with the drive wheels rotating. A four-wheel drive tractor which has positive front wheel drive can descend slopes with greater safety than a two-wheel drive tractor, because the front wheels are engine-braked.

Power take-offs

A power take-off (PTO) shaft transfers power from the tractor to the trailed equipment drawn behind. A tractor power take-off and the power take-off shaft are extremely dangerous if used in an unguarded or incorrectly guarded condition. The Agriculture (Power take-off) Regulations 1957 place specific duties on employers concerning safety aspects of PTOs and PTO shafts. The tractor PTO must be covered while the engine is in motion by a shield constructed of metal or other material which, when attached to the tractor, must be capable of supporting at least 113.4 kilograms. The shield must protect the worker and his clothing from coming into contact with the PTO from above or from either side. When the PTO is enclosed by a fixed cover, the shield is not necessary (Reg 3(1)). The PTO shaft, while in motion, must be enclosed in a guard extending along its whole length from the tractor to the first fixed bearing on the machine. Shaft guards should be substantially constructed and maintained in good condition. Moreover, workers must not use any tractor or machine that does not comply with these requirements (Reg 4).

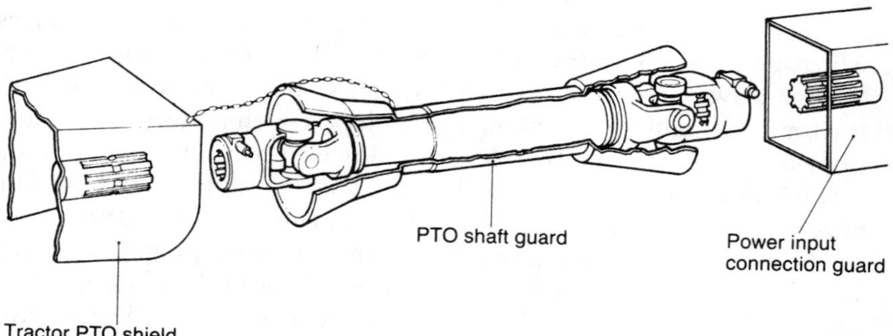

Fig. 40.1 Guards for PTO shaft, power input connection and tractor PTO

Braking systems

The use of tractor/trailer combinations without adequate braking systems has led to accidents, jack-knifing and overturning. The safe use of tractors and trailers on the road or in the field requires that they can be stopped safely within a reasonable distance, under the most adverse conditions. When small trailers are being towed, the tractor brakes alone may be adequate to brake the combination satisfactorily.

The Agriculture (Field Machinery) Regulations 1962 require that a field machine be properly maintained so that it is safe when used by an agricultural worker. Trailer brakes must be adequately maintained and properly adjusted to meet this provision (Part II, Schedule 1, para 15).

When an agricultural trailer is used on a public highway, the requirements of the Motor Vehicles (Construction and Use) Regulations 1978 apply. Every agricultural trailer over 102 kilograms unladen weight must be fitted with efficient brakes. The brakes must be capable of being operated by the driver from his tractor seat unless the trailer is fitted with overrun brakes or there is another person in a position to operate the trailer brakes. Trailers fitted only with overrun brakes may be used up to a limit of 3.56 tonnes gross weight. When parked on a public highway, a detached trailer must have the brake applied or one of the wheels chained to prevent the wheels turning.

Safety cabs

(a) All new wheeled tractors weighing 560 kilograms or more *and* sold for use in agriculture must be fitted with an approved safety cab (Agriculture (Tractor Cabs) Regulations 1974, Reg 4).
(b) All tractors, when used by agricultural workers, must be fitted with an approved safety cab (Reg 5).
(c) New tractors can only be sold for use in agriculture if fitted with an approved safety cab with a noise level of not more than 90 dBA at the driver's cab (Reg 2(2)). (This is one of the very few statutory requirements at present controlling noise exposure.)

A safety cab includes a frame and comprises a rigid structure meeting BS 4063: 1973 'Specification for Requirements and Testing of Protective Cabs and Frames for Agricultural Wheeled Tractors'. The cab must be approved by the HSE and marked with an approval mark showing the make and model of tractor for which it is approved. A cab which satisfies the noise requirements will bear an approval mark with the letter 'Q' in an inverted triangle beneath it.

A safety cab or frame may only be fitted to the make and model of tractor for which it is approved. Further information relating to the sale of safety cabs and/or frames, the fitting of them and their use and

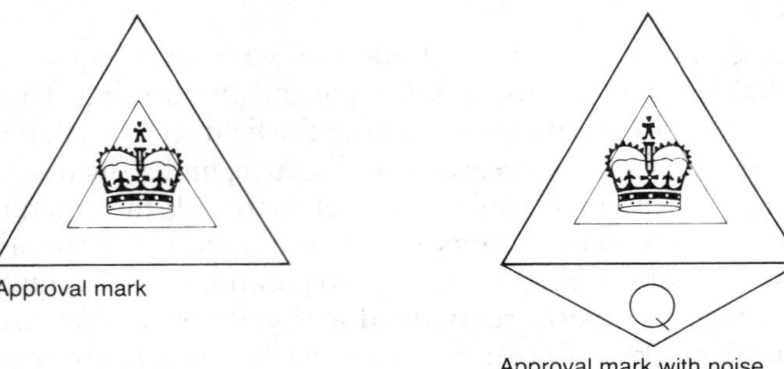

Fig. 40.2 Approval marks

maintenance is outlined in the Agriculture (Tractor Cabs) Regulations 1974.

Electricity

There is no specific legislation concerning the safe use of electricity in agriculture. To ensure maximum safety, therefore, the requirements of the Electricity Regulations relating to factories should be followed. Moreover, installations should comply with the IEE Regulations and appliances with the appropriate British Standards. In particular, electrical equipment exposed to the weather should be adequately protected against water penetration and corrosion, and electrical circuits should be capable of withstanding (as appropriate) dampness, steam, fumes from ammonia, acids, coke, oil, sulphur and other chemical effects, together with high temperatures and adverse weather conditions. Electrical installations should be maintained and protected from shock through correct methods of earthing, double insulation or other approved systems.

Soil warming transformers

Such transformers should have electrically separate input and output windings so that, in the event of an insulation failure, the extra low voltage winding will not rise to a dangerous potential above earth. The windings, core and input terminals should be contained in a sealed metal enclosure. Transformers should be protected against dampness and adverse weather conditions, have output terminals so placed or protected as to prevent accidental short circuits, and be adequately earthed.

Milking machines

Electrical motor driven pumps should be earthed or otherwise protected. The vacuum line should be electrically separated from the pump by means of a length of rubber tube.

Motors

Motors exposed to corrosive fumes, e.g. in places where grain is dried by combustion fumes, should be of the pipe-ventilated type. Motors exposed to dust should be totally enclosed or pipe-ventilated. Motors, unless of the submersible type, should not be mounted in well shafts.

Electrical accidents in agriculture

Common causes of electrical accidents are

(a) incorrect wiring of plugs and the use of self-made extensions to existing circuits;
(b) the use of unsuitable trailing flexes, including joining one length of cable to another with insulating tape or inappropriate cable couplers;
(c) the use of faulty electrical appliances;
(d) the use of fuses with ratings different from the correct one for the circuit; in some cases, nails or pieces of wire have been used in place of the correct type of fuse;
(e) the use of damaged lamp bulbs, switchgear and insulation; and
(f) the contact with overhead power lines by machinery and equipment, ladders, pipes and nesting poles.

Children and young persons

Agriculture is the only major industry which has to accommodate the constant presence of children and young persons within its confines. Largely because of this, 257 of the 1086 people killed (i.e. 24 per cent) as a result of agricultural activities between 1970 and 1979, were children under 16 years. This notwithstanding, there are many tasks on a farm that can be undertaken by young people without risk to their health and safety, provided that they are adequately trained and supervised.

Employment outside school hours of children aged 13 years or more is at present mainly governed by local authority by-laws made under powers given by the Children and Young Persons Act 1933 and the Children and Young Persons (Scotland) Act 1937. Local authorities are also empowered to make by-laws permitting parents or guardians to employ their children over the age of 13 years on light agricultural or horticultural work. Employment of children and young persons in occupations recognised as undesirable, although not physically dangerous, is generally prohibited.

NOTE: By definition:

(a) a child is a person under compulsory school-leaving age; that is, at present, 16 years;
(b) a young person is a person over 16 years but under 18 years of age.

Prohibitions on tasks performed by children and young persons

General

Children: A child under the age of 13 years must not

(a) drive, or ride on, tractors, vehicles or other prescribed classes of machine while they are being used in the course of agricultural operations, or are going to or from such operations (Agriculture (Avoidance of Accidents to Children) Regulations 1958, Regs 3 and 4);
(b) ride on agricultural implements while the implements are being towed or propelled; (Reg 5).

NOTE: It is also an offence for a person to cause or permit a child under 13 years to ride on, or drive, a tractor or machine, or to ride on an agricultural implement, in contravention of these Regulations (Agriculture (Safety, Health and Welfare Provisions) Act 1956, sec 7 (3)).

A child under the age of 16 years must not

(a) operate or assist at a circular saw (Agriculture (Circular Saws) Regulations 1959, Part III, Schedule 2, para 2);
(b) remove a guard from a field machine (Agriculture (Field Machinery) Regulations 1962, Part IV, Schedule 1, para 17);
(c) remove a guard from a stationary machine or prime mover (Agriculture (Stationary Machinery) Regulations 1959, Part III, the Schedule, para 9).

Young Persons: A young person under the age of 18 years must not

(a) lift, move or carry a load so heavy as to be likely to cause injury to himself or herself (Agriculture (Lifting of Heavy Weights) Regulations 1959, Reg 3);
(b) feed produce into the drum feeding mouth of a thresher (Agriculture (Threshers and Balers) Regulations 1960, Part III, the Schedule, para 14);
(c) operate a circular saw except under the supervision of a person over 18 years with a thorough knowledge of its working (Agriculture (Circular Saws) Regulations 1959, Part III, Schedule 2, paras 1(2) and 2);

(d) in any circumstances, work on scheduled operations, or on any other operations involving the use in agriculture of a smoke generator or smoke shreds (Poisonous Substances in Agriculture Regulations 1984, Reg 14).

Hazardous Operations

The following agricultural operations are considered hazardous and should not be undertaken by any persons without arrangements being made to ensure, so far as is reasonably practicable, the safety and absence of risks to health of those undertaking the operation, and others who might be affected.

In particular, a child should not

(a) work inside
   (i) a fruit, forage or grain store designed to retain an oxygen deficient or toxic atmosphere;
   (ii) a tower silo containing silage during or after filling; or
   (iii) a slurry pit or tank;
(b) drive a tractor unless it is fitted with an approved safety cab;
(c) couple up or operate a PTO machine;
(d) drive a tractor on steep hillsides or adjacent to any dykes, ditches, or ponds or other hazards, such as silage heaps, where there is a risk of the tractor overturning;
(e) drive a tractor for winching or other similar extraction work;
(f) operate any of the following categories of machines:
   (i) rotary cultivators;
   (ii) forage harvesters, or trailers with built-in conveying, loading, unloading or spreading mechanisms;
   (iii) hedgecutters or trimmers;
   (iv) balers or bale handlers;
   (v) root harvesters;
   (vi) combine harvesters;
   (vii) pea viners;
   (viii) manure spreaders, including slurry tankers;
   (ix) chain-saws;
   (x) post hole diggers or post drivers;
   (xi) fore and rear end loaders;
   (xii) fork lift trucks or tractors fitted with a fork lift attachment;
(g) enter or work in a yard, pen or stall occupied by a bull, boar, sow with suckling pigs or cow with a new-born calf;
(h) climb, or work form, a fixed or portable ladder at a height of more than 6 metres;
(i) handle or use explosives or be present at the site of blasting operations;
(j) enter an open silo or storage bin containing grain;

(k) carry out or assist at any maintenance or other work on the roof of a building;
(l) carry or use a shot gun or other firearm (including a humane killer);
(m) handle or use crop additives or other acid or corrosive material;
(n) handle liquid sheep dip, or work at a dipping trough during sheep dipping operations;
(o) handle or manoeuvre irrigation equipment or electric fencing near to, or under, overhead power lines.

Dangerous substances

A wide range of dangerous substances are used in agriculture, including pesticides, hydrofluoric acid (for cleaning horticultural glass), cyanide-based products – e.g. 'Cymag', for the destruction of rats and rabbits – and herbicides. The vast majority of dangerous substances used in agriculture and related activities are controlled by the Poisonous Substances in Agriculture Regulations, 1984, made under the Health and Safety at Work etc., Act 1974. The precautions to be taken are prescribed, including the protective clothing to be worn, when the substances specified in Schedule 2 to the Regulations are used in agriculture in the operations described in Schedule 1. An operations register, the notification of sickness or absence and the exclusion from this work of persons under 18 years are required by Regulations 10, 12 and 14 respectively. The Regulations apply to the self-employed as well as to employers and employees.

Health hazards to agricultural workers

Agricultural workers are exposed to many chemical substances. Whilst direct poisoning is uncommon, many suffer ill health from frequent contact with chemicals, generally through inhalation and skin contact. The use of unmarked containers for the storage of small quantities of substances presents a hazard to the unwary, and has resulted in gassing accidents.

Lifting and carrying

The Agriculture (Lifting of Heavy Weights) Regulations 1959 indicate the maximum weight of a sack or bag which a worker employed in agriculture may lift or carry, unaided, as 81.65 kilograms. These Regulations are distinct from the provisions in the Agriculture (Safety, Health and Welfare) Provisions Act 1956 to the effect that a young person may not be employed to lift, carry or move a load so heavy as to be likely to cause injury to that person.

Guns

Accidents with firearms, particularly shotguns, are common in agriculture, the principal reason being lack of training in safe gun handling. Only firearms in good condition and working order should be used. A gun should be loaded only with the ammunition designed for it, and buckshot should be kept separate from other cartridges. Guns should not be loaded until they are about to be used, and should not be left loaded when stored. Furthermore, all guns and ammunition should be locked away safely when not in use.

Loaded guns should not be carried in a vehicle or over ground in such a manner that the person carrying them is liable to cause danger to himself or others. Most safety catches only prevent the trigger from being pulled. A gun may still be discharged if dropped or jarred, particularly if the lock mechanism does not incorporate intercepting safety sears. A gun should always be carried in the 'broken' manner when out shooting.

Occupational diseases

Whilst the majority of occupational diseases associated with agriculture are dealt with in Chapter 19, it is important to emphasise several diseases which frequently occur amongst farmers and agricultural workers.

Farmer's lung

This follows the exposure to certain spoiled vegetable produce, particularly mouldy hay and corn, of persons who have become sensitised. It is an allergy, not an infection. The micro-organisms responsible for the condition are those which grow well in overheated produce and their spores may be present in mouldy hay and corn which has overheated. The spores are common in litter and various stored fodders, including silage. When this produce is disturbed in grinding corn or feeding cattle, the dust containing the spores can be inhaled. This exposure sensitises some individuals and later even quite low concentrations of the spores will produce symptoms which are similar to those of influenza, i.e. fever, headache, dizziness, nausea, vomiting or generalised muscle pains leading to coughs, chest pain and breathing difficulties, often accompanied by rapid weight loss. Approximately two people die every year from farmer's lung.

Basic precautions include

(a) use of the appropriate respirator, and keeping upwind when forking or handling sheaves of corn during threshing;

(b) provision of effective ventilation when handling produce indoors;
(c) careful handling of hay to reduce disturbance to a minimum; and
(d) frequent washing of protective clothing which can hold dust.

Anthrax

This disease is caused by the anthrax bacillus, a specific organism which can be transmitted to Man by contact with infected animals. (*See* Chapter 19.)

Weil's disease (Leptospirosis)

This disease, which is carried by rats, was once commonly encountered in agricultural workers, but is rare these days. (*See* Chapter 19.)

Tetanus

This condition is caused by *Clostridium tetani* which lives in the intestine of animals, particularly horses, and occasionally Man. Spores of the bacillus can remain in dead tissue or the soil for many years. Contamination of a wound with tetanus spores results in release of a most poisonous toxin resulting in the typical spasm of the voluntary muscles and the classic 'lockjaw'. Untreated tetanus infection is often fatal.

Noise-induced hearing loss

Noise-induced hearing loss is a common problem amongst older tractor drivers who have not had the benefit of using the newer form of 'Q' cab which is now a legal requirement. The design of a tractor safety cab must now ensure that noise at the driver's ear does not exceed 90 dBA. One of the adverse effects of producing a cab which cuts out noise outside, however, is the problem of drivers failing to hear warning shouts from people working in close proximity.

Vibration-induced conditions

Vibration-induced white finger (VWF) has been common amongst chain saw operators. However, the incidence of this condition has reduced following the introduction of anti-vibration handles and diminution at source by improved design. A further problem is that of whole body vibration of tractor drivers. BS 6055: 1981 'Measurement of Whole Body Vibration of the Operators of Agricultural Wheeled Tractors and Machinery' specifies methods of measuring and reporting vibration transmitted to operators by way of the seat or the foot platform. Other vibration paths, e.g. through the controls or the steering wheel, are not considered, however.

Tree felling and land clearance

The felling of large trees requires special skills, tools and equipment, and sound judgment based on experience. It should only be carried out by trained and experienced operators, particularly in the case of trees with a diameter larger than the length of the chain-saw guidebar. Diseased elm trees pose special problems in that the outer area of the tree can become hard while the heart can be soft or hollow. Such trees can fall in an unpredictable manner. In all cases of when large trees are to be felled, the operator must ensure that there is an unobstructed escape route from the base of the tree.

Land clearance of small trees and scrub can be undertaken using a tractor, with or without a winch, by hand winching or bulldozing. In each case, specific precautions are required. Persons not engaged in the operation should be kept well clear, particularly during a winching operation due to the risk of the cable snapping and its subsequent recoil.

The use of explosives to remove stumps or complete trees should only be carried out by trained operators who understand the use and placing of charges and the handling of detonators.

Ladders

Defective ladders are one of the principal causes of accidents in agriculture. The Agriculture (Ladders) Regulations 1957, Regs 3(1) and (2), require that employers must not allow agricultural workers to use a ladder, steps or trestle ladder, unless it is of good construction and sound material and properly maintained. In particular

(a) the grain of wooden stiles and rungs must run lengthwise;
(b) there must be no weakening defect apparent in the wooden stiles or rungs;
(c) rungs of a wooden-stiled ladder must not be solely supported by nails or screws;
(d) wooden rungs must be fitted into stiles by rabbet, notch or mortise;
(e) metal tie rods must be fitted not more than 0.61 m from each end of the ladder and not more than 2.438 m apart throughout its length, although this is not necessary if the rungs are through-tenoned and wedged in the stiles;
(f) steps or a trestle ladder must be fitted with an effective device to prevent the back support from spreading; and
(g) apart from trestle ladders, the distance between adjacent rungs must be no more than 0.305 m centre to centre.

Both employers and employees are responsible for the safe use of ladders. They must ensure that

(a) the ladder is strong enough for the purpose and manner of its use;
(b) it has no rung missing;
(c) it is equally supported on each stile and is securely placed or held in position; and
(d) the top of the ladder (except for steps or a trestle ladder) must extend above any point at which the worker has to get off or on, unless there is some secure handhold available apart from the ladder itself (Regs 4(1) and (2)).

Workers must inform the employer immediately if it is found that any ladder supplied for their use is defective. This applies to missing rungs, cracked or broken wooden stiles or rungs and any missing or broken stop or cord or steps of a trestle ladder (Reg 5).

Stationary machinery

A wide range of fixed and/or stationary machinery is used in agriculture. The Agriculture (Stationary Machinery) Regulations 1959 lay down specific requirements for machinery designed or adapted for stationary use only. Within this category are included root cutters, grain driers, corn mills, grain cleaning plant, meal mixers and hop picking machines. Transmission machinery used with such machines is also included along with prime movers. Thus, a tractor, when used to provide power for stationary machinery, is subject to the requirements for guarding prime movers generally. The prime mover is often built into the machine but must still meet relevant requirements.

Field machinery

The Agriculture (Field Machinery) Regulations 1962 control the safe use and guarding of farm machines which operate while travelling over the ground, along with trailers and power driven hand tools. A new field machine may not be sold or let on hire unless these guarding requirements are met. Specific provisions apply to workers. For instance, a worker may not ride on, and the employer must not allow him to ride on, the drawbar or other linkage of any machine or trailer while towing or propelling, nor get on or, except in an emergency, get off a self-propelled machine while it is engaged in towing or propelling (Part III, Schedule 1, para 16). The latter practice is one of the principal causes of fatal and serious accidents to agricultural workers. Moreover, a worker may not set a self-propelled field machine in motion over the ground except from the driving position, nor leave this position while the machine is travelling, except in an emergency. These requirements apply also to persons other than workers if it exposes a worker to risk of injury (Part V, Schedule 1, para 19).

The Agriculture (Threshers and Balers) Regulations 1960 lay down safety requirements for stationary threshers, hullers, balers and trussers, i.e. those permanently converted for stationary use only, used by farm workers. They do not apply to pea viners or combine harvesters, even when used as threshers, unless they have been permanently converted for stationary use. A thresher includes a huller and a baler includes a trusser. Specific guarding requirements apply to this equipment along with transmission machinery, e.g. shafting, pulleys, flywheels.

Livestock

Every year there are two or three deaths associated with livestock handling, principally bulls, but occasionally rams and boars. All mature male animals are unpredictable and can be extremely dangerous after the age of 10 months. The system for housing such animals, together with their handling, is important on the farm, at cattle-breeding centres, zoos and safari parks.

Bull housing

Whilst the following recommendations principally apply to the safe control of bulls, many of these recommendations apply equally well in the case of boars, rams and certain classes of zoo animals.

Any structure used for housing one or more bulls should be designed with the following safety requirements in mind

(a) appropriate strength of the structure,
(b) facilities for securing the bull(s), and
(c) escape facilities for use by the stockman or keeper in an emergency.

The structure should be of such strength and design to ensure the bull can be safely secured. It should be sited where the bull can see daily activities, including the presence of other cattle. Accommodation should be at least 1.5 metres high, and should allow the bull to be fed and watered without the stockman entering the enclosure. Enclosures, including all gates, should be so designed that a child cannot readily pass under, through or over them. A refuge or escape route should be provided and kept free from obstruction, but should be impassable to children and dogs from the outside. Apart from at artificial insemination centres, a service pen should be incorporated, and designed so that the stockman, operating from outside, can exclude the bull during the admittance of a cow or heifer and return him to his pen afterwards. Safety signs, 'WARNING – BULLS – KEEP OUT', should be exhibited at the entrance to any building used for housing bulls.

Control devices

Facilities for housing a stock bull should include a device whereby he can be safely secured by a person outside the accommodation area, e.g. a yoke, which will secure him by the neck, situated above the feeding trough. The use of yokes or bull rings set in the wall to hold the bull during veterinary treatment places the attendant at risk from a sudden upward movement of the bull's head, or of being trapped in the pen between the bull's body and the pen wall. A purpose-built cattle crate or 'crush' will give maximum protection.

All stock bulls should be fitted with a nose ring. The ring and its retaining screw or rivet should be of compatible material to avoid corrosion, and inspected regularly for wear. Whenever a bull is taken from his accommodation, e.g. for exercise, he should be attached to and controlled by a bull pole, or head and lead chains with ropes, or a combination of halter and ropes, preferably held by two handlers, one on each side of the animal. A bull undergoing semen collection should be controlled by use of a bull pole or by a handler on each side using ropes. A bull giving natural service should be separated from his handler by a secure barrier.

Fire

Agricultural buildings generally are allowed a relaxation of the requirements under planning legislation and building regulations. In view of the materials stored – e.g. hay, straw, fertilisers – and the materials and mode of construction, the potential for fire and fire spread far outweighs that of other forms of building. Every consideration should, however, be given to good fire protection practice, provision of fire fighting equipment in particular.

Straw or stubble burning, an annual practice following the harvest has, in the past, been responsible for numerous farm fires through failure to provide adequate firebreaks, fire fighting facilities, and control and supervision of the operation. Dangerous straw burning puts at risk farm workers, livestock, and members of the public using public highways and footpaths. Whilst there is a Ministry of Agriculture, Fisheries and Food Straw Burning Code, which is supported by the National Farmers' Union and local authorities, the degree of compliance varies considerably. Furthermore, even a well-controlled 'burn' can, in the space of a minute following a change in wind direction, turn into a raging inferno, engulfing the whole area, including motorways adjacent to the field, with dense smoke and sparks. Needless to say, there has been considerable pressure from many authorities to place a total ban on this activity.

Chain saws

Whilst many power tools are used in agriculture, the tool which has been most responsible for serious injuries is the chain saw. Apart from precautions prior to felling trees mentioned earlier, the following points need consideration.

(a) Operators should secure a good footing, remove all obstructions from the path of the saw, and ensure that no one is in the way of the falling tree.
(b) One-man power saws should not be placed in a position where they can slip.
(c) A power saw should not be cleaned or serviced with the engine running or, in the case of an electrically operated saw, when connected to the power supply.
(d) Power saws should be inspected by the operator at least once per shift and periodically by a competent person. (The term 'competent person' is dealt with in Chapter 13.)
(e) Operators should wear close-fitting clothing.

Personal protective equipment

Reference has already been made in this chapter to the Poisonous Substances in Agriculture Regulations 1984 which outline the personal protective equipment necessary when using 'scheduled substances' in 'scheduled operations'. However, consideration must also be given to the specific protective clothing and equipment which is necessary for external working, work in high noise levels, when using chain saws, working in confined spaces – e.g. breathing apparatus – and when handling livestock. Further information on this subject is provided in Chapter 24.

Bibliography and further reading

Chapters 1–5

Cusworth, G. R. N. (1975), *Health and Safety at Work Act, 1974*, Butterworths, London.

Dewis, M. (1978), *The Law on Health and Safety at Work*, Macdonald & Evans, Plymouth.

Dewis, M. (1983), *Tolley's Health and Safety at Work Handbook*, Tolley Publishing Co. Ltd, Croydon, and RoSPA, Birmingham.

Fife, Judge Ian, and Machin, E. A. (1980), *Health and Safety at Work* (excluding factories and mines), Butterworths, London.

Fife, Judge Ian, and Machin, E. A. (1982), *Redgrave's Health and Safety in Factories*, Butterworths, London.

Munkman, J. (1979), *Employer's Liability at Common Law* (9th edn), Butterworths, London.

Secretary of State for Employment (1972), *Report of the Committee on Safety and Health at Work* (Robens Report) (Cmnd 5034), HMSO, London.

Chapter 6

Arscott, P., and Armstrong, M. (1982), *An Employer's Guide to Health and Safety Management*, Kogan Page, London.

Bird, F. E., and Loftus, R. G. (1984), *Loss Control Management*, RoSPA, Birmingham.

Fletcher, J. A., and Douglas, H. M. (1971), *Total Loss Control*, Associated Business Programmes, London.

Health and Safety Commission (1977), *Safety Representatives and Safety Committees*, HMSO, London.

Health and Safety Executive (1980), *Effective Policies for Health and Safety*, HMSO, London.

Pirani, M., and Reynolds, J. (1976), 'Gearing up for Safety', *Personnel Management*, 8, 2, 25–9.

Secretary of State for Employment (1972), *Report of the Committee on Safety and Health at Work* (Robens Report) (Cmnd 5034), HMSO, London.

Shipp, P. J., and Sutton, A. S. (1972), *A Study of the Statistics Relating to Safety and Health at Work*, Committee on Safety and Health at Work Research Paper, HMSO, London.

Chapter 7

Hammer, W. (1976), *Occupational Safety Management and Engineering*, Prentice-Hall Inc., New Jersey.

Health and Safety Executive (1986), *The Reporting of Injuries, Diseases and Dangerous Occurrences*, HMSO, London.

Chapter 8

Chemical Industries Association Ltd (1975), *Safety Audits*, Chemical Industries Association, London.

Chemical Industries Association Ltd (1977), *A Guide to Hazard and Operability Studies*, Chemical Industries Association, London.

Chapter 9

Chemical Industries Association Ltd (1974), *Recommended Procedures for Handling Major Emergencies*, Chemical Industries Association, London.

Health and Safety Executive (1978), *Hazardous Installations (Notification and Survey) Regulations, 1978*, HMSO, London.

Home Office and Scottish Home and Health Department (1977), *Guide to the Fire Precautions Act, 1971; No. 2 Factories*, HMSO, London.

Chapter 10

Department of Employment (1973), *Safety Training Needs and Facilities in One Industry*, HMSO, London.

Department of Employment and Productivity (1978), *Glossary of Training Terms*, HMSO, London.

Food, Drink and Tobacco Industry Training Board (1976), *Training for Health and Safety at Work*, Food, Drink and Tobacco Industry Training Board, Gloucester.

Chapter 11

Bird, F. E. (1974), *Management Guide to Loss Control*, Institute Press, Atlanta, Georgia.

Fletcher, J. A., and Douglas, H. M. (1971), *Total Loss Control*, Associated Business Programmes, London.

Morgan, P., and Davies, N. (1981), The Cost of Occupational

Accidents and Diseases in Great Britain, *Employment Gazette*, HMSO, London.

Chapter 12

Bird, F. E., and Loftus, R. G. (1984), *Loss Control Management*, RoSPA, Birmingham.
Department of Employment (1974), *Accidents in Factories: The Pattern of Causation and Scope for Prevention*, HMSO, London.
Handley, W. (1977), *Industrial Safety Handbook*, McGraw-Hill, London.
Heinrich, H. W. (1931), *Unsafe Acts and Conditions*, McGraw-Hill Book Company (1959 edn), London.
International Labour Organisation (1976), *Accident Prevention*, International Labour Organisation, Geneva.
Powell, P. I., Hale, M., Martin, J., and Simon, M. (1971), *2000 Accidents*, National Institute of Industrial Psychology, London.
Royal Society for the Prevention of Accidents (1971), *Factory Accidents: Their Causes and Prevention*, RoSPA, Birmingham.

Chapter 13

Department of Employment (1974), *Accidents in Factories: The Pattern of Causation and Scope for Prevention*, HMSO, London.
Stevenson, A. (1980), *Planned Safety Management*, Alan Osborne & Associates, Cradley Heath.

Chapter 14

Bassett, W. H. (1982), *Clay's Handbook of Environmental Health*, H. K. Lewis & Co. Ltd, London.
Engineering Equipment Users Association (1973), *Factory Stairways, Ladders & Handrails*, EEUA Handbook No. 7, Engineering Equipment Users Association, London.
Health and Safety Executive (1978), *Road Transport in Factories*, Guidance Note GS9, HMSO, London.
Health and Safety Executive (1982), *Transport Kills*, HMSO, London.

Chapter 15

American Conference of Government Industrial Hygienists (1980), *Threshold Limit Values for Chemical Substances and Physical Agents in the Workroom Environment with Intended Changes of 1980*, ACGIH, Cincinatti, Ohio.
British Occupational Hygiene Society (1975), 'A Guide to the Design and Installation of Laboratory Fume Cupboards', *Ann. Occ. Hyg.*, Pergamon Press, London, **18**, 273–89.

Electricity Council, *Better Office Lighting*, Electricity Council, London.

Grundy, J. W., and Rosenthal, S. G. (1978), *Vision and V.D.U.s*, Association of Optical Practitioners, London.

Health and Safety Executive (1980), *Flame Arrestors and Explosion Reliefs*, HMSO, London.

Illuminating Engineering Society (1976), *I.E.S. Code*, Illuminating Engineering Society, London.

Incorporated National Association of British and Irish Millers Ltd (1967), *Dust Explosions in Flour Mills and Bulk Flour Containers*, Incorporated National Association of British and Irish Millers, London.

Institution of Chemical Engineers (1977), *User Guide to Fire and Explosion Hazards in the Drying of Particulate Materials*, Institution of Chemical Engineers, Rugby.

Lyons, S. (1984), *Management Guide to Modern Industrial Lighting*, Butterworths, Sevenoaks.

National Fire Protection Association (USA) (1979), *Explosion Venting, 1978*, National Fire Protection Association Inc., Quincy, MAO2269.

Chapter 16

Bassett, W. H. (1982), *Clay's Handbook of Environmental Health*, H. K. Lewis & Co. Ltd, London.

Chapter 17

Alcock, P. A. (1983), *Food Poisoning*, H. K. Lewis & Co. Ltd, London.

Bassett, W. H. (1982), *Clay's Handbook of Environmental Health*, H. K. Lewis & Co. Ltd, London.

Cornwell, P. B. (1973), *Pest Control in Buildings*, Hutchinson & Co., London.

Graham-Rack, B., and Binstead, R. (1973), *Hygiene in Food Manufacturing and Handling*, Food Trade Press Ltd, London.

Hobbs, B. C. (1968), *Food Poisoning and Food Hygiene*, Edward Arnold Ltd, London.

Hobbs, B. C., and Christian, R. (1974), *The Microbiological Safety of Food*, Academic Press, London.

Sprenger, R. A. (1982), *The Food Hygiene Handbook*, Institution of Environmental Health Officers, London.

Chapter 18

Buchwald, H. (1972), 'The Elusive Miasma: Problems of Abnormal

Responses to Atmospheric Contaminants', *Ann. Occ. Hyg.*, Pergamon Press, London, **15**, 370–91.

Health and Safety Executive, *Guidance Notes in the Environmental Hygiene and Medical Series*, HMSO, London.

Health and Safety Executive (1982), *A Guide to the Notification of New Substances Regulations, 1982*, HMSO, London.

Health and Safety Executive (1984), *Occupational Exposure Limits*, Guidance Note EH40, HMSO, London.

Patty, F. A. (1963), *Industrial Hygiene and Toxicology*, vols I and II, Interscience Publishers, London.

Plunkett, E. R. (1976), *Handbook of Industrial Toxicology*, Heyden & Son, London.

Sax, N. I. (1979), *Dangerous Properties of Industrial Materials*, Reinhold Book Corporation, New York.

Trevethick, R. A. (1980), *Environmental and Industrial Health Hazards*, William Heinemann, London.

Chapter 19

Atherley, G. R. C. (1978), *Occupational Health and Safety Concepts*, Applied Science Publishers Ltd, London.

Department of Employment (1972), *Code of Practice of Reducing the Exposure of Employed Persons to Noise*, Department of Employment, London.

Department of Health and Social Security (1983), *Notes on the Diagnosis of Occupational Diseases*, HMSO, London.

Gray, H. (1977), *Anatomy, Descriptive and Surgical*, Bounty Books, New York.

Hunter, D. (1976), *The Diseases of Occupations*, English Universities Press, London.

Industrial Injuries Advisory Council (1981), *Report of the Industrial Injuries Advisory Council*, Cmnd 8393, HMSO, London.

International Labour Organisation (1977), *Protection of Workers Against Noise and Vibration in the Working Environment*, International Labour Organisation, Geneva.

Taylor, W., and Palmear, P. L. (1975), *Vibration White Finger in Industry*, Academic Press, London.

Wingate, P. (1972), *The Penguin Medical Encyclopedia*, Penguin Books, Harmondsworth.

Chapter 20

Health and Safety Executive (1981), *Health Surveillance by Routine Procedures*, Guidance Note MS18, HMSO, London.

Health and Safety Executive (1982a), *Guidelines for Occupational Health Services*, HMSO, London.

Health and Safety Executive (1982b), *Pre-employment Health Screening*, Guidance Note MS20, HMSO, London.
International Labour Organisation (1984), *Occupational Health Services*, International Labour Organisation, Geneva.
McDonald, J. C. (1981), *Recent Advances in Occupational Health*, Churchill Livingstone, London.
Royal College of Nursing (1975), *An Occupational Health Service*, Royal College of Nursing, London.
Schilling, R. S. F. (1975), *Occupational Health Practice*, Butterworths, London.

Chapter 21

Beranek, L. L. (1971), *Noise and Vibration Control*, McGraw-Hill, New York.
Bilsom International, *In Defence of Hearing*, Bilson International Ltd, Henley-on-Thames.
Bruel & Kjaer, *Noise Control*, Bruel & Kjaer, Naerum, Denmark.
Bruel & Kjaer (1981), *Measuring Vibration*, Bruel & Kjaer, Naerum, Denmark.
Bruel & Kjaer (1984), *Measuring Sound*, Bruel & Kjaer, Naerum, Denmark.
Burns, W. (1973), *Noise and Man*, John Murray, London.
Burns, W., and Robinson, D. W. (1970), *Hearing and Noise in Industry*, HMSO, London.
Department of Employment (1972), *Code of Practice for Reducing the Exposure of Employed Persons to Noise*, HMSO, London.
Harland, I. (1972), *Woods' Practical Guide to Noise Control*, Woods Acoustics, Colchester.
Hassal, J. R., and Zaveri, K. (1979), *Acoustic Noise Measurement*, Bruel & Kjaer, Naerum, Denmark.
Health and Safety Executive (1976), *Noise and the Worker*, HSW Booklet 26, HMSO, London.
Health and Safety Executive (1983), *100 Practical Applications of Noise Reduction Methods*, HMSO, London.
International Labour Organisation (1977), *Protection of Workers Against Noise and Vibration in the Working Environment*, ILO, Geneva.
Jones, G. R., *et al.* (1967), *Acoustics*, English Universities Press, Frome and London.
Noise Advisory Council (1978), *A Guide to Measurement and Prediction of Equivalent Continuous Sound Level – Leq*, HMSO, London.
Peterson, A. G., and Gross, E. E., Jr (1967), *Handbook of Noise Measurement*, General Radio Company, Mass.

Sutton, P. (1974), *The Protection Handbook of Industrial Noise Control*, Alan Osborne & Associates, London.
Taylor, B. (1970), *Noise*, Pelican Books, London.
Waring, R. A. (1970), *Handbook of Noise and Vibration Control*, Trade & Technical Press, London.

Chapter 22

Atherley, G. R. C. (1978), *Occupational Health and Safety Concepts*, Applied Science Publishers, London.
Gill, F. S., and Ashton, I. (1982), *Monitoring for Health Hazards at Work*, RoSPA, Birmingham.
Hackett, W. J., and Robbins, G. P. (1979), *Safety Science for Technicians*, Longmans, London.
Health and Safety Executive (1975), *Principles of Local Exhaust Ventilation*, HMSO, London.
Schilling, R. S. F. (1975), *Occupational Health Practice*, Butterworths, London.

Chapter 23

Central Electricity Generating Board (1981), *Radiation – Its Origin and Effect*, CEGB, London.
Council of the European Communities (1980), 'Council Directive of 15th July, 1980 amending the Directives laying down the Basic Safety Standards for the Health Protection of Workers against the Dangers of Ionising Radiation', *Official Journal of the European Communities*, **23**, *L246*.
Department of Employment and Productivity (1969), *Ionising Radiations: Precautions for Industrial Users*, HSW Booklet 13, HMSO, London.
Department of Health and Social Security (1972), *Code of Practice for the Protection of Persons Against Ionising Radiations Arising from Medical and Dental Use*, HMSO, London.
Department of the Environment (1975a), *Code of Practice for the Carriage of Radioactive Materials by Road*, HMSO, London.
Department of the Environment (1975b), *Code of Practice for the Carriage of Radioactive Materials in Transit*, HMSO, London.
Department of the Environment (1975c), *Code of Practice for the Carriage of Radioactive Materials through Ports*, HMSO, London.
Hackett, W. J., and Robbins, G. P. (1979), *Safety Science for Technicians*, Longmans, London.
Harvey, B., *et al.* (1983 onwards), *Handbook of Occupational Hygiene – Ionising Radiations*, Kluwer Publishing, London.
Health and Safety Executive (1977), *Guidance Notes for the*

Protection of Persons Exposed to Ionising Radiations in Research and Teaching, HMSO, London.

HM Factory Inspectorate (1975), *Code of Practice for Site Radiography*, Kluwer-Harrap, London.

Home Office (1974), *Safety Precautions Relating to Intense Radiofrequency Radiation*, HMSO, London.

International Commission on Radiological Protection (1977), *Recommendations of the International Commission on Radiological Protection*, ICRP Publication 26, Pergamon Press, Oxford.

National Radiological Protection Board (1977), *Protection against Ultra Violet Radiation in the Workplace*, HMSO, London.

National Radiological Protection Board (1981), *Living with Radiation*, HMSO, London.

Nero, A. V., Jr (1979), *A Guidebook to Nuclear Reactors*, University of California Press.

Taylor, F. E., and Webb, G. A. M. (1978), *Radiation Exposure of the U.K. Population*, HMSO, London.

United Kingdom Atomic Energy Authority (1982), *Nuclear Facts*, UKAEA, London.

Chapter 24

Hamilton, M. (1983), *The Hand Book*, RoSPA, Birmingham.

Sutton, P. (1982), *The U.K. Handbook of Hearing Protection*, Alan Osborne & Associates, London.

Waring, A. E. (1983), *The Health and Safety Officers' Reference Book and Buyers' Guide*, Millbank Publications, London.

Chapter 25

American Conference of Governmental Industrial Hygienists (1971), *Documentation for Threshold Limit Values*, ACGIH, Cincinnati, Ohio.

Atherley, G. R. C. (1978), *Occupational Health and Safety Concepts*, Applied Science Publishers, London.

Cullis, C. F., and Firth, J. G. (1981), *Detection and Measurement of Hazardous Gases*, Heinemann, London.

Gill, F. S., and Ashton, I. (1982), *Monitoring for Health Hazards at Work*, RoSPA, Birmingham.

Harvey, B., *et al.* (1983 onwards), *The Handbook of Occupational Hygiene*, Kluwer Publishing, London.

Health and Safety Executive (1984), *Occupational Exposure Limits*, Guidance Note EH40, HMSO, London.

Jones, A. L., Hutcheson, D. M. W., and Dymott, S. (1981), *Occupational Hygiene*, Croom Helm Ltd, London.

Thain, W. (1980), *Monitoring Toxic Gases in the Atmosphere for Hygiene and Pollution Control*, Pergamon, Oxford.

Chapter 26

Department of Employment (1972), *Code of Practice for Reducing the Exposure of Employed Persons to Noise*, HMSO, London.

Harvey, B., *et al.* (1983 onwards), *Handbook of Occupational Hygiene*, Kluwer Publishing, London.

Schilling, R. S. F. (1975), *Occupational Health Practice*, Butterworths, London.

Chapter 27

Bell, C. R. (1974), *Men at Work*, George Allen & Unwin Ltd, London.

Brown, B. L., and Martin, J. T. (1977), *Human Aspects of Man-Machine Systems*, Open University Press, Milton Keynes.

Carpenter, J., and Cazamian, P. (1977), *Night Work*, International Labour Organisation, Geneva.

Edholm, O. G. (1967), *The Biology of Work*, World University Library, London.

McCormick, E. J. (1976), *Human Factors Engineering*, McGraw-Hill, New York.

Murrell, K. F. H. (1965), *Ergonomics, Man and his Working Environment*, Chapman & Hall, London.

Shackel, B. (1974), *Applied Ergonomics Handbook*, IPC Science and Technology Press, Guildford.

Singleton, W. T. (1974), *Man-Machine Systems*, Penguin Books, Harmondsworth.

Singleton, W. T. (1976), *Human Aspects of Safety*, Keith Shipton Developments, London.

Chapter 28

Anderson, P. W. (1984), *Safety Manual for Mechanical Plant Construction: Lifting and Handling*, Kluwer Publishing, London.

Anderson, T. M. (1969), *Human Kinetics*, RoSPA, Birmingham.

Creber, F. L. (1967), *Safety for Industry*, RoSPA and Queen Anne Press, London.

Hooper, E. G. (1980), 'Kinetic Handling – Have We Got it Right', *Occupational Safety & Health*, RoSPA, Birmingham, September issue.

International Labour Organisation (1984), *I.L.O. Encyclopaedia: Lifting and Carrying*, ILO, Geneva.

Mason, I. D., and Haig, A. R. (1980), *Evaluation of Kinetic Handling*, HSE Project 1540, University of Aston in Birmingham.

Nicholson, A. S. (1984), 'Manual Handling', *Safety Practitioner*, Victor Green Publications Ltd, London, September and October issues.
Payne, D. A. (1980), 'Condition not Position', *Occupational Safety & Health*, RoSPA, Birmingham, September issue.
Ring, L. (1977), *Facts on Backs*, RoSPA, Birmingham.

Chapter 29

Health and Safety Commission (1981), *Approved Code of Practice: Health and Safety (First Aid) Regulations, 1981*, HMSO, London.
Health and Safety Executive (1981), *First Aid at Work*, HSS Booklet HS(R)11, HMSO, London.
St John's Ambulance Association and Brigade (1972), *First Aid Manual*, SJAB, London.
Ward Gardner, A., and Roylance, P. J. (1967), *New Essential First Aid*, Pan Books Ltd, London.

Chapter 30

Cox, T. (1978), *Stress*, Macmillan Press, London.
Department of Employment (1973), *On the Quality of Working Life*, Manpower Paper No. 7, HMSO, London.
Harrington, J. M. (1978), *Shift Work and Health – A Critical Review of the Literature*, HMSO, London.
Selye, H. (1936), *The Stress of Life*, revised 1976, McGraw-Hill, New York.
Warr, P. B. (1971), *Psychology at Work*, Penguin Books, Harmondsworth.

Chapter 31

Beatson, C. G. (1984), 'Robots', Safety Representative, Royal Society for the Prevention of Accidents, Birmingham.
Booth, R. T. (1976), *Machinery Guarding*, Technical File No. 36, *Engineering*.
British Standards Institution (1975), *Code of Practice: Safeguarding of Machinery* (BS 5304:1975), BSI, London.
Department of Employment (1967), *Drilling Machines: Guarding of Spindles and Attachments* (HSW 20), HMSO, London.
Department of Employment (1968a), *Safety in the Use of Guillotines and Shears* (HSW 33), HMSO, London.
Department of Employment (1968b), *Safety in the Use of Machinery in Bakeries* (HSW 9), HMSO, London.
Department of Employment (1969), *Safety in the Use of Woodworking Machines* (HSW 41), HMSO, London.

Department of Employment (1970a), *Guarding of Cutters of Horizontal Milling Machines* (HSW 43), HMSO, London.

Department of Employment (1970b), *Safety in the Use of Mechanical Power Presses* (HSW 14), HMSO, London.

Department of Employment (1971), *Safety Devices for Hand and Foot Operated Presses* (HSW 3), HMSO, London.

Department of Employment (1972), *Safety at Drop Forging Hammers* (HSW 12), HMSO, London.

Department of Employment and Productivity (1970), *Electrical Limit Switches and their Applications* (HSW 24), HMSO, London.

Engineering Industry Training Board (1977), *Instruction Manual: Mechanical Maintenance for Engineering Craftsmen*, EITB, Watford.

Health and Safety Executive (1981), *Microprocessors in Industry: Implications in the Use of Programmable Electronic Systems* (HSE Occasional Paper OP2), HMSO, London.

Waring, R. H. (1982), *Robots and Robotology*, Lutterworth Press, Lutterworth.

Chapter 32

Chemical Industries Association, *Guide to the Storage and Use of Highly Flammable Liquids*, CIA, London.

Department of Employment (1975), *Dust Explosions in Factories* (HSW 22), HMSO, London.

Fire Offices Committee (1973), *Classification of Fire Hazards in Buildings*, FOC, London.

Fire Protection Association, *Compendium of Fire Safety Data* (vols 1 to 6), FPA, London.

Fire Protection Association (1982), *Fire, Safety and Security Planning in Industry and Commerce*, Fire Data Sheet MR2, FPA, London.

Freeman, N. T., and Thacker, B. W. (1975), *Appointment with Fire*, Alan Osborne & Associates, London.

Home Office (1977), *Guide to the Fire Precautions Act, 1971*, HMSO, London.

Home Office, *Manual of Firemanship* (Books 1 to 12), HMSO, London.

Lees, F. P. (1980), *Loss Prevention in the Process Industries*, Butterworths, London.

Lyons, W. A. (1981), *Action Against Fire*, Alan Osborne & Associates, London.

Underdown, G. W. (1979), *Practical Fire Precautions*, Gower Press, Farnborough.

Wharry, D. M., and Hurst, R. (1974), *Fire Technology, Chemistry and Combustion*, Institution of Fire Engineers, Leicester.

Chapter 33

Anderson, P. W. P. (1984), *Safety Manual for Mechanical Plant Construction*, Kluwer Publishing, London.

Associated Offices Technical Committee, *Guide to the Inspection and Testing of Cranes*, AOTC, Manchester.

Dickie, D. E. (1981a), *Crane Handbook*, Butterworths, London.

Dickie, D. E. (1981b), *Lifting Tackle Manual*, Butterworths, London.

Health and Safety Executive, *Precautions in the Working of Lifts* (SHW 276), HMSO, London.

Health and Safety Executive, *Avoidance of Danger from Overhead Electrical Lines* (Guidance Note GS6), HMSO, London.

Health and Safety Executive (1981), *Safety in Working with Lift Trucks* (HS(G)6); HMSO, London.

National Joint Industrial Council for the Flour Milling Industry (1956), *Health and Safety Handbook*, NJICFMI, London.

Chapter 34

Handley, W. (1977), *Industrial Safety Handbook*, McGraw-Hill, London.

Ministry of Power (1958), *The Efficient Use of Fuel*, HMSO, London.

Chapter 35

Beckingsale, A. A. (1976), *The Safe Use of Electricity*, RoSPA, Birmingham.

Health and Safety Executive, *Electricity Regulations* (SHW 928), HMSO, London.

Health and Safety Executive (1980), *Electrical Testing: Safety in Electrical Testing* (HSE Booklet HS(G)13), HMSO, London.

Hughes, E. (1978), *Electrical Technology*, Longmans, London.

Imperial College of Science and Technology (1976), *Safety Precautions in the Use of Electrical Equipment*, ICST, London.

Institution of Electrical Engineers (1981), *Regulations for Electrical Installations*, 15th edn, IEE, London.

Manpower Services Commission (n.d.), *Safety Recommendations for Off-the-Job Training in Electrical Skills*, MSC, Sheffield.

Manpower Services Commission (n.d.), *Safety Recommendations for On-the-Job Training in Electrical Skills*, MSC, Sheffield.

St John's Ambulance Association and Brigade (1972), *First Aid Manual*, SJAB, London.

Chapter 36

Anderson, P. W. P. (1984), *Safety Manual for Mechanical Plant Construction*, Kluwer Publishing, London.

Armstrong, P. T. (1980), *Fundamentals of Construction Safety*, Hutchinson, London.

Health and Safety Executive (n.d.), *Roofwork: Prevention of Falls* (Guidance Note GS10), HMSO, London.

International Labour Organisation (1982), *Safety and Health in Building and Civil Engineering Work*, ILO, Geneva.

Royal Society for the Prevention of Accidents (1982), *Construction Regulations Handbook*, RoSPA, Birmingham.

Royal Society for the Prevention of Accidents (n.d.), *The Supervisors' Guide to the Construction Regulations*, RoSPA, Birmingham.

Chapter 37

Health and Safety Executive (1979), *Lift Trucks*, HMSO, London.

Health and Safety Executive (1980), *Safe Working with Lift Trucks* (HS(G)6), HMSO, London.

Royal Society for the Prevention of Accidents (1967), *Industrial Training Manual for Power Truck Operators*, RoSPA, Birmingham.

Royal Society for the Prevention of Accidents (1975), *Training Manual for Power Truck Operators*, RoSPA, Birmingham.

Chapter 38

Atherley, G. R. C. (1978), *Occupational Health and Safety Concepts*, Applied Science Publishers, London.

Health and Safety Commission (1981), *Approved Code of Practice: Classification of Dangerous Substances for Conveyance in Road Tankers and Tank Containers*, HMSO, London.

Health and Safety Commission (1983a), *Approved Code of Practice: Operational Provisions of the Dangerous Substances (Conveyance by Road in Road Tankers and Tank Containers) Regulations, 1981*, HMSO, London.

Health and Safety Commission (1983b), *Authorised and Approved List: Approved Substance Identification Numbers, Emergency Action Codes and Classification for Dangerous Substances Conveyed in Road Tankers and Tank Containers*, HMSO, London.

Health and Safety Commission (1984a), *Authorised and Approved List: Information Approved for the Classification, Packaging and Labelling of Dangerous Substances for Supply and Conveyance by Road*, HMSO, London.

Health and Safety Commission (1984b), *Approved Code of Practice: Packaging of Dangerous Substances for Conveyance by Road*, HMSO, London.

Health and Safety Executive (1979), *A Guide to Tanker Marking Regulations*, HMSO, London.

Health and Safety Executive (1984), *Classification, Packaging and Labelling of Dangerous Substances*, HMSO, London.
Hunter, D. (1978), *The Disease of Occupations*, English Universities Press, London.
Imperial College of Science and Technology (1977), *Safety in Chemical Laboratories and in the Use of Chemicals*, ICST, London.
Kinnersley, P. (1974), *The Hazards of Work: How to Fight Them*, Pluto Press, London.
Kletz, T. A. (1983), *HAZOP and HAZAN*, Institution of Chemical Engineers, Rugby.
Muir, G. D. (1974), *Hazards in the Chemical Laboratory*, Royal Institute of Chemistry, London.
Parkes, W. R. (1974), *Occupational Lung Disorders*, Butterworths, London.
Royal Institute of Chemistry (1976), *Code of Practice for Chemical Laboratories*, RIC, London.
Sax, N. I. (1979), *Dangerous Properties of Industrial Materials*, Reinhold Book Corporation, New York.
Schilling, R. S. F. (1981), *Occupational Health Practice*, Butterworths, London.

Chapter 39

Bassett, W. H. (1982), *Clay's Handbook of Environmental Health*, H. K. Lewis & Co. Ltd, London.
Health and Safety Commission (1982), *Principles of Good Laboratory Practice*, HMSO, London.
Health and Safety Executive (1983), *Visual Display Units*, HMSO, London.
Institution of Electrical Engineers (1981), *Regulations for Electrical Installations*, 15th edn, IEE, London.
Road Transport Industry Training Board (1975), *Basic Safety Training in Motor Vehicle Workshops, Stores and Forecourts*, RTITB, Wembley.
Royal Society for the Prevention of Accidents (1972), *Safety in Offices and Shops*, RoSPA, Birmingham.
Royal Society for the Prevention of Accidents (1976), *Catering Care*, RoSPA, Birmingham.

Chapter 40

Health and Safety Executive, Agricultural Series Leaflets 1–24, HMSO, London.
Health and Safety Executive (1978a), *A Guide to Agricultural Legislation*, HMSO, London.

Health and Safety Executive (1978b), *Poisonous Chemicals on the Farm*, HMSO, London.

International Labour Organisation (1973), *Safety and Health in Agricultural Work*, ILO, Geneva.

International Labour Organisation (1979), *Guide to Health and Hygiene in Agricultural Work*, ILO, Geneva.

Index

accident, 62–3, 64–5, 90, 111–16, 133
  analysis, 120–29
  investigation, 58, 67–76
  results of, 119–20
accident prevention, 62, 133–4
  economic motivation, 64–5, 111–16
  principles of, 119–29
accidents, 67–70, 83, 125–9, 206, 584
  fatal and major, 89–91
acid cleaning preparations, 190
adhesives, 124
Advisory, Conciliation and Arbitration Service (ACAS), 46, 49, 51
aerosol dispensers, 556
agriculture, 4, 574–89
air sampling, methods of, 306–10
alcohol, 48, 232–3, 250–1, 355
  see also stress
alkali cleaning preparations, 190
anthracosis (caused by coal dust), 215
anthrax, 236, 584
appeal
  courts of, 7, 9–10
  procedures, 7
Approved list of dangerous substances, 547, 548, 551, 552
'arc eye' (from welding), 573
Area Health Authority, liaison with, 246
arsenic poisoning, 234
artificial respiration, 343
asbestosis, 13, 215, 216, 217

barrier creams, 301–2
'beat' conditions *see* bursitis

behaviour, human, 105, 124, 133, 157, 348–55
 'human factor', 124, 126, 129, 130
behaviour modification, 66
benzine poisoning, 228–9
bleeding, first aid for, 343
boiler, steam, 450, 451–4
breathing apparatus, 275, 290, 300–1
broken bones, first aid for, 343, 345
brucellosis, 235, 237–8
burns, first aid for, 345
bursitis, 240–1
byssinosis (caused by cotton), 215–18

cancer, 13, 223–5, 290
carbon disulphide poisoning, 233
carbon monoxide poisoning, 233
carbon tetrachloride poisoning, 229
catering operations, hazards in, 569–70
causation, breach and, 12, 390
ceilings, 160, 172
chains: safety aspects of, 435, 440–2
chain-saws, safety of, 589
chemicals, dangers of, 220–35
 see also dangerous substances
children, 3, 4, 5
 in agricultural work, 574, 579–82
chlorinated hydrocarbons, 229–31
chromium poisoning, 228
civil action, trade union initiated, 11
civil law; accident actionable in, 10
civil liability, 10–11, 294
cleaning, 131, 186–91, 271, 272, 275
 staff, 127
clothing, 70, 182, 184–5
 see also protective clothing
coal tar pitch derivatives: hazards, 543
codes of practice, approved, 28, 42, 78, 548
colour: environmental importance, 160, 172
colour-blindness: effect on safety, 249
common law, 3, 5–6, 9, **14–25**
 employer's duty under, 15, 25, 28
companies, responsibilities under HSWA, 34–5
compensation, 11, 112
compressed gases, 544–7
construction industry, **486–508**
 contractors: safety status in, 500–8
construction safety, 486–508

contact scheme, 80–1
contamination, 305–10
  hand-to-mouth, 124, 315, 538, 566
contract and tort, law of, 5, 15
contract of employment, 5, 46, 48, 49, 62
  breach of, 29, 31, 315
  contractual duties, 31, 122, 133
contractors, 58, 137
  see also construction *and* construction safety
conveyors, safety of, 509–17
corporations, duties of, under HSWA, 39
courts, 7, 9–10
cramp, 240
criminal liability, 7–9, 12, 19, 42, 294

damage control (costing), 83
damages, award of, 6, 7, 10, 12, 363, 508
  employee's negligence: effect, 20, 23–4
dangerous substances, 121, 505–6, 532–62, 582
data sheets, designers', manufacturers', 34
deafness, occupational, 205–11
death at work, 6, 10
decompression sickness, 218–19
decontamination procedures, 315
demolition work, hazards of, 497–500
Department of Health and Social Security: accidents, 91
dermatoses (skin conditions), 220
  dermatitis, 220–3
design, 82, 262, 320–1
detergent cleaning preparations, 190
disabled persons, 123, 128–9, 244
disciplinary procedures, 46, 49, 66
diseases and conditions, occupational, 6, 73, 202–41, 583–4
  non-occupational, monitoring for, 244–5
  prescription test, 201
  time limit for action for damages, 13
disinfectants, 191
dismissal, 31, 47, 48–51
  unfair, law regarding, 29, 50–1
doctrine of common employment, 14
'double-barrelled action': in law, 12, 22
drilling machines, 378–9
drinking and drunkenness *see* alcohol
drowning, first aid for, 343
drug addiction, 248–9
  see also stress
dry clothing processes, 570

dust, **265–76**, 537, 571
  occupational diseases, cause of, 215–18, 220
  protection, respiratory, 297–300

earnings, loss of, 10
elderly people at work, 244, 574
electrical safety, 151–4, 469–85
electric arc welding, 572–3
electricity, **476–8**
  public supply systems, 473–4
electric shock, 469–73
  first aid, 343
elevators, safety of, 517–8
emergency, major, 58, 90–5, 286–7
  equipment, 246, 300
Emergency Action Code, 551
Emergency Controller, 93
employee, 19–20, 49, 316
  duties under HSWA, 25, 30–2, 124
employer
  compulsory liability insurance, 24
  duties to employees, 15–19, 29–30, 62, 305, 311, 314
    to others, 19–20, 32
  exemption from duty, 29
enforcement of health and safety legislation, 3, 38–44, 75, 79, 91
environment, organisation of, 69–70, 157–62, 163–7
  outside: protection of public, 271
  working safety, 4, 127, 130
environmental control, 58, 246
environmental health officers, 9, 246
equipment
  defective, 70
  safety of, 420–9, 476–80, 489, 564, 565
ergonomic design, 129, 318–19, 567
ergonomics ('man-machine interface'), 130, 317–21
  anthropometry (body measurement), 319–20
ethers, poisoning by, 233
eyesight, 168, 249–50
  first aid, 435
  protection of, 295–6, 304, 381, 382
excavation work, hazards of, 489, 496–7
exposure limits, 198–9, 213

Factories Act Register, 186
Factory Inspectors, 246
factories, welfare amenities in, 178–85

fail-safe (failure to safety), 367
farmer's lung (aspergillosis), 239, 583–4
fault-free analysis, 62
fencing of machinery, 8, 34
fibreglass, hazards of, 543
fines as penalties, 7, 9
fire, 391–419, 564, 566–7, 570, 571, 585
  escape from, 415–6
  prevention, 58, 131, 413–5, 503–4, 542
  regulations, 4
  risks, 168, 173–4
first aid, 245–6, 316, 340–7, 566
floors, 126, 172
  safety of, 158
food and drink facilities, 178, 183
  see also contamination
food industries, 242, 569–70
fork lift trucks *see* trucks
fume cupboard, 538, 546
fumes, 265, 275–6, 537

gas welding, 572
gas, 300, 306, 309, 537
  see also compressed gases
gassing, 343, 582
General Duties under HSWA, 28–34
General Medical Practitioners (GPs), 246
generators, electric, 474–5
glanders fever, 236–7
grinding machines, 380–1
guards, machinery, 516–7
  see also fencing; safety devices
guillotines, 383
guns, safe handling of, 583

handbooks, employee: information, 62
hazard and operability studies, 81–3
health education, 245
Health and Safety at Work etc., Act 1974, (HSWA), 26–36, *et passim*
  work places not covered until, 5
Health and Safety Commission (HSC), 6, 26, 27, 63, 198, 199
  radiological safety proposals, 284–6, 291
health and safety committee, 79, 80, 136
Health and Safety Executive (HSE), 5, 26, 44, 89, 246, 363
  enforcing authority, as, 38–49
  first aid training, regarding, 347

Health and Safety Executive (*contd.*)
policy statements: guidance, 58
radiation, regarding, 291
Seveso Directive, 557
threshold limit values, on use of, 198
HSE Inspectors, 26, 27, 31, 34, 36, 40, 52
health and safety policy statement *see* Statement of Health and Safety Policy
health and safety specialists, 60–1, 78
health and safety survey, 78–9
hearing, 206–9, 249–50, 296–7
loss, noise-induced, 206–9
heat: cause of diseases and conditions, 204–5
heating, 3, 131, 563, 565, 567
fire risk from, 167–8, 566
hepatitis, viral, 239
hernia, 324
history, legislative, of occupational health and safety, 3, 4, 14
hoists, 421–2
housekeeping, 187–9, 271, 275, 565, 567, 569, 575
bad, as cause of accidents, 69, 127, 490
dangerous substances, regarding, 538
inspections, 314–5, 415
safe system of work, procedures in, 131
waste disposal, regarding, 160–1
hygiene, 186–191
occupational, 305–10, 575
personal, 124, 301, 538

imprisonment: penalty under HSWA, 9, 44
improvement notices, 37, 40, 41
industrial relations law regarding health and safety, 46–53
industrial tribunal, 31, 41, 50, 51
information, 28, 33–4, 52, 58, 61–2
sources of, 63, 132–3
injuries, 6, 14–24, 323–5
inspection, health and safety, 27, 79–80
inspectors, 3, 79
see also HSE inspectors
Institution of Occupational Health and Safety: training syllabus, 109
insurance, 10, 11, 22, 24
insurance company, 11, 74, 89, 91, 112
insurance cover, 112, 501
insurer, employer's, 24–5, 112
International Labour Organisation (ILO), 266
isocyanates, poisoning by, 231–2

job description, 46, 122, 132–3
Job Safety Analysis, 62, 75, 83, 131, 133–6
  training objectives, defining, 98

Kinetics, 330–8

laboratories, safety in, 564–6
ladders, safe use of, 159, 487, 492–3, 585–6
land reclamation, hazards of, 505, 585
lasers as source of radiation, 281
lathes, hazards of, 583–4
law, health and safety, 3–53
lead, 225–6, 275
learning systems in training, 100–8
legislation, occupational health and safety, 3–6
leptospirosis *see* Weil's disease
leukaemia and radiation, 290
liability, 120, 206, 499, 505
  civil, 5, 9–13, 294
  for machinery safety, 390
  vicarious, 21–2, 489
lifting machinery, 420–35
lifting tackle, 435–49
ligamental strain, 323–4
lighting of working environment, 3, 163–75, 542, 545, 564, 567, 569
  as fire risk, 413
  occupational diseases, cause of, 204–5
  poor, as cause of accidents 70, 126, 163, 168, 293
  safe system of work, regarding, 131
litigation, private interparty, 10–11
lithosis (caused by stone particles), 215
livestock handling, hazards of, 587–8
local authorities, 34–5, 93, 562, 579
  as enforcing authority, 5, 27, 38, 39
loss, financial, 62, 111

machinery, 7–8, 130, 564, 569, 586–7
  fire hazards, 414
  safety, 360–90
  see also construction; construction safety; lifting machinery
maintenance, 126–7, 131, 187–91, 314–5, 575
management, 122–3, 128, 293–4, 538
  duties towards accident prevention, 68
manual handling, 323–8
manuals, operating, 128
mechanical handling equipment, 201, 509–31

media: post-accident communication, 90
medical examination, 123, 242
medical expenses *see* damages, 'special'
mercury poisoning, 226–8
methyl bromide poisoning, 230
methyl chloride poisoning, 231
microcomputers in machinery safety, 374
microprocessors in machinery safety, 374
microwaves as source of radiation, 281
milling machines, hazards of, 382–3
miner's nystagmus, 204–5
misconduct, gross, 49–50
mists *see* dangerous substances; dust and fumes
mixers, vertical spindle bowl: safety, 385
mobile handling equipment, 518–30
motivation: safety incentive scheme, 84–5
muscle strain, 323–4

National Arrangements for Incidents involving Radioactivity (NAIR), 286
National Examination Board in Occupational Safety and Health, 109
National Radiological Protection Board, 291
negligence, 7, 10, 22, 35, 499, 526
  at common law, 31, 390
  contributory by employee, 23–4, 31
  employer's, 11, 15, 49, 120
  insurance covering, 11, 501
noise, 6, 70, 131, 293, 563, 571, 577
  control, 58, 128, 132, 261–2, 502
  diseases and conditions caused by, 205–11, 584
  measurement, 255–61
  vibration and, 252–64
notification sequence: fatal and major accidents, 89
Nuclear Installations Inspectorate, 291

occupational diseases, causes of
  biological, 203, 235–9
  chemical, 203, 220–4
  ergonomic, 203, 239–41
  physical, 202–3, 204–20
occupational health practice, 242–51
occupiers of buildings, General Duties under HSWA, 32–3
offices, 5, 178–83, 566–7
Orf (contagious pustular dermatitis), 238–9
osteoarthritis, vibration-related, 213
oxygen enrichment; welding hazard, 572

painting, exterior, hazards of, 507–8
penal duties, 7–8
penalties, 11, 42–4
permit to drive system, 162, 528
permit to work, 83, 136, 137, 141, 142
  work requiring, 140, 429, 434, 477, 504, 571
permit to work system, 58, 83, 136–43, 313, 497
  contractors, regarding, 496, 502, 504
  electricity, regarding, 434, 477
  welding, regarding, 504, 571
phosphorus poisoning, 234–5
platform, working, 126, 432–5, 487–8, 491, 529–30
pneumoconiosis, 215–16
police, 9, 286
pollution on construction site, 505–6
Portland cement, handling hazards, 543
power presses, 381–2
pressure vessels, 450–68
printing machines, 386–8
production: costs and efficiency, related
  to safety awareness, 83, 113–14, 128
prohibition notice, 37, 40, 41, 311
prosecution under HSWA, 37, 41–2
  employer's defences, 22–4
  payment demand for health and safety provision, 43
protective clothing, 290, 302–4, 315–16, 538
protective equipment, personal, 58, 124, 292–304
  deficiencies as cause of accidents, 128
  disadvantages of, 315–16
  failure to use, 69
  radiological, 277–91
  see also under appropriate headings such as fumes; radiation, etc.
public, protection of, 499, 547, 557, 562
'publication in series' list (HSE), 63
Publications Catalogue (HSE), 63
public relations officer (PRO), post-accident duty, 90

Q fever, 238
quarries, legislation regarding work in, 4

radioactive materials, 539
radiation, 198–9, 215, 277–91
records
  accident, 62
  health, 247–8
'relevant statutory provisions', 37–8, 41–2, 44–5

remedial orders, 9
resins, hazards of, 543–4
respiratory protection, 297–301
rheumatism, 298
Robens Committee, 60–64
Robens Report, 27, 37, 64
robots, dangers of, 374–7
Royal Society for the Prevention of Accidents (RoSPA)
  fork lift trucks, training for, 162
  information sources, 63
  safe driving awards, 84
  safety incentive scheme, 84
  training centres run by, 109
roofs, work on, 488–9, 492–6
ropes, safety aspects, 435, 436–40
rule book, failure to obey, 29
rules, works, 47, 128

'safe person' strategies, 123–5, 293
safe system of work, 52, 61–2, 130–54, 497, 502
  duty of employer, 15–19, 29–30
  occupational hygiene control strategies, 121–5, 293
  safe place strategies, 121–5, 293, 314–16
safety
  awareness, 128
  audit, 58, 62, 77, 84, 85–8
  budgets, 64–5
  committee, 30, 52–3, 78
  contact scheme, 80–1
  devices for machinery, 68, 364–5, 370–4
  see also fencing; guards
  equipment, 303–4
  incentive schemes, 84–5
  inspections, 58, 62, 79–80
  orders, disobeying, 20–1
  officers, 35, 58, 79, 81, 96
  performance, 62–3, 116
  propaganda, 65–6, 85, 316
  representatives, 26, 30, 51–2, 74, 90
  sampling, 81
  tours by company management, 80
  training, 58, 123
sanitation: statutory requirements, 178–81
saws, hazards of, 385–6
scaffolds, safety of, 490–2
scalds, first aid for, 345
self-employed, 19, 28, 33

Seveso Directive, 557, 562
shops, 5, 178–83
siderosis (caused by iron particles), 215
silicosis, 215
skin conditions, occupational, 124
  irritants, resistance to, 221–2
  protection, 315
'slipped disc', 324
smoke as dangerous substance, 537
smoking at work, 47–8, 250, 315, 538, 566
social security benefit, 10, 114, 120, 202, 209, 211
soft tissue injuries, 213
solvents, 124, 190–1
Statement of Health and Safety Policy, 29–30, 46–7, 57–9, 95, 124–5
  exemption from, 29, 57
  monitoring, 77
state, costs to, as results of accident, 114
statute law: occupational health and safety, 6
statistics, accident, 133
statutory civil liability, 9–13
statutory duties, 21–5, 46–7
statutory protection: establishments
  unprotected until HSWA, 5
stress, 126, 129, 164–6, 348–55, 569
  personal counselling for, 245
structural safety, 158–60
subrogation, doctrine of, 24
suffocation, first aid for, 343
supervision, 17, 28, 122–3, 127, 538
supervisors, 80–1, 122, 128
survey, health and safety, 78–9

Task Analysis, 98, 133
teagle openings: potential hazard, 126, 422
temperature, environmental, 131, 163–8
tetanus, 584
tetrachlorethane poisoning, 230
tools, portable electric, accidents with, 478, 489, 564, 569
tort, law of contract and: employer's civil liability in, 6, 15
toxicology and health, 195–201
toxic substances, 196–201
tractors, dangers of, 575–8
traffic control system, 157, 161–2
trades union, 11, 26, 51, 74, 91
trading standards departments as enforcement agencies, 9
training, health and safety, **97–110**
  contractor's staff, 142

training, health and safety (*contd.*)
dangerous substances, handling, 538
employer's duty to provide, 17, 28
first aid, 346–7
inadequate as cause of accidents, 127–8
permit to work system, 142
propaganda, use of, 65–6
reinforcement, need for regular, 128
safe system of work, use of, 61
training officers, offences committed by, under HSWA, 35
transport, safe, of materials, 28
treatment service, provision of, 243
tree-felling, hazards of, 585
trial
on indictment, 43
summary, 43
trichlorethylene poisoning, 229
trucks, classification of, 519–23

unconsciousness, first aid for, 343
ultraviolet
as radiation source, 281
as welding hazard, 571
unfair dismissal, law relating to, 50

vapour: dangerous substances, 265, 537
vehicles, safety of, 489, 507, 530–1, 564
ventilation, 275–6, 414, 563, 570
dangerous substances, in storage of, 542, 544, 545
dust control measure, as, 271
systems, 175–7, 201
vibration, 131, 211–4, 262–4
hearing, effect on, 254
sources of, 253
vibration induced white finger (VWF), 211–13
visitors to building, plant or site, offences under HSWA, 35
personal protection, protection of, 293
visual display units (VDUs), 174–5, 567–9
volenti non fit injuria, 14, 22–3, 504
'vulnerable' persons, 123–4, 244

walls, 160, 172, 542, 544
warning systems, inadequate, 69
washing arrangements, emergency facilities, 304, 542
waste products, 160–1, 290–1, 505, 565, 566

fire risk, 414–5
Weil's disease, 235, 237, 584
'welder's lung' (siderosis), 275, 571
welding, 275–6, 480–1, 504, 570–3
welfare amenity provision, **178–85**
occupational hygiene, 315
window cleaning, hazards of, 507–8
women in employment, 123, 312, 323
workplaces, 126, **157–62**
location of, 157–8
work rate: health and safety, 319
workshops, 563–4
work study techniques, 132

X-rays, 280

young persons in employment, 17, 123, 244
in agriculture, 574, 579–82
definition of, 580
Youth Training Scheme: link to health and safety training programme, 109